D0593964

Gas Chromatography
Principles, Techniques and Applications

Gas Chromatography

Principles, Techniques and Applications

A. B. LITTLEWOOD

King's College
University of Durham
Newcastle upon Tyne, 1
England

1962

ACADEMIC PRESS · *New York and London*

ACADEMIC PRESS INC.
111 Fifth Avenue, New York, New York 10003

United Kingdom Edition published by
ACADEMIC PRESS INC. (LONDON) LTD.
Berkeley Square House, London W.1

LIBRARY OF CONGRESS CATALOG CARD NUMBER: *62-14804*

First Printing, 1962
Second Printing, 1966

PRINTED IN THE UNITED STATES OF AMERICA.

PREFACE

The aim of this book is to present a self-contained description of all aspects of gas chromatography other than the detailed technology of particular pieces of apparatus. It is designed as a textbook for those who use the technique and for research workers. It does not presuppose any knowledge of the subject, which is introduced in the first chapter.

After the introduction, the first half of the book is primarily concerned with the ability of gas chromatography to perform separations. The theory of the operation and design of gas chromatographic columns, both packed and capillary, is treated in detail, and it is shown how columns may be designed to secure any required separation. The other function of gas chromatographic apparatus is to perform quantitative analysis. This is a function not of the chromatographic column, but of the "detector" at its outlet, which detects and measures separate effluent vapours. Approximately one quarter of the book, therefore, describes the principles of operation and design of the various devices which are used for this purpose.

The final chapter, which occupies the remaining quarter of the book, is a series of essays in each of which the literature describing the gas chromatography of a particular class of chemical compound is surveyed. References to each essay are listed separately, so that each list forms a selective bibliography of the gas chromatography of each class. Wherever possible, quantitative data relating to the chromatography of the compounds surveyed is tabulated. In writing this chapter, papers published up to the middle of 1961 have been considered.

I should like to thank all those who have helped me in the preparation of the text. Dr. K. F. Oldham, Mr. W. A. Wiseman, and Mr. E. R. Adlard and his colleagues have each read sections of the typescript in various stages of completion, and their critical comments have been of great value in preparing the final version. I should also like to thank the Gas Chromatography Discussion Group of the Institute of Petroleum, London, and their abstractors for their "Gas Chromatography Abstracts," issued quarterly, and published annually by Butterworths. These abstracts have greatly reduced my labor in searching the literature and in compiling lists of references. They are not referred to in the main text of the book, and they require special mention in this preface.

Newcastle upon Tyne, England
August, 1962

A. B. LITTLEWOOD

ACKNOWLEDGMENTS

The author would like to acknowledge the kindness of the following organisations, journals, and individuals in allowing him to reproduce copyright material.

The American Chemical Society (Journal, Journal of Physical Chemistry, Analytical Chemistry)
The Biochemical Society (The Biochemical Journal)
The British Council (British Medical Bulletin)
The Chemical Society, London (Journal)
The Institute of Petroleum (Journal)
The Institute of Physics and the Physical Society (Journal of Scientific Instruments)
The National Research Council of Canada (Canadian Journal of Chemistry)
The New York Academy of Sciences (Annals)
The Society of Chemical Industry (Chemistry and Industry)
Academic Press Inc., New York (Proceedings of International Symposia organised by the Instrument Society of America)
Butterworths & Co., London (Proceedings of International Symposia organised by the Institute of Petroleum and others)
Elsevier Publishing Company, Amsterdam (Journal of Chromatography, Anal. Chim. Acta)
The Macmillan Company, New York (Nature)
Pergamon Press Inc., New York (Chemical Engineering Science)
Reinhold Publishing Corporation, New York ("Gas Chromatography" by A. I. M. Keulemans)
Dr. Robert L. Bowman, Mr. Nathaniel Brenner, Dr. J. E. Callen, Mr. E. W. Ciepelinski, Dr. F. van der Craats, Mr. D. H. Desty, Mr. R. D. Eanes, Dr. A. Goldup, Dr. A. T. James, Dr. J. H. Knox, Dr. J. E. Lovelock, Dr. I. G. McWilliam, Dr. L. Ongkiehong, Mr. C. S. G. Phillips, Professor V. Pretorius, Mr. G. R. Primavesi, Dr. J. H. Purnell, Dr. F. C. Snowden, Dr. G. A. P. Tuey.

CONTENTS

Chapter 5
Column Performance—Mechanisms

Chapter 6
The Preparation and Use of Columns

Chapter 7
The Use of Detectors for Quantitative Analysis

Chapter 8
Ionisation Detectors

Chapter 9
Thermal Conductivity Detectors

Chapter 10
Other Detectors—Ancillary Apparatus

Chapter 11
Applications of Gas Chromatography

Chapter 1

Definitions and Technical Terms

1.1. Gas Chromatography

Gas chromatography is a method for separating components of mixtures of volatile compounds. In most applications, the separations are made to identify and determine the quantity of each component of a sample of the mixture, and analytical gas chromatographic apparatus includes additional devices for this purpose. In some applications, separations are made for preparative purposes, but the scale is not generally greater than that required for quantities of the order of 100 g. The technology and applications of gas chromatography are almost completely independent of other chromatographic techniques (*1–3*), to which little reference will be made.

The central item in the apparatus for gas chromatography is the chromatographic *Column*, a long tube packed permeably with some adsorbent (in the general, rather than the specifically chemical, sense). In the commonest technique of gas chromatography, the *Elution* technique, a stream of inert gas, the *Carrier* gas, passes continuously through the column, and the mixture to be separated is introduced instantaneously at the beginning of the column (Fig. 1.1) as a sample either of a gas or a volatile liquid. Let us suppose that the sample consists of one pure component. After introduction, it is swept by the carrier gas on to the column, first evaporating to form a *Vapour* if it is introduced as a liquid. When it reaches the column, it is largely adsorbed, but an equilibrium is set up between the column and the gas in the interstices of the column so that a proportion of the sample always remains in the gas phase. This portion moves a little further along the column in the carrier gas stream, where it again equilibrates with the column. At the same time, material already adsorbed in the column re-enters the gas phase so as to restore equilibrium with the clean carrier gas which follows up the zone of vapour. This process is shown by the arrows in Fig. 1.1b, which is an idealisation of the column in which the carrier gas is assumed to flow down the left-hand half and the adsorbent is contained in the right-hand half. The interface between the phases is used as a length abscissa along the column, and positive ordinates in each phase represent the concentrations of vapour therein. The process in which carrier gas containing the vapour is stripped by the adsorbent in front of the zone while the vapour enters the carrier gas at the rear goes on continuously, with the result that the zone of vapour moves along the column in a more or less compact zone.

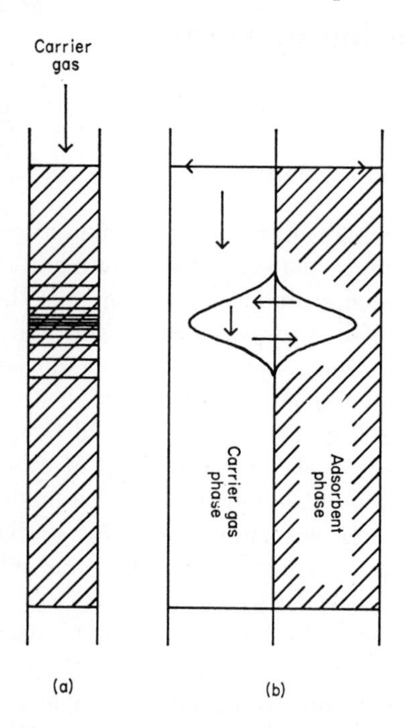

FIG. 1.1. Diagram of a permeably packed column and its idealisation in which gas and adsorbed phases are represented separately.

The speed at which the zone moves depends mainly on two factors, the rate of flow of the carrier gas and the extent to which the vapour is adsorbed. The faster the flow of carrier gas the faster the zone moves; and the more strongly the vapour is adsorbed on the column, the more slowly the zone moves. The quantitative relations describing this are given in Chapter 2. When two or more components are present in the sample, each usually behaves independently of the others, so that for a given carrier gas flow rate, the speed of the zone of each component will depend on the extent to which it is adsorbed. Since different substances differ in their adsorption, they may therefore be separated by making use of their different speeds of progress through the column. If they are eluted to the far end of the column, they will appear one after the other in the gas stream, the fastest first and the slowest last.

It remains to specify the nature of the adsorbent. We have used this word in a general sense, rather than in the strict chemical sense of a substrate which will retain a vapour on its surface. In a few cases, some of which are important, adsorbents in the chemical sense, such as carbon, alumina, or silica gel, are used as the packing material for columns, but in more than 90% of applications, the column material is a liquid held in place on the column by being *absorbed* on an inert solid support. Gas chromatography with this kind of column is called *Gas Liquid Chromatography* (G.L.C.). This method is a direct extension of liquid-liquid partition chromatography used for separating solutes from mixed solutions, since the vapour in the carrier gas is exactly analogous to the solute in the eluting liquid. The distribution of solute between eluting liquid and stationary liquid in partition chromatography is described by the same law as the distribution of vapour between eluting gas and stationary liquid in gas-liquid chromatography, so that G.L.C. has often been called "Gas Partition Chromatography," though international convention no longer favours this name. In the case of G.L.C., the solution of a vapour in a liquid is described by Henry's law, which is:

$$q = \beta c, \tag{1.1}$$

where q is the concentration of vapour in the stationary phase, c is the concentration of vapour in the gas phase, and β is a constant. The constant β is a measure of the adsorption of a vapour in the adsorbent, and therefore determines the speed of the zone of vapour through the column. Though it should strictly be called the "Henry's Law Constant," it is conventionally called the *Partition Coefficient* by virtue of the analogy with liquid-liquid chromatography. The illogicality of refusing to use the word "Partition" in the name of the technique, but using it in the name of the principal quantitative measure in the technique is too well established to change.

Though the elution technique is the most common, there are two other techniques by which gas chromatography can be used, *Displacement* and *Frontal* analysis. Both techniques apply only when chemical adsorbents are used for the columns, and chemical adsorbents are more suitable for use with these techniques than with elution. Displacement and frontal techniques will be described in part of Chapter 6. The rest of the book is concerned solely with elution chromatography.

1.2. Basic Apparatus of Gas Chromatography

The instrumentation of gas chromatography is remarkably simple compared to many other recent analytical techniques. Figure 1.2 shows a block schematic diagram of a typical gas-liquid chromatography apparatus, such as might be used for analysis.

Carrier gas from the tank of compressed gas first passes to a controller, the usual purpose of which is to maintain a constant flow of gas. The gas then passes to the beginning of the column, at the inlet to which is a *Sample Injector* through which the sample to be analysed can be introduced. The carrier gas then elutes the components of the mixture through the column. At the far end is a device, the *Detector*, the purpose of which is to detect the separate components of the mixture as they emerge one by one. The detector uses some physical or chemical property of the vapours by which they can be indicated and, if possible, measured. A further piece of apparatus not always incorporated is a *Flowmeter* to measure the rate of flow of gas.

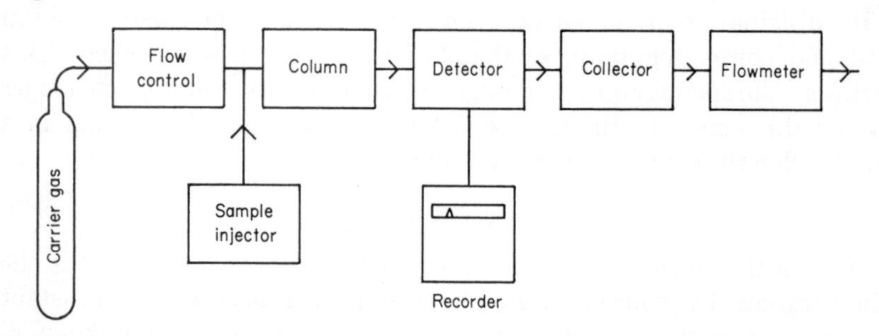

FIG. 1.2. Block schematic diagram of apparatus for analytical gas chromatography.

The details of the design of the apparatus for chromatography will be considered in later chapters. For the moment it is sufficient to outline the operation of the various sections of the apparatus simply to indicate how the technique works and to introduce technical terms.

(1) Any gas which is easily distinguishable in the detector from any components of the mixture can be chosen as the carrier gas. In most cases a permanent gas such as helium, argon, nitrogen, or hydrogen is used.

(2) Flow controls can either be true flow controls, which allow a definite rate of flow of gas, or they can be pressure controls which control the input pressure to the column. Since the column generally acts as a constant choke, a constant input pressure will itself ensure a constant flow. Pressure controls are simpler than flow controls and are used more commonly.

(3) For analytical purposes, reasonable dimensions for a permeably packed column might be 6 feet long by $\frac{1}{4}$ inch diameter. In G.L.C. the actual dissolving agent is a liquid which must remain stationary in the column without draining. It is therefore absorbed or otherwise held upon

an inert solid support of some porous material which will allow the passage of gas. Kieselguhr, which can absorb up to 40% by weight of a liquid without becoming unduly moist, is commonly used. The application of this property in making dynamite is, of course, well known. More recently other supporting materials have been used, such as ground firebrick, glass beads, etc., and these will be discussed in detail in Chapter 6. A further necessary property of the supporting material is that it should not itself adsorb any of the components of the mixture, and therefore must be inert. The supporting material is often simply called the *Support*. The liquid solvent is called the *Stationary Liquid*. The two together are called the *Stationary Phase*, though this phrase is often used for the stationary liquid alone.

Another kind of column consists of a long fine tube of which the inner surface is coated with stationary liquid. Such columns, called *Capillary Columns*, are particularly useful in the analysis of microscopic samples, and their use is increasing, though there are some applications for which they are not at present suitable.

The stationary liquid must be of such a nature as to dissolve all the components of the mixture (with the possible exception of one) and furthermore it must be completely involatile relative to any of them. For relatively involatile mixtures, columns are operated at elevated temperatures. The best temperature at which to run the column for a given mixture depends upon the design of the column and upon the mixture; the temperature of the column may be anything between 100°C above and 100°C below the boiling points of components in the mixture. Stationary liquids must have boiling points which are high in comparison with the boiling points of the components of the mixture. Almost any high-boiling liquid may be used, for example, silicone oils, high-boiling esters such as phthalates, high-boiling paraffins, and many others. Factors affecting the choice of stationary liquids and other column conditions are discussed in Chapter 3.

(4) One of the most commonly used properties for detecting the vapours is the thermal conductivity of the gas, which changes when a vapour is present. The thermal conductivity cell, or catharometer, generally consists of some kind of electrically heated element situated in the gas stream. The resistance of the element is continuously measured by a Wheatstone's bridge, which also serves to supply the electrical heating current. When pure carrier gas is passing through the cell, the thermal conductivity is constant. In these conditions, the heated element is continually losing heat by conduction to the walls of the cell, and an equilibrium is reached in which the rate of heat input from the electric current is balanced by the rate of loss of heat by conduction, so that the temperature, and therefore the resistance, of the heated element is constant. If a vapour comes through the end of the column into the thermal conductivity cell, the thermal con-

ductivity of the carrier gas is changed by its presence, and this disturbs the equilibrium. Either more or less heat is conducted to the walls, and the temperature of the hot element changes; this causes a change in its resistance, which in turn causes the bridge to go off balance. Usually the galvanometer of the bridge is a recording meter, and so the record of the meter will be a straight line when no vapour is coming through, while zones of vapour emerging from the column will show as temporary deflections of the line. The straight line corresponding to pure carrier gas is called the *Base Line*, and the deflections corresponding to the presence of vapours are called *Peaks*. The plot given by the recording meter of the detector is called the *Chromatogram*. Thermal conductivity detectors are considered in Chapter 9.

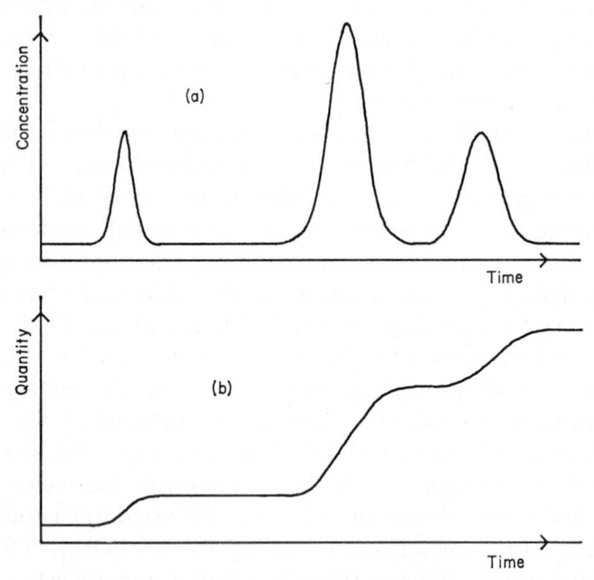

FIG. 1.3. (a) Peaks given by a differentiating detector. (b) Steps given by an integrating detector.

Many other kinds of detector are used, and these can be classified in many different ways. One important classification gives two classes (Fig. 1.3):

(i) *Differentiating detectors*, which record concentrations ($\partial w/\partial V$) or rate of flow of mass of vapour ($\partial w/\partial t$) rather than actual masses (w). The chromatogram given by these consists of peaks (Fig. 1.3a). If the deflection of the meter is proportional to the concentration of vapour, then the total amount of vapour present in the zone corresponding to a peak is proportional to the area of the peak. Differentiating detectors are used in the great majority of applications and in all discussion the chromatogram should be assumed to be of the differential class unless it is specified otherwise.

(ii) *Integrating detectors*, in which the deflection is proportional to the total quantity rather than to the concentration. When no vapour is passing through, the recorder gives a straight line. As a zone of vapour passes through, the recorder moves across the strip-chart by a distance proportional to the quantity of vapour that has appeared. When another vapour appears, the recorder moves further across the chart, and so on (Fig. 1.3b). The chromatogram of an integrating detector consists of a series of steps, the sloping part of each step corresponding to the appearance of a peak in a differential detector. It is clear from Fig. 1.3 that the upper chromatogram is the plot of the differential coefficient of the lower one. For general convenience, and accurate work, differential detectors are more satisfactory than the integrating class, though there are a few useful applications of the latter.

Detectors in general are discussed in Chapter 7. Other kinds of detector are discussed in Chapters 8 and 10.

(5) There remain the items of auxiliary apparatus, sample injectors, sample collectors, flowmeters, together with the apparatus for temperature control of the column and other apparatus. Details of sample injectors are given in Section 10.6. Details of sample collectors are given in Section 6.6. Other items, being familiar pieces of general scientific equipment, are not discussed.

1.3. The Chromatogram

Analytically useful information obtainable from the chromatogram is of three kinds.

The simplest thing a chromatogram can show is whether or not a given sample is pure. If the chromatogram contains more than one peak, the sample contains more than one component. Very often this technique is used as a test of purity of substances. When one is looking for possible trace impurities in a sample of nearly pure substance, the detector must be sufficiently sensitive to be able to detect possible traces. This application is considered in more detail in Chapter 7.

The second use of the chromatogram is to enable one to identify the individual components of a mixture qualitatively. This information is sometimes obtainable directly by measuring the distance on the strip-chart from the point corresponding to the beginning of a run to the centre of the peak, which, for given conditions of operation, is characteristic of the component. As mentioned above, the speed of movement of a zone through the column is governed, amongst other things, by the ease of adsorption of the vapour, which in the case of G.L.C. is measured by the partition coefficient. The speed of movement of the zone through the column determines the total time it takes to move from one end of the column to the other, and it is this time that is registered by the above distance measured on the strip-chart. Thus, the distance on the strip-chart is determined by the partition coefficient of the vapour in the column, which is a characteristic of the vapour. The time taken by a zone to traverse the column is called the *Retention Time.*

The retention time of a component is itself a function of the many variables of column operation which are discussed in Chapter 2. Among the more important of these is the flow rate of the carrier gas. The greater the flow rate, the smaller the retention time, and to a first approximation, the retention time and the flow rate are inversely proportional so long as the pressure drop across the column is small. The constant product of the flow rate and the retention time is equal to the total volume of gas required to move a component from one end of the column to the other. This volume can also be used as a characteristic of the component in a given column, and has the advantage that it is independent of at least one operating variable, the flow rate; it is called the *Retention Volume.*

Retention volumes are themselves functions of many other column operating variables, which in routine analytical work are not generally measured. In order that retention data may still be used without measuring all these variables, use can be made of the fact that change in many of the operating variables affects all retention volumes by a similar factor, so that retention volumes stand in the same ratios one to another whatever the conditions. Hence, in many cases one substance of which the retention volume is set arbitrarily at unity is chosen from a mixture, and the retention volumes of all other components are quoted relative to this. Such a reference substance is called an *Internal Standard* for *Relative Retention Volumes.* If the internal standard is not a component of a mixture of interest, it is added to the mixture before chromatographing.

Gas chromatography provides only one number as a characteristic of each vapour. This is insufficient to characterise any particular one from the totality of volatile substances, since retention volumes can only be measured with an accuracy of about 0.1 to 1%, and many vapours have virtually identical retention volumes on a given column. The scope of retention data for qualitative identification can be somewhat enlarged by comparing chromatograms of a mixture obtained on two different columns (Section 3.10), but even with this, gas chromatography should not be regarded as an absolute means of qualitative analysis. Its use in this field is generally in conjunction with some other source of information. In this connection, the separative power of the technique is relevant, for a vapour giving an unknown peak can be condensed separately from the gas stream and submitted to more unambiguous analysis, for example, chemical analysis, infrared spectrophotometry, or mass spectrometry. Many such applications can be found in the literature.

The third kind of information obtainable from the chromatogram is a quantitative analysis of the mixture, which is provided by the detector rather than the column. With most detectors, the deflection of the meter is proportional to the concentration of vapour, and so, if the flow rate is constant, the area of the peak will give the total amount of vapour. This may be made the basis for an exact quantitative analysis. Gas chromatography is mainly used for quantitative analysis, for the method is particularly suitable for the routine analysis of industrial samples, the interpretation of the data is simple, and the apparatus does not require skilled personnel.

It has been assumed hitherto that the components of a mixture are completely separated on their appearance at the far end of the column. There remains another factor to consider; the ability of the column to

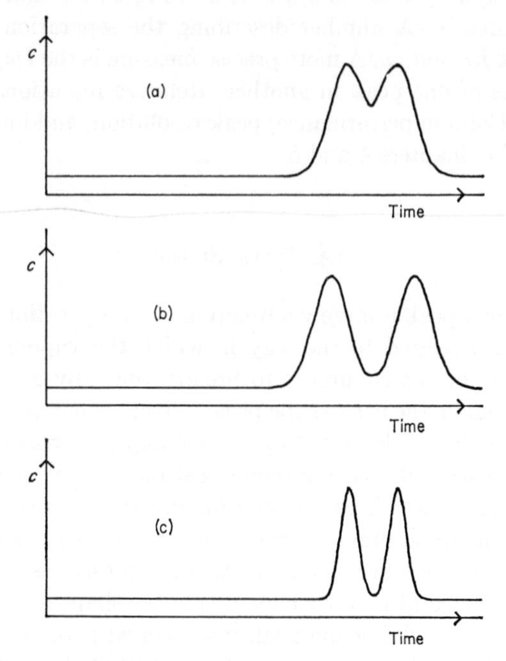

FIG. 1.4. (a) Incompletely resolved peaks. (b) The same resolved by increasing the relative retention. (c) The same resolved by increasing the column performance.

perform its separations. In the case of two components of which the partition coefficients are not very different, the retention times also will not be very different and the two zones may be incompletely separated. The chromatogram resulting from such a case is shown in Fig. 1.4a. The overlap of the two peaks is produced by two causes: (1) the closeness of the peaks and (2) the width of the peaks. These two causes are largely independent. The overlap could be reduced either by arranging the peaks to lie further apart (Fig. 1.4b) or by making each peak narrower (Fig. 1.4c). The first is due to the closeness of the partition coefficients, which is a function of the chemical natures of the components concerned and the nature of the stationary liquid, and separations can often be improved by judicious choice of stationary liquid. The second is a function of the column design and the manner of operation; attention to these can often make the peaks narrower. The closeness and width of peaks are each described by numerical quantities. The closeness is measured by the *Relative Retention*, which is the ratio of the retention volumes of the two components (subject to the qualifications given in Chapter 2). The peak width is measured by the *Column Performance*, which is related to the ratio of the standard deviation of the peak to its retention volume, σ/V. The separation as a whole is improved by increasing the relative retention and improving the column performance. A number describing the separation as a whole is called the *Peak Resolution*. A more precise measure is the *Impurity Fraction* of the contents of one peak in another. Relative retentions are discussed in Chapter 3. Column performance, peak resolution, and impurity fraction are discussed in Chapters 4 and 5.

1.4. Peak Shape

The shape of a peak is largely a function of the operation of the column, though it is also related to the way in which the vapour is introduced. The usual effect of the column is to broaden out any given input distribution so as to make the peak shape progressively wider and shallower; it is this broadening that is described by the column performance. Broadening factors can be specified, and for theoretical purposes it is also possible to specify a column in which broadening factors are absent, though no such column can be made in practice. Such a column is called an *Ideal* column. A real column in which broadening factors are present is called *Non-ideal*.

A further important factor which affects the shape of peaks is the way in which the vapour giving the peak interacts with the stationary phase. For every vapour and every stationary phase there is a relation between the concentration of vapour in the gas phase and its concentration in the stationary phase when there is equilibrium between the two. This can be expressed by an equation which is called the *Isotherm* of interaction between the phases; the use of the word isotherm implies that the temperature must be specified for the equation to hold.

The simplest isotherm that can hold is the *Linear* isotherm, in which the concentration in the gas phase (c) and the concentration in the stationary phase (q) are connected by Eq. (1.1). In the case of ideal chromatography with a linear isotherm, it can be shown (Chapter 2) that whatever the input distribution of a particular component, the output distribution will

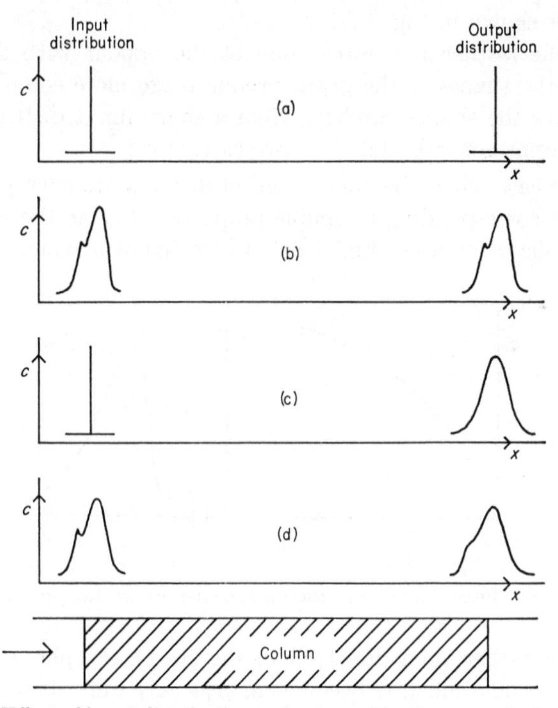

FIG. 1.5. Effect of input distribution and column ideality on peak shape. (a) Linear ideal chromatography, sharp input. (b) Linear ideal chromatography, non-sharp input. (c) Linear non-ideal chromatography, sharp input. (d) Linear non-ideal chromatography, non-sharp input.

have exactly the same shape. Figure 1.5a illustrates the output distribution for a sharp input distribution, and Fig. 1.5b illustrates the output distribution for a non-sharp input distribution. For good separations, the input distribution should be as narrow as possible, so that the output distribution can be similarly narrow, and, in practice, sample injectors are designed with this end in view.

In the case of non-ideal chromatography with a linear isotherm, such as is found in practical gas-liquid chromatography, the broadening factors operate upon the input distribution, and it can be shown (*4*) that they do this in such a way that any input distribution tends to be broadened out into a distribution that is very close to the distribution of the normal curve of error, or "Gaussian Distribution." In the case of a sharp input distribution, the output distribution is virtually an exact Gaussian distribution (see, however, Section 5.4). This is illustrated in Fig. 1.5c. In the case where the input distribution is not sharp, the output distribution is more or less a Gaussian distribution superimposed upon the input distribution, as is shown in Fig. 1.5d.

When the isotherm of interaction of the vapour with the phases is not linear, the shapes of the peaks produced are more complex. We shall consider only the shapes resulting from a sharp input distribution. Non-linear isotherms generally fall into two categories:

(1) The case when the concentration in the stationary phase (q) lags behind that corresponding to simple proportionality as the concentration in the gas phase (c) rises (Fig. 1.6a), which happens when the vapour is

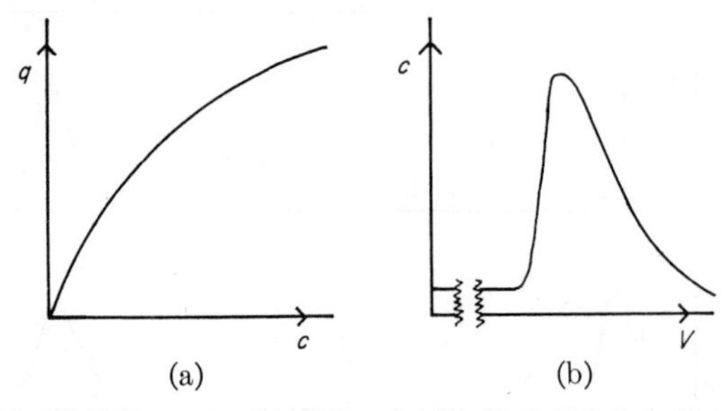

FIG. 1.6. Peak shape for isotherms concave toward the pressure axis.

adsorbed on rather than dissolved in the stationary phase. As sites for adsorption become filled, it becomes increasingly difficult for any further vapour to enter. The effect of this in the chromatography of the vapour is as if the partition coefficient were lower at higher concentrations of vapour. The lower the partition coefficient, the more rapidly the chromatographic zone moves, and since the concentration is highest in the middle of the zone, the middle of the zone tends to move faster than the edges. This results in the zone becoming skewed towards the outlet of the column, so that the peak shape shows a sharp front profile and a diffuse rear profile (Fig. 1.6b). The extent of this skewing depends on the degree of curvature of the isotherm; the greater the curvature, the greater the skewing.

(2) The opposite case also occurs sometimes; here the isotherm is such

that the concentration in the stationary phase exceeds that of simple proportionality at higher concentrations (Fig. 1.7a). The partition coefficient is effectively higher at the higher concentrations, with the result that the centre of the peak tends to lag, and the chromatogram shows a peak with a diffuse front profile and a sharp rear profile (Fig. 1.7b).

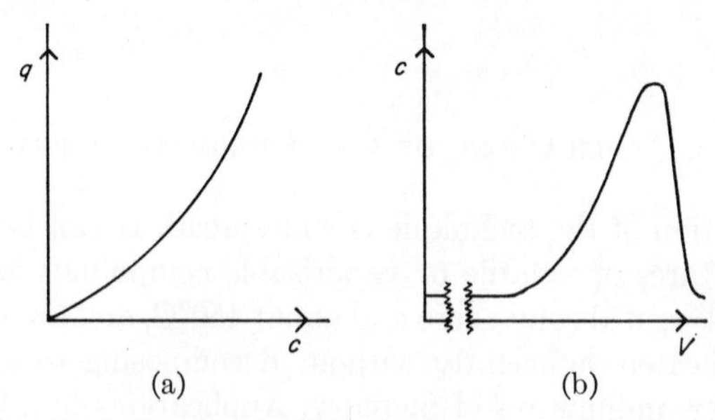

FIG. 1.7. Peak shape for isotherms convex toward the pressure axis.

The most common case of the first kind of non-linearity occurs when the vapours are adsorbed according to the Langmuir adsorption isotherm:

$$q = \frac{ac}{1 + bc}, \tag{1.2}$$

where a and b are constants. The equation gives a virtually linear relation between q and c when c is small compared with $1/b$, but this ceases to be so when c becomes appreciable compared with $1/b$. When c is large, so that it is large compared with $1/b$, then q becomes virtually independent of c; this corresponds to saturation of the adsorbent. The asymmetry of peaks from columns of adsorbents was formerly a serious drawback to their use by the elution technique, so that in the first couple of years of elution gas chromatography, adsorbents were almost totally neglected. However, more recently, the sensitivity of methods of detection of vapours has increased so much that adsorbent columns can be effectively used with samples of vapour so small that the concentration is always small compared with $1/b$. In these circumstances, the part of the isotherm that is used is nearly linear, and the asymmetry produced is small. Such adsorbent columns are regularly used for the analysis of permanent gases and other substances of very low boiling point, and can be used for less volatile compounds if required.

Non-linearity of the second kind described is rarer than adsorption non-linearity. There is no case reported where it is useful, and when it appears, its removal is desirable. This kind of isotherm arises when the vapour has a greater affinity for itself than for the stationary phase. At first the stationary phase adsorbs or dissolves a small quantity of the vapour, and after that the quantity already adsorbed or dissolved attracts more of itself. This isotherm, therefore, tends to arise with strongly polar vapours having strong mutual attraction, for instance, with water upon charcoal. Further cases often arise in partition chromatography when the vapour is polar but the stationary phase is not. These cases are treated in Section 3.5.

1.5. Applications of Gas Chromatography

The application of the technique is widespread. It can be used for the analysis of mixtures of volatile or vaporisable compounds boiling at any temperature between absolute zero and about 450°C, and for any substance which can be heated sufficiently without decomposing to give a vapour pressure of a few millimetres of mercury. Applications to a large range of specific classes of compound are considered in Chapter 11.

The size of sample used in gas chromatography may vary over a wide range. Analyses may be easily performed on quantities of the order of micrograms, and with a little care on quantities of the order of millimicrograms. There is no theoretical upper limit to the size of sample that may be handled if the chromatographic apparatus is built to accomodate it, but in gas chromatography, the ratio of price to throughput is so great that commercial considerations are limiting. Preparative apparatuses dealing with up to hundreds of grams of sample are available.

In addition to analytical and preparative applications, gas chromatographic methods have also been used in pure scientific studies, e.g., for the determination of partition coefficients, heats of solution, etc. Such applications are implicit in Chapter 3.

1.6. History

Several reports of techniques similar to gas chromatography appeared in the 1930's, but the first publications recognising it as a separate technique were those of Claesson *et al.* (*5*), who used columns of chemical adsorbents, and somewhat insensitive catharometers as detectors. As previously explained, these were not very suitable for use with elution chromatography, and Claesson used displacement and frontal techniques.

The development of gas chromatography was enormously accelerated by the introduction in 1952 of gas-liquid chromatography by James and Martin (*6*), following an earlier suggestion made by Martin and Synge (*7*). Since then the subject has expanded rapidly in a manner resembling logarithmic growth. After James and Martin's papers, a few workers developed the subject, till in the middle of 1956 there were some tens of papers on gas-liquid chromatography which contained most of the basic principles of the subject. Since 1956, a steadily increasing number of papers, particularly on applications, has appeared, and at present there are at least 3000 papers, articles, and communications on the subject.

References

1. Lederer, E., and Lederer, M., "Chromatography," 3rd ed. Elsevier, Amsterdam, 1959.
2. Cassidy, H. G., "Fundamentals of Chromatography," Vol. X of "Technique of Organic Chemistry" (A. Weissburger, ed.). Interscience, New York, 1957.
3. Williams, T. I., "An Introduction to Chromatography," Chemical Publ., New York, 1947; Blackie & Son, London, 1949.
4. Klinkenberg, A., and Sjenitzer, F., *Chem. Eng. Sci.* **5**, 258 (1956).
5. Claesson, S., *Arkiv. Kemi Mineral Geol.* **23A** (1), (1946).
6. James, A. T., and Martin, A. J. P., *Eiochem. J.* **50**, 679 (1952).
7. Martin, A. J. P., and Synge, R. L. M., *Eiochem. J.* **35**, 1358 (1941).

Chapter 2

Retention Volume and Column Variables

2.1. Introduction

The relations between retention volume, retention time, flow rate, partition coefficient, and other quantities which were defined in the last chapter can all be specified mathematically. Equations relating the various quantities are important in practice because they provide a method for quoting gas chromatographic results in a form independent of variables governing only the particular column on which the results were obtained, so that they become universal to all columns and all workers. Use of such equations also enables fundamental quantities, such as partition coefficients, heats of solution, or entropies of solution, to be calculated from measured retention times.

An attempt to secure uniformity in the presentation of data has been made by a committee under IUPAC. The preliminary recommendations have been published (*1*), and the nomenclature of this book generally conforms with these.

2.2. The First Order Conservation Equation

The quantitative theory may be explained simply and concisely through a first order partial differential conservation equation with the concentrations of the vapour in the gas and the liquid phases as dependent variables, and the volume of gas passed and the distance along the column as independent variables. An oversimplified form of the equation was first given by Wilson (*2*) and this was modified by DeVault (*3*) to give the equation that appears below [Eq. (2.4)].

Let V = volume of gas passed through the column (cc),
x = distance from inlet end of the column (cm),
q = concentration of the vapour in the stationary phase (mole/g),

c = concentration of the vapour in the gas phase (mole/cc),
m = mass of stationary phase per unit length of column (g/cm),
a = volume of gas phase per unit length of column (cm^2).

Consider a small cross section of infinitesimal thickness dx chosen so as to be in a zone of vapour in the chromatographic column (Fig. 2.1). At

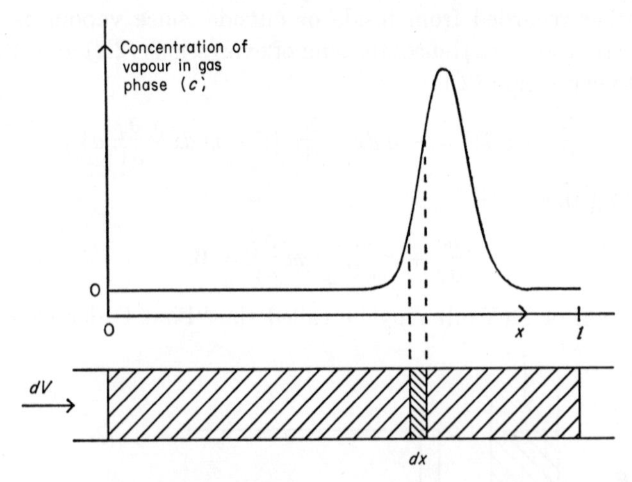

FIG. 2.1. Cross section of thickness dx in a chromatographic zone.

any instant, the cross section will contain a certain amount of vapour, some in each phase. The change in this amount when a volume of eluting gas dV is passed will be considered from two points of view: (1) that of an observer outside the cross section, and (2) that of an observer inside the cross section. Since mass is conserved, the observations made from each point of view must be equal.

(1) The concentration difference of vapour in the gas phase across the cross section is:

$$\frac{\partial c}{\partial x} \cdot dx.$$

Hence, the decrease in the total mass of vapour in the zone as a result of passing dV of eluting gas is:

$$\frac{\partial c}{\partial x} \cdot dx\, dV. \tag{2.1}$$

(2) From the point of view of an observer inside the cross section, the vapour is distributed between two phases. The decrease in the total amount of vapour due to change in the amount in the gas phase is:

$$-a\, dx \cdot \frac{\partial c}{\partial V} \cdot dV. \tag{2.2}$$

Similarly, the decrease in the total amount of vapour due to the change in the amount in the stationary phase is:

$$-m\,dx \cdot \frac{\partial q}{\partial V} \cdot dV. \tag{2.3}$$

However, the amount of solute removed from the cross section must be the same whether regarded from inside or outside, since vapour is not lost inside the cross section. Hence, the sum of expressions (2.2) and (2.3) must be equal to expression (2.1):

$$\frac{\partial c}{\partial x} \cdot dx\,dV = -a\,dx \cdot \frac{\partial c}{\partial V}\,dV - m\,dx \cdot \frac{\partial q}{\partial V}\,dV,$$

or, cancelling the $dx\,dV$,

$$\frac{\partial c}{\partial x} + a\,\frac{\partial c}{\partial V} + m\,\frac{\partial q}{\partial V} = 0. \tag{2.4}$$

This equation of DeVault may be called the "First Order Conservation

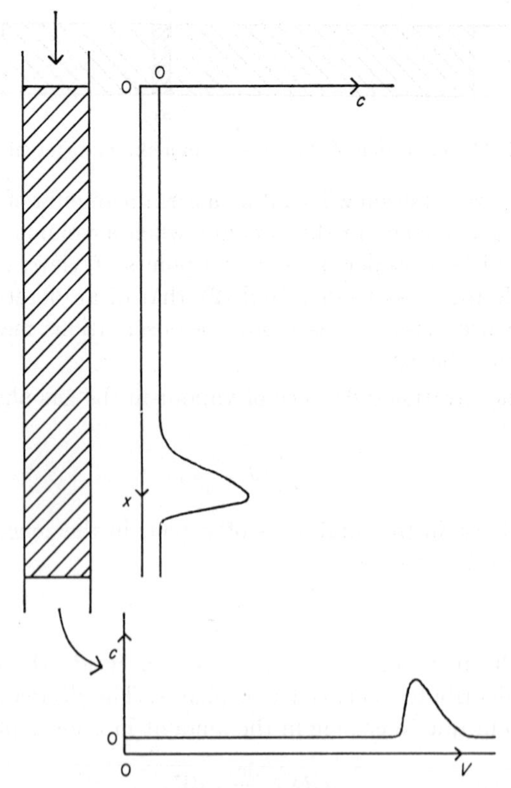

FIG. 2.2. Distinction between $c(V)$ and $c(x)$.

Equation" of chromatography. When an isotherm between c and q is specified, and boundary conditions are given, this equation may be solved for c or q. When diffusion occurs in the column, the time, t, is also a significant variable; the use of the equation in these circumstances is considered in Chapter 5. In the present chapter, diffusion in the column is to be neglected.

In any isotherm observed in practice, $\partial c/\partial q$ is always positive, so that $\partial c/\partial V$ always has the same sign as $\partial q/\partial V$, and, since a and m are both positive, it necessarily follows from Eq. (2.4) that $\partial c/\partial V$ and $\partial c/\partial x$ have opposite signs. This fact and its importance are illustrated in Fig. 2.2. If the chromatogram, regarded as a function of c against x, has a given shape while it is in the column, its shape when it is regarded as a function of c against V at the far end of the column will be the mirror image. In the figure, while the asymmetric peak is in the column, its sharp profile is further along the column than its diffuse profile, and consequently at the end of the column the sharp profile appears first, with the diffuse profile coming later at a greater value of V. This is not significant in the case of symmetrical peaks such as are usually found in partition chromatography, but it should be remembered in the discussion of asymmetrical peaks such as appear by elution from adsorbents or in partition chromatography in conditions where symmetrical peaks are not obtained.

2.3. The Conservation Equation for Linear Isotherms

When the isotherm of interaction of a vapour between the phases is linear as in the case of partition chromatography, the relation between q and c is simply:

$$q = \beta c, \tag{2.5}$$

where β is the partition coefficient. If this is substituted in the conservation equation, the result is:

$$\frac{\partial c}{\partial x} + (a + m\beta)\frac{\partial c}{\partial V} = 0, \tag{2.6}$$

which has the general solution:

$$c = \phi\{V - x(a + m\beta)\}, \tag{2.7}$$

where ϕ is an arbitrary function. The form of ϕ is determined by the initial conditions, that is, by the way in which the vapour is introduced into the beginning of the column. In partition chromatography using the elution technique, the ideal method of introduction is that of an infinitely thin band of vapour instantaneously introduced, which minimises overlap between successive bands of different vapours at the end of the column.

Such an input distribution may be expressed by the "Delta Function," defined by:

$$\delta(y) = 0 \qquad (y \neq 0),$$
$$\int_{-\infty}^{+\infty} \delta(y) = 1. \tag{2.8}$$

Using this, Eq. (2.7) becomes:

$$c = \delta\{V - x(a + m\beta)\} \tag{2.9}$$

which has a non-zero value only when

$$V = x(a + m\beta). \tag{2.10}$$

When the distance x is defined to be the length of the column, l, V becomes the volume of gas required to move the delta-function plug of vapour from one end of the column to the other. By definition, this is the retention volume (see, however, Section 2.5), for which the recommended symbol is $V_R{}^0$. Hence,

$$V_R{}^0 = l(a + m\beta). \tag{2.11}$$

Equation (2.11) is basic to gas chromatography, for it relates the retention volume of a vapour to its partition coefficient; that is, it relates the most important chromatographic characteristic of the vapour to a purely thermodynamic characteristic which is independent of the actual column used. Normally, a, m, and l are all easily measurable quantities, so that Eq. (2.11) enables the chromatographic behaviour of the vapour to be predicted from its partition coefficient with complete certainty. The direct use of Eq. (2.11) as it stands, however, is complicated by the fact that $V_R{}^0$ is not obtained simply by multiplying the measured retention time and the measured carrier gas flow rate, and the discussion of the following three sections is required before *observable* chromatographic quantities can be related to partition coefficients.

Two assumptions are made in the derivation of Eq. (2.11). The first is that the input distribution is that of a delta function. Such a distribution is never possible in practice, for a finite weight of pure vapour occupies a finite volume. However, the width of the input distribution measured in volume units is small compared to the retention volume, so that the effect of the input distribution on the retention volume is usually only a minor one (Section 2.9). The second assumption is that there is no broadening in the column as the zone of vapour moves along. In fact, this is not so; the zone broadens, largely because of diffusion occurring in the column. It is shown in Sections 5.3 and 5.4, however, that if the vapour has a linear isotherm and the volume $V_R{}^0$ is the retention volume of the maximum of the broadened peak, Eq. (2.11) still holds in most circumstances. Thus, the two assumptions that have been made are made as simplifications. If they are not made, a slightly more accurate, but very much less simple version of Eq. (2.11) is obtained.

In Eq. (2.11), the product *al* is the total gas hold-up, or dead volume, of the column, and the product *ml* is the total weight of stationary phase in the column. If these are given the symbols V_M^0 and W, respectively, the equation becomes:

$$V_R^0 = V_M^0 + W\beta. \tag{2.12}$$

The retention volume is seen to consist of two parts. The first is equal to the gas hold-up, and is merely the volume that would be required to move a vapour from one end of the column to the other as if it were not dissolved by the stationary phase at all. The second, and from a practical point of view the more important, part is the volume which serves to move the vapour slowly along the column while it is moving in and out of the stationary phase. The equation shows that the greater the partition coefficient the greater the retention volume.

The total gas hold-up may easily be determined by introducing a small sample of a vapour not dissolved by the stationary phase, such as air, or some permanent gas other than the carrier. In this case, β is zero, and the volume of gas passed between introduction and emergence from the column is the gas hold-up. Substances which are separated by the column necessarily have non-zero values of β, and thus their retention volumes are greater than V_M^0. As a general rule, most practical separations involve retention volumes from 3 times to about 200 times the gas hold-up with packed columns, and from 1.2 to about 20 times with capillary columns.

The gas hold-up, measured as above, also includes volume between the sample injector cavity and the column, and volume between the column and the detector. Chovin (*4*) has drawn attention to this, and has proposed a distinction between observed retention volumes which include these spurious volumes and "true" retention volumes from which they have been subtracted out. The "true" value of V_M^0, therefore, would consist only of the interstitial volume of the column, whereas the observed value would be greater. The distinction is not made in the IUPAC preliminary recommendations, except in that the two words "gas hold-up" and "interstitial volume" are both presented, presumably as distinct entities. The practical significance of the distinction is usually small, since the spurious volumes are small. They are in effect considered in the sections dealing with the effect of sample and detector volumes (Sections 2.9 and 5.8).

2.4. Retention Volume and Retention Time

So far the retention of a vapour has been considered exclusively in terms of its retention volume, but in practice it is a retention time that is measured, for the experiment consists of noting the time at which a vapour was introduced and measuring the time taken before the peak maximum appears at the end of the column. The retention time is related to the retention volume by the equation:

$$V_R{}^0 = \dot{V} t_R, \tag{2.13}$$

where $\dot{V}$ is the volume flow rate of carrier gas in units, for example, of cubic centimetres per second or cubic centimetres per minute. When there is an appreciable pressure drop across the column, $\dot{V}$ is not constant, and Eq. (2.13) must be given a more general form [Eq. (2.29)].

By dividing Eq. (2.12) by $\dot{V}$ and substituting Eq. (2.13), an equation for the retention time of a vapour is obtained:

$$t_R = \frac{V_M{}^0}{\dot{V}} + \frac{W\beta}{\dot{V}}. \tag{2.14}$$

The retention time, like the retention volume, consists of two parts. The first term on the R.H.S. is the time taken for the carrier gas to sweep out the gas hold-up of the column, and hence is the retention time for a plug of undissolved gas for which β is zero; it may be called the "gas hold-up time," t_M. The second term on the R.H.S. gives the delay imposed upon a vapour by the action of the stationary phase, different delays for different vapours being provided by different values of β. It is clear that the remarks made about the ratio of gas hold-up to retention volume also apply to the ratio of gas hold-up time to retention time.

The ratio of the delay time to the gas hold-up time is significant in the theory of chromatography, particularly in connection with separation efficiency. A suitable name for the quantity is "retardation ratio," following a suggestion by Primavesi (*5*), and a suitable symbol is k, e.g., as used by Golay (*6*) and by van Deemter, Zuiderweg, and Klinkenberg (*7*).* Thus, k is defined by:

$$k = \frac{W\beta}{V_M{}^0} = \frac{m\beta}{a}. \tag{2.15}$$

Practical values of k are usually between about 2 and 200 for packed columns and between about 0.2 and 20 for capillary columns.

The division of the retention time into two terms, one due to the gas phase and one due to the stationary phase, suggests that the chromatographic process itself can be regarded in terms of times rather than volumes. The equilibrium of a vapour between the phases is a dynamic one in which the molecules of vapour are continually changing phase. The life history of a particular molecule of vapour in the column consists partly of periods in

* The symbol a has been used by Scott and Hazeldean (*8*), and σ by Bosanquet and Morgan (*9*), and by Bosanquet (*10*).

the gas phase, when it is moving down the column with the carrier gas at a volume speed $\dot{V}$, and partly of periods in the stationary phase, when it is still. The sum of the residence times in each phase is the total residence time of the molecule in the column, which is the retention time. The residence time in the gas phase is merely the gas hold-up time of the column, for while the molecule is in the gas phase it is moving at the carrier gas flow rate. The ratio of residence time in the stationary phase to the residence time in the gas phase is given by k, so that from Eqs. (2.14) and (2.15), the total residence time of the molecule is given by:

$$t_R = \frac{V_M{}^0}{\dot{V}}(1 + k). \tag{2.16}$$

A theory of chromatography in terms such as these has been given by Giddings and Eyring (*11*), Giddings (*12,13*), and by Beynon *et al.* (*14*). This "Stochastic" theory takes into account the fact that there is a spread in the total residence times of the molecules, and by calculating this arrives at conclusions similar to those given in Chapter 5. Giddings (*13*) has shown that the stochastic theory and the theory given here and in Chapter 5 are equivalent.

The quantity usually employed in liquid-liquid partition chromatography as a characteristic of the retention of a vapor is the retardation factor, R_F, defined as the ratio of the speed of the zone of solute to the speed of the eluting solvent. The common gas chromatographic equivalents of R_F are related to it by any of the equations:

$$R_F = \frac{1}{1 + k} = \frac{V_M{}^0}{V_M{}^0 + W\beta} = \frac{t_M}{t_M + (W\beta/\dot{V})}. \tag{2.17}$$

Though the flow rate as measured by the flowmeter is a volume flow rate, it is often more convenient to express flow rates as the average linear gas velocity in the column. If this is denoted by u, its connection with $\dot{V}$ is easily seen to be:

$$\dot{V} = au. \tag{2.18}$$

In terms of the measurable quantities $V_M{}^0$ and l, this becomes:

$$\dot{V} = \frac{V_M{}^0}{l} \cdot u. \tag{2.19}$$

In analytical columns, u is generally of the order of 1 to 10 cm/second.

2.5. Effect of Pressure Gradient

In a gas chromatographic column, the gas flows in the narrow interstices between the particles of packing, which offer resistance to flow, and thus, because of the finite viscosity of the gas, there is a pressure gradient along the length of the column. Such a pressure gradient would have no effect upon retention volumes and retention times were it not for the fact that the gas is compressible. Because of this the existence of a higher pressure at the inlet than at the outlet means that the density of the gas is greater at the inlet than at the outlet, and since the number of molecules per second flowing past a given point at the inlet must be the same as that flowing past a point at the outlet, it follows that the volume flow rate is greater at the outlet than at the inlet. Thus, a velocity gradient is an inevitable consequence of the pressure gradient in the column. These two gradients have several consequences in gas chromatography, one of which is an effect on the measurement of retention volumes. See also Section 5.19.

Normally, the flow rate is measured at the outlet from the column, so that the measured flow rate is greater than the flow rate at any other point in the column. Hence, a measured retention volume obtained by multiplying the observed retention time by the outlet flow rate is greater than the true retention volume. In order to correct for this, the form of the velocity gradient in the column must be known, and this in turn depends on the form of the pressure gradient. Following the original work of James and Martin (*15*) the forms of these gradients will be calculated and then a correction factor to convert the retention volume measured as above into the true retention volume will be produced [Eq. (2.34)].

(*a*) *The Pressure Gradient*

The pressure gradient, dP/dx, and the linear velocity, u, in a column are connected by the equation:

$$\frac{dP}{dx} = -\frac{\eta}{K}u, \tag{2.20}$$

where η is the gas viscosity and K is the "Column Permeability," which measured the conductance of the column to gas. It is more convenient to use volume flow rate than linear flow rate, so that, substituting Eq. (2.18), this becomes:

$$\frac{dP}{dx} = -\frac{\eta}{Ka}\dot{V}. \tag{2.21}$$

In this equation, $\dot{V}$ is a function of x. By a simple extension of Boyle's law, $\dot{V}(x)$ can be substituted by $P(x)$, since

$$P_o\dot{V}_o = P\dot{V}, \tag{2.22}$$

where P_o and $\dot{V}_o$ are the values at the outlet. Substitution of Eq. (2.22) into Eq. (2.21) gives:

$$\frac{dP}{dx} = -\left[\frac{\eta P_o\dot{V}_o}{Ka}\right]\frac{1}{P}. \tag{2.23}$$

The solution of this equation is simplified by the fact that the gas viscosity is independent of pressure, so that all the quantities in the square bracket can be regarded as constant. If the contents of the square bracket are denoted by $-K'$, the solution to Eq. (2.23) is simply:

$$x = \frac{P^2}{2K'} + K'', \tag{2.24}$$

where K'' is another constant. The two constants can be obtained from the initial and final conditions, for, if the inlet pressure is P_i and the outlet pressure P_o,

$$\begin{aligned} P &= P_i, \qquad \text{when } x = 0; \\ P &= P_o, \qquad \text{when } x = l. \end{aligned} \tag{2.25}$$

Substituting these in Eq. (2.24) gives:

$$K' = \frac{P_o^2 - P_i^2}{2l}, \qquad K'' = -\frac{P_i^2}{2K'}. \tag{2.26}$$

When these are substituted back in Eq. (2.24), the result is an equation for the pressure at any point in the column,

$$\frac{x}{l} = \frac{P_i^2 - P^2}{P_i^2 - P_o^2}. \tag{2.27}$$

The other quantities in the equation, P_o, P_i, and l, are all easily measurable. Figure 2.3 shows a plot of P/P_o as a function of x/l for various values

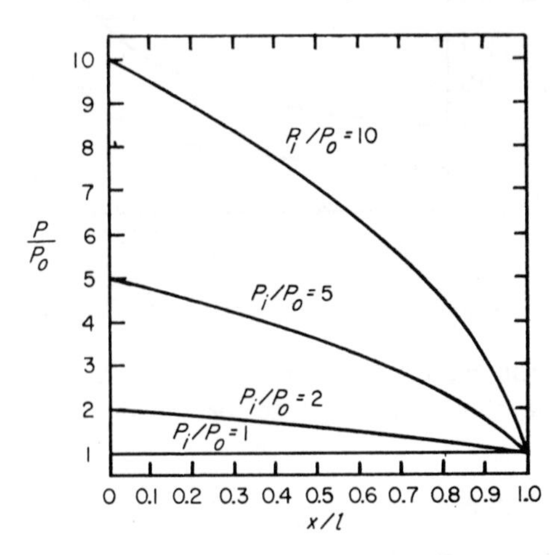

FIG. 2.3. Plots of P/P_o against x/l with P_i/P_o as parameter.

of the pressure ratio across the column, P_i/P_o. The fact that the lines are curved is a result of the compressibility of the gas in conjunction with the fact that the viscosity is independent of pressure. Were the moving phase not compressible, as in liquid-liquid chromatography, the plot would be linear. Note that the curves steepen towards the outlet end of the column, particularly at high pressure ratios, since in the later regions of the column, the gas velocity is greater and thus the pressure gradient must be greater in order to maintain that velocity.

(b) The Velocity Gradient

This is obtained from Eqs. (2.27) and (2.22). The result is:

$$\frac{x}{l} = \frac{(P_i/P_o)^2 - (\dot{V}_o/\dot{V})^2}{(P_i/P_o)^2 - 1}. \tag{2.28}$$

In Fig. 2.4, $V/\dot{V}_o$ is plotted as a function of x/l for various values of the pressure ratio. Note that when the pressure ratio is large, the great majority of the change in velocity takes place at the end of the column, almost

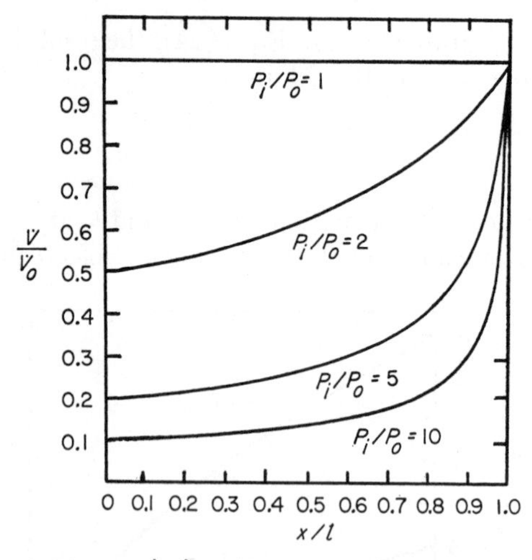

FIG. 2.4. Plots of $\dot{V}/\dot{V}_o$ against x/l with P_i/P_o as parameter.

as if the end of the column were acting as a choke. This observation is significant for the choice of flow rate for the best column performance (Section 5.19).

(c) Retention Volume

Equation (2.13), connecting retention time and retention volume, holds in any small region of the column, and over the whole column when the flow rate is the same throughout, but when the flow rate is a function of distance down the column, a more generalised form must be used. Regarding volume rather than distance as the independent variable, the general relation is easily seen to be:

$$t_R = \int_0^{V_R^0} \frac{dV}{\dot{V}}. \tag{2.29}$$

Using Eq. (2.22), this becomes:

$$t_R = \int_0^{V_R^0} \frac{PdV}{\dot{V}_o P_o}. \tag{2.30}$$

Changing the variable of integration by means of Eq. (2.10),

$$t_R = (a + m\beta) \int_0^l \frac{Pdx}{\dot{V}_o P_o}, \tag{2.31}$$

and again by means of Eq. (2.23), the result is:

$$t_R = (a + m\beta) \int_{P_i}^{P_o} \frac{P^2 dP}{K' \dot{V}_o P_o}. \tag{2.32}$$

Substituting the value of K' from Eq. (2.26), integrating, and rearranging,

$$t_R \dot{V}_o = l(a + m\beta) \times \left[\frac{2}{3} \cdot \frac{(P_i/P_o)^3 - 1}{(P_i/P_o)^2 - 1}\right]. \tag{2.33}$$

In this equation, the L.H.S., i.e., the product of the outlet flow rate and the measured retention time, is the measured retention volume. The first term of the product on the R.H.S. is seen by reference to Eq. (2.11) to be the true retention volume. Thus, the expression in square brackets is the correction factor required to correct the measured retention volume for the effect of the pressure drop across the column. The equation can be rewritten

$$V_R^0 = V_R \times \frac{3}{2} \cdot \frac{(P_i/P_o)^2 - 1}{(P_i/P_o)^3 - 1} = jV_R, \tag{2.34}$$

where V_R is the measured retention volume. The symbols V_R, V_R^0, and

$$j = \frac{3}{2} \cdot \frac{(P_i/P_o)^2 - 1}{(P_i/P_o)^3 - 1} \tag{2.35}$$

are internationally accepted. The measured quantity V_R is called the "Retention Volume" without any qualification. The quantity V_R^0 is called *Corrected Retention Volume*, thus modifying the definition given in Section 2.3. If V_M (uncorrected for pressure drop) is subtracted from V_R, the difference is called the *Adjusted Retention Volume*, V_R'. If j is applied to the adjusted retention volume, V_R', rather than to V_R, the result is the *Net Retention Volume*, V_N. It will be appreciated that the gas hold-up considered hitherto is a corrected quantity.

A plot of the correction factor as a function of the pressure ratio is given in Fig. 2.5. When the pressure ratio is less than 1.5, the correction factor is given by:

$$\frac{1}{j} = \frac{1}{2} + \frac{1}{2} \cdot \frac{P_i}{P_o} \tag{2.36}$$

within $\frac{1}{2}\%$. When the pressure ratio is large compared with unity, the correction factor approximates to $j = 3P_o/2P_i$. The correction factor has the value of unity when $P_i = P_o$, and is less than unity when $P_i > P_o$.

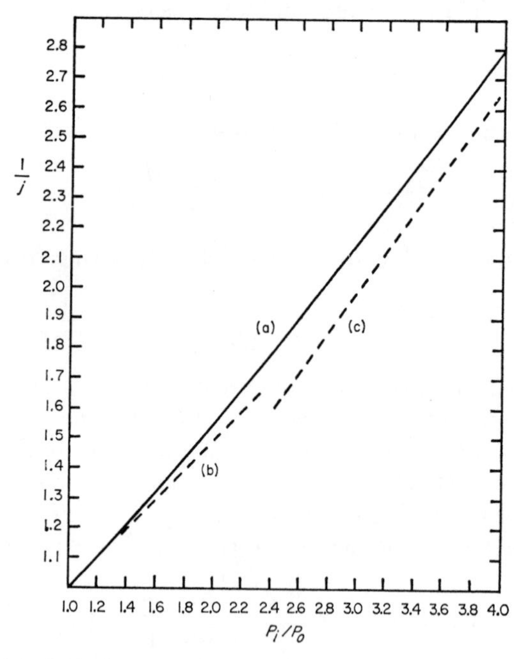

FIG. 2.5. Plot of the inverse correction factor, $1/j$. (a) As given by Eq. (2.34). (b) As given by approximation (2.36). (c) As given by the approximation $j = 3P_o/2P_i$.

The above calculation has been made on the assumption that the flowmeter is on the outlet side of the column, so that the measured retention volume involves $\dot{V}_o$. A similar calculation can be made in which the measured retention volume is assumed to be the product of the inlet flow rate and the retention time. In this case, the equivalent of Eqs. (2.33) and (2.36) is:

$$V_R = V_R{}^0 \left[\frac{2}{3}\left(1 + \frac{P_o/P_i}{1 + P_i/P_o}\right)\right] \simeq V_R{}^0 \left(\frac{1}{2} + \frac{1}{2}\frac{P_o}{P_i}\right). \tag{2.37}$$

It is interesting to note that in this case measured retention volumes are smaller than the true retention volumes, and also that the size of the correction is smaller than in the previous case. This corresponds with the fact that most of the velocity gradient is at the outlet end of the column.

2.6. Retention Volume and Column Temperature

A further correction to the retention volume may be necessary if the flow rate is measured at a temperature other than that of the column. In most common practice, the flowmeter operates at room temperature, whereas the column may operate at almost any temperature either hotter or cooler. During its passage through the column, the carrier gas takes the temperature of the column, and the volume rate of flow of the gas is determined by its temperature through Charles' law. The volume of a given mass of gas at constant pressure is related to its absolute temperature T by:

$$\frac{V}{T} = \frac{V_o}{T_o}, \tag{2.38}$$

and thus, using the principle of conservation of mass, the flow rate is connected with the temperature by a similar relation. In particular, if $\dot{V}_0$ is the flow rate at 0°C, the flow rate at any other temperature T (°K) is given by:

$$\dot{V}_T = \dot{V}_0 \frac{T}{273}. \tag{2.39}$$

If the flow rate at 0°C is measurable, then the above equation can be used to find the flow rate inside the column, which, when multiplied by the retention time, will give the retention volume inside the column corrected for this factor.

In practice, the flowmeter will probably be calibrated at room temperature, so that the flow rate at the column temperature will be given by:

$$\dot{V}_{T_c} = \dot{V}_{T_f} \times \frac{T_c}{T_f}, \tag{2.40}$$

where T_f (°K) is the temperature at which the flowmeter is calibrated and T_c (°K) is the temperature of the column. In connection with the use of Eq. (2.40), it should be noted that the temperature at which the flowmeter is calibrated is not necessarily the temperature of the flowmeter. For example, a conceivable arrangement is one in which the flowmeter is held in a thermostat at 25°C, while the calibration is done at a room temperature of 22°C. In this case, T_f is 295°K, not 298°K. Flowmeters can be divided into two classes in order to discuss the variation of their readings with temperature. In one class are those in which the flow rate is measured by the time taken for a given volume to flow, for example, soap-bubble flowmeters. The calibration of these is the same at all temperatures, so that if T_f stands for the flowmeter temperature, Eq. (2.40) will be true at all flowmeter temperatures. Thus, such a flowmeter does not require a thermostat in order to obtain accurate results. In the other class are those in which the flow rate is measured by a physical property, usually viscosity, for example, rotameters or capillary flowmeters. In these cases, the viscosity is a function of temperature, so that for accurate measurements, the flowmeter should be placed in a thermostat. With this class, the calibration depends on the temperature.

2.7. The Correction of Retention Volumes

The analysis of the previous three sections has shown that the retention volume as measured by the product of the outlet flow rate and the retention time is a function of several variables concerned with the operation of the column, the gas hold-up, the pressure drop across the column, and the temperature of the column. For practical purposes it is useful to be able to quote some property of the chromatogram related to the retention time which is not dependent on the manner in which the column is operated, but only on the column packing and the vapour. This property can then be used for quotation, and should be reproducible from column to column and from operation to operation. The variables which determine the retention volume of a vapour can be divided into two classes; first, those connected with the operation of the column, and second, those concerned with the actual process of interaction of the vapour between the phases. These two classes can conveniently be called "Column Variables" and "Thermodynamic Variables," and are listed below.

(1) *Column variables*
- (i) Dead volume
- (ii) Pressure drop across the column
- (iii) Temperature of the carrier gas as it affects the flow rate
- (iv) Weight of stationary phase or stationary liquid

(2) *Thermodynamic variables*
- (i) Chemical nature of the vapour
- (ii) Chemical nature of the stationary phase
- (iii) Temperature of the column as it affects the thermodynamics

The procedure used to correct a measured retention time so as to give the required invariant quantity involves the elimination of the column variables, using the results derived in the previous sections.

The most direct procedure from a measured retention time to the invariant quantity involves five steps. These are laid out formally below in equations in which the operation of each lettered step on the retention time is indicated by the letter placed *subscriptum.*

Step (*a*). Multiply the measured retention time, t_R, by the outlet flow rate, $\dot{V}_o$,

$$V_a = t_R \times \dot{V}_o \qquad (= V_R). \tag{2.41}$$

Step (*b*). Correct for the gas hold-up by subtracting the product of the retention time at the same inlet and outlet pressures and temperature of an undissolved substance, e.g., air, and the outlet flow rate,

$$V_{ab} = V_a - t_M \dot{V}_o \qquad (= V_R'). \tag{2.42}$$

Step (*c*). Correct for the pressure drop across the column using the correction factor given in Eq. (2.34) [or Eq. (2.37)],

$$V_{abc} = jV_{ab} \qquad (= V_N). \tag{2.43}$$

Step (*d*). Correct retention volumes from temperature of measurement T_f to the temperature of the column, T_c,

$$V_{abcd} = V_{abc} \times \frac{T_c}{T_f}. \tag{2.44}$$

Step (*e*). Divide by the weight of the stationary phase, W,

$$V_{abcde} = V_{abcd}/W. \tag{2.45}$$

V_{abcde} is the required column-independent quantity.

The logic of this procedure and the meaning of the above five operations may be appreciated by multiplying together Eqs. (2.41)–(2.45) above, to give:

$$V_{abcde} = \frac{1}{W} \cdot \frac{T_c}{T_f} \cdot j \cdot (t_R - t_M) \dot{V}_o. \tag{2.46}$$

Making use of Eqs. (2.40) and (2.34) differentiated with respect to t, this simplifies to:

$$V_{abcde} = \frac{(t_R - t_M)\dot{V}}{W}, \tag{2.47}$$

where $\dot{V}$ is the true flow rate in the column. Now substituting Eq. (2.14), and the equation $t_M = V_M/\dot{V}$,

$$V_{abcde} = \beta. \tag{2.48}$$

The partition coefficient β is a purely thermodynamic quantity which can, if required, be determined independently of chromatography, and hence V_{abcde} is independent of column operation.

The procedure described above is probably the most logical, but in practice it is better to modify it in two respects: (i) Calibrate all flowmeters at 0°C, so that T_f is always 273°K. (ii) Omit step (*d*). The quantity so obtained is called the *Specific Retention Volume*, the internationally approved symbol for which is V_g. A simple extension of the arguments of Eqs. (2.46)–(2.48) will show that

$$V_g = V_{abce} = \beta \cdot \frac{273}{T_c}. \tag{2.49}$$

There are two reasons for adopting this modification:

(1) Specific retention volumes for tabulation are in any case functions of temperature on account of the steep temperature dependence of β. In fact the dependence of β upon temperature is very much steeper than the variation of retention volume with temperature on account of the Charles' law correction alone. Hence, it seems pointless to correct for a comparatively small proportion of the total temperature dependence.

(2) One of the uses of specific retention volumes is to determine the heats of solution of the vapour in the stationary phase (Section 3.6). It will be shown that to do this, a retention volume including the step (*d*) would have to be multiplied by the factor $273/T_c$, thus removing step (*d*) by operating upon the retention volume with its inverse. It is clearly more satisfactory not to apply the step in the first place.

The subscript in the symbol for the specific retention volume conveys the fact that it is a retention volume *per gram* of stationary phase. V_{abcde} will be given the simplified symbol of $V_g{}^c$, in which the superscript denotes the fact that it refers to the column temperature.

The steps connecting a measured retention time with V_g or $V_g{}^c$ may be varied for greater experimental convenience in handling a large number of data, but care should be taken on account of the fact that step (*b*) does not commute with the others. If one column is used at a range of flow rates and temperatures, it may not be convenient to measure an air peak for every run. If the retention time of an air peak is measured at one temperature and flow rate, and steps (*a*), (*c*), and (*d*) are applied, study of Eqs. (2.41), (2.43), and (2.44) will show that

$$V_{acd}^{\text{air}} = al = V_M{}^0. \tag{2.50}$$

This value of al is independent of T and $\dot{V}$ so that in an alternative procedure for correcting retention times to give values of $V_g{}^c$, the gas hold-up given by Eq. (2.50) can be subtracted *after* steps (*c*) and (*d*). This alternative procedure is outlined below.

Step (*a*)* = *Step* (*a*).
Step (*b*)* = *Step* (*c*).
Step (*c*)* = *Step* (*d*).
Step (*d*)* = *Subtract* $V_{acd}^{\text{air}} = al = V_{a^*b^*c^*}^{\text{air}}$.
Step (*e*)* = *Step* (*e*).

The result of these steps is the same as that of the previous five steps, but the procedure is more convenient for measuring large numbers of results on one column, since the air peak need only be run once.

The simple revised procedure using the starred steps is not correct in the determination of specific retention volumes, V_g, as opposed to V_g^c values, since there is no stage at which one can subtract an invariant gas hold-up. Instead, the following procedure is probably the simplest.

Preliminary step. Determine the true dead volume $V_M{}^0$ by Eq. (2.50).

*Step (a)*** = *Step (a)*.
*Step (b)*** = *Step (c)*.
*Step (c)*** = *Subtract* $273V_M{}^0/T_c$.
*Step (d)*** = *Step (e)*.

The result of carrying out these steps is the specific retention volume,

$$V_{a^{**}b^{**}c^{**}d^{**}} = V_g. \tag{2.51}$$

The above relations are rather fussy, and failure to appreciate them may not produce a very large error in quoted retention data. However, such neglect is unwise, since, as column performances improve, more and more accurate knowledge of relative retentions becomes useful. Much retention data of a few years ago is of comparatively little use owing to failure to specify conditions with sufficient accuracy or to use a satisfactory correction procedure. In order to illustrate the methods of correction more fully, we give below some worked examples of such calculations, and include a few other minor points not previously mentioned.

Example 1. Unstarred Procedure. In a chromatogram run at 55°C, the retention time of a component was 25.6 minutes. The retention time of an air peak in similar conditions was 2.0 minutes. The outlet flow rate, flowmeter calibrated at 0°C, was 15.7 cc/minute; atmospheric pressure was 75 cm Hg; inlet pressure was 25 cm Hg above atmospheric. The weight of stationary phase on the column was 2.8 g. Calculate V_g^c and V_g.

(*a*) $V_a = 25.6 \times 15.7$.
(*b*) $V_{ab} = 15.7(25.6 - 2.0) = 15.7 \times 23.6$.
(*c*) $P_i = 100$ cm Hg, $P_o = 75$ cm Hg, $P_i/P_o = 1.33$.

Using Eq. (2.35) for small pressure ratios, the correction factor is approximately

$$(\tfrac{1}{2} + \tfrac{1}{2} \times 1.33)^{-1} = 0.855.$$

Hence,

$$V_{abc} = 15.7 \times 23.6 \times 0.855.$$

(*d*) Using Eq. (2.44),

$$V_{abcd} = 23.6 \times 15.7 \times 0.855 \times 328/273.$$

(*e*) Using Eq. (2.45),

$$V_{abcde} = V_g{}^c = \frac{15.7 \times 23.6 \times 0.855 \times 328}{273 \times 2.8} = \mathit{136\ cc/g}.$$

Also, omitting step (*d*),

$$V_{abce} = V_g = \frac{15.7 \times 23.6 \times 0.855}{2.8} = \mathit{113\ cc/g}.$$

In measuring a number of peaks on one chromatogram, it is convenient to multiply together steps (*c*), (*d*), and (*e*) to give one joint correction factor which can then be used on each peak in turn.

Example 2. Starred Procedures. The air peak in a column (W = 4.5 g) has a retention time of 3.3 minutes at a flow rate of 10.3 cc/minute, with the flowmeter calibrated at 0°C. For the air peak, P_i = 85 cm Hg, P_o = 76 cm Hg. When the same column is used at 225°C and a flow rate of 22.8 cc/minute, P_i = 112 cm Hg, P_o = 76 cm Hg. A component of interest has a retention time of 9.8 minutes. Calculate V_g and $V_g{}^c$.

Preliminary.

$$V_a^{\text{air}} = 3.3 \times 10.3.$$

$$V_{ac}^{\text{air}} = 3.3 \times 10.3 \Big/ \left(\frac{1}{2} + \frac{1}{2} \cdot \frac{85}{76}\right) = \frac{3.3 \times 10.3}{1.05}.$$

$$V_{acd}^{\text{air}} = \frac{3.3 \times 10.3 \times 298}{1.05 \times 273} = 35.4 \text{ cc}.$$

(*a*)* = (*a*)** $V_{a^*} = 9.8 \times 22.8.$

(*b*)* = (*b*)** $P_i/P_o = 1.473.$

From Fig. 2.5, the correction factor is 1/1.252, whence,

$$V_{a^*b^*} = \frac{9.8 \times 22.8}{1.252} = 178.5.$$

(*c*)* From Eq. (2.44),

$$V_{a^*b^*c^*} = \frac{9.8 \times 22.8 \times 498}{1.252 \times 273} = 326.$$

(*d*)* $V_{a^*b^*c^*d^*} = 326 - 35.4 = 291.$

(*e*)* $V_{a^*b^*c^*d^*e^*} = \beta = 291/4.5 = \mathit{64.7\ cc/g}.$

(*c*)** $V_{a^{**}b^{**}c^{**}} = 178.5 - \dfrac{35.4 \times 273}{498} = 159.1.$

(*d*)** $V_g = 159.1/4.5 = \mathit{36.2\ cc/g}.$

Note the large difference between $V_g{}^c$ and V_g at high temperatures. Note also that failure to correct for the gas hold-up in the right place would make an error of 10% in V_g in this case.

Example 3. Procedure Reversed. The specific retention volume of *n*-heptane on tricresyl phosphate at 80°C is 36.0 cc/g. What is the retention time of *n*-heptane at 80°C on a column of 0.91 g tricresyl phosphate with a flow rate of 19.0 cc/minute (flowmeter calibrated at 25°C), $P_o = 77$ cm Hg, $P_i = 103.9$ cm Hg? The gas hold-up of the column is 29.0 cc.

$((d)^{**})^{-1}$ $\quad V_{a^{**}b^{**}c^{**}d^{**}} = 36.0$ cc/g.

$$V_{a^{**}b^{**}c^{**}} = 36.0 \times 0.91 = 32.75 \text{ cc.}$$

$((c)^{**})^{-1}$ Add the dead volume corrected to column temperature,

$$V_{a^{**}b^{**}} = 32.75 + \frac{29.0 \times 273}{353} = 55.15 \text{ cc.}$$

(Note that in reversing the procedure, one adds rather than subtracts the corrected gas hold-up, but the correction remains the same.)

$((b)^{**})^{-1}$ $P_i/P_o = 1.365$, and from Fig. 2.5, the correction factor is $(1/1.191)^{-1} = 1.191$, whence $V_{a^{**}} = 55.15 \times 1.191 = 65.7$ cc.

$((a)^{**})^{-1}$ The flow rate from a flowmeter calibrated at 25°C is 19.0 cc/minute, so that the flow rate given by a flowmeter calibrated at 0°C would be $19 \times 273/298 = 17.4$ cc/minute. Hence, the required retention time is

$$t_R = 65.7/17.4 = \mathit{3.77\ minutes.}$$

2.8. The Presentation of Relative Retentions

The presentation of specific retention volumes described in the last section requires calculation, and also requires measurements of column variables to be at least as accurate as the retention times. This has been considered an unnecessary labour by many analysts, and most published retention data are presented as relative retentions, that is, retention volumes or times relative to the retention volume or time of a single internal standard. To standardise procedures, the IUPAC committee has recommended that where possible, one of the following substances should be used as a standard (*1*):

n-butane
2,2,4-trimethylpentane
benzene
p-xylene
naphthalene
methyl ethyl ketone
cyclohexanone
cyclohexanol.

In order for relative retentions to be useful, they should be independent of column variables, and, therefore, they should be prepared from corrected retention times. It is, however, necessary only to correct for quantities which are *added* to the retention time as a result of the individual column used, for quantities which *multiply* the retention time by a factor are all divided out when the two retention times are divided one by the other. Thus, of the five steps for correction listed in the previous section, only step (*b*), that is, the subtraction of the gas hold-up, need be performed. The commonest procedure is to prepare a chromatogram including a peak due to the standard substance and including a peak produced by an undissolved substance, e.g., air. Distances on the chart paper are measured from the air peak to all other peaks, and these distances are then divided by the distance given by the peak due to the standard substance. The resulting quotients are the required relative retentions. It should be emphasised that relative retentions prepared without subtraction of the gas hold-up time are incorrect.

Though tables of relative retention data are useful in studying the separation of all compounds contained in the table, they cannot be extended to the study of compounds not in the table even if these are contained in other tables. Since it is desirable to make relative retention data as universally useful as possible, some means of relating together different tables of relative retention data should be used. One method is always to use one or more of the standards listed above. Another more desirable method, the use of which appears to be growing in recent papers giving relative retention data, is to tabulate relative retention data and to include the specific retention volume of the standard. Quoted in this way, it is implied that the accuracy of the specific retention volume is less than that of the relative retention data. If the results are obtained in such a way that the specific retention volumes are as accurate as the relative retention volumes, it would be natural for the relative retention volumes to be multiplied by the specific retention volume of the standard, so that all the data are thereby specified.

When certain kinds of detectors are used (e.g., ionisation detectors, Chapter 8), no undissolved substance can be found which produces a peak from which retention times can be measured. In such a case, it may be possible to calculate the gas hold-up from the dimensions of the column, especially in the case of capillary columns. In capillary columns, however, where values of the retardation ratio, k, are generally small, a particularly accurate knowledge of the gas hold-up is required, not only because a small error in the gas hold-up produces a relatively large error in the relative retention volumes, but also because accurate values of relative retention volumes are significant on account of the high column performance. One method for finding the gas hold-up makes use of the fact (Section 3.7) that a plot of log V_R' against carbon number is accurately linear for any homologous series, so that the retention times of successive homologs are in geometrical progression, as illustrated in Fig. 2.6. With higher members of

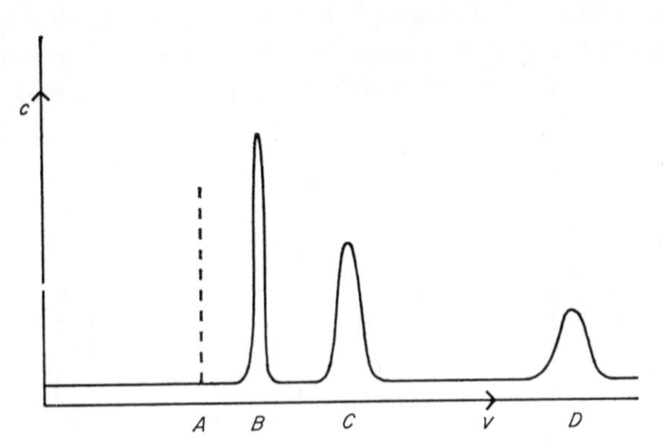

FIG. 2.6. A chromatogram in which retention times measured from a given point for successive homologs are in geometrical progression. A is point corresponding to $V_M{}^0$; $AC/AB = AD/AC$.

homologous series, it is apparent that as the homolog number declines, peaks converge rapidly as the retention becomes negligible, and the limiting point gives the retention of an unabsorbed component. In practice, if a few successive homologs are incorporated in a mixture (if not already present), a point is easily found by trial and error such that successive relative retention volumes measured from it are constant. A more systematic procedure has been defined by Peterson and Hirsch (*16*). Include three homologs the carbon numbers of which satisfy the relation $n_2 - n_1 = n_3 - n_2$, and measure the distances to their peaks from an arbitrary point (y_1, y_2, y_3). Then the distance δ of the arbitrary point from the point corresponding to the gas hold-up time is given by:

$$\delta = \frac{y_2{}^2 - y_3 y_1}{y_3 + y_1 - 2y_2}. \tag{2.52}$$

2.9. Effect of Input Distribution on Retention Volume

In practice, the delta-function input distribution which has been assumed throughout is unattainable, since both the vapour and the sample injector cavity occupy a finite volume. As previously mentioned, the effect of these on the retention volume is small, but in accurate work it is necessary to consider it. Two extreme kinds of possible input distribution have been recognised by Porter, *et al.* (*17*) who have considered the effect of these on retention volumes. In the first extreme, it is assumed that the vapour goes onto the column as a compact plug of finite volume within which there is a uniform vapour concentration. This would happen if the sample were completely evaporated in the sample injector cavity, and then swept out by the carrier gas without any mixing. The effect of non-ideal linear chromatography upon such an input distribution is to superimpose a Gaussian distribution upon the plug of vapour as described in Section 1.4. The resulting output distribution is illustrated in Fig. 2.7a, which is merely a

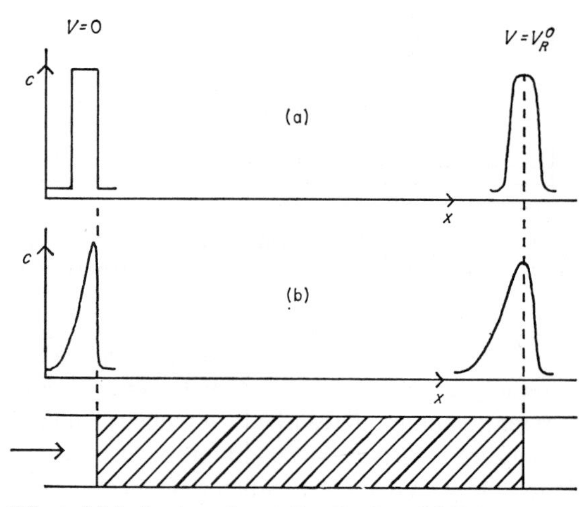

FIG. 2.7. Effect of (a) plug type input distribution, (b) Poisson type input distribution on the chromatogram.

specific form of Fig. 1.5d. The output distribution is symmetrical, and its maximum corresponds to the mid-point of the plug in the input distribution. Thus, if the retention time is measured from the instant that the front of the plug enters the column, as is usual practice, the retention volume measured to the maximum of the output distribution will be greater than the retention volume corresponding to a delta-function input distribution by half the width of the plug measured in volume units. If the measured retention volume is $V_R{}^0$, the true retention volume corresponding to Eq. (2.11) is $V_r{}^0$, and the volume of the plug is V_i,

$$V_R{}^0 = V_r{}^0 + \tfrac{1}{2}V_i \qquad (2.53)$$

(cf. Section 2.3, also Chovin (*4*)). In practice, the volumes both of the sample vapour and of the sample injector cavity should be less than about 1/100 of a retention volume, so that the error involved in neglecting the above correction is almost certainly less than 1%.

The other extreme considered by Porter *et al.* is that in which complete mixing occurs in the sample injector cavity, so that the input distribution is of the Poisson type (Fig. 2.7b). In this also, the measured retention volume is slightly greater than the true retention volume if the time zero is the instant the front of the distribution reaches the column. There is, however, no simple formula corresponding to Eq. (2.53). Porter *et al.* show that in experiments using specific sample injectors of their design, the behaviour lies between the two extreme cases of plug flow and complete mixing.

2.10. Effect of Sample Size on Retention Volume

Sample size has a definite effect on retention volumes, but the effect may vary according to the circumstances; increase in sample size can cause an increase or a decrease in the retention volume. No complete or quantitative discussion is yet possible. The effect of sample size on retention volumes in non-linear chromatography is very much larger than in linear chromatography; non-linear chromatography will be treated separately in the next section.

There are probably two principal reasons for variation of retention volume with sample size in linear chromatography: (1) non-sharp input distribution and (2) finite vapour concentration in the column. The magnitude of each of these can be roughly assessed, though there are no specific experimental checks that can be applied. The best possible practical input distribution for a finite sample is one in which a plug of pure sample vapour

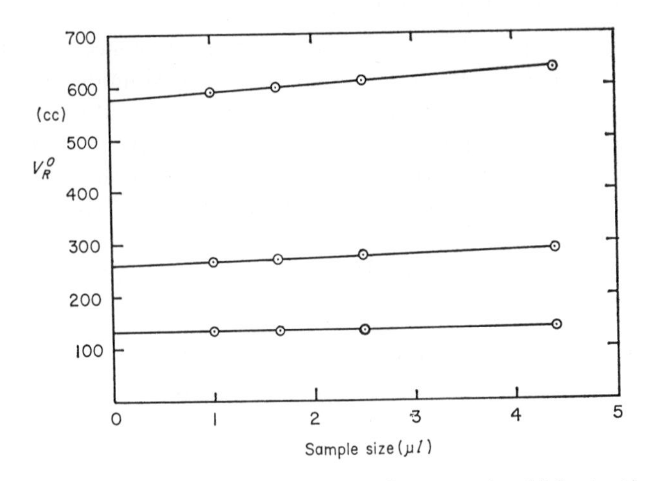

Fig. 2.8. Effect of sample size on retention volume; case in which retention volumes increase with increase in sample.

undiluted with carrier gas enters the column. If the sample weighs w mg, and its molecular weight is M, the volume of its vapour at NTP is $24w/M$ cc, and its volume at any other temperature and input pressure is easily calculable. For example, a sample consisting of 10 mg of n-hexane ($M = 86$) cannot have an input distribution narrower than about 3 cc (see Section 5.20). Moreover, in the introduction of liquid samples, there may be a period during which the sample is evaporating, so that, particularly with large samples of less volatile components, the input distribution is broadened on this account. Thus, the general effect of a non-sharp input distribution will be to make retention volumes increase with the quantity of sample. This is illustrated in Fig. 2.8, which shows retention volume plotted against sample size (writer's results). It is noteworthy that the least volatile component shows the largest effect.

The effect of the finite vapour concentration in the column is to cause retention volumes to decrease with increase in sample size. The total pressure inside a zone in the column is not different from the total pressure elsewhere in the column (neglecting the over-all pressure gradient). Hence, since there is a finite vapour pressure of sample, the partial pressure of carrier must be correspondingly reduced. Since the mass flow rate of carrier gas in the column must remain constant along its length, it follows that the carrier velocity is greater inside the zone than elsewhere, particularly in those parts of the zone where the concentration is high. The effect of this is to move the centre of the zone through the column more rapidly than the other parts, so that it becomes skewed towards the end of the column, and so that a slight asymmetry is imposed upon the peaks, making their front profiles sharper than their rear profiles.

The quantitative aspects of the effect of vapour concentration have been considered in detail by Bosanquet and Morgan (*9*) and by Bosanquet (*10*), who, however, studied saturation and elution fronts rather than peaks in order to be able to correlate experiment with an exact theory. A crude estimate of the magnitude of the effect on the retention volumes of peaks can be made as follows. Let c'_{max} be the concentration of vapour measured in mole fraction units in the gas phase in the maximum of the peak. It can be proved that (Section 4.3)

$$c'^2_{max} V \simeq K, \qquad (2.54)$$

where K is a constant. If the retention volume is $V_R{}^0$, and $c'_{R\,max}$ is the value of c'_{max} as the peak emerges from the column,

$$c'^2_{R\,max} V_R{}^0 \simeq K$$

so that

$$c'_{max} \simeq c'_{R\,max} \sqrt{\frac{V_R{}^0}{V}}. \qquad (2.55)$$

Normally, the retention volume is given by

$$V_R{}^0 = \int_0^{t_R} \dot{V}\, dt.$$

However, in this case the velocity of the carrier gas in the centre of the peak is raised by a factor $1/(1 - c'_{\max})$, so that the retention volume corrected for this factor, V_R^{0*}, is given by

$$V_R^{0*} = \int_0^{t_R} (1 - c'_{\max})\dot{V}\, dt. \tag{2.56}$$

Substitution of Eq. (2.55) into Eq. (2.56), followed by integration, yields

$$V_R^{0*} = V_R{}^0(1 - 2c'_{R\max}), \tag{2.57}$$

so that the percentage reduction in the measured retention volume caused by this effect is approximately 200 $c'_{R\max}$. The quantity $c'_{R\max}$ is calculable from the height of a peak on a chromatogram and the sensitivity of the detector (Section 7.2). In unfavourable circumstances it may amount to about 0.02 to 0.05 mole fraction, giving as much as 10% error in the measurement of the retention volume, but in normal

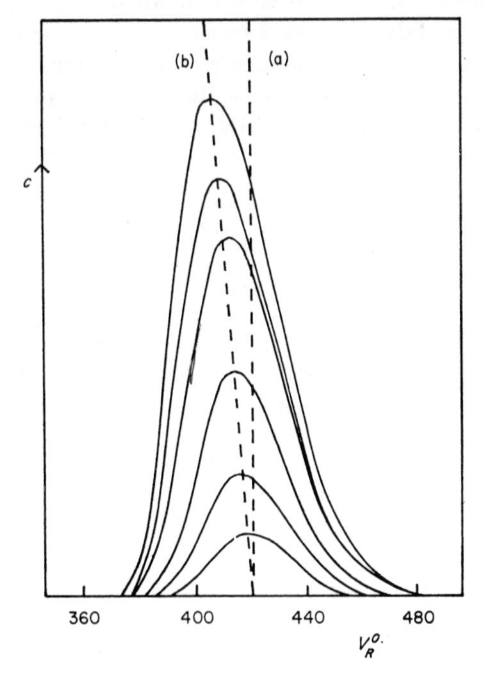

FIG. 2.9. Effect of sample size on retention volume; case in which retention volumes decrease with increase in sample [after Pollard and Hardy (*18*)]. (a) Retention volume of small sample. (b) Line of decreasing retention volumes with increasing sample.

operation it is generally small enough to make its effect on the retention volume negligible.

A case in which retention volume declines with increase in sample size is given by Pollard and Hardy (*18*), who demonstrate the effect by superimposing chromatograms of samples of different weights of chloroform, using a column of dibutyl phthalate (Fig. 2.9). When measurements are made from this diagram, it is found that the change in retention volume roughly obeys Eq. (2.57), though whether for the reason under discussion or for a combination of other reasons cannot be ascertained. Further remarks relevant to this subject are included in the discussion under Eq. (3.26) (Section 3.3).

2.11. Retention Volumes in Non-Linear Chromatography

Whereas in linear chromatography the effect of the sample size on the retention volume is small, in non-linear chromatography, where the speed of a zone depends on the concentrations inside it, the effect is so large that retention volumes often cease to be useful. In the case of Langmuir isotherms, where the speed of the zone increases as the concentrations increase, the larger the sample, the smaller the retention volume measured to the maximum of the peak. In the case of its anti-Langmuir type isotherm, the opposite applies, and the larger the sample, the larger the retention volume (Fig. 2.10).

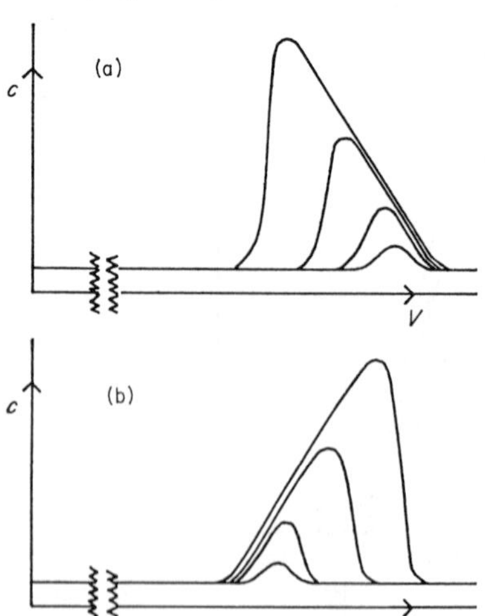

Fig. 2.10. Peak shapes and retention volumes for various sample sizes in nonlinear chromatography. (a) Langmuir isotherms. (b) Anti-Langmuir isotherms.

In normal practice, there is no way of calculating the change in retention volume as a function of the sample size. There is, however, one part of the peak produced in chromatography on a non-linear isotherm that changes but little with change in sample size: when the concentration is very small, the isotherm is virtually linear, and a small change in concentration will not affect the speed, so that a part of the peak in which the concentration is always small will move at a speed more or less independent of the total sample size. In the Langmuir case, this part is the bottom of the rear profile, with the result that as sample sizes are increased, though retention volumes measured to the peak maximum decrease, retention volumes measured to the very end of the peak are very nearly constant. This is illustrated in Fig. 2.10a, where chromatograms from a number of sample sizes are superimposed. With anti-Langmuir type isotherms, it is the beginning of the front profile that is nearly constant, as in Fig. 2.10b. This observation has been made the basis of an empirical method for correcting retention volumes for asymmetry in anti-Langmuir type peaks (*19*), in which a volume corresponding to the time occupied by the rear profile is added to the retention volume of the beginning of the front profile of the peak. Such a procedure is only approximate, for the beginning of the front profile is not easily observed, and also, as the quantities increase, the rear profile tends to become sharper (Section 5.5), so that the volume occupied by the rear profile is smaller than that occupied by the front profile of the equivalent symmetrical peak for a linear isotherm.

The conclusion from the above observations is that retention volumes from columns and vapours with non-linear isotherms have meaning only when the whole peak is formed at a very low concentration, so that the non-linearity is small and has little effect. This means that such retention volumes are significant only for very small samples. The fact that retention volumes are not significant, however, does not mean that stationary phases giving non-linear isotherms are not useful in quantitative analysis (Section 11.1).

References

1. "Preliminary Recommendations on Nomenclature and Presentation of Data in Gas Chromatography," see preprints of the Third Symposium on Gas Chromatography, Edinburgh, June, 1960.
2. Wilson, J. N., *J. Am. Chem. Soc.* **62,** 1583 (1940).
3. DeVault, D., *J. Am. Chem. Soc.* **65,** 532 (1943).
4. Chovin, P., Informal Symposium of the Gas Chromatography Discussion Group of the Institute of Petroleum, London, held at Liverpool, England, October, 1960.
5. Primavesi, G. R., Informal Symposium of the Gas Chromatography Discussion Group of the Institute of Petroleum, London, held at Liverpool, England, October, 1960.
6. Golay, M. J. E., *in* "Gas Chromatography 1958," Proceedings of the Second Symposium, Amsterdam, May, 1958 (D. H. Desty, ed.), p. 36. Academic Press, New York, 1958.

7. Van Deemter, J. J., Zuiderweg, F. J., and Klinkenberg, A., *Chem. Eng. Sci.* **5,** 271 (1956).
8. Scott, R. P. W., and Hazeldean, G. S. F., Third Symposium on Gas Chromatography, Edinburgh, June, 1960 (Preprint).
9. Bosanquet, C. H., and Morgan, G. O., *in* "Vapour Phase Chromatography," Proceedings of the First Symposium, London, May, 1956 (D. H. Desty, ed.), p. 35. Academic Press, New York, 1957.
10. Bosanquet, C. H., *in* "Gas Chromatography 1958," Proceedings of the Second Symposium, Amsterdam, May, 1958 (D. H. Desty, ed.), p. 107. Academic Press, New York, 1958.
11. Giddings, J. C., and Eyring, H., *J. Phys. Chem.* **59,** 416 (1955).
12. Giddings, J. C., *J. Chem. Phys.* **26,** 169 (1957).
13. Giddings, J. C., *J. Chromatog.* **2,** 44 (1959).
14. Beynon, J. K., Clough, S., Crookes, D. A., and Lester, G. R., *Trans. Faraday Soc.* **54,** 705 (1958).
15. James, A. T., and Martin, A. J. P., *Biochem. J.* **50,** 679 (1952).
16. Peterson, M. L., and Hirsch, J., *J. Lipid Research* **1,** 132 (1959).
17. Porter, P. E., Deal, C. H., and Stross, F. H., *J. Am. Chem. Soc.* **78,** 2999 (1956).
18. Pollard, F. H., and Hardy, C. H., *in* "Vapour Phase Chromatography," Proceedings of the First Symposium, London, May, 1956 (D. H. Desty, ed.), p. 115. Academic Press, New York, 1957.
19. Littlewood, A. B., Phillips, C. S. G., and Price, D. T., *J. Chem. Soc.* p. 1480 (1955).

Chapter 3

Retention Volume and Thermodynamic Variables

3.1. Introduction

The preceding chapter describes how the measured retention volume is related to the partition coefficient and the column variables. In any particular chromatographic run, the column variables are the same for each vapour (see, however, Section 6.5), and so the separation depends on the values of the partition coefficients; if these are sufficiently different, there will be adequate separation; if not, there will not. The difference between two partition coefficients is normally expressed by their ratio, the relative retention (Section 1.3). In this chapter, therefore, the factors determining partition coefficients are discussed in detail, and it is shown how a knowledge of these factors may be applied to predict the relative retention of a given pair of solutes in a given stationary phase, so that the stationary phase may be chosen to provide the most satisfactory relative retention. These factors are best discussed in terms of the thermodynamic functions governing the equilibrium of the vapour between the gas and the stationary phase. In the discussion, vapours are generally called *solutes*, and, for consistency, the word solute is used even though the process of interaction may not always be one of solution.

3.2. General Relations between Retention Volumes, Partition Coefficients, and Relative Retention

The partition coefficient of a solute is the ratio of its concentration in the liquid phase to that in the gas phase. Concentrations can be expressed in several kinds of units, and therefore the partition coefficient can be expressed in several different forms. It is convenient to use one of the three forms described below, which should be clearly distinguished.

The most fundamental form is

$$\alpha = \frac{\text{weight of solute per cc of stationary phase}}{\text{weight of solute per cc of gas at column temperature}}.$$

This is a dimensionless quantity, but its use in practice is restricted because the volume of the stationary phase is not easily known. For this and other reasons, we define

$$\beta = \frac{\text{weight of solute per gram of stationary phase}}{\text{weight of solute per cc of gas at column temperature}}.$$

In practice it is more convenient to use β than α, for the total weight of stationary phase on the column is an easy quantity to measure, and the theory is discussed in terms of β rather than α. The form β has already been used in Chapter 2 in discussing the relation of retention volume to column variables.

In addition to the above two forms, it is convenient also to use the form:

$$\zeta = \frac{\text{weight of solute per gram of stationary phase}}{\text{weight of solute per cc of gas at 0°C}},$$

which equals the specific retention volume, V_g, of a solute. This form should be used in the calculation of heats of solution from retention data (Section 3.6).

The above three forms of the partition coefficient are related. The forms α and β are related by

$$\alpha = \beta\rho, \tag{3.1}$$

where ρ is the density of the stationary phase at the temperature at which α and β are measured. Also

$$\zeta = \beta \cdot \frac{273.16}{T_c}, \tag{3.2}$$

where T_c (°K) is the absolute temperature of the column, and

$$\alpha = \zeta \frac{T_c\rho}{273.16}. \tag{3.3}$$

The partition coefficients can now be related with two different forms for the corrected retention volume. As described in Section 2.7, $V_g^c = \beta$, and also V_g and V_g^c are related by Eq. (2.49). From these, the following six relations between retention volumes and partition coefficients may be obtained:

$$V_g = \frac{273.16}{T_c\rho} \cdot \alpha \tag{3.4}$$

$$V_g^c = \frac{1}{\rho} \cdot \alpha \tag{3.5}$$

$$V_g = \frac{273.16}{T_c} \cdot \beta \tag{3.6}$$

$$V_g^c = \beta \tag{3.7}$$

$$V_g = \zeta \tag{3.8}$$

$$V_g^c = \frac{T_c}{273.16} \cdot \zeta. \tag{3.9}$$

These relations are discussed in part by several authors (*1–4*). It is clear from Eqs. (3.7) and (3.8) that some condensation of symbols could be achieved by using the V symbols for β and ζ. This has not usually been done in the literature, and for purposes of explanation and logical consistency the chromatographic quantities, V, should be kept distinct from the thermodynamic quantities, α, β, and ζ; it should be borne in mind that Eqs. (3.7) and (3.8) are not identities.

As described in Section 2.8, the relative retention may be expressed by the ratio of any retention times or retention volumes from which the effect of the gas hold-up has been subtracted; in particular, it may be expressed as the ratio of specific retention volumes, and, by Eq. (3.8), as the ratio of the partition coefficients ζ of the two solutes. Since, also, the relations between the different forms of partition coefficient involve only column variables which are static throughout the chromatography (see, however, Section 6.5), the relative retention may also be expressed as the ratio of either of the other forms of partition coefficient. Thus, if the relative retention of two solutes denoted by subscripts 2 and 3 is r_{23}, then

$$r_{23} = \frac{V_{g2}}{V_{g3}} = \frac{\zeta_2}{\zeta_3} = \frac{\alpha_2}{\alpha_3} = \frac{\beta_2}{\beta_3}. \tag{3.10}$$

3.3. Thermodynamic Equations for Partition Coefficient

The system which is defined by any of the partition coefficients described above consists of the vapour of the solute in equilibrium with the solution of the solute in the stationary liquid. This system is familiar in thermodynamics, and thermodynamic equations relating the partition coefficients with measurable properties of solvent and solute may be derived [Eqs. (3.19), (3.20), and (3.23)].

(a) *Properties of the Ideal Solution*

In the case that the solute forms an *ideal solution* in the solvent, its vapour pressure above the solution, p_2, is given by Raoult's law,

$$p_2 = p_2^0 x_2, \tag{3.11}$$

where p_2^0 is the vapour pressure of the pure liquid solute, and x_2 is the *mole fraction* of the solute in the solution. The mole fraction is a unit of concentration, defined as the proportion of moles of solute in the solution. Raoult's law is derived from the general definition of ideal solution, which may be found in texts on thermodynamics [e.g., ref. (*5*)], but it is sufficient in this discussion to assume that an ideal solution may be defined as one obeying Raoult's law. No real solution is ideal; the ideal solution is commonly regarded as a standard to which others are referred, and in many cases departures from ideality are not very great.

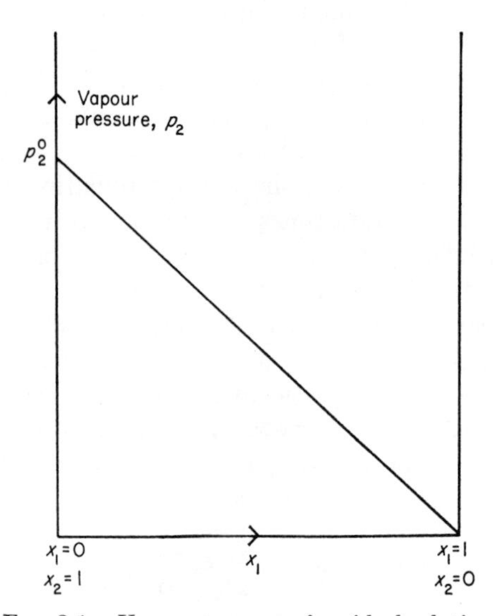

FIG. 3.1. Vapour pressure of an ideal solution.

The behaviour of an ideal solution is illustrated in Fig. 3.1, which shows a plot of vapour pressure, p_2, against mole fraction. In gas chromatography, the concentration of solute is small, so that only the bottom end of the line is relevant. The top end of the line is familiar in elementary physical chemistry, where the fact that the depression of vapour pressure of a volatile solvent by an involatile solute is proportional to the mole fraction of the latter is used for the determination of molecular weights.

(*b*) *Equation for the Partition Coefficient in an Ideal Solution*

In Eq. (3.11), x_2 is a measure of the concentration of the solute in the stationary phase, and p_2 is a measure of the concentration of the solute in the gas phase. Thus, p_2 and x_2 are measures of the denominators and numerators of the partition coefficients described in the previous section. By converting the units of x_2 and p_2 into those contained in the definitions of the partition coefficients, expressions for the latter may be obtained. Let

$$\beta = \frac{\mathcal{W}_2'}{\mathcal{W}_2''}, \tag{3.12}$$

where $\mathcal{W}_2'$ and $\mathcal{W}_2''$ are the values of the numerator and the denominator of the definition of β. We derive expressions for $\mathcal{W}_2'$ and $\mathcal{W}_2''$ in the next two paragraphs.

If n_1 and n_2 are the number of moles of solvent and solute in an arbitrary weight of solution, then

$$x_2 = \frac{n_2}{n_1 + n_2},$$

from the definition of mole fraction. We assume that the solute concentration is always small enough that $n_1 \gg n_2$, so that n_2 may be neglected in comparison with n_1 in the denominator of the above. Also, the number of moles, n, may now be converted into weight units, w, by the relations:

$$\begin{aligned} w_1 &= M_1 n_1, \\ w_2 &= M_2 n_2, \end{aligned} \tag{3.13}$$

where M_1 and M_2 are the molecular weights of the solvent and solute, respectively. Hence,

$$x_2 \approx \frac{M_1 w_2}{M_2 w_1} = \frac{M_1 \mathcal{W}_2'}{M_2}. \tag{3.14}$$

Except where the approximation is discussed specifically, this is regarded as an equation.

The general form of the gas law may be written:

$$PV = RT, \tag{3.15}$$

where R has the same value for one mole of any vapour. Hence, for a weight w_2' of vapour, the gas law is:

$$PV = RT \frac{w_2'}{M_2},$$

using Eq. (3.13). If the volume of gas, V, is 1 cc, then w_2' becomes $\mathcal{W}_2''$, the denominator of β. Thus, for vapour of pressure p_2,

$$p_2 = RT \frac{\mathcal{W}_2''}{M_2}. \tag{3.16}$$

We may now substitute Eqs. (3.16) and (3.14) into Eq. (3.11), to give:

$$RT \frac{\mathcal{W}_2''}{M_2} = p_2^0 \frac{M_1 \mathcal{W}_2'}{M_2},$$

which, after substitution in Eq. (3.12) and rearrangement, gives:

$$\beta = \frac{RT}{M_1 p_2^0}. \tag{3.17}$$

If p_2^0 is measured in mm Hg and T in °K, the units of R are cc (mm Hg)/(mole °K), and its value is 62,370.

(c) *Quantitative Description of Non-Ideality*

In practice, solutions of a volatile solute in a non-volatile solvent are frequently not even approximately ideal. Usually the plot of the vapour pressure of a volatile solute as a function of its mole fraction is like either curve I or curve II of Fig. 3.2, in which the vapour pressure is either

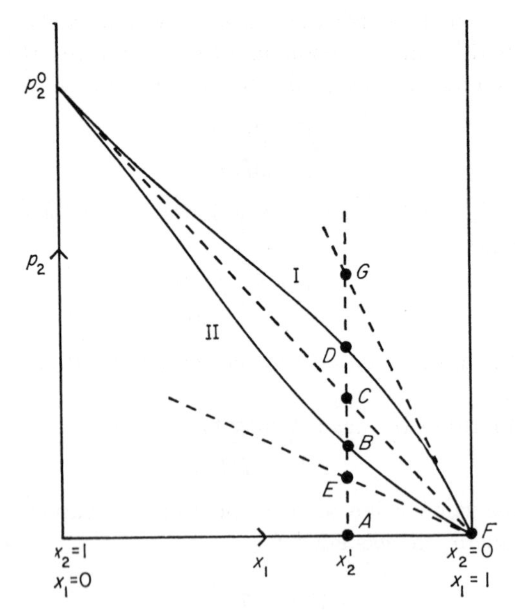

FIG. 3.2. Vapour pressure of a non-ideal solution.

greater or smaller than the ideal vapour pressure given by Eq. (3.11). In most cases, except when there are definite compounds formed between solute and solvent, the curves are of either of the shapes given, and differ from system to system only in the degree of "bowing" away from the straight line given by the ideal law. If the proportion of non-volatile component is small, the vapour pressure curve generally follows the ideal curve, so that the classical method of determining molecular weights from Raoult's law can still be used even though the solution is not ideal. However, if the proportion of volatile component is small, this is not generally true, and there is a real difference between the slope of the actual vapour pressure curve and the slope given by Eq. (3.11) even as x_2 tends to zero. When x_2 is small, the rate of change of slope of the vapour pressure curve, i.e., its curvature, is small, so that there is still a linear relation between p_2 and x_2, but the proportionality constant is not given by Eq. (3.11). The linear relation between p_2 and x_2 in general is called "Henry's law."

The departure from ideality of a particular solution is expressed quantitatively as the ratio of the vapour pressure actually exerted above the solution to the vapour pressure it would have if it were ideal. This ratio is called the *Activity Cceffcient*, γ, of the solute. In Fig. 3.2, the activity coefficient at a mole fraction x_2' is given by the ratio of the distance AB/AC for curve II and AD/AC for curve I. We also define the *activity coefficient at infinite dilution* as the ratio of the slope of the line FG to the slope of the ideal line, FC, in the case of curve I, and by the ratio of the slopes of FE and FC and the case of curve II.

It is useful to remember that when activity coefficients are *less* than unity, vapour pressures are *smaller* than they would be ideally, so that partition coefficients are *greater* than they would be ideally; and when activity coefficients are *greater* than unity, vapour pressures are *larger* than they would be ideally, so that partition coefficients are *less* than they would be ideally. These relations can easily be seen from the figure and from Eq. (3.17).

The activity coefficient γ is defined here in terms of departures from Raoult's law. It is also possible to define an activity coefficient in terms of departures from Henry's law. Thus, in Fig. 3.2, the activity coefficient could also be defined by the ratios AE/AB or AG/AD, in which an infinitely dilute solution is taken as the standard. These cases have been clearly distinguished, for example, by Guggenheim, (*5*, p. 246). In gas chromatography, the activity coefficient is always relative to an ideal solution defined by Eq. (3.11) and not relative to an infinitely dilute solution.

(*d*) *Partition Coefficients in Non-Ideal Solutions*

From the definition of activity coefficient, Eq. (3.11) for the ideal solution is replaced by:

$$p_2 = \gamma p_2^0 x_2 \tag{3.18}$$

for the non-ideal solution. Hence, Eq. (3.17) can be corrected for non-ideality by replacing p_2^0 by γp_2^0,

$$\beta = \frac{RT_c}{M_1 \gamma p_2^0} = \frac{62{,}370\ T_c}{M_1 \gamma p_2^0}. \tag{3.19}$$

Substitution of Eqs. (3.6) and (3.8) into this equation gives a similar, but more convenient form:

$$V_g = \zeta = \frac{273R}{M_1\gamma p_2^0} = \frac{1.7027 \times 10^7}{M_1\gamma p_2^0}. \tag{3.20}$$

In the case that the chromatography is linear, the partition coefficient must be constant, and thus, in the case of non ideal solutions, the concentration of solute must be sufficiently small that the activity coefficient is constant and equal to the activity coefficient at infinite dilution. In subsequent discussion of activity coefficients, they are assumed to be those at infinite dilution except in specific discussions of activity coefficients at large values of x_2.

Equations (3.19) and (3.20) are of great importance, for they connect specific retention volumes or partition coefficients with four quantities [three in the case of Eq. (3.20)] which can be either determined or estimated with some degree of accuracy. The temperature of the column can be measured directly, and M_1 can easily be determined; the separation of different solutes on a given column depends upon the vapour pressure of the pure liquid solute and the activity coefficient. Both of these vary in a more or less regular manner with chemical composition, and thus discussion of γ and p_2^0 with respect to chemical composition enables one to use Eq. (3.19) or (3.20) for the calculation of retention volumes. Sections 3.4–3.7 deal with each of the quantities on the right-hand side of Eq. (3.19) in turn. The practical importance of the discussion is that by use of general relations involving the activity coefficients and the vapour pressures of the components in a given mixture, the correct stationary phase and the correct conditions can be chosen so as to give the greatest relative retentions. This is considered in general in Sections 3.8 and 3.9, and in particular in Chapter 11.

An idea of the order of magnitude of the quantities in Eqs. (3.19) and (3.20) can be suggested by an example. For ethyl acetate partitioning on dinonyl phthalate at 56°C,

$$\begin{aligned} T &= 329°\text{K} \\ M_1 &= 418\ [C_6H_4(COOC_9H_{19})_2] \\ p_2^0 &= 350 \text{ mm Hg (from tables, see Section 3.4)} \\ \gamma &= 0.52. \end{aligned}$$

Substitution of these figures in Eq. (3.19) gives

$$V_g^c = 183 \text{ cc/g},$$

and in Eq. (3.20),

$$V_g = 152 \text{ cc/g}.$$

For most stationary phases other than high polymers, values of M_1 lie between about 100 and 1000. In normal gas chromatography, the vapour pressure of the solutes at column temperature may vary from a few millimetres to a few thousand millimetres. The result is that specific retention volumes usually lie between about 10 and 1000 cc/g. Table 3.1 gives a

TABLE 3.1

SAMPLE PARTITION COEFFICIENTS[a] IN DIDECYL PHTHALATE

Solute	b.p. (°C)	Partition coefficient (α), at 105°C
n-Hexane	68.3	27.0
n-Heptane	98.4	57.6
n-Octane	125.6	121
n-Nonane	150.8	240
Methylcyclopentane	71.8	38.2
Cyclohexane	80.7	52.3
Methylcyclohexane	100.9	83.5
Methanol	64.6	12.6
Ethanol	78.3	20.9
Propanol-1	97.4	46.2
Butanol-1	117.7	107
Butanol-2	99.5	77.4
2-Methylpropanol-2	82.8	30.8

[a] See Pierotti *et al.* (8).

short list of partition coefficients measured by gas chromatography. The most notable property is the rapid increase in partition coefficient with increase in molecular complexity and boiling point of the solutes.

Equations (3.19) and (3.20) are implicit in many texts, for example, Glasstone (6, p. 702), and Hildebrand and Scott (7, p. 22), where the equation corresponding to the case in which the mole fraction of solute is not necessarily small is also given. An equation similar to Eq. (3.19) is given by Pierotti *et al.* (8) and by Porter *et al.* (9) in which the inverse molar volume of the solvent, N_1, replaces its molecular weight, M_1. The quantities N_1 and M_1 are connected by

$$N_1 = \frac{1000\rho}{M_1} \text{ moles/litre,} \tag{3.21}$$

so, substituting this into Eq. (3.19),

$$\beta = \frac{62.4 T_c N_1}{\rho \gamma p_2^0}. \tag{3.22}$$

Using Eq. (3.1), this becomes

$$\alpha = \frac{62.4 T_c N_1}{\gamma p_2^0}, \tag{3.23}$$

which is the form used by the above authors. A similar equation is also used by Kwantes and Rijnders (*10*) in the calculation of activity coefficients. Equation (3.23) has the advantage that it gives the fundamental α rather than the derivative β, but for practical purposes it has the drawback that the determination of N_1 requires a knowledge of the density of the stationary phase. Even if this is known at one temperature, it is probably not known at the column temperature. Of Eqs. (3.19), (3.20), and (3.23), Eq. (3.20) is the most convenient for practical use.

Hoare and Purnell (*11*) give the following equation for the partition coefficient:

$$\alpha \approx \frac{RTN_1}{k(p_2^0)^a}, \tag{3.24}$$

where k is a constant characteristic of solute and solvent, and a is equal to $\Delta H_s/\Delta H_v$, the ratio of the heat of evaporation of the solute from the solution to the heat of evaporation of the pure liquid solute (Section 3.6). This equation becomes identical with Eq. (3.23) if

$$\ln \gamma = (a - 1)\ln p_2^0 + \ln k. \tag{3.25}$$

Equation (3.25) may be obtained from subsequent discussion by combination of Eqs. (3.42) and (3.30), in which case $\ln k = A(1 - a)$ where A is the constant of Eq. (3.30).

(e) *Approximations Involved in the Derivation of Eqs. (3.19), (3.20), and (3.23), and Their Effect*

The derivations given above for non-ideal solutions take account of non-ideality in the solution phase, but imply that the vapour in the gas phase behaves as a perfect gas. This assumption is unjustified, since the vapours of solutes used in gas chromatography are usually far below their critical temperature, though the carrier gas may not be. In practice, the non-ideality of the vapour is often sufficient for Eq. (3.15) to be several per cent in error. However, such an error has little effect on the quotation of partition coefficients, since the error in Eq. (3.15) is incorporated in the value of the activity coefficient of Eq. (3.18). In thermodynamics, a distinction may be made between activity coefficients as defined here, and activity coefficients from which gas phase non-ideality has been specifically excluded. Adlard *et al.* (*4*) have considered gas phase non-ideality in the course of determining accurate thermodynamic properties by gas chromatography, and discuss the matter further, but, at present, most practical aspects of gas chromatography are unaffected by assuming gas ideality.

An explicit approximation is made in the derivation of the equations for the partition coefficient by neglecting the molar proportion of the solute in the solution in the derivation of Eq. (3.14). If this approximation is not made, the exact form of Eq. (3.14) is:

$$x_2 = \frac{w_2 M_1}{w_1 M_2} \left\{ \frac{1}{1 + (w_2 M_1 / w_1 M_2)} \right\} \approx \frac{w_2 M_1}{w_1 M_2} \left(1 - \frac{w_2 M_1}{w_1 M_2} \right). \qquad (3.26)$$

In this, the second form of writing uses the first term in the binomial expansion of the first form of writing, and is a better approximation to x_2 than is given by Eq. (3.14). It is seen that, so long as x_2 is not so large that further terms in the expansion are appreciable, the fractional error in Eq. (3.14) is approximately equal to the mole fraction itself. Thus, if the mole fraction is 0.01, the percentage error in Eq. (3.14) is about 1%. The operation of Eq. (3.26) rather than Eq. (3.14) when x_2 is not small causes the partition coefficient to become a function of vapour concentration, thus affecting the retention volume. This effect works in opposition to the effect of vapour concentration on the retention volume described in Section 2.9, and the relative magnitudes of the effect of the non-zero concentration of solute in the gas phase and the non-zero concentration of solute in the liquid phase depend on the values of β, M_2, and M_1.

Another source of error arises if the concentration of solute is great enough that the activity coefficient becomes appreciably different from the activity coefficient at infinite dilution. This is most serious for activity coefficients much greater than unity, for, as is seen from Fig. 3.2, in this case, activity coefficients change rapidly at relatively small values of x_2. The theory of the shape of the curves of Fig. 3.2 is complex, and is treated in textbooks, e.g., ref. (7). Practical consequences of the variation of activity coefficients with concentration are described in Sections 5.6 and 5.15.

3.4. Effect of the Vapour Pressure of Solutes on Their Partition Coefficient

The vapour pressure of the solute affects the partition coefficient, and hence the retention volume, through the p_2^0 that appears in the denominator of Eq. (3.20), so that the larger the vapour pressure of a solute at the temperature of the column, the smaller is the partition coefficient. This is apparent from the sample results of Table 3.1. When the solutes and the stationary phase are such that there are no differences in activity coefficient from solute to solute, separation occurs solely on account of difference in p_2^0 between solutes.

In a general way, the higher the boiling point of a solute, the smaller its vapour pressure at a given temperature. Thus, when differences in vapour pressure are the main factor in producing a separation in a chromatographic column, the components will emerge in order of increasing boiling point. There are in fact many applications of this kind in gas chromatography, where differences in activity coefficients cannot be made to, or are not required to, enhance separations. In such cases, a knowledge of p_2^0 will enable one to determine, approximately at any rate, the retention volume and relative retention of two solutes with similar activity coefficients.

The vapour pressure of a solute is a very steep function of the temperature, with the result that the retention volume is similarly very much dependent upon temperature. It is important to select the right column temperature with respect to the solutes to be separated so that retention volumes should be neither too large nor too small. This requires knowledge of absolute values of vapour pressures at different temperatures, which may then be used in Eq. (3.19) or (3.20). As an illustration, consider the chromatography of *n*-heptane on di-isodecyl phthalate, for which it has been found that γ is virtually unity (*10*), whence Eq. (3.17) may be used. Table 3.2 shows the vapour pressure of *n*-heptane at various temperatures,

TABLE 3.2

VAPOUR PRESSURE AND PARTITION COEFFICIENT ON DI-ISODECYL PHTHALATE OF *n*-HEPTANE AS A FUNCTION OF TEMPERATURE

Temperature (°C)	Vapour pressure (mm Hg)	β (cc/g)
25	46	905
75	360	135
95	700	75.7
105	940	56.3
115	1220	44.5
135	2010	28.9
150	2780	21.3

and the partition coefficients β calculated from them by Eq. (3.17). Since specific retention volumes should normally be in the range 10–1000, it is seen from the table that the column should be operated between about 20° and 150°C, and probably somewhere in the middle of this range. In a mixture of wide boiling range, not all the components can give moderate retention volumes, and it is not generally practical to chromatograph at a fixed temperature a mixture of which the boiling range is greater than about 125°C, except when activity coefficients act so as to compress the chromatogram into a smaller range. For mixtures with greater boiling range, the programmed temperature technique described in Section 6.5 may be used.

An instructive guide to the temperature at which to chromatograph a mixture is found by considering the partition coefficient of any solute at its boiling point assuming unit activity coefficient. In these circumstances, p_2^0 has the value of 760 mm Hg, so that Eqs. (3.19) and (3.20) become, substituting $\gamma = 1$,

$$\beta = \frac{82.2T_B}{M_1}, \tag{3.27}$$

$$\zeta = \frac{22{,}420}{M_1}. \tag{3.28}$$

For example, on didecyl phthalate, ζ is 50.3 for all solutes at their boiling point, and for *n*-heptane on didecyl phthalate, β is 68.4 at its boiling point (98°C). Since M_1 is generally of the order of 100 to 1000, the partition coefficient of a solute at its boiling point is usually suitable for practical chromatography. Columns designed for good column performance work better when partition coefficients are large, e.g., 100 to 1000, so that such columns are generally best operated some tens of degrees below the boiling points of the solutes. Capillary columns may operate 100°C or more below the boiling points.

At temperatures other than the boiling points of the solutes, vapour pressures must be sought or calculated. A knowledge of vapour pressure is required in many branches of technology, with the result that there are several useful compilations of such data, in which vapour pressures are given as functions of temperature either as tables, graphs, or formulae. Some useful sources of such data are given below:

"Handbook of Chemistry and Physics." Chemical Rubber Publ., Cleveland, Ohio, published annually.

Jordan, T. Earl, "Vapor Pressure of Organic Compounds." Interscience, New York, 1954.

Rossini, F. D., *et al.*, American Petroleum Institute Research Project 44. Selected values published for the American Petroleum Institute by Carnegie Press, Pittsburgh, Pennsylvania, 1953.

Timmermans, J., "Physico-Chemical Constants of Pure Organic Compounds." Elsevier, Amsterdam, 1950.

Stull, D. R., *Ind. Eng. Chem.* **39**, 517 (1947).

Other compilations to be found in the literature are referred to in the above. The compilation of Jordan gives many curves of vapour pressure against temperature for a large range of organic compounds.

For solutes of which the vapour pressures are not available in the literature, approximate values can generally be found by calculation, particularly if the boiling point is known. These can never be made exact, but are sufficiently useful to estimate the order of magnitude of retention volumes with some degree of accuracy and sometimes to make useful estimates of relative retentions. The vapour pressure of a solute is a function of its chemical composition and of temperature. The second of these can be treated fairly exactly, but the effect of composition is less predictable.

The variation of vapour pressure with temperature is described by the Clausius-Clapeyron equation. In the form relevant here, it is

$$\frac{d \ln p_2{}^0}{dT} = \frac{\Delta H_v}{RT^2}, \tag{3.29}$$

where ΔH_v is the heat of vaporisation of the pure liquid solute. On integration, this gives

$$\ln p_2{}^0 = -\frac{\Delta H_v}{RT} + A, \tag{3.30}$$

where A is a constant of integration. This equation possesses two parameters, ΔH_v and A, and when these are known for a particular solute, the equation is known as a "Young's" equation for the vapour pressure. Equations of this kind are not accurate over large temperature ranges, since ΔH_v is itself slightly dependent on temperature. Thus there are many kinds of vapour pressure equation containing more than two parameters that are more exact than Eq. (3.30). One such form, the "Antoine" equation:

$$\log_{10} p_2{}^0 = A - \frac{B}{t + C}, \tag{3.31}$$

where t is the centigrade temperature, is very often used for quoting vapour pressure data, and can also be used for quoting retention data [Eq. (3.60).] This equation becomes identical with Eq. (3.30) if $C = 273$, but it is usual for heats of evaporation to decline with increase in temperature, with the result that $C < 273$. Hala *et al.* (*12*) report the following empirical relations for the constant C:

(1) for hydrocarbons with n carbon atoms:

$$C = 271 - 7.6n, \tag{3.32}$$

(2) for other substances other than elements and substances boiling below -150°C:

$$C = 240 - 0.19t_B, \tag{3.33}$$

where t_B is the boiling point in °C.

In the absence of published data, the constants in the approximate

Eq. (3.30) can be calculated from the boiling point of the solute, for this is connected with the heat of evaporation by Trouton's rule:

$$\frac{\Delta H_v}{T_B} \approx 22 \text{ cal/(mole °C)}, \tag{3.34}$$

where T_B is the boiling point in °K. If Eq. (3.30) is considered at the boiling point of the pure liquid solute, $p_2{}^0 = 760$ mm Hg, so that

$$\ln 760 = 6.6 \approx \frac{-22}{R} + A = \frac{-22}{2} + A,$$

whence $A \approx 17.6$, and is a universal constant. Hence

$$\ln p_2{}^0 \approx \frac{-22T_B}{RT} + 17.6,$$

or, using common logarithms and substituting the value of R,

$$\log_{10} p_2{}^0 \approx 7.7 - 4.8 \frac{T_B}{T}. \tag{3.35}$$

Equation (3.35) gives a very simple means of calculating the vapour pressure of a solute at any temperature given its boiling point. Its virtue is simplicity rather than accuracy, but it holds within a few per cent within some tens of degrees of the boiling point except for polar compounds such

TABLE 3.3

TESTS OF APPROXIMATION (3.35)

Substance	b.p. (°C)	V.P. at 50°C calc.	V.P. at 50°C true	V.P. at 100°C calc.	V.P. at 100°C true	V.P. at 150°C calc.	V.P. at 150°C true
n-Hexane	68.3	407	400				
n-Heptane	98.4	144	145				
2,2,4-Trimethyl-pentane	99.2	138	140				
n-Decane	174.1	10.5	7.5	83	70	398	380
Benzene	80.1	269	270	1380	1370		
p-Xylene	138.3	37	33	251	235	1047	1030
n-Butylbenzene	183.1	7.9	5.3	64	53	316	300
Ethyl acetate	77.1	295	282	1470	1510		
Diethyl carbonate	125.8	55	39	346	320		
Methyl benzoate	199.5	4.5	2.0	39	30	204	197
Ethanol	78.4	288	222	1480	1690		
Pentanol-2	119.7	69	32	426	350		
Ethylene glycol	197.2	4.9	—	43	1.45	219	20

as alcohols, for which Trouton's constant is abnormal. Vapour pressures of various classes of organic substances at different temperatures are compared with values given by Eq. (3.35) in Table 3.3. It is seen that only for the alcohols is the approximation unusable.

Many other relations involving vapour pressure and boiling point and also relations including the critical parameters of vapours have been described. See, for example, Hala *et al.* (*12*).

The other variable of interest with regard to vapour pressures is chemical composition. The vapour pressure above a vapour is the pressure exerted when liquid and vapour are in equilibrium. In these circumstances, if the liquid is assumed incompressible and the vapour is assumed ideal, the difference in the free energies of liquid and vapour, each referred to a standard pressure, $P\dagger$, is:

$$\Delta G\dagger = G^{\dagger}_{\text{gas}} - G^{\dagger}_{\text{liquid}} = RT \ln \frac{p_2{}^0}{P\dagger}. \tag{3.36}$$

The difference between $G^{\dagger}_{\text{liquid}}$ and $G^{\dagger}_{\text{gas}}$ is that the former includes the interactions of all the molecules with the field of force provided by sur-

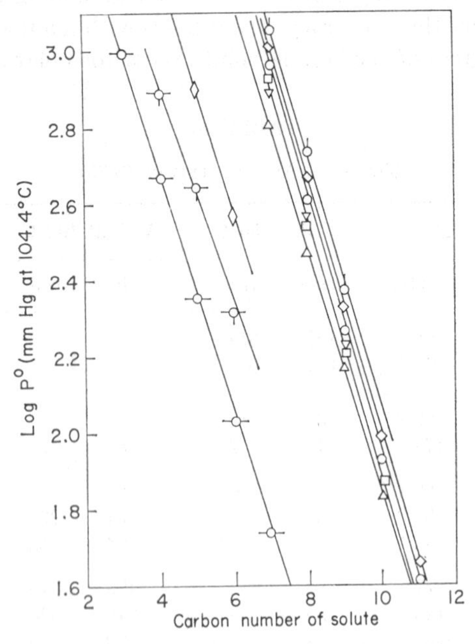

FIG. 3.3. Logarithms of vapour pressures of members of homologous series as a function of carbon number. From Pierotti *et al.* (*8*). ○, *n*-Alkanes; ○ 2-methylalkanes; △, *n*-alkylbenzenes; ▽, *n*-alkylcyclopentanes; □, *n*-alkylcyclohexanes; ▱, 1-alkenes; -○-, 1-alkanols; -○-, 2-alkanols; ◇, 2-alkanones.

rounding molecules, whereas the latter does not. Hence, $\Delta G^\dagger$ is a measure of the forces acting on the molecules in the liquid state. It is clear that, in general, the bigger the molecule and the more polar groups between which specific electric interactions can occur, the smaller is the vapour pressure; this is familiar experience.

Detailed theories of intermolecular interactions in liquids are complex and incomplete. In the case of homologous series, however, each successive methylene group appears to add an almost constant increment to $\Delta G^\dagger$. This can be shown by plotting the logarithm of the vapour pressure of the members of any one homologous series at any one temperature against the number of carbon atoms in the molecule (carbon number), as has been done by Pierotti *et al.* (*8*) and by Herington (*13*). Herington also quotes the relation:

$$\ln p_2^0 = A + Bn, \tag{3.37}$$

where n is the carbon number, and A and B are constants. Figure 3.3 (*8*) shows a plot of the logarithm of the vapour pressure against carbon number (or homolog number) for several different homologous series. It is seen that the lines corresponding to the different series all have very nearly the same slope, which indicates that the constant increment to the standard free energy change is independent of the end-group of the series. The constancy of this increment has been studied by Pierotti *et al.* (*8*), some of whose results are shown in Table 3.4. This shows the increments in $\log_{10} p_2^0$ for addition of one methylene unit, which for the several homologous series shown is about 0.35 $\log_{10}$ units. The increments begin to deviate a little for

TABLE 3.4

INCREMENTS IN $\log_{10} p_2^0$ AT 85°C (*a*) FOR ADDITION OF ONE CARBON ATOM IN A HOMOLOGOUS SERIES, (*b*) FOR CHANGE OF HOMOLOGOUS SERIES[a]

Homologous series	Increment in $\log_{10} p_2^0$
(*a*)	
n-Alkanes	0.35 ± 0.03
2-Methylalkanes	0.35 ± 0.03
3-Methylalkanes	0.37 ± 0.03
1-Alkanols	0.35 ± 0.03
2-Alkanols	0.34 ± 0.03
(*b*)	
n-Alkanes—1-alkanols	1.50 ± 0.15
n-Alkanes—2-methylalkanes	0.22 ± 0.05
2-Methylalkanes—2,2-dimethylalkanes	0.22 ± 0.05
n-Alkanes—3-methylalkanes	0.22 ± 0.05

[a] See Pierotti *et al.* (*8*).

the figures given for small carbon numbers, and generally constancy is obtained only above C_5 or above the first member of the series, whichever is first. The difference in vapour pressure between homologs can also be checked from the boiling points, using Eq. (3.35), from which the increment in $\log_{10} p_2^0$ at temperature T is:

$$\log_{10} \frac{p_2^0}{p_3^0} = \frac{4.8(T_{B3} - T_{B2})}{T}. \tag{3.38}$$

As an example, the difference in boiling points between *n*-heptane and *n*-octane is about 27°C. From Eq. (3.38), the logarithm of the ratio of vapour pressures at 85°C is 0.36, which agrees well with the results of Pierotti *et al.* Note from Eq. (3.38) that the ratio of vapour pressures increases the lower the temperature. This point is discussed further in Section 3.6.

The vapour pressures of branched-chain isomers of members of homologous series are always higher than those of the straight-chain isomers, so that their boiling points are lower, but it is not possible to correlate the vapour pressure with the amount of branching. Table 3.5 gives the boiling

TABLE 3.5

BOILING POINTS OF THE HEPTANES

Substance	b.p. (°C)
n-Heptane	98.4
3-Ethylpentane	93.5
3-Methylhexane	91.8
2-Methylhexane	90.1
2,3-Dimethylpentane	89.8
3,3-Dimethylpentane	86.1
2,2,3-Trimethylbutane	80.9
2,4-Dimethylpentane	80.5
2,2-Dimethylpentane	79.2
Cycloheptane	118.9
Ethylcyclopentane	103.5
Methylcyclohexane	100.9
cis-1,2-Dimethylcyclopentane	99.5
trans-1,2-Dimethylcyclopentane	91.9
trans-1,3-Dimethylcyclopentane	91.7
cis-1,3-Dimethylcyclopentane	90.8
1,1-Dimethylcyclopentane	87.8

points of all the heptanes, from which it is seen that there are double-branched isomers with lower boiling points than a triple-branched isomer. Table 3.5 also includes the cyclic heptanes, and it is seen that these have higher boiling points than the alkanes. These trends apply to all hydrocarbons in homologous series. A result of branched-chain homologs having higher vapour pressures than the corresponding straight-chain compounds is that the addition of a methylene as a branch in the middle of a chain rather than at the end causes a smaller increment in $\log_{10} p_2^0$, as is shown by the last two entries in Table 3.4.

3.5. Activity Coefficients

Although in many cases the difference in partition coefficients of two solutes largely parallels differences in vapour pressure, there are many other cases where differences in their activity coefficients may also be very significant. For gas chromatography, this is particularly useful, since separations depending only on differences of vapour pressure are directly comparable with separations by distillation; but when separations involve differences in activity coefficients, a separating factor is present that is absent in distillation. It is the fact that separations by gas chromatography can use differences in activity as well as differences in volatility that so increases its range and in many cases enables it to perform separations that could not be made by volatility differences alone. For performing separations, a knowledge of the values of the activity coefficients for the solutes in the stationary phase is clearly important. Often the stationary phase can be chosen so as to make the greatest possible use of differences in activity coefficients in performing a given separation.

A simple physical explanation of the meaning of activity coefficients can be given in terms of the free energies of evaporation of the solute from its own liquid and from a solution in a solvent. The free energy of evaporation from an ideal solution is given by

$$\Delta G_{\text{ideal}} = -RT \ln p_2^0, \tag{3.39}$$

and the free energy of evaporation from a real solution by

$$\Delta G_{\text{real}} = -RT \ln \gamma p_2^0. \tag{3.39a}$$

If we define an "Excess Free Energy of Evaporation" for the real solution in comparison with the ideal solution,

$$\Delta G_{xs} = \Delta G_{\text{real}} - \Delta G_{\text{ideal}} \tag{3.40}$$

and substitute this in Eqs. (3.38) and (3.39),

$$\Delta G_{xs} = -RT \ln \gamma. \tag{3.41}$$

The free energy given in Eq. (3.39) is yielded when the solute condenses to form a liquid. This can be regarded as the solute dissolving from the vapour into itself, and this free energy is composed of the sum of a number of terms consisting of all the different forms of interaction of the different parts of the condensing molecules with their environment. In Eq. (3.39a), the free energy is that yielded when the solute condenses into an environment which is largely that of solvent molecules. The detailed interactions between the condensing solute molecules and the environment provided by the solvent are different from those between solute molecules and the environment provided by other solute molecules. This difference is expressed by ΔG_{xs}, which is related to the activity coefficient by Eq. (3.41). When the environments provided to a condensing molecule by both the liquid solute and by the solvent are the same, then the free energies of Eqs. (3.39) and (3.39a) are the same, so that ΔG_{xs} is zero. In this case Eq. (3.41) gives the value of unity for the activity coefficient, and the solution is ideal.

The calculation of activity coefficients from easily accessible molecular properties of solute and solvent is not generally possible, for there is no sufficiently complete theory of liquid structure. However, there are several partial and semi-quantitative attempts at such calculations for restricted classes of compounds based upon more or less realistic models of solutions. Three such models will be described, of which the last has been applied specifically to gas chromatography.

A model of the solution which is slightly more realistic than the ideal solution is the "Regular Solution," in which the heat of mixing of the two components is not necessarily zero. For this case, calculation shows that (5) if ΔH_v is the heat of evaporation of the pure liquid solute, and ΔH_s is the heat of evaporation of a solute from a solvent, then

$$\ln \gamma = \frac{\Delta H_v - \Delta H_s}{RT}. \tag{3.42}$$

Therefore, for a regular solution, if ΔH_s is greater than ΔH_v, the activity coefficient is less than unity, and if the heat of evaporation is the greater, the activity coefficient is greater than unity. This is generally observed to be true, as is shown in Section 3.6, although the solutions involved in gas chromatography are not even approximately regular. A prerequisite of regular solutions, and a necessary condition for Eq. (3.42) to hold, is that the entropy of mixing is an entropy of dilution only. In solutions involved in gas chromatography, this is not normally true since, in order to be less volatile than the solute, the molecules of solvent are of necessity larger than those of the solute, which leads to non-ideal entropy of mixing.

Whereas the regular solution considers the non-zero heat of mixing, but not the difference in size between the molecules, another model considers the difference in size between the molecules but not the heat of mixing.

This is likely to apply with greatest accuracy to cases where non-polar solutes dissolve in non-polar solvents. For very small values of the concentration of a solute of molar volume V_2 in a solvent of molar volume V_1, the activity coefficient can be calculated to be (*5*)

$$\gamma = \frac{V_2}{V_1} \exp\left(1 - \frac{V_2}{V_1}\right), \tag{3.43}$$

assuming that the difference in molar volume is the only factor producing non-unit activity coefficient. Another relation for the activity coefficients of molecules of unequal size has been given by Bronstead and Koefoed [see ref. (*8*)] for mixtures of *n*-alkanes:

$$\ln \gamma = -D(n_1 - n_2)^2 \tag{3.44}$$

where D is a constant and n_1 and n_2 (n_1, $n_2 < 16$) are the carbon number of solvent and solute, respectively. The constant D was found to vary slightly with temperature, and at 60°C was 55×10^{-5}. Both Eq. (3.43) and Eq. (3.44) predict that as the difference in homolog number between solute and solvent increases, the activity coefficient should decrease. Equation (3.44) has been tested by Kwantes and Rijnders (*10*), using gas chromatography to determine activity coefficients through Eq. (3.23), and with solutions of alkanes in higher alkanes as stationary phases, they confirmed that activity coefficients fall as the difference in carbon number between solute and solvent increases, but the quantitative agreement with Eq. (3.44) is poor. For example, the measured activity coefficient of *n*-heptane in *n*-C_{35} alkane is 0.63. Calculation by Eq. (3.44) gives 0.34, calculation by Eq. (3.43) gives 0.44.

The effect of the difference in molecular size in different solutes has little effect upon relative retentions in practical chromatography, since for two solutes to have appreciably different activity coefficients through this effect, they would be so different in size that they would separate with greatest ease merely through vapour pressure differences.

The two approaches to activity coefficient given above each apply to extreme cases, and are in principle mutually exclusive. In spite of this, however, study of published data suggests that a useful guide to the behaviour of activity coefficients of solute-solvent systems exhibiting both differences in molecular size and non-zero heats of mixing may be obtained by multiplying together Eqs. (3.42) and (3.43). This will be seen in Section 3.7 and in many places in Chapter 11, where it is shown that polymeric stationary phases with very large molecular weights cause all solutes to have very small activity coefficients as predicted by Eq. (3.43), yet changes in these activity coefficients from solute to solute are in accord with the predictions of Eq. (3.42).

The phenomenological approach given above has restricted use in practice, since the molecular structure of the solutes and solvents are probably known, but heats of solution, etc., are almost certainly not known except in a very general way. Pierotti *et al.* (*8*) have considered activity coefficients in terms of structure in a case which is still restricted, but is of considerable application in gas chromatography; that in which members of homologous series are used both as solutes and solvents. The actual solvents used by the authors in obtaining their experimental results were generally more volatile than are used in gas chromatography, but the principles arising are of general application, and make a good basis for further discussion of stationary phases.

If the solute is called R_2-X_2 and the stationary phase R_1-X_1, then Pierotti *et al.* assume that the forces acting on the solute in its own liquid may be expressed as the sum of all possible interactions of R_2 and X_2 in pairs and that the forces acting on the solute in the stationary phase may be expressed as the sum of all possible interactions of R_1, R_2, X_1, and X_2 in pairs. Complete specification of all the interactions in terms of the structural parameters of the molecules would give the free energies of evaporation of the solute from the liquid solute and from the solvent, and the difference of the two would give ΔG_{xs}, from which the activity coefficient may be obtained by Eq. (3.41). As has been mentioned, this cannot be done in general, but Pierotti *et al.* restrict themselves by the introduction of two parameters only, the carbon number of the solute (n_2) and the carbon number of the solvent (n_1). In this case they find experimentally that γ is given by the equation

$$\ln \gamma = -\frac{\Delta G_{xs}}{RT} = f(a) + f(b) + f(c) + f(d) + f(e) + f(f) \qquad (3.45)$$

where the six functions $f(a)$ to $f(f)$ of n_1 and n_2 are given in Table 3.6. In

TABLE 3.6

SPECIFICATION OF FUNCTIONS COMPRISING $\ln \gamma^a$

Function	Dependence on carbon number of solute and solvent	Interactions involved
$f(a)$	A	$X_1 - X_2$, $X_1 - X_1$, $X_2 - X_2$
$f(b)$	Bn_2/n_1	$X_1 - X_1$, $R_2 - X_1$, $R_1 - X_1$
$f(c)$	$C/(n_2 + C')$	$X_2 - X_2$, $R_2 - X_2$
$f(d)$	$D(n_2 - n_1)^2$	$R_1 - R_2$, $R_1 - R_1$, $R_2 - R_2$
$f(e)$	$(En_1/n_2 = 0)$	$R_1 - X_2$
$f(f)$	$F/(n_1 + F')$	$X_1 - X_1$, $R_1 - X_1$, $X_1 - X_2$

[a] See Pierotti *et al.* (*14*).

these functions, the capital letters A to F are all constants which must be empirically determined, but are independent of the carbon numbers.

Pierotti *et al.* do not attempt to explain the functions listed in Table 3.6, which are essentially empirical, but obviously chosen with regard to the mechanics of the systems to which they apply. It is possible to rationalise them as a rough aid to understanding as follows.

The term $f(a)$ includes all interactions not involving n_1 or n_2, which are those involving the characteristic groups X_1 and X_2 only. Of these, there are X_2-X_2 interactions in the solute liquid which are replaced by X_1-X_2 interactions in the solution. In addition, the formation of X_1-X_2 interactions in the solution necessitates the break-up of X_1-X_1 interactions in the solvent.

The term $f(b)$ describes the change in X_1 on passing from an environment containing solvent alkyl groups to an environment also containing solute alkyl groups. Thus, B represents the free energy of interaction between X_1 and one methylene. As would be expected, $B \geqslant 0$.

The term $f(c)$ describes the free energy change in lifting a solute molecule out of its own liquid. When n_2 is small, so that the alkyl proportion of the solute molecule is small, the term approximates to C/C', which is constant; when n_2 is large, $f(c)$ becomes inversely proportional to n_2. The term $f(f)$ similarly describes the free energy required in passing a solute molecule into the solvent. Terms $f(c)$ and $f(f)$ together are supplementary to term $f(b)$ in that they roughly describe the same changes in a different analytical form. This enables a

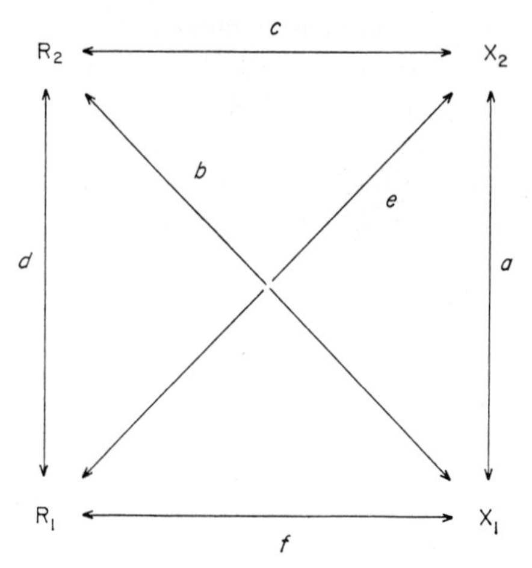

FIG. 3.4. Scheme of interactions relevant in determining partition coefficients of solutions of homologs. From Pierotti *et al.* (*8*).

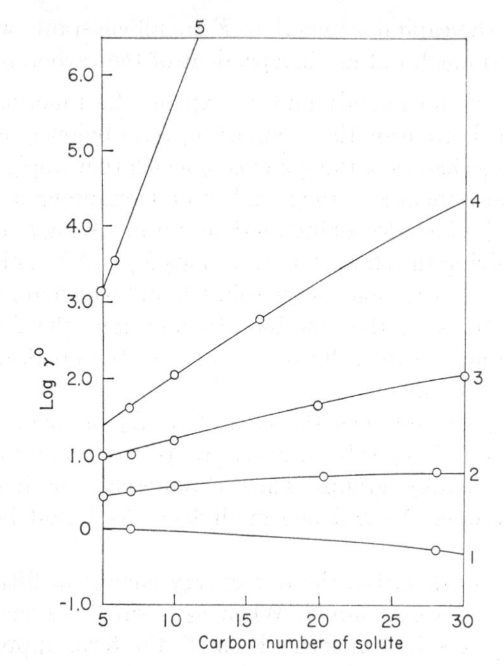

FIG. 3.5. Activity coefficients of alkanes as a function of carbon number in various solvents. From Pierotti *et al.* (8). 1, *n*-Heptane at 90°C; 2, 2,2-butanone at 90°C; 3, phenol at 90°C; 4, triethylene glycol at 90°C; 5, water at 25°C.

large range of experimental data to be accommodated in Eq. (3.45) by empirical adjustment of the parameters. Terms $f(c)$ and $f(f)$ are only required to account for the more complicated behaviour of mixtures of compounds of low carbon numbers. At high values of n_1 and n_2, γ is completely defined by A, B, n_1, n_2, and $f(d)$.

The term $f(d)$ has already been discussed.

Finally, the term $f(e)$ would describe the change in the environment of X_2 on encountering R_1 groups. Pierotti *et al.*, however, find that the results can be adequately represented without its use, so that $E = 0$.

Pierotti *et al.* have illustrated the principal interactions involved in the definitions of $f(a)$ to $f(f)$ by Fig. 3.4.

The validity and use of this approach may be shown by discussing special cases in which all variables but one are held steady. The simplest case to consider is that in which the solutes are a series of *n*-alkanes, and the stationary phase is given. In these circumstances, $f(a)$ and $f(f)$ are both constants, and C is equal to zero since there are no end-groups on the solutes between which interactions can occur. As described above, D is of the order of 10^{-4} to 10^{-3}, so for ranges of n_2 not spanning more than about 10 carbon atoms, $f(d)$ may be neglected, or regarded as constant. Hence, the general equation (3.45) reduces to

$$\ln \gamma = K + \frac{B}{n_1} \cdot n_2, \tag{3.46}$$

where K is a composite constant. Equation (3.46) has been independently derived, as Herington (*13*) has pointed out. Figure 3.5 shows experimental plots of $\ln \gamma$ against carbon number for *n*-alkanes on a selection of stationary phases (*8*). It is seen that the plots are virtually straight lines, in agreement with Eq. (3.46). When the solvent is another alkane, B is zero and also K is zero, so that Eq. (3.46) becomes $\ln \gamma = 0$. In fact, the line is seen to be nearly horizontal, and the slight decline in γ with increase in carbon number is due to the small $f(d)$ term which was omitted from Eq. (3.46), but is described by Eq. (3.43) or (3.44). In other solvents, both K and B have positive values, with the result that activity coefficients increase with carbon number and also have large absolute values. These observations are reasonable from a molecular point of view; in the more polar stationary phases, the polar groups have more attraction for each other than for the

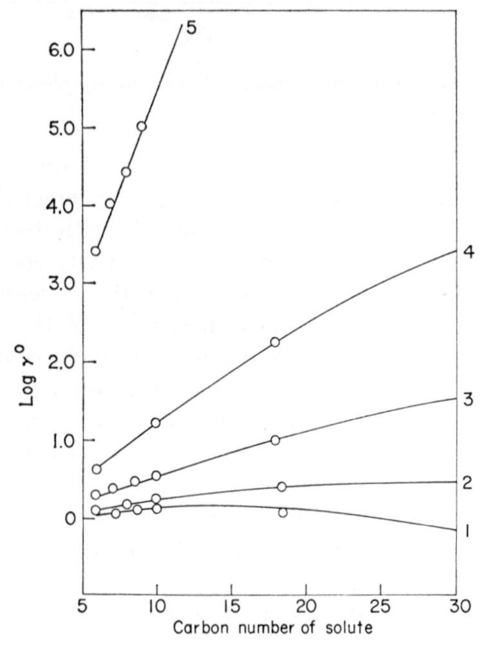

FIG. 3.6. Activity coefficients of alkylbenzenes as a function of carbon number in various solvents. From Pierotti *et al.* (*8*). 1, *n*-Heptane at 90°C; 2, 2,2-butanone at 90°C; 3, phenol at 90°C; 4, triethylene glycol at 90°C; 5, water at 25°C.

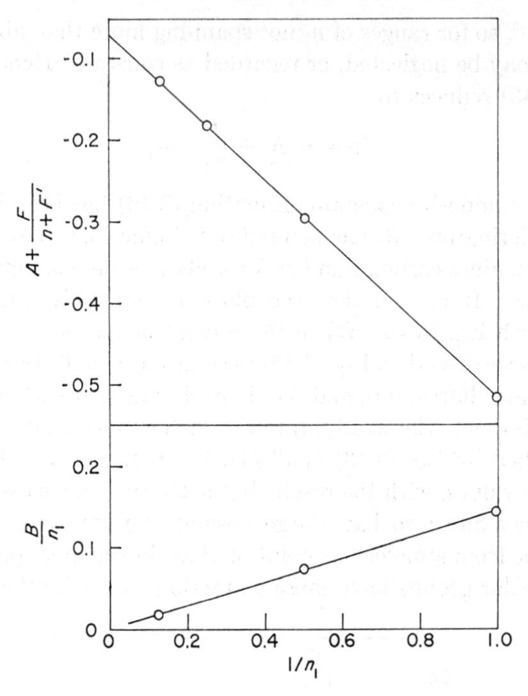

FIG. 3.7. Effect of the carbon number of the stationary phase on terms contributing to ln γ for n-alkanones in alcohol solvents.

alkanes, and hence the presence of alkanes breaks up these interactions, leading to a positive value of A. Furthermore, the larger the alkane solute molecule, the greater the effect of each molecule, with the result that B has a positive value. In the extreme cases, where activity coefficients are very large, the alkane solutes are immiscible with the solvents; large activity coefficients usually imply incomplete miscibility of the solvent and the liquid solute. From Fig. 3.5 it is apparent that by choice of the stationary phase, one can chromatograph alkanes without any activity effects, with moderate activity effects, as with butanone or phenol, or with gross activity effects, as with triethylene glycol or water. The use of such variety of choice is described in Section 3.9.

In another example, Pierotti *et al.* (*8*) show the activity coefficients of a homologous series of alkylbenzenes on different stationary phases. In this case, the C term is no longer zero, and the expression for the activity coefficient on each stationary phase as a function of the carbon number becomes

$$\ln \gamma = K + K'n_2 + \frac{C}{n_2 + C'}.$$

C' is found empirically to equal 4, so that when the homolog number is large, the plot of $\ln \gamma$ against carbon number is approximately a straight line as with alkane solutes, but when the homolog number is small, there is some curvature of the plot. Figure 3.6 shows the experimental results. Apart from the slight curvature, the general shape of the plots is much the same as with the alkanes, but though the values of B are the same, the values of A are smaller for the alkylbenzenes than for the alkanes. This enables non-paraffinic solvents to be used effectively for the separation of alkanes and alkylbenzenes of the same boiling range (Section 11.3).

Pierotti *et al.* have also investigated the effect of changing the homolog number of the stationary phase. The full expression for the activity coefficient in these authors' terms is

$$\ln \gamma = \left[A + \frac{F}{n_1 + F'}\right] + \left[\frac{B}{n_1}\right] n_2 + \frac{C}{n_2 + C'} + D(n_1 - n_2)^2, \tag{3.47}$$

where the terms in square brackets are constant for a given solvent. The authors have chromatographed a series of solutes on each of a homologous series of solvents, and thus determined values of the quantities in brackets for each of the solvents. Results for alkanol solvents ranging from methanol to octanol-1 are given in Fig. 3.7, in which the quantities in brackets of the expression for γ are plotted against $1/n_1$. From the fact that a straight line plot is obtained in each case, it is seen that for this system, A is small, F' is small, and that the general equation of Pierotti *et al.* appears to hold well. If the comparatively small C and D terms are omitted from Eq. (3.47), we obtain a form of Eq. (3.46) in which the dependence of K of Eq. (3.46) on n_1 is specified,

$$\ln \gamma = \left[A + \frac{F}{n_1 + F'}\right] + \left[\frac{B}{n_1}\right] n_2. \tag{3.48}$$

For a given series of stationary phases, F and F' are constant, but A and B depend upon the chemical type of the solutes. The result of this is that the way in which K and B/n_1 of Eq. (3.46) vary with the molecular type of the solutes depends on the homolog number of the solvent. This can clearly form the basis of a subtle way of varying the selectivity of the stationary phase. Increasing its carbon chain makes it behave more like a paraffinic stationary phase; decreasing the length of its carbon chain makes it behave more according to the character of its end-group. There are few reports of this effect being used specifically, but there are several pieces of evidence in the literature reflecting this behaviour. One specific example has been pointed out by Keulemans *et al.* (*15*) who have found that olefins are more selectively retained relative to alkanes on dibutyl phthalate than on dinonyl phthalate. The former stationary phase contains a larger proportion of groups other than the alkyl chains of methylenes, and it is these that cause the specific retention of olefins.

When the consideration of partition coefficients is broadened from homologous series to all compounds, the principal factor involved is the standard excess free energy produced by the interaction of the characteristic groups of the solvent with the characteristic groups of the solute, which is analogous to a general form of the parameter A of the treatment of Pierotti *et al.* When the characteristic groups are the same in solute and solvent, A is small, so that activity coefficients near unity will generally arise in solutions of "Like in Like." Polar solutes have activity coefficients close to unity in media of about the same polarity, as have aromatics in aromatics and alkanes in alkanes. Mixtures of like in like may give activity coefficients of somewhat less than unity, but rarely less than about 0.5 except as a result of unequal molecular size, for very small activity coefficients do not result from simple binary solutions of non-electrolytes. Generally dissimilar kinds of chemical form mutual solutions of large activity coefficient, whether it is solute or solvent that is more polar.

In certain cases there are specific chemical effects which can be introduced to influence activity. Thus, if silver nitrate is dissolved in a stationary phase, the activity coefficients of alkenes and dienes becomes abnormally small through chemical combination of the double bonds with the silver ion (*16*). The effect is more marked for 1-alkenes than for others. Other examples of this kind of specific behaviour are the large activity coefficients of *o*-alkyldiphenyls on aromatic stationary phases through steric hindrance (*17*); the separation of pyridines on glycerol (*18*); or the separation of amines and other compounds on columns using metal salts of higher fatty acids as stationary phase (*19*). Such specific chemical effects are obviously very useful in practice, but are not amenable to a general theoretical treatment. They are described where relevant in Chapter 11.

3.6. Effect of Temperature on Partition Coefficients

Partition coefficients are affected by temperature through variation of three of the quantities appearing in Eq. (3.19). Firstly, there is the temperature itself; secondly, the vapour pressure of the pure solute, p_2^0, is very dependent upon the temperature; and thirdly, the activity coefficient is to some extent a function of temperature, particularly when it is large.

Of these three, the first requires no further comment, and to begin with, the other two can be considered together. The product γp_2^0 is the Henry's law constant for the distribution of the solute between the phases. As shown in the derivation of Eq. (3.19)[see Eq. (3.18)], it is the ratio of the concentration of the solute in the gas phase to that in the stationary phase. Thermodynamic theory requires that the distribution coefficient such as the above is connected with the temperature T by the relation:

$$\frac{d \ln (\gamma p_2^0)}{dT} = \frac{\Delta H_s}{RT^2}, \tag{3.49}$$

where ΔH_s is the differential heat of evaporation of the solute from the solvent.

Equation (3.49) can be split up into two parts, firstly for the vapour pressure of the solute,

$$\frac{d \ln p_2^0}{dT} = \frac{\Delta H_v}{RT^2}, \tag{3.29}$$

and secondly for the activity coefficient,

$$\frac{d \ln \gamma}{dT} = \frac{\Delta H_{xs}}{RT^2}, \tag{3.50}$$

where the two heats are related by:

$$\Delta H_{xs} = \Delta H_s - \Delta H_v. \tag{3.51}$$

Equation (3.29) is the Clausius-Clapeyron equation for the variation of the vapour pressure with temperature already given in Section 3.4, and ΔH_v is the heat of evaporation of the pure liquid solute. For the case of regular solutions, ΔH_{xs} is related to the activity coefficient by Eq. (3.42), and to the excess free energy of evaporation [Eq. (3.40)] by the relation:

$$\Delta G_{xs} = \Delta H_{xs} - T\Delta S_{xs}, \tag{3.52}$$

where ΔS_{xs} is the corresponding difference in the entropy terms. Combination of Eqs. (3.51), (3.52), (3.41), and (3.42) shows that for regular solutions, $\Delta S_{xs} = 0$. In the case that the activity coefficient is neither very large nor very small, ΔH_{xs} is small compared to ΔH_s, so that ΔH_s is not very dif ferent from ΔH_v.

If Eq. (3.49) is substituted into Eq. (3.19), the result is:

$$\frac{d \ln (RT/M_1\beta)}{dT} = \frac{\Delta H_s}{RT^2}. \tag{3.53}$$

Rearranging this, and omitting the temperature independent terms inside the logarithm, gives

$$\frac{d \ln (\beta/T)}{dT} = -\frac{\Delta H_s}{RT^2}. \tag{3.54}$$

Substitution of Eq. (3.2) gives

$$\frac{d \ln \zeta}{dT} = -\frac{\Delta H_s}{RT^2}. \tag{3.55}$$

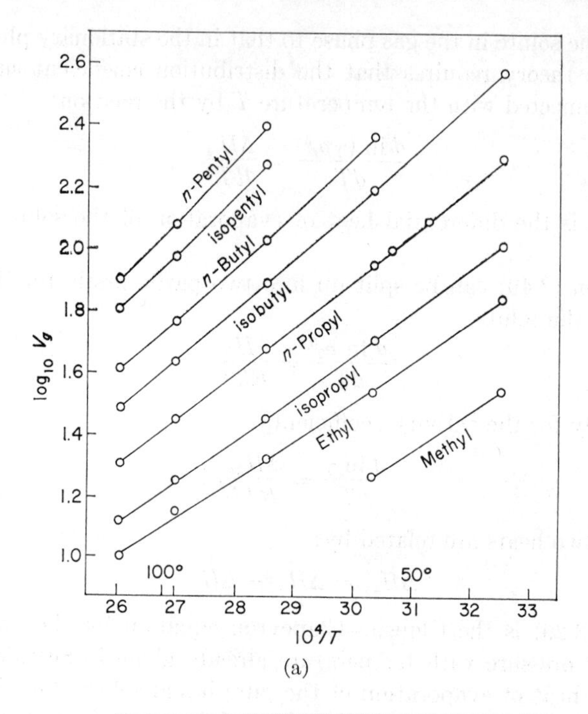
2.6
2.4
2.2
2.0
1.8
1.6
1.4
1.2
1.0
$\log_{10} V_g$
n-Pentyl
isopentyl
n-Butyl
isobutyl
n-Propyl
isopropyl
Ethyl
Methyl
100°
50°
26
27
28
29
30
31
32
33
$10^4/T$
(a)

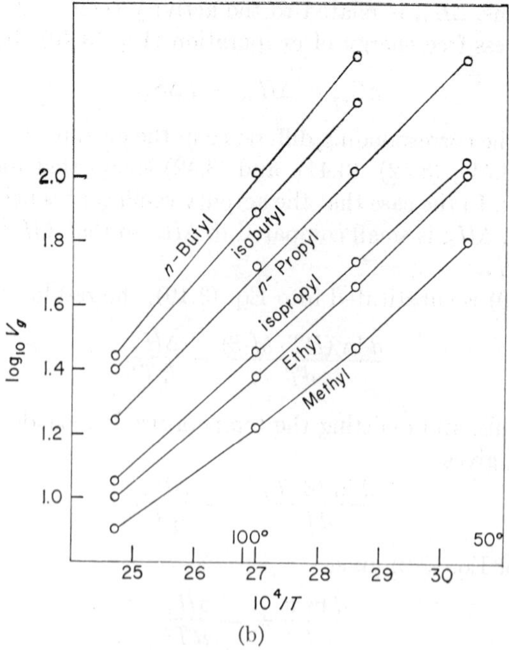
2.0
1.8
1.6
1.4
1.2
1.0
$\log_{10} V_g$
n-Butyl
isobutyl
n- Propyl
isopropyl
Ethyl
Methyl
100°
50°
25
26
27
28
29
30
$10^4/T$
(b)

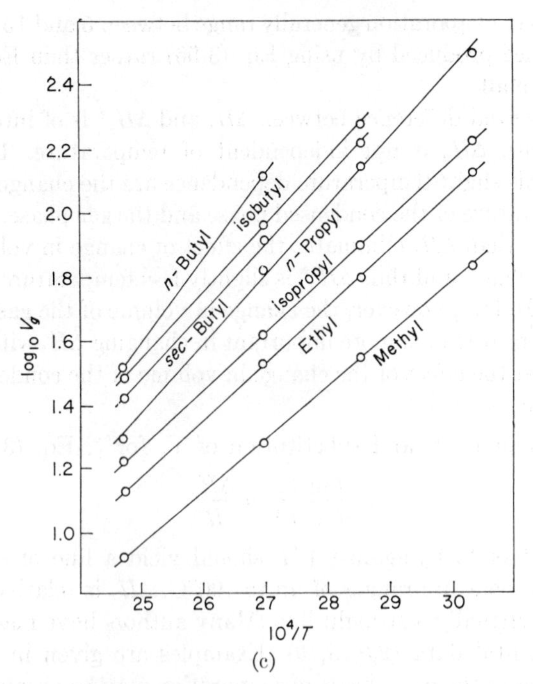

(c)

FIG. 3.8. Plots of log V_g against inverse temperature. From Littlewood *et al.* (*2*). (a) Alcohols on silicone oil DC 702. (b) Alcohols on tricresyl phosphate. (c) Acetates on tricresyl phosphate.

Equations (3.54) and (3.55) describe the variation of partition coefficient with temperature.

Some authors (*2, 9*) have given an equation similar to Eq. (3.54) in α rather than in β:

$$\frac{d \ln (\alpha/T)}{dT} = -\frac{\Delta H_s{}^*}{RT^2} \tag{3.56}$$

where $\Delta H_s{}^*$ is a quantity obeying the above equation but not quite equal to the heat of evaporation of the solute in the solvent. It is easily shown that the difference between the two forms is

$$\Delta H_s{}^* - \Delta H_s = RT^2\eta \tag{3.57}$$

where η is the coefficient of expansion of the solvent. The coefficient of expansion for most stationary phases is, within a factor of 2, equal to 10^{-3} °C^{-1} at or near room temperature. Thus, the difference between the two forms of the heat term for a substance at or near room temperature is

$$2 \times 273^2 \times 0.001 \approx 180 \text{ cal/mole.}$$

Since heats of evaporation generally range between 5 and 15 kcal/mole, the difference produced by using Eq. (3.56) rather than Eq. (3.57) is relatively small.

The essential difference between ΔH_s and ΔH_s^* is of interest. As is shown below, ΔH_s is not independent of temperature. Two of the causes of this slight temperature dependence are the change in volume with temperature of the condensed phase and the gas phase. The use of ΔH_s^* rather than ΔH_s eliminates the effect of change in volume of the condensed phase, and thus ΔH_s^* is slightly less temperature dependent than ΔH_s. In fact, however, the change in volume of the gas phase and other factors are much more important in changing ΔH_s with temperature, so that the effect of the change in volume of the condensed phase is negligible.

On rearrangement, and substitution of V_g for ζ, Eq. (3.55) becomes

$$\frac{d \ln V_g}{d(1/T)} = \frac{\Delta H_s}{R} \tag{3.58}$$

so that a plot of ln V_g against $1/T$ should yield a line of slope $\Delta H_s/R$. Since over temperature ranges of up to 100°C, ΔH_s is relatively constant, such a plot is virtually a straight line. Many authors have made such plots from experimental data (*2,9,18,19*). Examples are given in Fig. 3.8 (*2*). From the slopes of the lines, heats of evaporation may be obtained. Heats of

TABLE 3.7

HEATS OF EVAPORATION OF SOLUTES FROM TRICRESYL PHOSPHATE, HEATS OF EVAPORATION OF THE PURE LIQUID SOLUTES, AND THEIR DIFFERENCE

	kcal/mole		
Solute	ΔH_s	ΔH_v	$-\Delta H_{xs}$
2-Methylpentane	5.3	5.9	0.6
n-Heptane	6.3	6.8	0.5
n-Octane	7.2	7.5	0.3
Benzene	7.6	6.4	−1.2
Toluene	7.9	7.6	−0.3
p-Xylene	8.5	8.0	−0.5
o-Xylene	8.6	8.0	−0.6
Methanol	6.5	9.1	2.6
Ethanol	7.1	9.7	2.6
Isopropanol	8.0	10.2	2.2
n-Propanol	9.0	10.8	1.8
Isobutanol	9.8	11.0	1.2

evaporation have been obtained by many authors (*2,9,18–20*), some of whom give tables of values.

Table 3.7 gives a selection of the heats of evaporation for a number of solutes. It is observed that, in general, the heats of evaporation increase with increasing molecular complexity of the solutes. This is reasonable, from a mechanical point of view, for the more atoms there are in a molecule, the more energy is required in order for the molecule to escape from the environment of the solvent into the gas phase. The fact that heats of evaporation rise with molecular complexity corresponds with the fact already noted that boiling points and heats of evaporation of pure liquid solutes both increase with increasing molecular complexity. In the case of homologous series, each methylene group added to the solute appears to produce a constant increment to ΔH_s, as is illustrated in Fig. 3.9 (*18*). This corresponds with the similar regularities observed with the vapour pressure.

Plots such as are shown in Fig. 3.8 are useful because the vertical distance between two lines is the logarithm of the relative retention of two solutes. If, for example, the logarithms on the ordinate are to the base of 10, then a distance between the lines of 0.04 units would represent a relative retention of 1.1. Heats of evaporation are greater for more complex molecules,

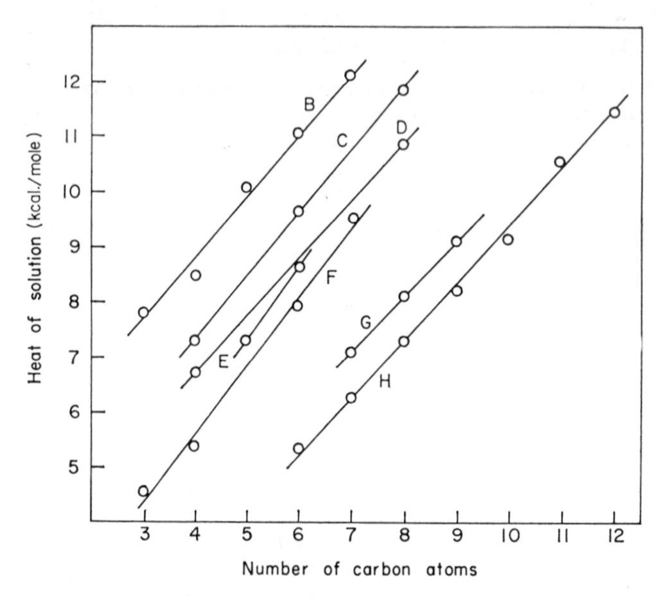

FIG. 3.9. Plots of heats of solution as a function of carbon number for members of homologous series. From Barber *et al.* (*18*). A, Amines; B, normal primary alcohols; C, 2-methyl alcohols; D, secondary alcohols; E, cyclic ketones; F, aliphatic ketones; G, aromatic hydrocarbons; H, aliphatic hydrocarbons.

so that the lines of $\log_{10} V_g - 1/T$ plots are not parallel. Since also the more complex molecules generally have the greater retention volumes, the result is that the lines tend to spread out in a fan, being closer together at high temperatures (small values of $1/T$) and further apart at low temperatures. The significance of this in practice is that generally, relative retentions are greater at low temperatures than at high temperatures. This forms an important rule which has been remarked many times in the literature. For example, the relative retention of *m*- and *p*-xylene can be considerably increased by reducing the temperature about 60°C (*21*). As described in Chapter 5, reduction in temperature generally increases column efficiencies, so that both on account of efficiency and on account of relative retention, operation at a low temperature is desirable. On the other hand, drawbacks to low-temperature operation are the length of time taken for an analysis, and also the necessity of using smaller samples in order to avoid overloading the column, which occurs more easily the lower the temperature (Sections 5.15 and 5.22).

Table 3.7 also includes values for the heat of evaporation of pure liquid solutes and the excess heat of solution. The latter quantity is interesting, for, through Eq. (3.50), it determines the variation of activity coefficients with temperature. Table 3.8 shows the values of the activity coefficients at

TABLE 3.8

ACTIVITY COEFFICIENTS AS A FUNCTION OF TEMPERATURE AND EXCESS HEATS OF SOLUTION FOR SUBSTANCES IN SILICONE 702 FLUID

	Activity coefficient					
Substance	34.5 °C	56.2 °C	77.0 °C	97.0 °C	111 °C	$-\Delta H_{xs}$ (kcal/mole)
Methanol	6.42	4.77				3.1
Ethanol	6.50	4.74	2.99	2.03	1.96	3.7
i-Propanol	5.81	4.06	2.76	1.92	1.76	3.8
n-Propanol	6.25	4.50	3.09	2.16	1.81	3.7
i-Butanol	5.13	3.98	2.91	2.17	1.79	3.2
Methyl acetate	0.98	0.96	0.94	0.88		0.1
Ethyl acetate	0.91	0.94	0.90	0.86	0.77	0.2
n-Propyl acetate		1.00[a]	0.93	0.92	0.89	0.2
Benzene	0.67	0.72	0.71		0.63	−1.2
Toluene			0.81	0.78	0.74	−0.8
p-Xylene			0.90	0.90	0.86	−1.4

[a] This activity coefficient was assumed, and was used to determine the effective average molecular weight of the stationary phase.

different temperatures for various solutes, and also the corresponding values of ΔH_{xs}. It is seen that a large value of ΔH_{xs} corresponds with a temperature-sensitive activity coefficient. From evidence so far available, it appears that both $\partial \ln \gamma / \partial T$ and ΔH_{xs} are largest for solutes with large activity coefficients, so that the large activity coefficients tend to decrease as the temperature rises. This implies that, at least in systems so far studied, Eq. 3.42 is at least approximately true.

The variation of γ with temperature is important, for it means that when activity effects are being used to secure a particular separation, some attention must be paid to the temperature at which the separation is carried out. Thus, from Table 3.8 it is apparent that activity effects can be used to separate alcohols from similarly boiling esters on a silicone column at low temperatures, for at low temperatures the activity coefficients of the alcohols are very much larger than those of the esters. However, at higher temperatures, the activity coefficients of the alcohols fall, with the result that their retention volumes become more comparable with those of the esters. In cases like these, the relative retentions between compounds of which the values of ΔH_{xs} are dissimilar vary sharply with temperature. This is expressed on $\log_{10} V_g - 1/T$ plots by two lines of dissimilar slope. It is possible for two solutes to have roughly similar retention volumes, but different heats of solution, particularly when one solute is of a different chemical type to the other and has a different activity coefficient. In this case, the lines of the $\log_{10} V_g - 1/T$ plots are close and non-parallel, and may easily cross, with the result that the solutes appear A after B at one temperature, B after A at another temperature, and together at an intermediate temperature. An example of this behaviour is shown in the three chromatograms reproduced in Fig. 3.10.

As with heats of evaporation of pure solutes, heats of evaporation of

TABLE 3.9

HEATS OF EVAPORATION FROM TRICRESYL PHOSPHATE AS A FUNCTION OF TEMPERATURE

	Heat of evaporation (kcal/mole)		
Solute	30°C	60°C	100°C
2-Methylpentane	6.1		5.3
n-Heptane	7.3		6.3
n-Octane	8.6		7.2
Toluene		8.4	7.9
p-Xylene		9.1	8.5
o-Xylene		9.2	8.6

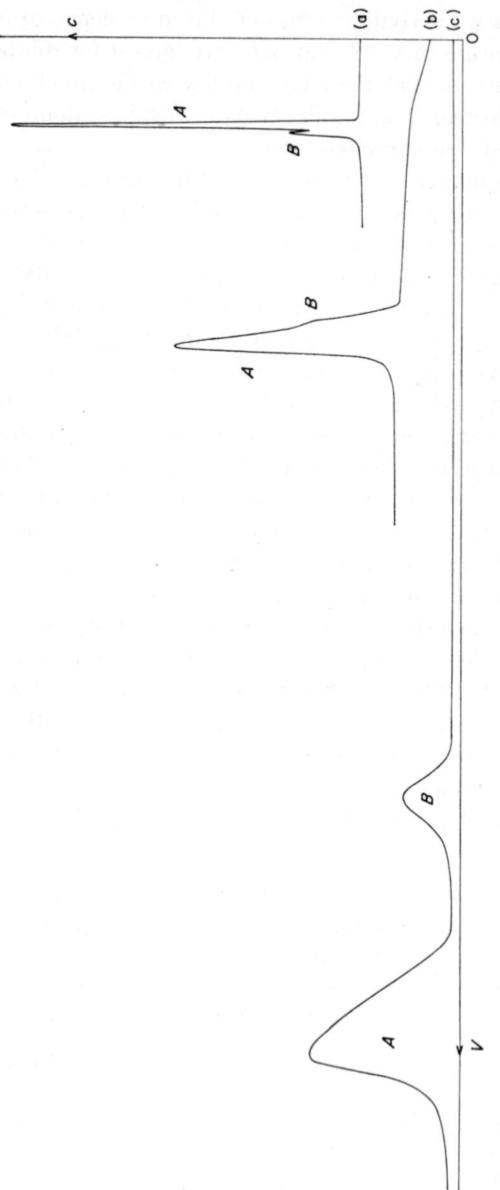

FIG. 3.10. Chromatograms of 2 parts of 3-methyl hexane (A) to 1 part of n-propanol (B) at (a) 100°C, (b) 50°C, (c) 22°C, on didecyl phthalate.

solutes from solution decrease slowly with increasing temperature, with the result that the lines of $\log_{10} V_g - 1/T$ plots are slightly convex downwards. The magnitude of the effect is illustrated by the results quoted in Table 3.9, and the curvature of $\log_{10} V_g - 1/T$ may be seen on the curve for methanol in Fig. 3.8. The variation of ΔH_s with temperature requires that, if values of ΔH_s are quoted, the temperature should also be mentioned; it also implies that no values of ΔH_s are very accurate, and indeed there is little point in quoting them to more than one decimal place.

If Eq. (3.55) is integrated, the result is

$$\ln V_g^0 = -\frac{\Delta H_s}{RT} + A, \tag{3.59}$$

which is a two-parameter equation for the retention volume as a function of temperature. Owing to the variation of ΔH_s with temperature, this cannot be used over any appreciable range of temperature, so Ambrose and Purnell (*22*) have suggested that Eq. (3.59) be replaced by a three-parameter equation similar to the Antoine equation (3.30) for vapour pressure:

$$\log_{10} V_g = A + \frac{B}{t' + C} \tag{3.60}$$

where A, B, and C are constants for any one solute on any one stationary phase, and t' is the temperature in degrees centigrade. If $C = 273$, Eq. (3.60) has the same form as Eq. (3.59), and implies that the $\log_{10} V_g - 1/T$ curve is straight. In the usual case that ΔH_s declines with increase in temperature, $C < 273$. The use of Eq. (3.60) in connection with the correction procedure of Section 2.7 enables the retention of a solute to be completely described by the three parameters of the above Antoine equation.

3.7. The Molecular Weight of the Stationary Phase

Equations (3.19) and (3.20) each contain M_1, the molecular weight of the stationary phase, in the denominator, so that retention volumes should be inversely proportional to M_1 if the other terms remain constant. In practice, however, a change in M_1 always causes a change in γ, since the molecular weight is roughly proportional to the molar volume, and Eq. (3.43) applies. When $V_2 \ll V_1$, Eq. (3.43) reduces to $\gamma \propto V_2/V_1$. This condition normally applies in gas chromatography, since the stationary phase must have a much larger molecular weight than any of the solutes in order to be involatile. If the rough proportionality of V_1 and M_1 is assumed, the variation of γ with molecular weight of the stationary phase cancels out the M_1 in Eqs. (3.19) and (3.20), so that partition coefficients vary little with change in molecular weight of the stationary phase, other things being equal. The truth of this is easily seen in comparing retention volumes given by polymeric stationary phases of varying molecular weight. For example, similar values of β can be obtained either on silicone pump oils (average molecular weight about 500) or on silicone grease (average molecular weight of order of 10^4). Adlard (*23*) has studied the specific retention volumes of paraffins and alcohols on samples of polyethylene glycol of average molecular weight varying from 200 to 1000, and finds that there is at most a factor of 2 between specific retention volumes on the least and on the mcst polymerised liquid. This factor appears only for paraffins, the solution of which in polyethylene glycols is very poor and much influenced by the proportion of end-groups. For alcohols, the solution of which is more ideal, the differences between V_g^c for P.E.G. 200 and for P.E.G. 1000 are very small.

Though there is ample theoretical and experimental evidence that the orders of magnitude of partition coefficients are independent of the molecular weight of the stationary liquid, there are often other reasons why the molecular weights of polymeric stationary phases should not be too large. The thermal stability of high polymers is often poorer than that of those of lower molecular weight, so that the high polymers are liable to break down at high temperatures. Also, higher molecular weight polymers are viscous, so that slow diffusion of solute within them causes peak broadening (Section 5.5).

A more significant property of the stationary liquid related to its molecular weight is its vapour pressure, which should ideally be zero, but which is finite in practice. A volatile stationary phase is deleterious in several respects, for the liquid evaporating from the column changes the characteristics of the column, causes noise in the detector, and contaminates any products that may be condensed from the effluent of the column. The maximum permissible ratio of the vapour pressure of the stationary phase to the vapour pressure of the least volatile solute depends very much on the sensitivity of the detector and the care with which the analysis is to be carried out. Probably in practice the stationary liquid should have a vapour pressure such that its response in the detector is not greater than its inherent noise (*24*).

The vapour pressure of the stationary phase rises with temperature, and so for any stationary phase there is an upper limit to the temperature of its operation above which its vapour pressure becomes too great. The vapour pressure of a stationary phase is connected with temperature by the same law as for solutes, i.e., Eq. (3.29), but the approximate equation (3.35) can seldom be used, for the boiling point at atmospheric pressure is rarely known and the extrapolation involved is too large. Since the boiling points of stationary phases are high, it follows from Trouton's rule that the latent heat of evaporation is greater than for solutes, so that the dependence of vapour pressure on temperature is steeper than that of solutes. Hence, the lower the temperature, the greater the ratio between vapour pressure of solute and solvent.

A reasonable working value for the maximum vapour pressure of the stationary phase would be about 0.1 mm Hg. For most substances boiling in the range 300°–500°C, reference to published data reveals that this pressure is generally reached about 250°C ± 20°C below the boiling point. For example, this conclusion suggests that dibutyl phthalate, which boils at 340°C, should not be used above 90°C in order not to exceed 0.1 mm Hg vapour pressure, whereas in fact the temperature at which its vapour pressure is 0.1 mm Hg is 89°C. Suggested values of maximum working temperatures for common stationary phases are listed in Table 3.11. These values can be exceeded if a slow bleed of stationary phase is permissible.

3.8. General Relations between Partition Coefficient and Structure

The partition coefficient of a solute has been related through Eq. (3.19) or (3.20) to its vapour pressure, which is discussed in Section 3.4, and to its activity coefficient in the stationary phase, which is discussed in Section 3.5. The accepted approach in gas chromatography at present is to think of retention volumes as determined principally by vapour pressures but modified by activity coefficients. However, this approach is unwieldy, for a solute's vapour pressure has no relevance whatever in determining its partition coefficient in another liquid. In terms of molecular interactions, the argument of this chapter is to:

(1) consider forces between solute molecules in the liquid solute, which thus determine the vapour pressure,

(2) compare forces of the solute molecules first in the solvent and then in the solute liquid, to give the activity coefficient,

and then to combine the two steps. In this procedure the interaction of the solute molecules with their own liquid is considered twice, once in determining the vapour pressure, and once in the course of the comparison involved in calculating the activity coefficient. When the product γp_2^0, is formed, the twice-considered solute-solute forces cancel out, leaving only the effect of the interaction of the solute with the solvent, which is what is required. It would clearly be preferable for economy of presentation to

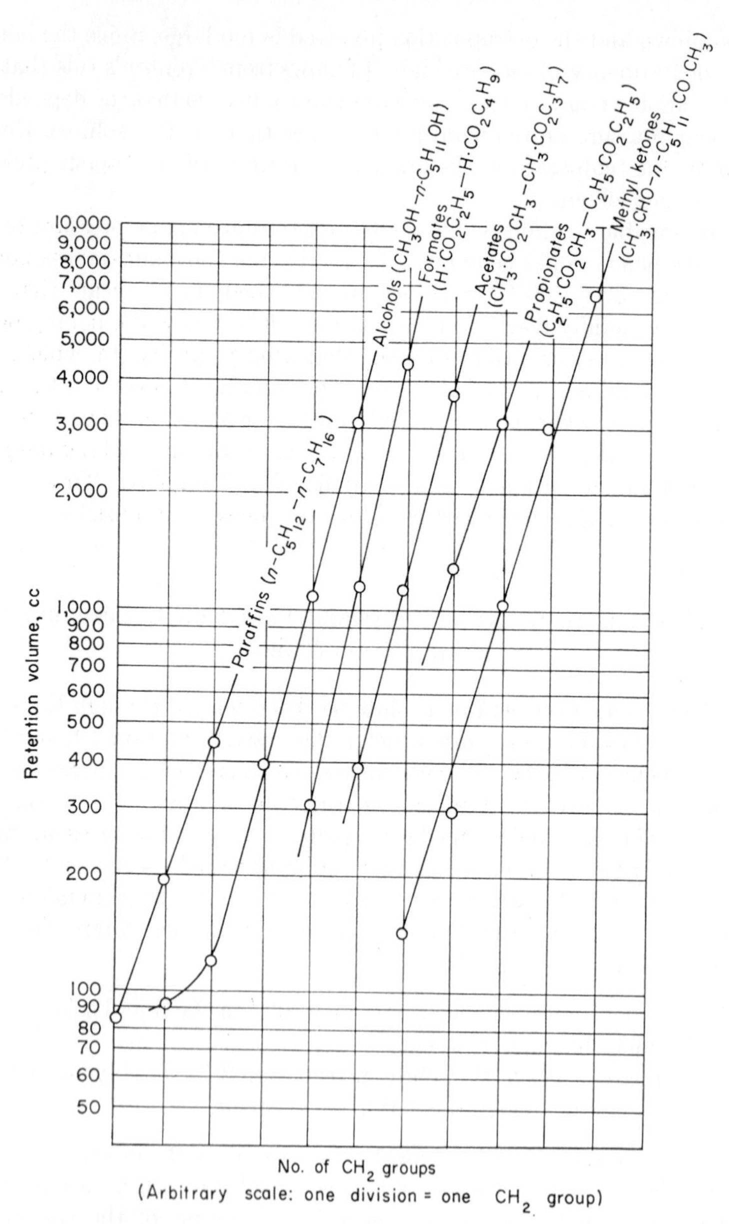

FIG. 3.11. Plots of log V_g against carbon number for various homologous series. From Ray (25).

avoid all reference to the irrelevant vapour pressure, and to describe direct relations between structure and partition coefficient. Such an approach has not yet been made systematically, and at present would probably yield less useful information than the more complicated approach described here, since at present there is a great deal more data about vapour pressures than about partition coefficients. However, direct correlation of solute and solvent structure with partition coefficients without reference to vapour pressures is implicit in some of the literature of the subject, and several semi-empirical quantitative relations between structure and partition coefficient as set out below can be constructed; these may be regarded as resulting from the combination of established semi-empirical relations involving vapour pressures and activity coefficients, or as semi-empirical relations in their own right.

(a) *Retention Volume and Carbon Number*

If the logarithm of the retention volume of members of a homologous series is plotted against the carbon number or homolog number, a straight line plot is obtained. This plot may be explained by adding Eqs. (3.37) and (3.46); alternatively, it may be argued that each successive methylene group adds a constant increment to the free energy of evaporation from the solvent. The constant increment to log V_g is not affected by the end-group of the series, so that different homologous series each give one of a family of parallel straight lines on the plot, as shown in Fig. 3.11 (*25*). Plots such as these have the same kind of practical value as plots such as those of Fig. 3.8, for the antilog of the vertical distance between the points for any two solutes is equal to their relative retention.

It is apparent from plots such as are shown in Fig. 3.11 that the slope of the lines and the difference in the intercepts may be such that a particular homolog of one series overlaps with a different homolog of another, and such plots are useful for seeing these overlaps at a glance. The slopes of all the lines and the intercepts of each are functions of the stationary phase and the temperature.

The variation with temperature for the case of paraffinic solvents of the slope of the lines such as are shown in Fig. 3.11 is easily understood and well documented. In this case, activity coefficients are not appreciably a function of the length of the carbon chain, and relative retentions of successive homologs are determined by vapour pressure ratios alone. Table 3.10 shows relative retentions of successive homologs as a function of temperature, using data taken from various sources. It is seen that in all cases the relative retentions decline with increase in temperature, providing another example of the general rule given in Section 3.6. The data of Table 3.10 can be approached theoretically using Eq. (3.38) to calculate the

TABLE 3.10

RELATIVE RETENTIONS OF SUCCESSIVE HOMOLOGS ON PARAFFINIC STATIONARY PHASES AS A FUNCTION OF TEMPERATURE[a]

Temperature (°C)	Relative retentions of successive homologs				
	Acids	Alkanes	Ethyl esters of fatty acids ($>C_3$)	Alkyl acetates	Eq. (3.38)
23	3.40				2.7
25		3.0			2.7
50			2.2	2.3	2.5
58.6	2.76				2.5
65	2.46	2.55			2.4
78		2.4			2.3
78.6	2.38	2.4			2.3
100	2.10	2.1	1.9	2.0	2.2
120		1.9			2.2
137	1.90				2.1
150	2.0	2.0	1.7	1.8	2.0
197	1.56				1.9

[a] Data taken from references (*26*) to (*31*) inclusive.

vapour pressure ratio for successive homologs. Reference to tables of boiling points shows that for substances boiling above 0°C up to at least C_9, the boiling point difference of successive homologs is within a few degrees of 25°C. On this basis, the calculated relative retentions of successive homologs are as tabulated in the last column of Table 3.10. It is seen that the theoretical values agree approximately with all the experimental values, and the scatter between the theoretical values and any one group of experimental values does not seem to be greater than the scatter among the experimental values themselves. The values indicated in the last column of Table 3.10, therefore, may be taken as a general guide to relative retentions of successive homologs on paraffinic stationary phases.

The variation of the relative retention of successive homologs with the nature of the stationary phase can be discussed in terms of the variation of the activity coefficient with the stationary phase in such terms as were used in the discussion of Eq. (3.48). General rules are given in Section 3.9.

In general, the vertical distance between the lines of plots such as that of Fig. 3.11 declines as the temperature rises, in accord with the general rule that relative retentions decline with increase in temperature. If the intercepts decline at the same rate as the slopes, all relative retentions decline equally; if the intercepts change at a different rate to the slopes, as is likely when the interaction of the solvent with methylene groups is very different from that with the end-group, there is the possibility of the reversal of peaks at different temperatures, as described in Section 3.6.

(*b*) *Retention Volume and Boiling Point*

A general relation of considerable importance is that between the boiling point of a solute and its retention volume. These two quantities can be connected by combining Eqs. (3.9), (3.20), and (3.35) to yield:

$$\log_{10} V_g \approx -0.5 - \log M_1 - \log \gamma + 4.8 \frac{T_B}{T}. \tag{3.61}$$

The constant term and the term involving M_1 need not be considered, and this equation can be rewritten as a relation between relative retention volumes and boiling point,

$$\log_{10} r_{23} \approx K'' - \log \gamma + \frac{4.8}{T} \cdot T_B, \tag{3.62}$$

where K'' is a constant depending on the stationary phase and the standard for the relative retention volumes. If γ is constant, the logarithms of relative retention volumes are approximately proportional to the boiling points, and all substances with the same γ will lie on the same straight line. In the case of homologous series, where γ can be expressed by Eq. (3.46), Eq. (3.62) becomes

$$\log_{10} r_{23} \approx K'' - \left(K + \left(\frac{B}{n_1}\right) n_2\right) + \frac{4.8}{T} \cdot T_B. \tag{3.63}$$

Since T_B is a linear function of n_2, the result is that the logarithms of relative retention volumes of members of homologous series are approximately proportional to boiling point, and that different series, having different values of the constants of Eq. (3.46), give different lines. Where differences in K of Eq. (3.46) are predominant and differences in B are small, as is usual on all but the most polar stationary phases, then the lines are parallel and differ only in their intercept. When both K and B alter appreciably from series to series, which is rather rare, the lines are not parallel. Plots of the logarithm of relative retention volumes against boiling point have been given by several authors, e.g., Desty and Whyman (*28*). In particular, Tenney (*32*) has made this plot the basis of his detailed study of the behaviour of different homologous series on a number of different stationary phases. Figure 3.12 (from Tenney) shows plots of relative retention volumes of many homologous series on β,β-oxydipropionitrile, a polar stationary phase. It is seen that the linear relation holds well for any solute containing a polar group, but some curvature is found for the alkanes, for which ac-

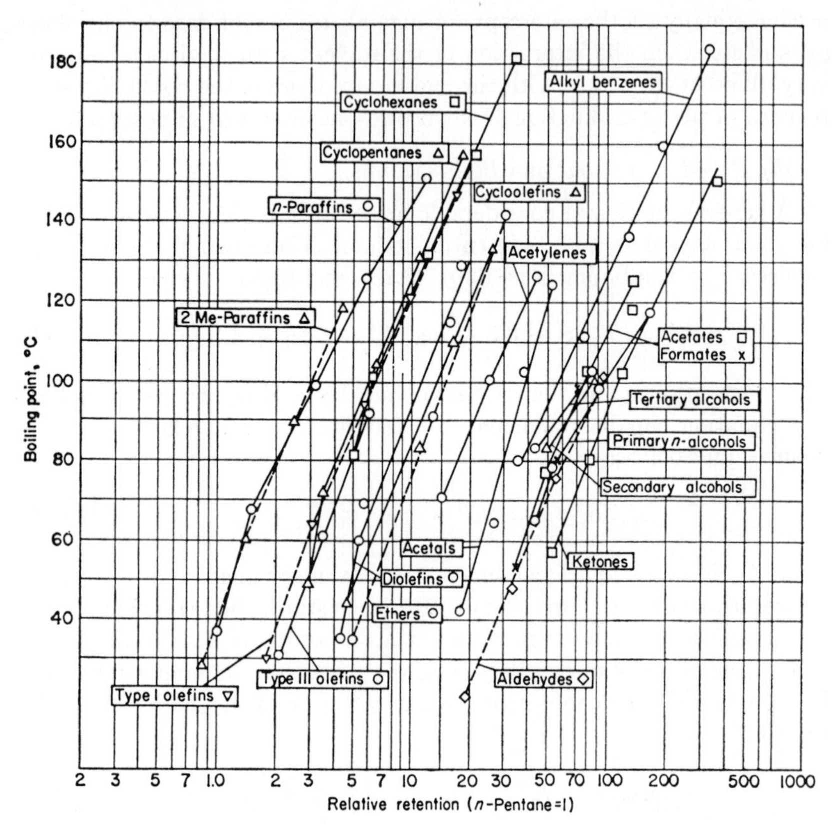

FIG. 3.12. Plots of the logarithm of relative retentions on β,β'-oxydipropionitrile as a function of boiling point for various homologous series. From Tenney (32).

tivity coefficients are large and retention volumes small. Curves such as are shown in Fig. 3.12 can be used to provide relative retention volumes by measuring the distance along the log r_{23} axis.

(c) *Solutes with Two or More Functional Groups*

Comparatively few bifunctional compounds have been chromatographed, and there is little experimental evidence from which to draw general conclusions. There is enough general evidence to draw the conclusion that, to a degree of approximation that is sometimes rather poor, each group adds a characteristic increment to log V_g independently of others. The operation of this rule is seen clearly from the retention volumes of methyl esters of unsaturated fatty acids containing different numbers of double bonds. It is seen from Fig. 11.12 that on polar stationary phases, which cause a moderate selective retention of olefins, the retention of an unsaturated ester relative to its saturated analog is multiplied by a constant factor for every successive ethylenic group. The rule holds less well, however, in the case of the chromatography of variously unsaturated fatty acid esters on Apiezon grease, e.g., Fig. 11.11, where it is seen that though one and two double bonds cause successive similar increments to the retention volume, the addition of a third causes no such increment, so that linoleic and linolenic acids are not resolved.

Among lower hydrocarbons, the general rule works with varying accuracy. Thus the data of Table 11.8 for C_5 hydrocarbons shows that in all cases, the retention of the pentadiene isoprene relative to *n*-pentane is approximately equal to the square of the relative retentions of the monopentenes. Similar evidence can be deduced from the retention data given for styrene in Table 11.7. If detailed calculations are performed, it is seen, however, that the rule is not sufficiently accurate to predict relative retentions of bifunctional compounds in general, though it is accurate enough to be of use in group separations, e.g., of all dienes from all monoenes of a particular carbon number.

(*d*) *The Accuracy of General Relations*

Nearly all the general relations presented in this section and Section 3.9 are approximate. By their means it is possible in principle and very often in practice to calculate relative retentions to within about 0.1 or 0.2 unit, but not generally to within any smaller margin of error. When relative retentions are large, e.g., 1.5, this error does not affect the separation, but when they are small, e.g., 1.05, the general relations are useless, and indeed cannot even predict the order of elution. General relations, therefore, are of greatest use in the prediction of group separations (see Section 3.9), and separations of individual solutes of different chemical class, but are not often usable for prediction of fine separations, e.g., between isomers. In the latter case, there is no substitute for experiment.

3.9. Choice of Stationary Phase for a Given Mixture

(*a*) *Criteria of Choice*

For a given mixture, the aim in choosing a stationary phase is to secure the required resolution of every component from every other component. The resolution of the column is a function of the column performance, the relative retention of the solutes, and the specific retentions, as described in Chapter 4, so that, if the column performance is given, all relative retentions and all specific retentions must be sufficiently large to secure the required separation. Thus the two conditions to be satisfied in the choice of the stationary phase are:

(1) Adequate relative retentions between all pairs of solutes.
(2) Adequate retention volumes for all solutes except, possibly, one.

It is important to remember the second condition; it is no use choosing a stationary phase in which one component comes through a thousand times as fast as another if they both come through in virtually no time.

In the case of complex mixtures, it is not always possible to secure adequate relative retentions for all components, for there may be so many components that the chromatogram is crowded with components following one after the other, and no amount of care in the selection of the stationary phase can avoid overlaps. For example, even on a column of good performance, one will scarcely see the base line of the chromatogram of a sample of commercial gasoline from first peak to last. In such cases, it is common practice to use two or more columns with different stationary liquids in which overlapping peaks from the first column are fed into a second column designed to resolve them, and any overlapping peaks remaining on the second column are fed into a third if necessary. For complex mixtures, it is often possible to devise a "Group Separation" in which different chemical classes are separated into separate groups of peaks more or less independently of boiling point on columns which give grossly different activity coefficients for each class.

Another minor aim in the choice of stationary phase where more important factors are not decisive is that the chromatogram should occupy as small a range of retention volumes as possible, so that the first peaks are not too tall and narrow, and the last peaks are not too wide, shallow, and slow. Though this can always be overcome if required by temperature programming (Section 6.5), it is not always convenient to do so.

For a given mixture, the values of the vapour pressures of the components are given, so that the choice of the stationary phase rests upon the values of the activity coefficients that it produces in the solutes. Relatively few values of absolute activity coefficients of solutes in different stationary phases have been published, and few general relations have appeared. However, in order to compare the *relative* retentions of different solutes in different stationary phases, one may use *relative* activity coefficients, which may be obtained from published retention data and published vapour pressures. If one solute (subscript 2) in a table of relative retention data is arbitrarily given a relative activity coefficient of unity, then from Eq. (3.19) or (3.20) it is seen that the relative activity coefficient of any other solute (subscript 3) is given by

$$\gamma_3^{\text{rel}} = r_{23} \frac{p_2^0}{p_3^0}. \tag{3.64}$$

Relative activity coefficients will be used in the course of discussing general relations in connection with condition (1) given above.

(*b*) *Classification of Stationary Phases*

A large number of stationary phases has been used in gas chromatography, and the commoner ones are listed in Table 3.11. To encourage uniformity, a committee in 1956 (*34*) suggested that one of six specified stationary liquids should be used where possible, so that a large body of retention data on these liquids should be built up. In conjunction with this, various chemical manufacturers, at least in the United Kingdom, marketed samples of these liquids in standard purity. The list given in 1956 quickly proved inadequate, and many more stationary phases were found to be useful and to perform separations not performed by members of the original list. The contents of Table 3.11 has been selected so that the table contains a sufficient number of stationary phases for most general purposes, but it does not contain stationary phases commonly used only for certain specific separations which by chance are not well performed by those in the list, e.g., isoquinoline for the separation of the hexanes. Many authors have used stationary phases not listed in Table 3.11, and the total number of stationary phases ever used probably runs into hundreds. Where possible, it is desirable that stationary phases used for published work should be easily accessible and reproducible chemicals in order that the results should be of universal value.

It is difficult to classify stationary phases objectively according to their properties, for they span the whole range of properties more or less continuously. An attempt has been made, however, to divide them into the five classes given in Table 3.11.

1. Paraffinic. Most evidence shows that relative retentions vary very little between different stationary phases consisting of alkanes, though there may be small differences; for example, Knight (*35*) finds that different paraffins give slightly different relative retentions of alkanes and naphthenes. Janak and Komers (*36*) have drawn attention to the fact that the methyl siloxane silicone liquids, which display methyl groups but no methylene groups, appear to show a slightly greater affinity for the aliphatic groups of phenols than Apiezon grease M, but the effect is not large. There is no definite report of any consistent difference in behaviour between paraffinic stationary liquids with many branches (thus containing more methyl groups and fewer methylenes) and those with straight chains. A frequently quoted rule is that paraffinic stationary phases separate substances in order of boiling point. This is approximately true for several classes of hydrocarbons, but for other classes of solute and even for some hydrocarbons there are many exceptions. It should be noted that some sili-

TABLE 3.11

STATIONARY PHASES IN GENERAL USE

Stationary phase	Formula	Maximum operating temperature	Notes
	(1) Paraffinic		
Hexadecane	$CH_3—(CH_2)_{14}—CH_3$	Room	Used only in experimental studies
Octadecane	$CH_3—(CH_2)_{16}—CH_3$	Room	Used only in experimental studies
Liquid paraffin	$CH_3—(CH_2)_n—CH_3$	Room–100	Commonly used on account of accesibility; maximum temperature depends on grade
Squalane	2,6,10,15,19,23-hexamethyltetracosane.	150	A standard stationary phase
n-Hexatriacontane	$CH_3—(CH_2)_{34}—CH_3$	100	
Vacuum pump oil, transformer oil		100–150	Commonly used on account of availability
Vacuum greases		300	For example, Apiezon products; commonly used for high-temperature work
Silicone oil	—O—Si(Me)(Me)—O—Si(Me)(Me)—O—	200	Commonly used; also phenylated silicones, e.g., pump oil
Silicone greases		300	Commonly used for high temperatures; may contain fillers which affect their properties

Carbon		325	Generally similar to paraffins in the elution order it produces; provides specific acceleration of naphthenes; not generally used at high temperatures
	(2) Intermediate		
Alkyl aryl sulfonate		250	Household detergent is a useful general purpose stationary phase ready for pouring into a column tube[a]
Di-isodecyl phthalate	$-COOC_{10}H_{21}$ $-COOC_{10}H_{21}$	150	General purposes
Dinonyl phthalate	$-COOC_9H_{19}$ $-COOC_9H_{19}$	150	Similar to the above
Dibutyl phthalate	$-COOC_4H_9$ $-COOC_4H_9$	100	Significantly more polar than the two above
Dioctyl sebacate	$C_8H_{17}OCOC_8H_{16}COOC_8H_{17}$	125	Generally similar to the phthalates, but not aromatic
Benzyl diphenyl	$-CH_2-$	100	
Tricresyl phosphate	$(C_6H_4CH_3O)_3PO$	125	Roughly similar to the above; all isomers are toxic, some very toxic

[a] See Desty *et al.* (*33*).

(*continued on following page*)

TABLE 3.11 (*Continued*)

STATIONARY PHASES IN GENERAL USE

Stationary phase	Formula	Maximum operating temperature	Notes
Dibenzyl ether	$C_6H_{11}—CH_2—O—CH_2—C_6H_{11}$ (two hexagonal rings joined by —CH₂—O—CH₂—)	50	The most polar in this class
Silica gel		300	
Alumina		300	
	(3) Polar		
Hexamethylphosphoramide		Room	Common general purpose polar liquids not too polar to be used with alkanes; generally similar, but with significant small differences
Dimethylsulfolane	$CH_3—CH—CH—CH_3$, with CH_2 under each CH, both CH_2 bonded to SO_2 (ring)		
β,β′-Oxydipropionitrile	$(CN—CH_2—CH_2)_2O$	100	
Various polyesters of dihydroxy compounds and dibasic acids, e.g., polyethylene glycol, adipic acid	$—CH_2—CH_2—O—CO—(CH_2)_4—CO—O—CH_2—CH_2—O—$	250	Extensively used as high-temperature polar stationary phases, especially for fatty acid ester analysis; polarity can be altered at will by choosing suitable monomers
2,5-Hexanedione	$CH_3—CO—CH_2—CH_2—CO—CH_3$	Room	

Polyethylene glycols, M.W. 200–10,000	$HO—CH_2—CH_2—[O—CH_2—CH_2—]_nOH$	100–250	Extensively used for oxygenated and other polar solutes; the smaller the M.W., the greater the polarity
Dimethylformamide	$HCONMe_2$	Room	Has a rather low boiling point (152°C)
	(4) Hydrogen bonding		
Diglycerol	$[C_3H_5(OH)_2]_2O$	150	Standard stationary phase suitable for analysis of alcohols, etc.
Glycerol	$CH_2OH \cdot CHOH \cdot CH_2OH$	100	Appreciably more polar than diglycerol
Erithritol	$C(CH_2OH)_4$	150	No retention of methylene groups
	(5) Specific		
Ethylene glycol–silver nitrate		50	Specific retention of alkenes in addition to ordinary polar properties
Benzyl cyanide–silver nitrate		50	As above, but solvent is less polar; more stable than the above
Perfluorocarbons			Retain other fluorocarbons, and have no retention of alkanes
Metal salts of higher fatty acids			Retain compounds which can form complexes with the metal, e.g., pyridines
Molecular sieves		300	Retain unbranched relative to branched alkyl groups

cone fluids contain phenyl groups; these should be included in the following class, and not among the paraffinic stationary phases.

2. Intermediate. Such stationary phases are intermediate between paraffins and polar liquids, and are composed of polar or polarisable groups in a more or less long alkyl chain. The principal characteristic of this class is that its members will dissolve both polar and non-polar solutes with moderate ease, so that they can be used to accommodate all kinds of solute. It will be noted that this class contains aromatic and aliphatic compounds. There appears to be a slight tendency for the aromatic members of the class to retain aromatic solutes with respect to aliphatic solutes, as can be seen from the figures of Table 3.16, but the effect is not marked, and aromatic or aliphatic solvents of this class can be used for separation of aromatic or aliphatic solutes. There are no very special selective properties in the class, but they are all sufficiently different from the classes either side to be useful in conjunction with them.

3. Polar. These liquids contain a large proportion of polar groups, and do not readily dissolve solutes not containing polar groups, but dissolve and differentiate well between all solutes containing such groups.

4. Hydrogen bonding. For many purposes, these can be regarded as a subclass of polar liquids. They have the additional property, however, that they have labile hydrogen atoms which can form hydrogen bonds with solutes capable of such bond formation, e.g., alcohols, ethers, amines, etc. A practical difference between the members of this class and those of the polar class is that alkanes may be chromatographed on polar stationary phases, albeit with large activity coefficients, but the activity coefficients of alkanes on hydrogen bonding stationary phases are impossibly great except for use in group separations.

5. Specific. The table contains a few examples of stationary phases which are used for specific separations on account of some specific chemical interaction between solute and solvent; these were referred to in Section 3.5.

Within the five classes given above, there are variations of degree, and the position of the dividing line between the classes is rather arbitrary. The classification is dominated by the fact that such a large proportion of the applications and published data of gas chromatography refer to members of homologous series. Given this, the basic property by which different stationary phases can be distinguished is their reaction towards methylene groups in relation to their reaction towards end groups. This property is normally described by the "Polarity," and in gas chromatography it is understood that the more "Polar" is a stationary phase, the greater is its ability to dissolve compounds other than paraffins. In general chemical usage the word "Polar" applies to substances the molecules of which have dipole moments, and it will be observed that all the stationary phases in class (3) are polar in this sense. However, in gas chromatography, the magnitude of the polarity is in no way related to molecular dipole moment, the molecular polarisability, or the molar polarisation of the solvent. The most significant relation between polarity as generally understood in the context of gas chromatography and the structure of a stationary phase is the ratio of methylene or methyl groups to polar or polarisable groups. Thus, non-polar stationary phases have nothing but methyl and methylene groups; intermediate stationary phases have more or less large alkyl groups together with either a few small polar groups or non-polar but polarisable groups; and polar stationary phases have polar groups associated with rather small alkyl chains.

The operation of the above idea is indicated quantitatively for a special case by Eq. (3.48). A clear example of the effect of altering the proportion of methylenes in a stationary phase is seen by comparing relative retention volumes and relative activity coefficients of solutes in polyethylene glycol and in polypropylene glycol, as are shown in Table 3.12 (*23*). It is apparent

TABLE 3.12

RETENTION VOLUMES V_g^c AND ACTIVITY COEFFICIENTS FOR SOLUTES IN POLYETHYLENE GLYCOL AND POLYPROPYLENE GLYCOL AT 100°C[a]

Solute	V_g^c in P.E.G. 400	V_g^c in P.P.G. 425	γ in P.E.G. 400	γ in P.P.G.425
n-Pentane	3.56	9.24	3.69	1.307
n-Hexane	5.87	19.85	5.65	1.47
n-Heptane	10.23	40.60	7.13	1.67
n-Octane	17.38	80.22	9.60	1.92
n-Decane	48.71		16.9	
Methanol	52.62	49.81	0.44	0.41
Ethanol	62.89	65.28	0.56	0.50
n-Propanol	109.4	130.7	0.66	0.50
n-Butanol	199.4	270.7	0.79	0.52
n-Pentanol	362.3	554.2	0.90	0.52

[a] See Adlard (*23*).

that alkanes are very insoluble in polyethylene glycol, but that the addition of an extra methylene per monomer unit creates an enormous difference, making them much more soluble. The difference in the activity coefficients for the lowest alcohols is small, but for the higher alcohols, in which there is a greater proportion of methylene chain, the activity coefficients are smaller in the stationary phase containing the more methylenes.

(c) *Specificity with Respect to Carbon Number and Isomeric Form of Solutes*

Since the affinity of methylenes for stationary liquids depends on the proportion of methylenes in the stationary liquids, relative retentions of successive homologs are greatest on paraffinic stationary liquids, and are smaller on all others, declining with reduction in the proportion of methylene in the stationary liquid molecule. In terms of the discussion of Sections 3.4 and 3.5, this may be explained by the fact that on stationary phases other than paraffins, activity coefficients rise with carbon number, as shown in Fig. 3.5, thus tending to cancel the drop in vapour pressure, so that the increase in β is smaller than would be anticipated from the change in vapour pressure alone. The operation of this effect in practice is shown in Table 3.13. With liquid paraffin, the retention ratios of successive homologs are similar to the vapour pressure ratios anticipated by Table 3.10. With dinonyl phthalate, most of which is still alkyl chain, there is a barely significant fall in relative retention. With polyethylene glycols, there is a significant reduction, and finally in the extreme case of solutes in erithritol and other sugar derivatives, which contain no methylene chains, there is apparently no retention of methylene groups, and higher homologs actually have slightly smaller retention volumes than lower ones.

Within any carbon number, paraffinic stationary phases separate isomers more or less according to boiling point. With alkanes, absolute activity coefficients are less than unity (*11*), the value being determined approximately by the difference in molar volume of solvent and solute. With groups of isomers of other compounds, e.g., alcohols, etc., activity coefficients are greater, and with polar compounds may be very great. A closer study of the activity coefficients of alkanes on paraffinic stationary phases shows that there are small deviations from isomer to isomer which are too large for experimental error, and which in many cases can be employed on an efficient column to secure separations that would not be anticipated from the boiling points. Table 3.14 shows boiling points and retention volumes of alkanes on two different paraffinic stationary phases determined at the same temperature by different workers, together with vapour pressures and activity coefficients relative to n-pentane. The table shows that though 2-methylhexane has a higher boiling point than 2,3-dimethylpentane, the former is eluted first. Another noteworthy irregularity occurs with n-heptane and 2,2,4-trimethylpentane. These two compounds boil only 0.8°C apart, and have very similar vapour pressures, but they are separable on a paraffinic column with a relative retention of about 1.08 to 1.10, the compound with the higher normal boiling point being eluted first. In several cases, relative activity coefficients of n-alkanes appear to be slightly smaller than those of branched chain alkanes of about the same boiling point, and

TABLE 3.13

RELATIVE RETENTIONS OF SUCCESSIVE HOMOLOGS ON DIFFERENT STATIONARY PHASES[a]

Stationary Phase:	Liquid paraffin			DNP		P.E.G. 1000	Glycerol	Apiezon L	Erithritol	P.E.G. 400
X:	Benzene	Hexane	Pyridine (m-isomers)	Benzene	Hexane	Benzene	Pyridine (m-isomers)	Phenol (m-isomers)	Phenol (m-isomers)	Pentane
Temp. (°C):	120	120	120	120	120	120	120	170	150	100
$\frac{\text{Me}X}{X}$	2.06	1.91	2.55	1.91	1.60	1.31	1.54	1.79	0.94	1.65
$\frac{\text{Et}X}{\text{Me}X}$	1.87	1.92	2.06	1.73	1.82	1.40	1.06	1.61	0.88	1.74
$\frac{n\text{-Pr}X}{\text{Et}X}$	1.97	1.97[b]		1.86	1.71[b]	1.48		1.55	0.80	1.7
$\frac{n\text{-Bu}X}{n\text{-Pr}X}$		1.97[b]			1.71[b]			1.73	0.97	1.65
Average	2.0	1.9	2.3	1.8	1.7	1.4	1.2	1.65	0.9	1.7

[a] Data taken from references (*23*), (*29*), (*36*), and (*37*).

[b] $\sqrt{(n\text{-Bu}X)/\text{Et}X}$.

TABLE 3.14

RELATIVE RETENTION VOLUMES AND ACTIVITY COEFFICIENTS FOR ALKANES IN PARAFFINIC STATIONARY PHASES AT 78.5°C[a]

Solute	b.p. (°C)	v.p. (78.5°C)	r in paraffin wax	r in $C_{36}H_{74}$	γ^{rel} in $C_{36}H_{74}$
n-Butane	−0.5			0.39	
Neopentane	9.50			0.44	
Isopentane	27.85		0.73	0.77	
n-Pentane	36.07	2620	*1.00*	*1.00*	*1.00*
2,2-Dimethylbutane	49.74	1746	1.34	1.34	1.03
2,3-Dimethylbutane	57.99	1393	1.90	1.83	1.03
2-Methylpentane	60.27	1294	1.87	1.83	1.11
3-Methylpentane	63.28	1197	2.17	2.12	1.03
n-Hexane	68.32	990	2.46	2.42	1.09
2,2-Dimethylpentane	79.20	740	3.1	3.00	1.18
2,4-Dimethylpentane	80.50	710	3.25	3.08	1.20
2,2,3-Trimethylbutane	80.88	710	3.6	3.49	1.06
3,3-Dimethylpentane	86.06	590	4.26	4.13	1.08
2,3-Dimethylpentane	89.78	510	4.67	4.55	1.15
2-Methylhexane	90.05	510	4.35	4.27	1.20
3-Methylhexane	91.85	480	4.8	4.68	1.17
3-Ethylpentane	93.48	470	5.26	5.18	1.08
n-Heptane	98.43	405	5.85	5.73	1.13
2,2,4-Trimethylpentane	99.24	400	5.40	5.28	1.24
2,2-Dimethylhexane	106.84	310	7.02	6.57	1.29
2,5-Dimethylhexane	109.10	285	7.51	7.13	1.29
2,4-Dimethylhexane	109.43		7.80	7.45	
2,2,3-Trimethylpentane	109.84		8.14	8.10	
3,3-Dimethylhexane	111.97	260	8.75	8.49	1.19
n-Octane	125.67	165	13.8	13.42	1.18
n-Nonane	150.80		32.4	30.96	

[a] See James and Martin (*26*) and Desty and Whyman (*28*).

this is supported by evidence from some other sources, for example, the results of Tenney (*32*) summarised in Table 3.15, but there is not enough evidence to make this a general rule. It can be seen from Table 3.14 that there is no obvious relation between relative activity coefficients and the amount of branching of the solute, any more than there is between boiling point and the amount of branching (Section 3.4).

With non-paraffinic stationary phases, the irregularities in relative activity coefficients inside any one carbon number increase with the polarity of the liquid, and this appears to be true whether the isomers are polar or not. Many examples of this can be seen in the tables of Chapter 11, where cases in which peaks do not appear in order of boiling point are seen to be generally on polar stationary phases; see, for example, Tables 11.12, 11.35, and 11.40. The difference between polar and non-polar stationary phases in their selectivity towards isomers makes the basis of a common kind of group separation. In a complex mixture of solutes containing many isomers of several different carbon numbers, a paraffinic stationary phase is used to separate the mixture into groups of peaks each of a given carbon number, after which isomers not resolved on the paraffinic stationary phase are chromatographed on a suitable polar stationary phase. In most cases, the deviations in relative activity coefficients produced by polar stationary phases at present appear to be random, and there is no systematic way of anticipating whether or not a particular polar liquid will give different activity coefficients with two given isomers. An exception to this is the case of *o*-isomers of aromatic compounds discussed in Sections 11.4, 11.7, and 11.8.

The actual retention ratio between first peak and last may not be very different on a polar stationary phase from that on a non-polar one, as, for example, is seen from the results for heptanes given in Table 11.13. The important thing, however, is that the relative retentions on polar stationary phases have a good chance of being *different*, even if not on average *greater*.

(*d*) *Relative Retentions of Different Homologous Series*

Figures 3.11 and 3.12 each show the logarithms of the relative retentions of members of different homologous series plotted to give more or less straight lines, the distance between which parallel to the $\log_{10} r$ axis defines a relative retention. In the case of Fig. 3.11, the distance between any two lines is the logarithm of the relative retention of compounds of the same carbon number in different series; in the case of Fig. 3.12, the corresponding distance along the $\log_{10} r$ axis is the relative retention of members of different homologous series but the same boiling point. In the latter case, there may not be homologs one in each series with the same boiling point; the distance between the lines can then be interpreted by regarding n in the alkyl group C_nH_{2n+1} as a continuous variable, so that the boiling point is a continuous monotonic function of n for each series, and then comparing retentions of similar boiling homologs in different series one or both of which may have fractional carbon numbers.

It is useful in practice to assume the rectilinearity of the lines of Figs. 3.11 and 3.12 in order to express the relative retention of two homologous series by means of a single approximate number with respect either to constant boiling point or to constant homolog number. A systematic study of the relative retentions of homologous series with respect to constant boiling point has been made by Tenney (*32*) who has given plots such as are shown in Fig. 3.12 for many homologous series on many stationary phases. For detailed information, the reader is referred to Tenney's paper, but a survey of some of his data is given in Table 3.15, which has been constructed from

TABLE 3.15

RELATIVE RETENTIONS OF DIFFERENT HOMOLOGOUS SERIES COMPARED ON COLUMNS OPERATING AT 100°C AT A COMMON "BOILING LEVEL" OF 100°C

	"Convoil 20," paraffin oil	Silicone oil DC 703	Dioctyl sebacate	Tricresyl phosphate	β,β'-Oxydipropionitrile at 67°C	Polypropylene glycol at120°C	Propylene glycol/$AgNO_3$ saturated at 65°C
n-Paraffins	*1.00*	*1.00*	*1.00*	*1.00*	*1.00*	*1.00*	*1.00*
2-Methyl paraffins	0.95	1.0	1.0	0.95	0.95	0.9	1.0
Olefins-1	1.00	1.2	1.1	1.25	2.00	1.2	3
2-Methyl olefins-1	1.00	1.2	1.1	1.25	2.15	1.2	1.3
Cyclopentanes	1.20	1.4	1.2	1.25	1.9	1.3	
Cyclohexanes	1.25	1.4	1.2	1.45	1.95	1.3	
Cycloolefins	1.30	1.8	1.5	2.1	4.3	1.6	6
Diolefins		1.4	1.2	1.55	3.6	1.3	
Acetylenes	0.80	1.5	1.3	2.1	8.0	1.9	
Alkylbenzenes	1.20	1.8	1.9	3.6	17.8	2.5	11
Alcohols, primary	0.25	0.6		2.5	31.3	2.6	
Alcohols, secondary	0.35	0.7		2.5	26.6	2.7	
Alcohols, tertiary	0.45	0.8		2.5	24.0	2.6	
Ketones	0.55	1.4		2.9	36	2.2	
Ethers	0.95	1.5			4	1.3	
Formates	0.60	1.4		2.7	24.7	2.2	
Acetates	0.60	1.6		2.7	24	2.2	
Aldehydes	0.60	1.4		3.5	29.7	2.2	

both tables and diagrams given in the paper. The table includes the relative retentions of different homologous series measured at a "Boiling Level" of 100°C; this means that the relative retentions listed are those that would apply to compounds the carbon number of which in their series is such that they would boil at 100°C. It will be appreciated that for compounds which actually boil at or close to 100°C, the figures given in Table 3.15 are the inverse of the relative activity coefficients. Tenney's figures and tables show that there is comparatively little variation in the figures of Table 3.15 at other boiling levels or at other column temperatures except when comparing solutes which have large activity coefficients. There are, however, small differences in some cases which appear to be greater than the experimental error. The accuracy of the figures in Table 3.15 is no greater than is indicated by the number of significant figures used, and may well be smaller.

There appears to be no systematic survey of relative retentions of homologous series with respect to constant homolog number, and there are rather few sets of results in the literature which give sufficient data from which to compose a table equivalent to Table 3.15. An attempt at such a table is given in Table 3.16, in which relative retentions of similar

TABLE 3.16

RELATIVE RETENTIONS OF SIMILAR HOMOLOGS OF DIFFERENT HOMOLOGOUS SERIES[a]

(a) Hydrocarbons		Didecyl phthalate, 100°C	Dinonyl phthalate, 120°C	Trixylenyl phosphate, 120°C	Dioctyl sebacate, 100°C	Polyethylene glycol, 100°C	Apiezon A, 100°C
n-Paraffins	RH	*1.00*	*1.00*	*1.00*	*1.00*	*1.00*	*1.00*
2-Methyl paraffins	R_{-3}—CH(Me)—CH_3	0.8			0.85		0.8
Olefins-1	R_{-2}—CH=CH_2		1.00	1.1			0.9
Alkylbenzenes	R_{-6}—C_6H_5	2.8	2.4	3.1	2.4	9	1.7
Primary alcohols	R—OH	20			19	100–200*	

(b) Polar compounds		Didecyl phthalate, 100°C	Dioctyl sebacate, 100°C	Polyethylene glycol, 100°C	β,β′-Oxydipropionitrile, 70°C	Apiezon L, 130°C
Primary alcohols	R—OH	*1.00*	*1.00*	*1.00*	*1.00*	*1.00*
Secondary alcohols	R—OH	0.55	0.6	0.5	0.4	
Tertiary alcohols	R—OH	0.3	0.3	0.3	0.3	
Formates	HCOOR				0.7	
Acetates	CH_3COOR	1.85	1.55	0.6	0.9	
Ethyl esters	RCOOEt	3.0	2.8	0.8	1.2	
Chloroalkanes	R—Cl				0.12	1.3
Bromoalkanes	R—Br					2.7
Aldehydes	R—CHO				0.6	0.45

* Depending on molecular weight.

[a] Data taken from references (*23*), (*29*)–(*31*), and (*38*).

homologs as tabulated in the second column are given for several stationary phases. Survey of the literature reveals many cases in which different workers have given inconsistent data, and so the data given in Table 3.16 has been selected so that there is at least one independent check on every entry.

3.10. Qualitative Analysis

As pointed out in Section 1.3, the value of the retention volume is insufficient characterisation of any one solute selected from all solutes and can only be used as qualitative identification when the peak is known to be that of one of a relatively small number of compounds of interest, all of which have significantly different retention volumes. In practice, however, the latter case is very common, and there are numerous reports in the literature of such qualitative identification from a restricted range of possibilities.

Gas chromatography may be effectively used for general qualitative analysis of a mixture by employing its separating power in conjunction with other more specific methods of analysis. It is particularly useful in connection with spectrometers, for the latter are effective in identifying single components, but become unreliable for complex mixtures. Several authors have described apparatus by which components may be trapped from a chromatographic column into cells which may be used in infrared spectrometers (*39–41*) and mass spectrometers (*42–45*). Of particular interest is the use of a time-of-flight mass spectrometer by Gohlke (*46*). The advantage of this instrument is that mass spectra may be scanned in a fraction of a second, so that the mass spectrum of a stream of gas may be continuously displayed on a cathode ray oscillograph. When it is connected to the effluent from a gas-chromatography apparatus, the appearance of every peak in the detector is accompanied by the appearance of the mass spectrum of the component. This may either be identified at the time, or photographed for later identification.

Gas chromatography may also be used in connection with chemical methods for qualitative analysis, e.g., an unidentified olefin may be hydrogenated before chromatographing to an alkane which can be identified, thus at least determining the skeletal structure of the olefin. Such methods are described in the appropriate sections of Chapter 11.

Another application of gas chromatography in qualitative analysis uses measurements of retention volumes on two or more stationary phases of different kinds. In effect, this squares or cubes the amount of information obtained, and enormously increases the range of compounds over which qualitative analysis is possible. The value of the technique lies in making use of different values of the activity coefficients of different solute end groups in different stationary phases as follows. If primes indicate one stationary phase, and double primes indicate another, the partition coefficients of a solute indicated by subscript 2 in each are given by

$$\zeta_2' = \frac{J'}{\gamma_2' p_2^0}, \qquad \zeta_2'' = \frac{J''}{\gamma_2'' p_2^0} \tag{3.65}$$

where J' and J'' are composite constants. If the stationary phases are at the same temperature, p_2^0 is the same in either case, so for the purposes of this argument it may be included in the constants J' and J''. If this is done, and γ is given by Eq. (3.46), the partition coefficients are given by

$$\log \zeta_2' = \log J' - K' - L'n_2$$
$$\log \zeta_2'' = \log J'' - K'' - L''n_2 \qquad (3.66)$$

where K', K'', L', and L'' are further constants, whence, eliminating n_2, the homolog number,

$$L'' \log \zeta_2' - L' \log \zeta_2'' = \mathcal{K} \qquad (3.67)$$

where the new composite constant, $\mathcal{K}$, includes J', K', L', J'', K'', and L'', but does not include n_2. This implies that a plot of the logarithm of the retention volumes of members of a homologous series on one phase against the same on another stationary phase would yield a straight line of slope L''/L' and intercept $\mathcal{K}/L'$. Figure 3.13 (*9*) shows that this is true. Furthermore, for two given stationary phases, change in the homologous series of the solute will produce a different straight line. Several such lines for different homologous series are shown in Fig. 3.13. The lines appear roughly

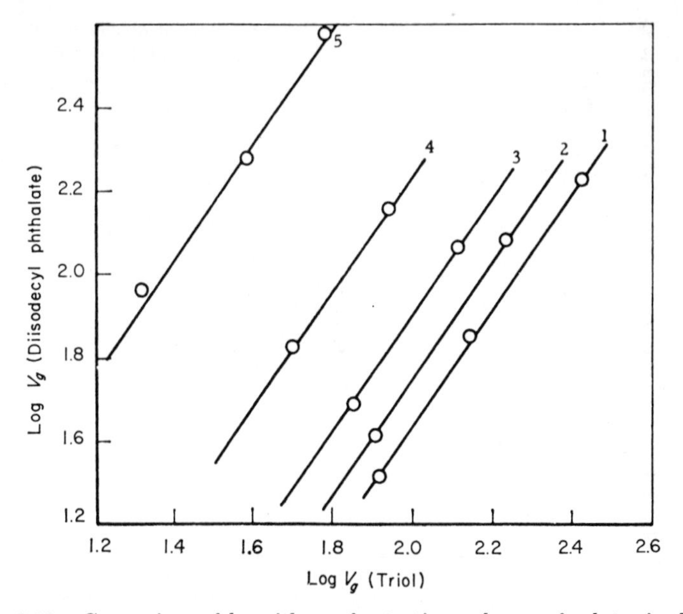

FIG. 3.13. Comparison of logarithms of retention volumes of solutes in different stationary phases; points due to solutes in a given homologous series lie on straight lines. From Pierotti *et al.* (*8*). 1, 1-alkanols; 2, *sec*-alkanols; 3, *tert*-alkanols; 4, alkanones; 5, *n*-alkanes.

parallel, giving further indication that the change from one series to another affects $\mathcal{K}$ more than L''/L'.

The possible use of plots such as those of Fig. 3.13 in qualitative analysis is evident. By chromatographing a substance on two different stationary phases, a solute is characterised by a point in an area rather than by a point on a line, and thus can be distinguished from a larger number of other solutes. James (*47*) has used this technique, using a non-polar phase and a polar phase, for the identification of the carbon number and the degree of unsaturation of fatty acid esters. The retention volume on the non-polar liquid serves to fix the carbon number, after which a run on a polar liquid serves to fix the degree of unsaturation. Figure 3.14 shows the lines given by variously unsaturated esters on complementary log V_g plots.

Another plot the intended purpose of which is similar to that of Fig. 3.13 has been given by James *et al.* (*48*) who plot the retention volumes themselves, and not their logarithms (Fig. 3.15). This plot has been used by Barber *et al.* (*18*) and by Cartoni and co-workers (*49*) for displaying the specific effects of different stationary phases. Such plots take the form of lines through the origin, one line for each solute homologous series. In the case that $L' = L''$ in Eq. (3.67), the lines are straight with a slope which

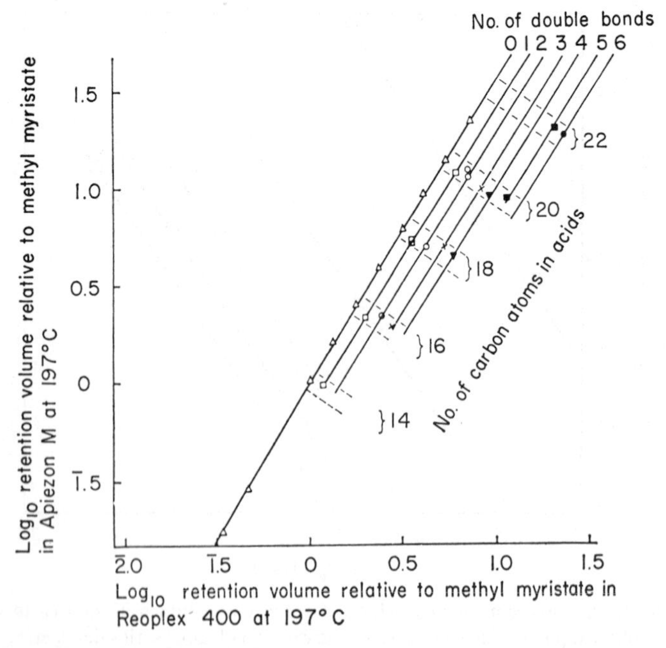

FIG. 3.14. Complementary plots of logarithms of relative retention volumes on two different stationary phases for fatty acid esters. From James (*47*).

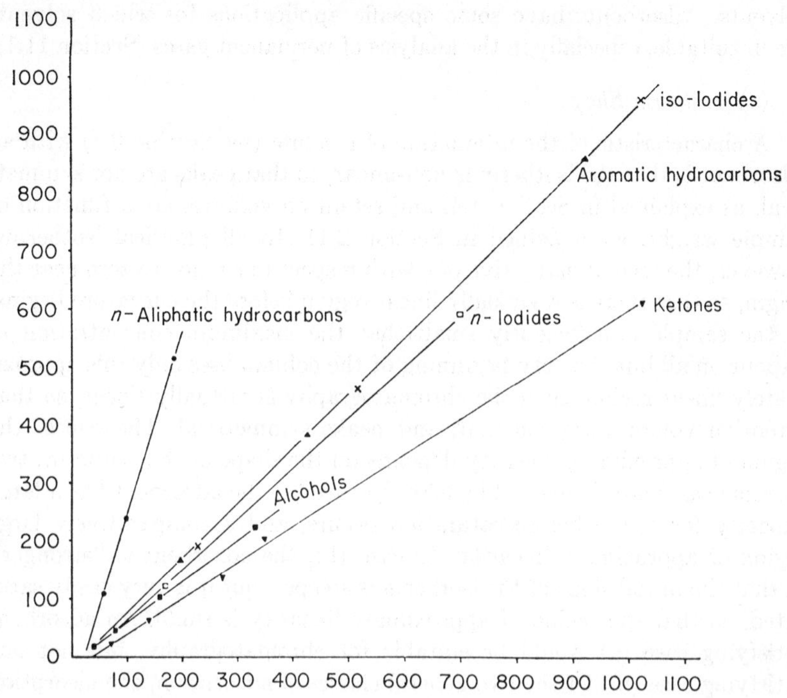

FIG. 3.15. Complementary plots of relative retention volumes on two different stationary phases for various homologous series. Abscissae: retention volume in benzyl diphenyl; ordinates: retention volume in paraffin. From A. T. James and A. J. P. Martin, *Brit. Med. Bull.*, **10**, 170 (1954).

is determined by the value of $\mathcal{K}$. There is no reason, however, why $L' = L''$, especially with very dissimilar stationary phases, and indeed, it can be seen from Fig. 3.13 that the slope of the lines is not unity.

Both plots given in Figs. 3.13 and 3.15 may be made and used with relative rather than with specific retention data; and this has occasionally been done. Wherever plots of the type described above have been given in the literature, they are used not for qualitative analysis but as a method of presentation, where they demonstrate the effect of differences in activity coefficients in different stationary phases. Their use in analysis is small.

3.11. Use of Adsorbents as Stationary Phases

The discussion hitherto assumes the use of liquid solvents as stationary phases, but although these are by far the most common, it is possible to use the same chromatographic technique with adsorbents rather than solvents. Adsorbents have some specific applications for which solvents are unsuitable, especially in the analysis of permanent gases (Section 11.1).

(*a*) *Isotherm Shape*

A characteristic of the interaction of a solute (see Section 3.1) with an adsorbent is that the isotherm is non-linear, so that peaks are not symmetrical, as explained in Section 1.4, and retention volumes are a function of sample weight, as explained in Section 2.11. In all practical isotherms, however, the second derivative of q with respect to c tends to zero near the origin, so that there is a virtually linear region before the curvature begins. If the sample is sufficiently small that the maximum concentration of vapour on all but the very beginning of the column uses only this approximately linear region, then the chromatography is virtually linear, so that retention volumes are constant, and peaks symmetrical. The size of the region of approximate linearity depends on the shape of the isotherm; two extreme cases are shown in Fig. 3.16. In case (a) the adsorbent has a large capacity for solute before saturation occurs, and a comparatively large region of approximate linearity. In case (b), the adsorbent is "stronger" in that the initial slope of the isotherm is steeper, but it is very easily saturated, so that the region of approximate linearity is small. An adsorbent satisfying case (a) would be suitable for chromatography, but not one satisfying case (b). Of the two general classes of adsorption, chemisorption and physical adsorption, chemisorption usually occurs at high temperatures, and the adsorbents give isotherms resembling (b). Physical adsorption occurs at lower temperatures, and gives isotherms resembling (a).

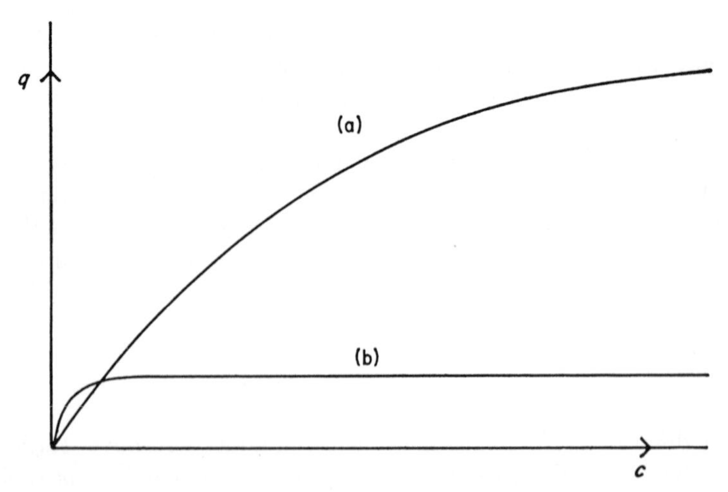

FIG. 3.16. Extreme examples of adsorption isotherms.

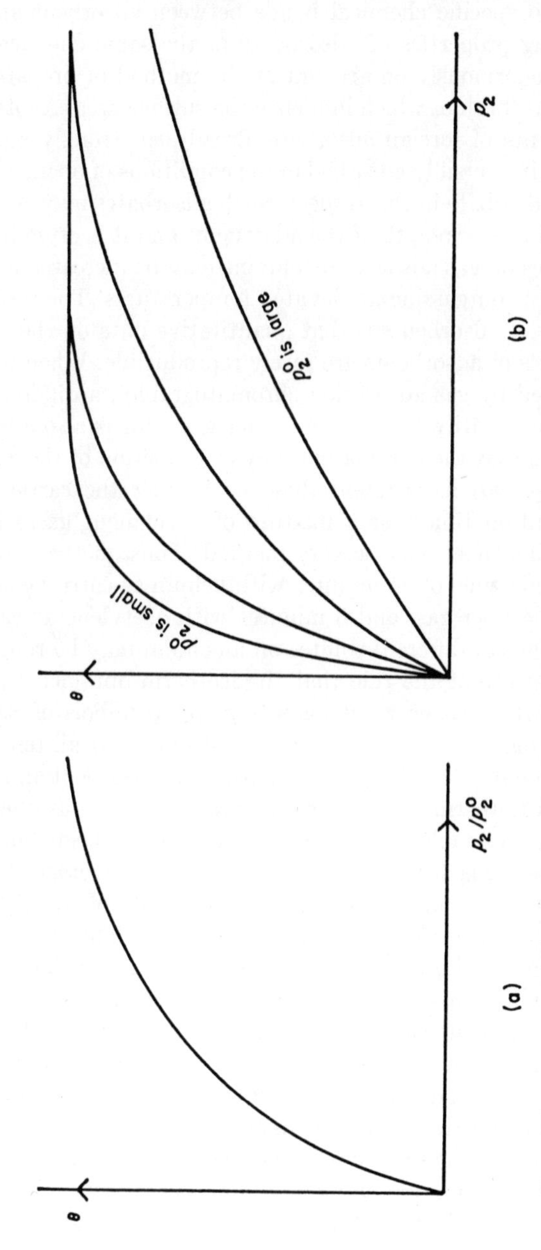

FIG. 3.17. The general adsorption isotherm (a) plotted as fractional surface coverage against p_2/p_2^0 and (b) plotted as fractional surface coverage against p_2 for various values of p_2^0.

Thus, the adsorption process occurring in chromatography is physical, and there are no specific chemical bonds between adsorbent and solute.

The adsorbing properties of adsorbents of the same chemical composition can vary enormously on account of the method of preparation and the pre-treatment, both of which influence the surface area. Another factor is varying amounts of foreign adsorbate already so strongly adsorbed as to be practically irreversibly adsorbed in the conditions of operation. Water is a ubiquitous adsorbate in this respect. Such adsorbates may cause a very great reduction in the strength of the adsorbent, and it is often found that retention volumes on gas adsorption columns may be increased as much as tenfold by suitable outgassing at elevated temperatures. The result of this irreproducibility of adsorbents is that quantitative data on the chromatographic properties of adsorbents are rarely reproducible. When permanent gases are analysed by gas adsorption chromatography, a different permanent gas must necessarily be used as carrier gas; this is also adsorbed by the adsorbent, so that the chromatography is a function of the carrier gas. Greene and Roy (*50*) have found that the heavier the carrier gas, the shorter are retention times for a mixture of permanent gases and light hydrocarbons. The effect may be very marked. Thus, methane was found to have a retention time of 34 minutes with helium as carrier gas, 15 minutes with air as carrier gas, and 5 minutes with acetylene as carrier gas.

The adsorptions of different solutes on a column may be roughly compared by making use of the rule that the isotherm obtained by plotting the fractional surface coverage, θ, against p_2/p_2^0 (symbols of Section 3.2 *et seq.*) is the same, or nearly the same, for all solutes at all temperatures on a given adsorbent (*51*). Thus, if for a particular adsorbent and temperature, the general isotherm is as appears in Fig. 3.17a, then isotherms plotted as p_2 against θ resemble this and each other in all respects but the scale of the abscissa, as in Fig. 3.17b. The fractional surface coverage, θ, is related to q by the equation $\theta = q/q_m$, where q_m is the quantity of adsorbed vapour required to make a complete monomolecular layer. The proportionality constant between θ and q is therefore a function of molecular size. If q is expressed in weight units, q_m varies comparatively little from solute to solute, and in any case, its variation is very much smaller than the variation in p_2^0. Volatile solutes have a large range of p_2 in which the isotherm is approximately linear, and progressively less volatile solutes have smaller linear ranges. This has the result that in chromatography, the less volatile the solute, the smaller the sample required in order to avoid peak asymmetry. The effect of chromatographing more or less equal samples of solutes of different volatility is shown in Fig. 3.18, in which the volatile components give symmetrical peaks, and the involatile components give increasingly asymmetrical peaks.

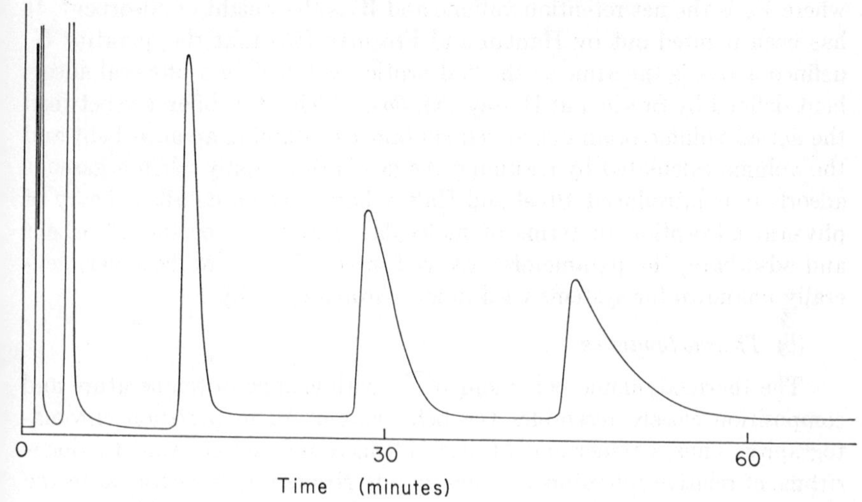

FIG. 3.18. Chromatogram of progressively less volatile solutes on an adsorbent, illustrating the increasing asymmetry of successive peaks. The chromatogram is of approximately 5 mg each of methane, ethane, propane, propene, and isobutene (together with a little air) on a 2-metre column of alumina. See Table 11.9 (author's result).

The range of approximate linearity of the adsorption isotherm is also influenced by the homogeneity of the adsorbent. If all adsorption sites are the same, the isotherm at low concentrations is approximately linear. If, as is common, the adsorbent has sites covering a range of activities, solute molecules will tend to fill the most active first, and when these are full, they will fill the next most active and so on. The slope of the isotherm is determined by the heat of adsorption of the sites, and thus the isotherm is curved. Hence, it is desirable for adsorbents to be homogeneous.

The greater the temperature, the greater is p_2^0, and for this and other reasons, the greater the region of linearity for a given solute. Thus, adsorption elution chromatography works most satisfactorily at high temperatures. Because of this, adsorption columns are normally used at temperatures from 50° to 200°C above the boiling point of the solutes used. Thus, air gases may be analysed at room temperature, and hydrocarbons up to C_4 require column temperatures of 100°C or more. With temperatures such as these in partition columns, the solute would scarcely be retained at all.

When the concentrations are such that the adsorption isotherm is linear, the measured retention volume can be corrected according to the procedures described in Section 2.7 to give an invariant quantity equivalent to a partition coefficient. Janak (*52*) has suggested the definition

$$U_g = \frac{V_N}{W}, \tag{3.68}$$

where V_N is the net retention volume and W is the weight of adsorbent. It has been pointed out by Hanlan and Freeman (*53*) that the quantity U_g defined above is the same as the "adsorption volume" of a physical adsorbent defined by Steele and Halsey (*54, 55*), which is the difference between the actual volume of an evacuated container containing an adsorbent and the volume calculated by assuming the gas laws to apply when a gaseous adsorbate is introduced. Steel and Halsey have given a detailed theory of physical adsorption in terms of molecular parameters of the adsorbent and adsorbate; the parameters involved in the theory are, however, generally unknown for systems used in gas chromatography.

(*b*) *Thermodynamics*

The thermodynamic behaviour of U_g with change in temperature and composition closely resembles the behaviour of V_g in partition chromatography. Thus, Cremer and Muller (*56*) have pointed out that the logarithms of relative retention volumes on adsorbents are proportional to the difference in the standard free energies of adsorption of the solutes,

$$\Delta G_2 \dagger - \Delta G_3 \dagger = RT \ln \frac{t_{R2}}{t_{R3}}. \tag{3.69}$$

Plots of log U_g against $1/T$ give straight lines (*57–59*) from which heats of adsorption may be obtained. Figure 3.19 shows such a plot (*58*); Table 3.17

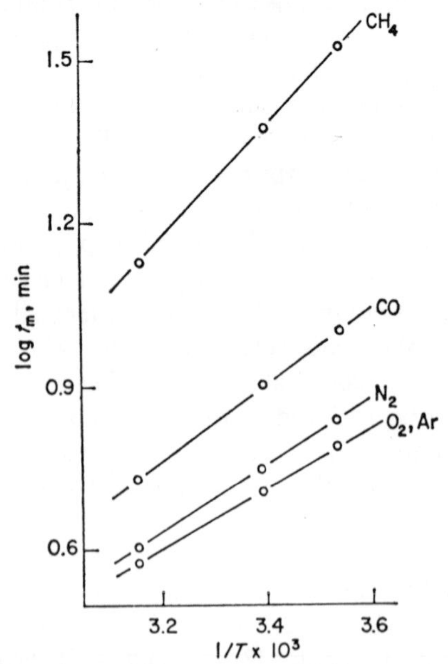

FIG. 3.19. Plots of the logarithm of retention time (t_m, $\propto U_g$) against inverse temperature for gases chromatographed on charcoal. From Greene and Pust (*58*).

TABLE 3.17

HEATS OF ADSORPTION OF GASES AND VAPOURS ON VARIOUS ADSORBENTS[a] ($-\Delta H$ kcal/mole)

	Adsorbent			
Solute	Carbon	Silica gel	Alumina	Molecular sieve 5A
Argon	2.7			1.5
Oxygen	2.7			2.0
Nitrogen	2.9			4.2
Krypton				3.2
Carbon monoxide	3.4			
Methane	4.8	2.8	2.5	4.0
Ethane		5.5	4.7	
Carbon dioxide		6.3		
Ethene		6.7	6.2	
Propane		8.0	7.2	

[a] See Greene and Pust (*58*).

gives values for the heats of adsorption of a number of volatile compounds on various adsorbents. It is seen that they are of the same order of magnitude as those obtained on partition columns. Habgood and Hanlan (*59*) have investigated the relation between the surface area of active charcoal and its adsorptive properties and find that the initial slope of the isotherm and the heat of adsorption increase with increase in surface area. A non-constant heat of adsorption indicates non-homogeneity of the adsorbent.

Another similarity of U_g to V_g is that a plot of log U_g against carbon number for homologous series is linear (*54,59–61*). Cremer (*60*) and Scott (*61*) have both found that the slope of the lines on the plot depends on the activity of the adsorbent; the more active the adsorbent, the greater the relative retention of successive homologs. Cremer (*60*) and Wolf and Bayer (*62*) have found that the surface area of the adsorbent is proportional to the slope of the plot, and have made this the basis of a method for determining surface areas. Scott (*61*) has recommended using adsorbents of low activity for accommodating a mixture of large boiling range on a single chromatogram (Section 11.2).

(c) *Selectivity of Adsorption Columns*

As with partition columns, the behaviour of solutes on adsorption columns can be regarded as determined principally by vapour pressure but modified by specific effects. The general relation between homolog number in homologous series and retention time is given above; in addition to this the tendency of adsorbents to accelerate naphthenes relative to alkanes in hydrocarbon mixtures has been referred to in Section 3.9. With common adsorbents such as carbon, silica gel, and alumina, there are no outstanding specific effects, though carbon would be classed as "non-polar" and silica gel and alumina are somewhat "polar." Use may be made of the ability of molecular sieves to retain compounds smaller than a certain size. In particular, molecular sieve 5A may be used to provide a wide separation of oxygen and nitrogen (Section 11.1). Another important use of molecular sieves is in the separation of *n*-alkanes and *n*-alkyl compounds, which are selectively retained, from any compounds possessing branched alkyl groups, which are not retained. This use of molecular sieves as "subtractors" for *n*-alkyl compounds was made by Brenner and Coates (*63*) and by Whitham (*64*) in connection with alkanes, and has been extended (*65*) to *n*-olefins and *n*-alcohols, which are retained while the corresponding iso- compounds are relatively slightly retained. The effect is a specific retardation of the *n*- compounds rather than a specific acceleration of the branched compounds, and in the right conditions, mixtures of branched compounds can be separated while the *n*- compounds are virtually irreversibly removed.

(*d*) *Use of Modified Adsorbents*

It is possible to remove much of the non-linearity of adsorbents by partially poisoning them with a stationary liquid added in small proportion. It is assumed that the liquid saturates the more active sites leaving a more uniform adsorbent containing relatively weak sites only. This was done first by Eggertsen, Knight, and Groennings (*66*), who found that the addition of 1.5% by weight of squalane to an active charcoal adsorbent completely prevented the tailing of peaks produced by alkanes. If the quantity of the modifying reagent is small, it will remove the tailing without greatly modifying the elution order of solute on the adsorbent. Thus, the charcoal modified as above is used in order to take advantage of the selective acceleration of naphthenes relative to alkanes referred to above, though the effect is not as great on the modified adsorbent as on the pure adsorbent. Scott (*61*) has similarly used alumina modified with silicone oil for separation of C_1—C_5 hydrocarbons. An extension of the modification of adsorbents is the use of a small proportion of a polar stationary phase, e.g., polyethylene glycol, to poison completely the adsorptive properties of a support for stationary liquids (Section 6.3).

A somewhat different technique of adsorbent modification in which the modification is chemical has been described by White *et al.* (*67–70*). In this, the adsorbent is a montmorillonite clay which has been modified by replacing the inorganic ion with an organic amine containing long alkyl chains. Thus, the authors used a commercial product in which the amine is the dioctadecyldimethylammonium ion. The result of this is a product which is essentially an adsorbent with a particularly uniform surface, but which, on account of the large proportion of methylene chain, behaves partly as a paraffinic partition liquid. With alkanes and naphthenes, symmetrical peaks are obtained, and separations are generally in order of boiling points. With aromatic compounds, however, unsymmetrical peaks with sharp front profiles are obtained, indicating ordinary adsorption with Langmuir type isotherms. The conclusion is that the interaction of the paraffins is with the alkyl groups, but the interaction of the aromatics is with the interior of the adsorbent. Of practical significance is the fact that the aromatics are very strongly selectively retained relative to the alkanes, as is shown by the figures of Table 3.18.

TABLE 3.18

COMPARISON OF THE RETENTION OF ALKANES, NAPHTHENES, AND AROMATICS ON ALKYLATED MONTMORILLONITE[a]

Solute	Relative retention volume on alkylated montmorillonite at 80°C	Specific retention volume on alkylated montmorillonite at solute b.p.	Specific retention volume on paraffin oil at solute b.p.
Benzene	1.00	139	66.3
Toluene	1.69	94	77.8
o-Xylene		78	66.7
Hexane	0.10	15.5	62.9
Cyclohexane	0.17	21.2	83.7
Heptane	0.20	15.2	63.0

[a] See White (*67*) and White and Cowan (*68*).

(e) *Applications of Gas Chromatographic Techniques in the Investigation of Adsorbents*

James and Phillips (*71*) have used a frontal technique (Section 6.7) for the determination of adsorption isotherms. The adsorbent is packed into a column and a stream of carrier gas is passed through it. At a measured instant the carrier gas is mixed with a measured concentration of a vapour, e.g., by diverting it through a saturator held at a known temperature, and the mixture is passed through the column. Before the column of adsorbent is in equilibrium with the vapour, it strips it out of the carrier gas, and the detector at the far end of the column shows no response. When all the adsorbent is in equilibrium with the vapour, the latter breaks through the far end of the column, and a step shows on the recorder. The time taken from the start to the breakthrough, the flow rate, and the vapour pressure of the vapour enable one to calculate the amount of vapour adsorbed. By repeating this procedure at different vapour pressures, e.g., by altering the temperature of the saturator, different points on the isotherm are obtained.

Nelsen and Eggertsen (*72*) have modified the procedure of James and Phillips in order to determine surface areas of adsorbents by a modification of the B.E.T. method. This method makes use of the fact that when a vapour is adsorbed on any adsorbent at or near its boiling point, adsorption proceeds with ease till a monomolecular layer is formed, after which there is a reduction in the rate of adsorption. This reflects in the shape of the isotherm, and by a suitable method of plotting, given the area of a single adsorbed molecule, the surface area may be determined. The modification of the above authors is essentially merely the use of helium as a carrier gas, and nitrogen as the adsorbed vapour, with the column at liquid nitrogen temperature. The results obtained closely resemble those obtained by the standard vacuum apparatus for B.E.T. area determinations. The authors find that it is also possible to use butane and ice in place of nitrogen and liquid nitrogen, but, as is generally recognised, B.E.T. areas obtained with large molecules may differ from those obtained from nitrogen.

References

1. Ambrose, D., Keulemans, A. I. M., and Purnell, J. H., *Anal. Chem.* **30,** 1582 (1958).
2. Littlewood, A. B., Phillips, C. S. G., and Price, D. T., *J. Chem. Soc.* p. 1480 (1955).
3. Johnson, H. W., and Stross, F. H., *Anal. Chem.* **30,** 1586 (1958).
4. Adlard, E. R., Khan, M. A., and Whitham, B. T., Third Symposium on Gas Chromatography, Edinburgh, June, 1960, Paper No. 17 (Preprint).
5. Guggenheim, E. A., "Thermodynamics," 3rd ed. North-Holland, Amsterdam, 1957.
6. Glasstone, S., "Textbook of Physical Chemistry," 2nd ed. Macmillan, New York, 1943.
7. Hildebrand, J., and Scott, R. L., "Solubility of Non-Electrolytes," 3rd ed., *Am. Chem. Soc.* Monograph No. 17. Reinhold, New York, 1950.
8. Pierotti, G. J., Deal, C. H., Derr, E. L., and Porter, P. E., *J. Am. Chem. Soc.* **78,** 2989 (1956).
9. Porter, P. E., Deal, C. H., and Stross, F. H., *J. Am. Chem. Soc.* **78,** 2999 (1956).
10. Kwantes, A., and Rijnders, G. W. A., *in* "Gas Chromatography 1958," Proceedings of the Second Symposium, Amsterdam, May, 1956 (D. H. Desty, ed.), p. 125. Academic Press, New York, 1958.
11. Hoare, M. R. and Purnell, J. H., *Trans. Faraday Soc.* **52,** 222 (1956).
12. Hala, E., Pick, J., Fried, V., and Vilim, O., "Vapour-Liquid Equilibrium." Pergamon Press, New York, 1960.
13. Herington, E. F. G., *in* "Vapour Phase Chromatography," Proceedings of the First Symposium, London, May, 1956 (D. H. Desty, ed.), p. 7. Academic Press, New York, 1957.
14. Pierotti, G. J., Derr, E. L., and Deal, C. H., *Ind. Eng. Chem.* **51,** 95 (1959).
15. Keulemans, A. I. M., Kwantes, A., and Zaal, P., *Anal. Chim. Acta* **13,** 357 (1955).

16. Bradford, B. W., Harvey, D., and Chalkley, D. E., *J. Inst. Petroleum* **41,** 80 (1955).
17. Beaven, G. H., James, A. T., and Johnson, E. A., *Nature* **179,** 490 (1957).
18. Barber, D. W., Phillips, C. S. G., Tusa, G. F., and Verdin, A., *J. Chem. Soc.* p. 18 (1959).
19. Anderson, J. R. A., *J. Am. Chem. Soc.* **78,** 5692 (1956).
20. Pollard, F. H., and Hardy, C. J., *Anal. Chim. Acta* **16,** 135 (1957).
21. Wiseman, W. A., *Nature* **185,** 841 (1960).
22. Ambrose, D., and Purnell, J. H., *in* "Gas Chromatography 1958," Proceedings of the Second Symposium, Amsterdam, May, 1958 (D. H. Desty, ed.), p. 369. Academic Press, New York, 1958.
23. Adlard, E. R., *in* "Vapour Phase Chromatography," Proceedings of the First Symposium, London, May, 1956 (D. H. Desty, ed.), p. 98. Academic Press, New York, 1957.
24. Gerrard, W., Hawkes, S. J., and Mooney, E. F., Third Symposium on Gas Chromatography, Edinburgh, June, 1960, Paper No. 13 (Preprint).
25. Ray, N. H., *J. Appl. Chem.* **4,** 21 (1954).
26. James, A. T., and Martin, A. J. P., *J. Appl. Chem.* **6,** 105 (1956).
27. James, A. T., and Martin, A. J. P., *Biochem. J.* **63,** 144 (1956).
28. Desty, D. H., and Whyman, B. H. F., *Anal. Chem.* **29,** 320 (1957).
29. Brooks, V. T., and Collins, G. A., *Chem. & Ind. (London)* p. 1921 (1956).
30. Raupp, G., *Z. anal. Chem.* **164,** 135 (1958).
31. Scott, R. P. W., Benzol Producers Ltd., London, Research Paper No. 8 (1957).
32. Tenney, H. M., *Anal. Chem.* **30,** 2 (1958).
33. Desty, D. H., and Harbourn, C. L. A., *Anal. Chem.* **31,** 1965 (1959).
34. Desty, D. H., ed., "Vapour Phase Chromatography," Proceedings of the First Symposium, London, May, 1956, p. xi. Academic Press, New York, 1957.
35. Knight, H. S., *Anal. Chem.* **30,** 9 (1958).
36. Janak, J., and Komers, R., *in* "Gas Chromatography 1958," Proceedings of the Second Symposium, Amsterdam, May, 1958 (D. H. Desty, ed.), p. 343. Academic Press, New York, 1958.
37. Brooks, V. T., and Collins, G. A., *Chem. & Ind.* p. 1021 (1956).
38. Kelker, H., *Angew. Chem.* **71,** 218 (1959). Kovats, E., *Helv. Chim. Acta* **41,** 1915 (1958).
39. Anderson, D. M. W., and Duncan, J. L., *Chem. & Ind.* p. 1662 (1958).
40. Anderson, D. M. W., *Analyst* **84,** 50 (1959).
41. Johns, T., Third Symposium on Gas Chromatography, Edinburgh, June, 1960, Paper No. 16 (Preprint).
42. Amberg, C. H., *Can. J. Chem.* **36,** 590 (1958).
43. Beynon, J. H., *Nature* **174,** 735 (1954).
44. Beynon, J. H., *Mikrochim. Acta* p. 437 (1956).
45. Beynon, J. H., Saunders, R. A., and Williams, A. E., *J. Sci. Instr.* **36,** 275 (1959).
46. Gohlke, R. S., *Anal. Chem.* **31,** 535 (1959).
47. James, A. T., *J. Chromatog.* **2,** 552 (1959).
48. James, A. T., Martin, A. J. P., and Smith, G. H., *Biochem. J.* **52,** 238 (1952).
49. Cartoni, G. P., Lowrie, R. S., Phillips, C. S. G., and Venanzi, L. M., Third Symposium on Gas Chromatography, Edinburgh, June, 1960, Paper No. 18 (Preprint).
50. Greene, S. A., and Roy, H. E., *Anal. Chem.* **29,** 569 (1957).
51. For this and other aspects of the theory of physical adsorption, see Brunauer, S., "Physical Adsorption of Gases and Vapors," Princeton Univ. Press, Princeton, New Jersey, 1943.

52. Janak, J., *Collection Czechoslov. Chem. Communs.* **18,** 798 (1953).
53. Hanlan, J. F., and Freeman, M. P., *Can. J. Chem.* **37,** 843 (1959).
54. Steele, W. A., and Halsey, G. D., Jr., *J. Chem. Phys.* **22,** 979 (1954).
55. Steele, W. A., and Halsey, G. D., Jr., *J. Phys. Chem.* **59,** 57 (1955).
56. Cremer, E., and Muller, R., *Z. Electrochem.* **55,** 217 (1951).
57. Cremer, E., and Prior, F., *Z. Electrochem.* **55,** 66 (1951).
58. Greene, S. A., and Pust, H., *J. Phys. Chem.* **62,** 55 (1958).
59. Habgood, H. W., and Hanlan, J. F., *Can. J. Chem.* **37,** 843 (1959).
60. Cremer, E., Symposium on the Use of Physical Chemical Methods for Analysis, Freiburg, West Germany, April, 1959.
61. Scott, C. G., *J. Inst. Petrol.* **45,** 118 (1959).
62. Wolf, F., and Bayer, H., *Chem. Tech.* **11,** 142 (1959).
63. Brenner, N., and Coates, V. J., *Nature* **181,** 1401 (1958).
64. Whitham, B. T., *Nature* **182,** 391 (1958).
65. Brenner, N., Ciepelinski, E., Ettre, L. S., and Coates, V. J., *J. Chromatog.* **3,** 230 (1960).
66. Eggertsen, F. T., Knight, H. S., and Groennings, S., *Anal. Chem.* **28,** 303 (1956).
67. White, D., *Nature* **179,** 1075 (1957).
68. White, D., and Cowan, C. T., *Trans. Faraday Soc.* **54,** 557 (1958).
69. White, D., and Cowan, C. T., "Gas Chromatography 1958," Proceedings of the Second Symposium, Amsterdam, May, 1958 (D. H. Desty, ed.), p. 116. Academic Press, New York, 1958.
70. Hughes, M. A., White, D., and Roberts, A. L., *Nature* **184,** 1796 (1959).
71. James, D. H., and Phillips, C. S. G., *J. Chem. Soc.* p. 1066 (1954).
72. Nelsen, F. M., and Eggertsen, F. T., *Anal. Chem.* **30,** 1387 (1958).

Chapter 4

Column Performance—Fundamentals

4.1. Introduction

It was pointed out in Chapter 1 that the separation of two substances depends on the relative retention and the column performance. The former is discussed in the two preceding chapters. The two following chapters describe the column performance, which determines the width of peaks relative to their retention volume.

It is simplest to imagine that a zone of vapour is put into a column instantaneously, as in Section 2.2, so that at the beginning of the elution it takes the form of a very narrow band which in the ideal case is infinitely narrow. This broadens while being eluted from one end of the column to the other. The problem is to define the degree of broadening by a suitable number, to find out the factors upon which the broadening depends, and finally to produce quantitative relations connecting the broadening with the factors which produce it. There are two ways of approaching this problem. The logical method, which is also the most useful, considers what happens to a band of vapour as it passes through the column in terms of the kinetics of vapour molecules as they move in and out of the stationary phase, a motion which is controlled by diffusion and by the geometry of the column. This method will be considered in the next chapter. Historically, however, it happened that another method of treatment came first, in which a very artifical model of the chromatographic column, the "Plate" model, was used, and which provided the number (number of theoretical plates) by which column performance is defined. The "Plate Theory" was first given in connection with liquid-liquid partition chromatography by Martin and Synge (*1*) and was subsequently developed by Mayer and Tompkins (*2*) and others. The discussion below also makes extensive use of papers by Klinkenberg and Sjenitzer (*3*) and by Gluekauf (*4*).

4.2. Plate Theory

Martin and Synge (*1*) imagine a chromatographic column divided along its length into a number of separate zones each of which is of such a length that within it there is complete equilibration of the vapour between the gas and the stationary phases. The zones, called "Theoretical Plates," form the imaginary basis of the model on which the plate theory is founded, and their length in the column is referred to as the "Height Equivalent to the Theoretical Plate," H.E.T.P., or the "Plate-Height." A similar model is used in describing the performance of distillation columns, but as is shown later, the theoretical plate in a chromatographic column and that in a distillation column do not have the same significance, though they may be defined in the same way.

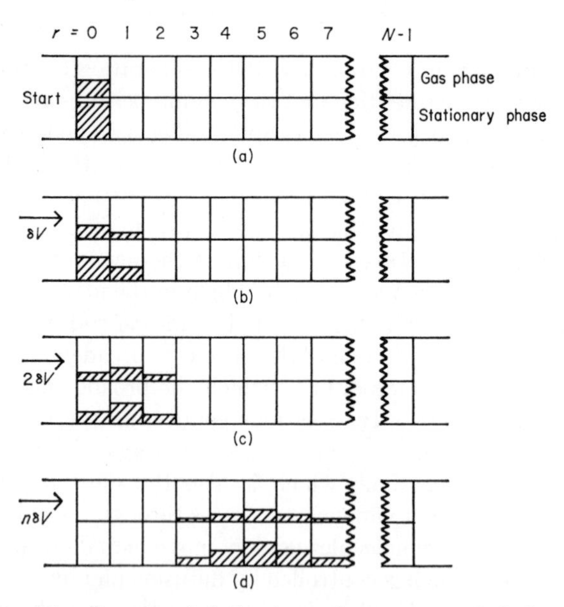

Fig. 4.1. Progress of elution in a column composed of plates.

Let us adopt the plate model of the column (Fig. 4.1) and imagine that at the beginning of the chromatography, a particular vapour is all contained in the first plate (Fig. 4.1a). On passing an incremental volume of carrier gas, δV, some of the vapour in the gas phase is swept onto the second plate, where it equilibrates with the stationary phase (Fig. 4.1b). Meanwhile, what remains in the stationary phase in the first plate equilibrates with the clean carrier gas that has entered. On passing further ncrements of carrier gas this process repeats (Fig. 4.1c) and slowly the vanguard of the vapour moves along the column while the concentration in the first plate becomes smaller and smaller till virtually none remains, and the whole zone has effectively moved along the column (Fig. 4.1d). The way in which the vapour is distributed among the plates after passage of a given number of increments of carrier gas depends on the amount of vapour transferred at each incremental passage. This in turn depends upon the relative cross sections occupied by the phases and upon the partition coefficient. Using mainly the notation of James and Martin (*5,6*), let

H = height equivalent to the theoretical plate (cm),
a = cross-sectional area of column occupied by the gas phase (cm^2),
b = cross-sectional area of column occupied by the stationary phase (cm^2),
α = partition coefficient defined in Section 3.2 (number),
c = concentration of vapour in the gas phase (g/cc),
δV = incremental volume of carrier gas (cc),

and we shall find the proportion of the contents of any plate moved into the following plate by passage of a single incremental volume, δV. The total vapour content of any plate is the sum of the contents of the gas phase and the stationary phase. The weight of vapour in the gas phase of one plate is the gas volume of the plate multiplied by the concentration in the gas phase, which is Hac. The concentration in the stationary phase is αc, so that the weight of vapour in the stationary phase is $Hb\alpha c$. Hence, the total weight of solute in the plate is $Hc(a + \alpha b)$. The passage of δV will remove from the plate a mass of vapour $c\delta V$. Hence the proportion of vapour moved out of the plate on passing δV (p) is

$$p = \frac{\delta V}{H(a + \alpha b)}. \tag{4.1}$$

Note that this is only the amount moved *out*, and does not take into account the vapour moved *in* from the previous plate.

Using Eq. (4.1), we now consider the distribution that results after a given number of incremental volumes (n) has been passed, assuming that before elution all the vapour is in the first plate. The distribution resulting from elution, expressed as a function of the concentrations existing in plates numbered from zero upwards (serial number of plate being r, the first plate being $r = 0$) and as a function of the number of incremental volumes, is tabulated for small values of the variables in Table 4.1. The amount of vapour has been normalised so that it is represented by a mass of unity. After passage of one increment δV, p is transferred from plate 0 to plate 1, leaving $1 - p$ in plate 0. Let $1 - p = q$. In the next passage of δV, a proportion p of the p already present in plate 1 is transferred from

TABLE 4.1

AMOUNTS OF VAPOUR OCCUPYING PLATES (r) AFTER PASSAGE OF n INCREMENTAL VOLUMES δV, GIVEN THAT ALL THE VAPOUR OCCUPIES THE ZEROTH PLATE WHEN $n = 0$

Number of incremental volumes δV (n)	Serial number of plate (r)						
	0	1	2	3	4	5	6
0	1						
1	q	p					
2	q^2	$2qp$	p^2				
3	q^3	$3q^2p$	$3qp^2$	p^3			
4	q^4	$4q^3p$	$6q^2p^2$	$4qp^3$	p^4		
5	q^5	$5q^4p$	$10q^3p^2$	$10q^2p^3$	$5qp^4$	p^5	
6	q^6	$6q^5p$	$15q^4p^2$	$20q^3p^3$	$15q^2p^4$	$6qp^5$	p^6

plate 1 to plate 2, giving p^2 in plate 2; from this transfer there remains pq in plate 1. Also, a proportion p of the q already present in plate 0 is transferred to plate 1, giving a further pq in plate 1. Thus plate 1 contains $2pq$. Plate 0 contains a proportion q of the q originally present, and thus contains q^2. In succeeding passages, this process is repeated, i.e., a proportion p from the contents of plate $r - 1$ is transferred to plate r, and a proportion q remains, the total contents of the plate being the sum of that remaining and that added by transfer from the previous plate. Study of Table 4.1 will make it evident that the amount in the rth plate after the nth incremental passage is

$$X \cdot p^r q^{(n-r)}$$

where the coefficient X is the sum of the coefficients of the terms above and to the upper left in the table. For small numbers, these coefficients are obtainable from "Pascal's Triangle," which is constructed in this way. The coefficients are those of the expansion of the binomial $(p + q)^n$ as a power series, and in general, the rth coefficient is given by the equation

$$X = \frac{n!}{r!(n - r)!}. \tag{4.2}$$

Hence, the mass distribution of the vapour among the plates as a function of r after the passage of n incremental volumes is

$$w(n,r) = \frac{n!}{r!(n - r)!} p^r q^{(n-r)} \tag{4.3}$$

where $w(n,r)$ is the proportion of the mass of vapour in the rth plate after passage of $n\delta V$.

The distribution of Eq. (4.3) is very common, and arises in many cases where some dependent property results from the repetition of a number of steps each of which has a given chance (p) of success or failure. First described by Newton, it is called the "Binomial Distribution," since the terms of the binomial expansion satisfy it. As a linear isotherm is assumed, w is proportional to c, the concentration in the gas phase of the plate, so that Eq. (4.3) is essentially the equation of the peak in the column as a function of r after a given amount of elution.

A little algebraic transformation of Eq. (4.3) is necessary to bring it into convenient analytical form, and this is done later in order to study the shapes of the peaks predicted by the plate theory. However, the retention volume and broadening of peaks can be obtained from familiar properties of binomial distributions without the necessity of obtaining the actual equation for the chromatogram.

In connection with any distribution there is a *mean*, $\bar{r}$, which is a point on the abscissa, r, such that a vertical line drawn through it bisects the area of the distribution, and there is a *standard deviation*, σ, or *variance*, σ^2, which measures the extent to which the distribution is spread out from the mean. These quantities are defined by the equations:

$$\bar{r} = \int rw(r)\, dr \tag{4.4}$$

and

$$\sigma^2 = \int (r - \bar{r})^2 w(r)\, dr. \tag{4.5}$$

For a binomial distribution it can be shown that (see, for example, Margenau and Murphy (*7*), Section 12.4)

$$\bar{r} = np \tag{4.6}$$

and

$$\sigma^2 = npq. \tag{4.7}$$

Substituting Eq. (4.1) in Eq. (4.6) to obtain an expression for the mean,

$$\bar{r} = \frac{n\delta V}{H(a + \alpha b)} \tag{4.8}$$

we obtain the serial number of the plate which has the same quantity of vapour on either side, i.e., the plate which bisects the area of the peak in the column. In the circumstances in which chromatography is normally used, it will appear that the distribution is nearly symmetrical with one maximum, so that the plate $\bar{r}$ is also the plate at which the concentration is the maximum. Also, the product $n\delta V$ is the total volume of eluting carrier gas passed, V, so that

$$\bar{r} = \frac{V}{H(a + \alpha b)}. \tag{4.9}$$

The product $\bar{r}H$ is the distance of the $\bar{r}$th plate from the beginning of the column, i.e., the distance of the peak maximum from the beginning of the column. Hence

$$V = x(a + \alpha b), \tag{4.10}$$

where V and x are the same symbols as used in Chapter 2. When x is equal to the length of the column, l, V is the volume of gas passed for the maximum to appear at the end of the column, i.e., the retention volume, V_R^0. Hence

$$V_R^0 = l(a + \alpha b). \tag{4.11}$$

This, using αb instead of the identical $m\beta$, is identical with the corresponding equation for the retention volume derived by the theory of Section 2.3 (Eq. 2.11). Hence, provided that the assumption that the peaks are symmetrical is valid, both theories give the same result.

The broadening can be obtained from the standard deviation, which, for the binomial distribution, is given by Eq. (4.7). In the most realistic interpretation of gas chromatography by means of the plate theory, p is small, so that q is approximately equal to unity. Thus the variance, σ^2, has the same form as the mean,

$$\sigma^2 = \frac{nq\delta V}{H(a + \alpha b)} \approx \frac{V}{H(a + \alpha b)}. \tag{4.12}$$

In order to obtain an expression for the broadening produced by the column, we require the standard deviation when the peak emerges from the column, that is, when $V = V_R^0$. Thus, substituting Eq. (4.11) for V_R^0,

$$\sigma_r^2 = \frac{l(a + \alpha b)}{H(a + \alpha b)} = \frac{l}{H} = \mathfrak{N}, \tag{4.13}$$

where $\mathfrak{N}$ is the number of plates in the column. The last equality of Eq. (4.13) derives from the fact that the product of the height of a plate and the number of plates equals the length of the column. The quantity defining the column performance is not the standard deviation itself, which increases continuously with either the plate-number or the length of the column, but, as stated in Section 1.3, the ratio of the standard deviation to the mean. Thus the measure of the performance is given by

$$\frac{(\bar{r})^2}{\sigma_r^2} = \frac{(V_R^0)^2/H^2(a + \alpha b)^2}{l/H} = \frac{l^2/H^2}{l/H} = \frac{l}{H} = \mathfrak{N}. \tag{4.14}$$

In this equation, neither standard deviation nor mean is in units easily accessible to measurement. However, if both numerator and denominator of the extreme L.H.S. of Eq. (4.14) are multiplied by $H^2(a + \alpha b)^2$, the plate units are changed into volume units by virtue of Eq. (4.9), so that $\sigma_{(\bar{r})}$ becomes $\sigma_{(V)}$ and $\bar{r}$ becomes V_R^0, and

$$\frac{(V_R{}^0)^2}{\sigma^2_{(\mathrm{V})}} = \mathfrak{N}. \tag{4.15}$$

Equation (4.15) is the fundamental justification of the plate theory. In Chapter 1, the criterion of column performance was defined as the ratio of the retention volume to the standard deviation of a peak produced by the column. The equation shows that the square of this quantity is in fact equal to the number of theoretical plates, so that the number of theoretical plates provides a number characteristic of column performance. This criterion is widely used, though the idea of the theoretical plate is in fact rather far removed from a directly measurable criterion of performance. The plate theory can do no more, for it cannot continue by making any predictions about the height of the theoretical plate in terms of column parameters, and the plate model of the chromatographic column is a model based solely on the answer it is required to give, which is Eq. (4.15). However, the notion of the theoretical plate is now so well established that it is convenient to express performances in terms of "Number of Plates," even in discussions in which it is fully recognised that there are no such things as plates, either in theory or practice. In all such cases, the plate number is defined by Eq. (4.15).

4.3. Peak Shape from Plate Theory

In Eq. (4.3), $w(n,r)$ is the amount of solute in plate r after the passage of n incremental volumes δV. If, as is normally the case, the zone of solute covers many plates, $w(n,r)$ can be considered as a function of a continuous variable r which is related to x, the distance from the start of the column, by the equation $Hr = x$ $(x \gg H)$. In this case, w is proportional to c or q, the concentrations in gas or liquid phases, since, by definition, there is equilibrium inside each plate and the isotherm is assumed to be linear. Thus, for a column with $\mathfrak{N}$ plates, the quantity $Kw(n)$ for a value of r given by $\mathfrak{N} - 1(\mathfrak{N} - 1$ rather than $\mathfrak{N}$ since the serial number of the first plate is zero), where K is a normalising constant, is the equation of the chromatogram as it emerges from the end of the column, and $K'w(r)$ at a given value of n is the equation of the zone inside the column after an elution volume $n\delta V$ has been passed.

Equation (4.3) cannot be plotted with ease in the algebraic form given except for small values of n and of r and except after specification of p and q. Normally, n and r are by no means small, and, as will be seen shortly, it is not convenient to give specific values to p and q. There are two different analytically convenient approximations to Eq. (4.3), the accuracy and applicability of which depends on the relative values of n, r, p, and q. One of these, to be described below, is generally applicable in chromatography.

In the case that $\bar{r}$ is sufficiently large that $1/\bar{r}$ may be neglected compared to unity, it can be shown that, as $n \to \infty$,

$$w(r) = \frac{1}{\sqrt{2\pi}\sigma_{(r)}} \exp\left[-(r - \bar{r})^2/2\sigma_{(r)}^2\right], \tag{4.16}$$

where $\sigma_{(r)}$ is given by Eq. (4.7). In these conditions, p is small in such a manner that $\bar{r} = np$ is finite as $n \to \infty$; the values of p and q are discussed below. Equation (4.16) is that of the well-known "Gaussian Distribution," and the conditions required for it are usually satisfied in gas chromatography. When $w(r)$ is plotted against r, it appears as a symmetrical peak whose maximum at $r = \bar{r}$ (Fig. 4.2). In this distribution, it can be shown

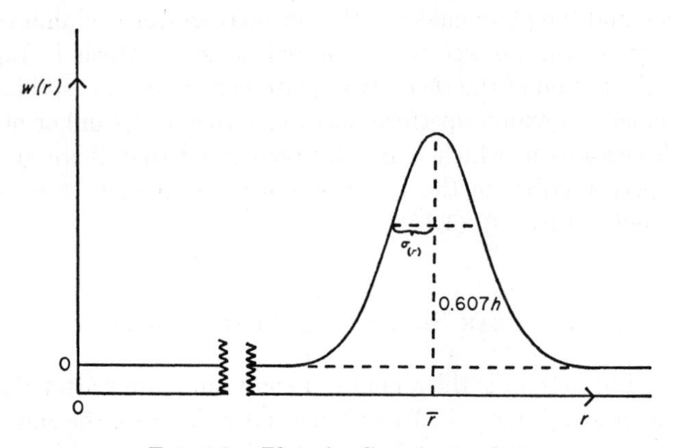

FIG. 4.2. Plot of a Gaussian peak.

that the standard deviation, $\sigma_{(r)}$, is represented by the half-width of the peak drawn at the points of inflection, which occur at points 0.607 up the height of the peak (Fig. 4.2). The quantity $1/\sqrt{2\pi}\sigma_{(r)}$ is a normalising constant such that the area of the peak is unity. Hence, the equation of a zone of vapour of mass w in the column is

$$c(r) = \frac{w}{\sqrt{2\pi}\sigma_{(r)}} \exp\left[-(r - \bar{r})^2/2\sigma_{(r)}^2\right] \text{ (g/plate)}. \tag{4.17}$$

This can also be written as a function of x rather than of the plate-number, so long as the unit of the standard deviation is changed correspondingly:

$$c(x) = \frac{w}{\sqrt{2\pi}\sigma_{(x)}} \exp\left[-(x - \bar{x})^2/2\sigma_{(x)}^2\right] \text{ (g/cm)}. \tag{4.18}$$

Since the peak is symmetrical, the concentration of an emerging zone can also be expressed in volume units:

$$c(V) = \frac{w}{\sqrt{2\pi}\sigma_{(V)}} \exp - (V - V_R{}^0)^2/2\sigma^2_{(V)} \text{ (g/cc)}, \tag{4.19}$$

where $V_R{}^0$ is the retention volume. Note that the fact that the peak as given by any of Eqs. (4.16)–(4.19) is symmetrical justifies $\bar{r}$ being identified with r_{max} in the derivation of Eq. (4.11). The maximum value of $c(V)$ for a peak in the column is when $r = \bar{r}$, and is given by:

$$c_{(max)} = \frac{1}{\sqrt{2\pi}\sigma_{(V)}}$$

for unit weight of vapour. Since $\sigma^2_{(V)} \propto V$ [Eq. (4.12)], the relation between the maximum concentration of a peak and its position in the column is:

$$c^2_{(max)} \propto \frac{1}{V} \propto \frac{1}{x}. \tag{4.20}$$

This equation is used in Section 2.9.

It will be noticed that the p and q of Eq. (4.3) only appear in Eq. (4.16) as the product $np = \bar{r}$. So long as p is small and n is large, the algebra involved in changing from one equation to the other is valid, and it is not necessary to have an exact value for p. However, the values of p and q have considerable interest; p depends directly upon δV [Eq. (4.1)], the size of which has not so far been discussed. Two extremes can be distinguished: (1) δV is equal to the gas volume of a plate, (2) δV is infinitesimally small.

In the former case, the theoretical model corresponds exactly with the familiar method of separation known as the "Countercurrent Extractor" [L. C. Craig (*8*)], in which solute is equilibrated between two immiscible liquids (Phases A and B) in a tube (serial number r), and, by a suitable mechanical arrangement, phase A passes on to equilibrate with phase B in the following tube $(r + 1)$ after which phase A from the previous tube $(r - 1)$ enters to fill the place of the phase A that has left. There is large number of such equilibration tubes, and the mixture to be separated is placed in the first. It is clear that here each tube is a "Theoretical Plate" in a real sense; the serial number of the tube is r; the number of transfers is n; and δV is the volume of phase A in each tube. This, however, is not quite the case in chromatography, for the gas is passing through the column continuously rather than intermittently. This fact is accounted for in the plate model of chromatography by regarding the continuous flow as the limiting case of n passages of δV as $n \to \infty$ and $\delta V \to 0$. Thus, in chromatography, the second choice of δV should be made. This is the essential justification for assuming p small in deriving Eq. (4.16) from Eq. (4.3).

It is interesting to examine the effect of the size of δV upon the variance of the resulting distribution. When δV is small, then, by Eq. (4.1), p is small, so that q is virtually equal to unity and the variance is given by the product np, that is, by the mean, $\bar{r}$, as described in the previous section. However, when δV is not small, as in the case of the countercurrent extractor, p may not be small, so that q may be less than unity, with the result that the variance may be less than the mean. Let us imagine a column composed of plates which can be operated with either small or large values of δV. If $\sigma_{(a)}$ is the standard deviation when the column is operated with values of δV of such a size that q is appreciably less than unity, and $\sigma_{(b)}$ is the standard deviation when it is operated with infinitesimal values of δV, the ratio of the two variances is given by:

$$\frac{\sigma^2_{(a)}}{\sigma^2_{(b)}} = \frac{npq}{np} = q. \tag{4.21}$$

Substituting Eq. (4.1),

$$\frac{\sigma^2_{(a)}}{\sigma^2_{(b)}} = 1 - \frac{\delta V}{H(a + \alpha b)}. \tag{4.22}$$

If, now, the value δV corresponding to $\sigma_{(a)}$ is made equal to the gas volume of a plate, Ha, this becomes:

$$\frac{\sigma^2_{(a)}}{\sigma^2_{(b)}} = 1 - \frac{Ha}{H(a + \alpha b)} = 1 - \frac{a}{(a + \alpha b)} \tag{4.23}$$

[see Klinkenberg and Sjenitzer (*3*)]. It is evident that, for a given mean, the variance is always less for large values of δV than for small ones. The reason for this can be seen as follows: Where δV is equal to the volume of the mobile phase in a plate, as in the countercurrent extractor, there is no mixing between the outgoing moving phase and incoming moving phase. However, in chromatography, where δV is small, since, by definition, complete equilibration occurs within a plate, there is always equilibrium between gas entering the plate and gas leaving it, with the result that, if there is a concentration gradient across the plates due to a solute, this gradient tends to become smeared out because of the mixing within each plate.

In cases where the mean of the distribution of the solute inside the column is not large, i.e., where the elution has only proceeded through a relatively small number of plates, the assumptions leading to Eq. (4.16) do not hold. In this case, a different approximation to Eq. (4.3) may be made which holds when the mean is relatively small, p is small, n is large, and of necessity q is close to unity, and which thus applies in theory to columns with few plates. The equation is:

$$w(r) = \frac{(np)^r \exp(-np)}{r!}, \tag{4.24}$$

and $w(r)$ is called the "Poisson Distribution." Substituting Eq. (4.6), this becomes:

$$w(r) = \exp(-\bar{r}) \cdot \frac{(\bar{r})^r}{r!}. \tag{4.25}$$

The plot of this is unsymmetrical, with the rear profile steeper than the front profile. Thus, by plate theory, columns with few plates give unsymmetrical peaks. There are many circumstances where gas chromatography gives unsymmetrical peaks, but none of these can be explained by the operation of a Poisson distribution, since the Poisson distribution is significantly different from a Gaussian distribution only in such circumstances that the plate model is a prohibitively bad representation of a chromatographic column.

4.4. Comparison of Theoretical Plates in Chromatography and Distillation

The expression of the performance of chromatographic columns in terms of the number of plates invites comparison with the similar term used in fractional distillation. Though the definition of the theoretical plate is the same in both cases, the number of plates required to perform a separation to a given degree of purity is very much greater in chromatography than in distillation, as has been pointed out by Herington (*9*) and others. Van Deemter, Zuiderweg, and Klinkenberg (*10*) have given a graph (Fig. 4.3) showing the number of plates required to obtain two products of 99.7% purity from 50-50 mixtures of two components as a function of the relative retention for gas chromatography and relative volatility for distillation. As expected (see Section 4.6) the number of plates required rises as the relative retention approaches unity, but the over-all number of plates required in chromatography is very much greater. Herington considers that the number of plates required in chromatography is about the square of the number required in distillation for the same degree of separation. The reason for this large difference is simple; in chromatography, only the part of the column occupied by the solutes is effective in performing the separations, and most of the column is empty most of the time; but, in distillation, all the column is working all the time in separating the components of the mixture.

Figure 4.3 shows that the very high plate-numbers achieved in chromatography are deceptive to those who are used to thinking of separations

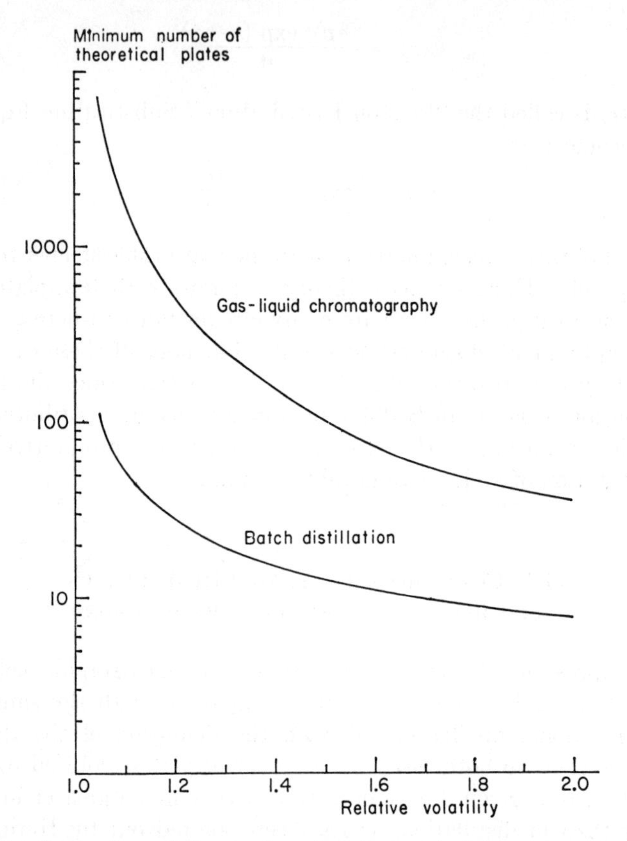

FIG. 4.3. Comparison of the number of plates required for a given separation by gas chromatography and by distillation. The curves show the number of plates required as a function of relative retention (G.C.) or relative volatility (distillation) to obtain fractions of 99.7% purity from an equimolar mixture. From van Deemter, Zuiderweg, and Klinkenberg (*10*).

in terms of distillation, though it should be emphasised that a plate in gas chromatography, although it may mean less than a plate in distillation, is very much easier to attain and to operate. Thus, though a distillation column of 100 plates is comparable with a chromatographic column of 10,000 plates for separation and analysis of small samples, the chromatographic column is much easier to construct and operate than the corresponding distillation column. A 10,000-plate chromatographic column could be used for the analysis of a small sample of a mixture in a few minutes, but a distillation column at 100-plate efficiency would require a long time on total reflux, with careful temperature control, and the allowable take-off rate would be very small. Chromatography also has the advantage that there is no equivalent of the "Hold-up Volume" of the distillation column, and no chasers are required.

4.5. Methods of Determining Plate-Numbers

The plate-number of a column may be found from a chromatogram by making measurements equivalent to the standard deviation and the retention of a peak, and by calculating the number of theoretical plates by Eq. (4.15). This equation is true whatever the units of the retention and the standard deviation so long as they are the same, and thus, for the greatest convenience, the quantities are measured as distances on the chromatogram as it appears on the strip-chart. Four methods for measuring plate-numbers have been reported:

(1) Measure L, the distance on the chart from the point corresponding to the start of the chromatogram to the peak maximum, and measure the standard deviation of the peak, $\sigma_{(L)}$. From these, the plate number will be given by:

$$\mathfrak{N} = \frac{L^2}{\sigma^2_{(L)}}. \tag{4.26}$$

This method was suggested by James and Martin (*5*).

(2) An adaption of the above method measures L and the peak-width half-way up the peak. If this latter quantity is $\omega_{1/2}$, the plate number is

$$\mathfrak{N} = 5.54 \frac{L^2}{\omega^2_{1/2}}. \tag{4.27}$$

A simple calculation will show that $\omega^2_{1/2}$ is equal to 5.54 $\sigma^2_{(L)}$, where $5.54 \equiv 8\ln(2)$. This method is illustrated in Fig. 4.4.

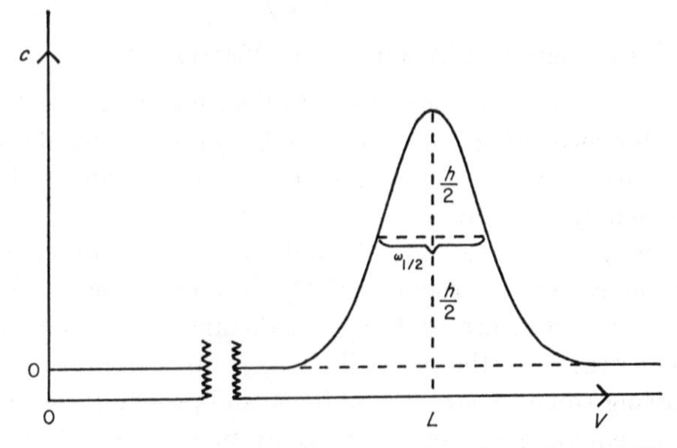

Fig. 4.4. Plate-number from retention and peak width at half-height.

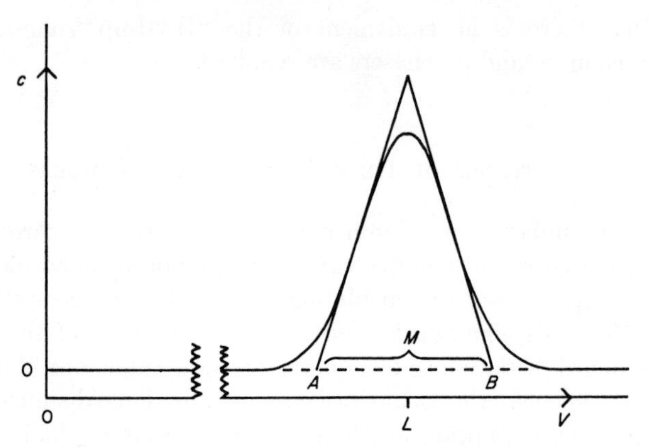

FIG. 4.5. Plate-number from retention and inflectional tangents.

(3) Draw tangents to the points of inflection of the peak, and produce the base line across the bottom of the peak (Fig. 4.5). A simple calculation that the distance AB (M) on the baseline between the points where the two tangents intersect it is of length $4\sigma_{(L)}$. Hence, if L is also measured, the plate-number is given by:

$$\mathfrak{N} = 16\frac{L^2}{M^2}. \tag{4.28}$$

This method has been recommended by Desty *et al.* (*11*).

(4) Measure the area of the peak, A; the height of the peak, h; and the retention distance, L; in such units as to make the quantity hL/A unitless. Thus, h and L could both be in centimetres, and A in cm². In this case, a simple calculation will show that the number of plates is given by:

$$\mathfrak{N} = 2\pi\left(\frac{hL}{A}\right)^2. \tag{4.29}$$

This method was suggested by James and Martin (*5*).

Of these, the first is too slow for practical use, since there is no easy construction for measuring $\sigma_{(L)}$. The fourth method demands some means of measuring area, such as a planimeter, and also involves the measurement of two lengths in addition, so this is relatively slow, though it has occasionally been used. Methods (2) and (3) are both quick and easy to use, and the choice between them probably depends on personal preference. Each involves the measurement of two distances; method (2) involves making a construction (the point half-way up the peak); method (3) involves drawing three constructional lines, and probably the two methods take about an equal time. There is possibly more personal error involved in drawing the tangents than there is in measuring $\omega_{1/2}$, and therefore method (2) might be expected to be more reliable. However, consistent results are easily obtained with method (3).

4.6. Purity of Separation of Pairs of Solutes

The separation of two solutes has been described in terms of their relative retention and the plate-number of the column with respect to the two solutes. As illustrated by Fig. 1.4, both of these are relevant in determining the over-all separation, and this section describes quantitatively the way in which they do this. The over-all separation can be described by the percentage purity of the zones as they emerge from the column, but, since in most cases of interest the purity will be nearly 100%, it is more useful to define the percentage impurity rather than the purity.

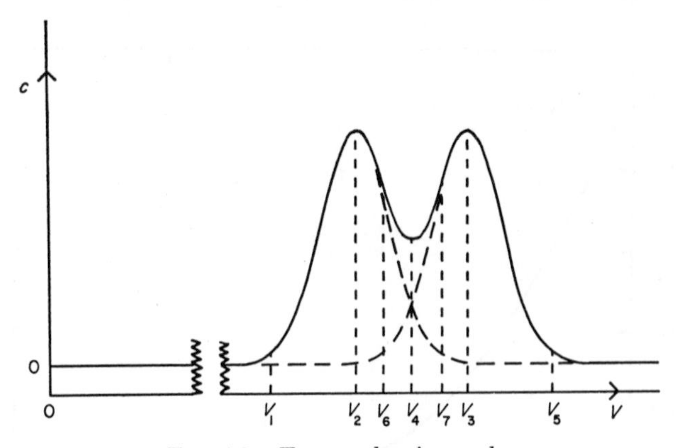

Fig. 4.6. Two overlapping peaks.

Figure 4.6 shows two slightly overlapping peaks, and it is evidently not possible to choose any two points on the volume axis between which an absolutely pure sample of either component could be obtained. In the figure shown, a nearly pure sample of A could be obtained between the limits V_1 and V_2; and of B between V_3 and V_5, but no single cut can be made so that material to the right is nearly pure A and to the left nearly pure B. In the case shown, where the area-proportions of A and B are equal, the sum of the impurity fractions obtained to the left and right of a single cut is a minimum when the impurity fractions are equal, and, in the case of two symmetrical peaks, the cut should be at the minimum of the col* between the peaks. Thus, the best possible single cut to obtain the purest possible samples of both A and B is at V_4. Gluekauf (*4*) has studied

* The word "col" is defined as a depression in a mountain chain.

the impurity fractions in this case as a function of the number of plates and the retention volumes of the two components. If the retention volumes are V_2 and V_3, and the number of plates is $\mathfrak{N}$, and if the impurity fraction of either component is $\eta_{1:1}$, Gluekauf gives:

$$\eta_{1:1} = 0.5 - \text{erf}\left[\frac{\sqrt{\mathfrak{N}}(\sqrt{V_3} - \sqrt{V_2})}{\sqrt[4]{V_2 V_3}}\right], \tag{4.30}$$

where

$$\text{erf}(x) = \frac{1}{\sqrt{2\pi}} \int_0^x \exp(-\xi^2/2)\, d\xi. \tag{4.31}$$

The error function, erf (x), is tabulated in many sources, for example in the "Handbook of Physics and Chemistry" (Section 3.4). A plot of 0.5 − erf (x) [sometimes called the complementary error function, erfc (x)] is given in Fig. 4.7. As expected its value drops sharply as x increases.

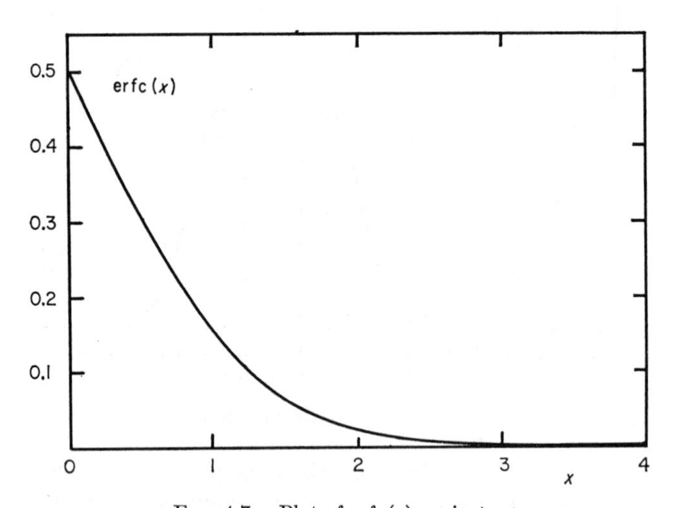

FIG. 4.7. Plot of erfc(x) against x.

Reference to tables shows that it becomes less than 0.01 (1%) when x exceeds 2.33 and less than 0.1% when x exceeds 3.08. Gluekauf (*4*) has given a plot of impurity fraction $\eta_{1:1}$ against plate-number $\mathfrak{N}$ with the ratio of the retention volumes as parameter (Fig. 4.8). This enables any two of $\eta_{1:1}$, $\mathfrak{N}$, and the ratio of retention volumes to be related with the third.

Equation (4.30) holds with accuracy only for cases in which the ratio of the retention volumes does not differ too much from unity, for, when this is not so, each peak will have a different value for $\mathfrak{N}$. However, with ordinary columns with performances of the order of thousands of plates, impurity fractions will be quite negligible before this factor begins to produce error in the use of Eq. (4.30). A little simplification of Eq. (4.30) makes it easier to use in the absence of a graph, and shows its structure more clearly. Let the ratio of the retention volumes of two solutes be expressed by a number greater than unity, and let

$$\frac{V_3}{V_2} = 1 + x, \tag{4.32}$$

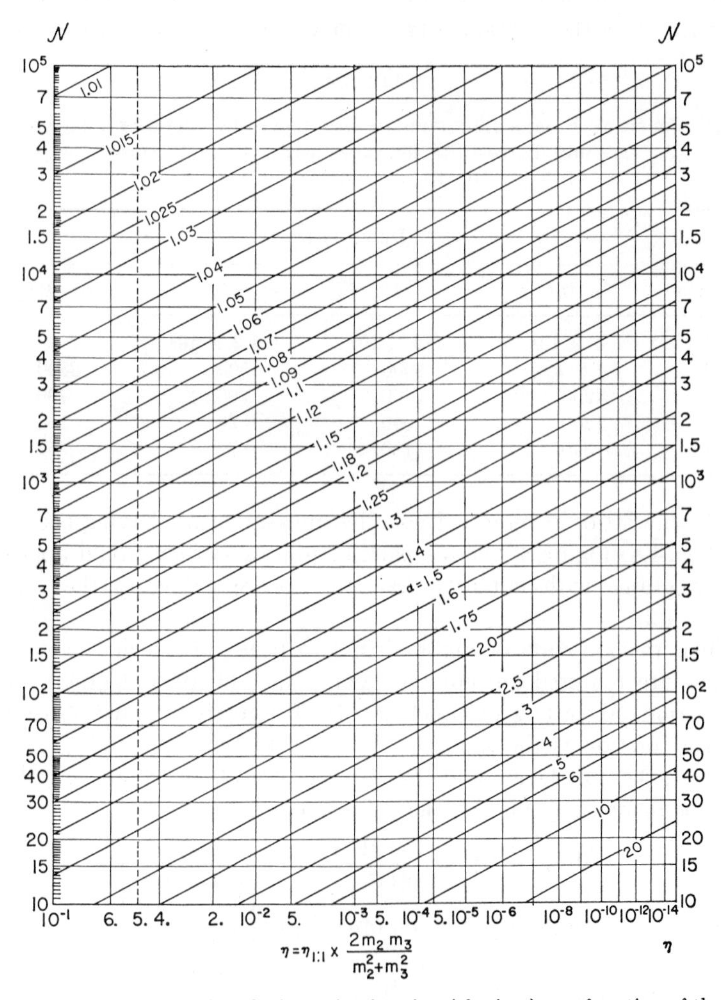

FIG. 4.8. Diagram giving the impurity fraction (abscissa) as a function of the number of plates (ordinate) with the ratio of retention volumes as parameter (*4*). From A. I. M. Keulemans, "Gas Chromatography." Reinhold, New York, 1957.

so that if the ratio is, for example, 1.2, then $x = 0.2$. In terms of x, Eq. (4.30) can be approximately rewritten

$$\eta_{1:1} = \operatorname{erfc}\left(\frac{x\sqrt{\mathfrak{N}}}{2}\right). \tag{4.33}$$

As with Eq. (4.30), this equation assumes equal peaks and a single cut at the col between them. It applies so long as impurity fractions are small.

It is useful to show a few examples of the use of Eqs. (4.30) and (4.33) to give an idea of the order of magnitude of the quantities involved. Table 4.2 gives the relation between plate-number and impurity fraction

TABLE 4.2

NUMBERS OF PLATES REQUIRED TO OBTAIN GIVEN IMPURITY FRACTIONS FROM PAIRS OF SUBSTANCES WITH GIVEN RATIOS OF RETENTION VOLUMES

Ratio of retention volumes	Impurity fraction (%)			
	0.1	1.0	5.0	10.0
1.01	4×10^5	2×10^5	1.2×10^5	7×10^4
1.05	1.6×10^4	9000	4500	2800
1.1	4200	2400	1200	700
1.2	1200	640	320	190
1.4	340	190	79	54

for different ratios of retention volumes, measurements having been made from Fig. 4.8. Figure 4.9 shows pairs of solutes as they would appear on chromatograms with impurity fractions corresponding to the columns in Table 4.2.

When the amounts of material in two peaks of which the impurity fractions are required are not the same, Eqs. (4.30) and (4.33) require modification. According to Gluekauf (*4*), if a cut is required so that the impurity fraction is the same in the zones to the right and to the left of the cut, then, if the amounts of material of peak are m_2 and m_3, the cut should be made at a point on the volume axis given by:

$$V = \sqrt{V_2 V_3} + \frac{2V_2 V_3}{\mathfrak{N}(V_3 - V_2)} \cdot \frac{m_2^2 - m_3^2}{m_2^2 + m_3^2}, \tag{4.34}$$

and the resulting impurity fraction of each zone is:

$$\eta_{m_2:m_3} = \frac{2m_2 m_3}{m_2^2 + m_3^2} \operatorname{erfc}\left\{\frac{\sqrt{\mathfrak{N}}(\sqrt{V_3} - \sqrt{V_2})}{\sqrt[4]{V_2 V_3}}\right\}. \tag{4.35}$$

Note that the cut is now no longer made at the col in between the two

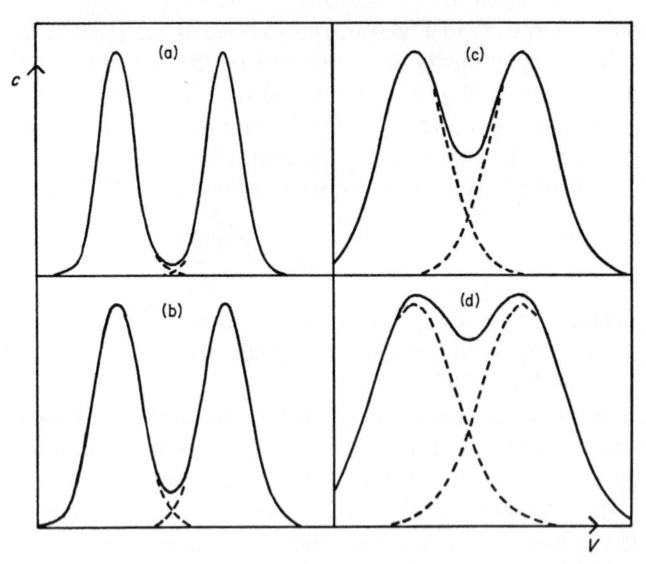

FIG. 4.9. Illustrations of overlapping peaks with given impurity fractions, see Table 4.2. (a) Impurity fraction 0.1%, (b) impurity fraction 1.0%, (c) impurity fraction 5%, (d) impurity fraction 10%.

peaks—indeed there may be no such col—but at a point which is nearer to the maximum of the peak of the minor component of the mixture. Also, since $2m_2m_3/(m_2^2 + m_3^2)$ is either less than or equal to unity, with a single maximum of unity when $m_2 = m_3$, the impurity fraction is less when the components are present in unequal amounts than when they are present in equal amounts. Figure 4.7 or Eq. (4.33) can still be used for cases where $m_2 \neq m_3$, with the quantity

$$\eta_{m_2:m_3} = \eta_{1:1}\left\{\frac{2m_2m_3}{m_2^2 + m_3^2}\right\} \tag{4.36}$$

replacing $\eta_{1:1}$, where $\eta_{m_2:m_3}$ is the corresponding impurity fraction. It should be noted that Eq. (4.36) holds whatever the units in which m_2 and m_3 are expressed, that the impurity fraction will be given in similar units, and that the position of the cut will give equal impurity fractions as expressed in those units. If measurements are made on peak areas, the units will be area units. If the relation between area and weight is the same for each substance in the incompletely resolved pair, then the impurity fractions will be given in weight units, but if not, m_2 and m_3 should be measured from the sample and not from the chromatogram.

The formulae so far given assume that two overlapping zones are separated by making the best possible single cut. In preparative work, a more likely procedure is to make two cuts, one each side of the col, for example, V_6 and V_7 in Fig. 4.6, and to discard the portion between the cuts. In this way, impurity fractions can be greatly reduced on account of the rapid decline in the value of erfc (x) with increase in x. A calculation derived from Eqs. (4.15) and (4.19) will show that for a peak of retention volume $V_R{}^0$, and plate-number $\mathfrak{N}$, the proportion of its area beyond a cut made at $V\dagger$, which may be either greater or less than $V_R{}^0$, is

$$\operatorname{erfc}\left\{\frac{|V_R{}^0 - V\dagger|\sqrt{\mathfrak{N}}}{V_R{}^0}\right\}. \tag{4.37}$$

This equation can be used, if required, to determine impurity fractions resulting from arbitrarily made cuts. Note that if $V_R{}^0 - V\dagger = \frac{1}{2}xV_R{}^0$, Eq. (4.37) gives Eq. (4.33).

Equation (4.33) is instructive in that it shows the relative importance of plate-number and the ratio of the retention, in determining the over-all separation of two solutes. Whereas the quantity x appears to the first power in the argument of the error function, the plate-number appears only to the power of $\frac{1}{2}$. Thus, doubling x is equivalent to multiplying the plate-number by 4, and the over-all separation is more sensitive to a change in the ratio of retention volumes than to a change in the plate-number.

Another means of defining the separation of the solutes is by the "Resolution" of two peaks. This quantity (*12*) has been accepted by the IUPAC committee in their preliminary proposals (*13*), and is defined by

$$R = \frac{2(L_3 - L_2)}{M_3 + M_2}, \tag{4.38}$$

where L_2, L_3, M_2, and M_3 are the distances L and M defined in Fig. 4.5 for each peak. The resolution, R, is easily related with the more precise impurity fraction. For two close peaks we shall assume $\mathfrak{N}_2 = \mathfrak{N}_3$, and $M_2 = M_3$; in this case, substitution of Eqs. (4.15), (4.32), and (4.28) yields

$$R = \frac{x\sqrt{\mathfrak{N}}}{4}, \tag{4.39}$$

so that

$$\eta_{1:1} = \operatorname{erfc} 2R \tag{4.40}$$

if the impurity fraction is small.

4.7. The Influence of Gas Hold-up on Resolution

The retention of solutes enters the definitions of impurity fraction and resolution as the ratio V_3/V_2. It is important to realise that this ratio is always smaller than the relative retention, for V_2 and V_3 each contain the gas hold up,

$$\frac{V_3}{V_2} = \frac{V_M + W\beta_3}{V_M + W\beta_2} = \frac{1 + k_3}{1 + k_2}, \tag{4.41}$$

where symbols are as in Chapter 2. In a case when the gas hold up is comparable with retention volume, there will be a considerable difference between V_3/V_2 and the relative retention, r_{23}, so that many more plates are required to obtain a given resolution than would be anticipated from the relative retention. It is seen that the larger the numerical value of the retardation ratio, k, the closer the ratio V_3/V_2 is to the limiting value, r_{23}. The distinction between relative retention and the ratio of retention volumes in determining the resolution can easily be included in the equations of the previous section, for,

$$x = \frac{1 + k_3}{1 + k_2} - 1 = \frac{k_3 - k_2}{1 + k_2} = (r_{23} - 1)\frac{k_2}{1 + k_2}, \tag{4.42}$$

so that, for close peaks, omitting the distinction between k_2 and k_3,

$$R = (r_{23} - 1)\frac{k}{1 + k} \cdot \frac{\sqrt{\mathfrak{N}}}{4} \tag{4.43}$$

and

$$\eta_{1:1} = \operatorname{erfc}\frac{1}{2}\left\{(r_{23} - 1)\frac{k}{1 + k} \cdot \sqrt{\mathfrak{N}}\right\}. \tag{4.44}$$

These relations have been discussed by Golay (*14*), Purnell (*15*), and by Loyd, Ayers, and Karasek (*16*). It is apparent that when k is large, Eqs. (4.43) and (4.44) tend towards Eqs. (4.33) and (4.39), since $(r_{23} - 1) \to x$ and $k/(1 + k) \to 1$. At the other limit, it is apparent that as $k \to 0$, $R \to 0$, whatever the values of $\mathfrak{N}$ or r_{23}. This corresponds to the circumstance referred to in Section 3.9, in which one might well fail to resolve two solutes with a very large relative retention on a very efficient column if both of them are virtually insoluble in the stationary phase. In practice, there is usually an optimum value of k, but, since this is determined by considerations such as the time required for the analysis and other variables concerned with the mechanism of column performance, it is discussed in the following chapter.

References

1. Martin, A. J. P., and Synge, R. L. M., *Biochem. J.* **35,** 1358 (1941).
2. Mayer, S. W., and Tompkins, E. R., *J. Am. Chem. Soc.* **69,** 2866 (1947).
3. Klinkenberg, A., and Sjenitzer, F., *Chem. Eng. Sci.* **5,** 258 (1956).
4. Gluekauf, E., *Trans. Faraday Soc.* **51,** 34 (1955).
5. James, A. T., and Martin, A. J. P., *Analyst* **77,** 915 (1952).
6. James, A. T., and Martin, A. J. P., *Biochem. J.* **50,** 679 (1952).

7. Margenau, H., and Murphy, G. M., "The Mathematics of Physics and Chemistry," 2nd ed. Van Nostrand, Princeton, New Jersey, 1956.
8. Craig, L. C., and Craig, D., *in* "Technique of Organic Chemistry" (A. Weissberger, ed.), Vol. III, Part 1. Interscience, New York, 1956.
9. Herington, E. F. G., *in* "Vapour Phase Chromatography," Proceedings of the First Symposium, London, May, 1956 (D. H. Desty, ed.), p. 30. Academic Press, New York, 1957.
10. Van Deemter, J. J., Zuiderweg, F. J., and Klinkenberg, A., *Chem. Eng. Sci.* **5,** 271 (1956).
11. Committee Recommendations, *in* "Vapour Phase Chromatography," Proceedings of the First Symposium, London, May, 1956 (D. H. Desty, ed.), p. xi. Academic Press, New York, 1957.
12. Jones, W. L., and Kieselbach, R., *Anal. Chem.* **30,** 1590 (1958).
13. "Preliminary Recommendations on Nomenclature and Presentation of Data in Gas Chromatography." See preprints of the Third Symposium on Gas Chromatography, Edinburgh, June, 1960.
14. Golay, M. J. E., *Nature* **182,** 1146 (1958).
15. Purnell, J. H., *J. Chem. Soc.*, p. 1268 (1960).
16. Loyd, R. J., Ayers, B. O., and Karasek, F. W., *Anal. Chem.* **32,** 698 (1960).

Chapter 5

Column Performance—Mechanisms

5.1. Broadening Factors and Column Variables

The principal criteria of quality in analytical columns are:

(1) plate-number, or column performance,
(2) resolution,
(3) time required for analysis.

The purpose of this chapter is to relate these criteria with all possible variables involved in the design and operation of columns, so that it is possible to design a column suitable for any particular analysis. There are many column variables each of which can influence all the criteria given above, and which in many cases affect the way in which another column variable influences the criteria; in other words, the column variables do not act independently. The description of the effect of column variables on the chromatography, therefore, is complicated and involves a large number of items of information.

In order to provide a formal scheme for the discussion, the ideal column defined in Chapter 1 will be taken as standard, for this is the best possible column as judged by the above criteria, in that two vapours with a relative retention infinitesimally different from unity are perfectly resolved in an infinitesimal time. Real columns depart from this standard in all three criteria, but in order to simplify the argument, we shall regard the first criterion as paramount, and the second two as subsidiary.

Real columns differ from the ideal column in that a zone of vapour broadens during elution. We shall specify the model of the column so that it contains a number of independent items each of which contributes to the broadening. The broadening factors each produce a variance σ_i^2 on an instantaneously introduced zone of sample, and we assume that they may be combined by the same rule that applies in the addition of the effects of independent sources of random error upon a distribution,

$$\sigma^2_{\text{total}} = \textstyle\sum_i \sigma_i^2. \qquad (5.1)$$

This equation will be used throughout the discussion. It is valid so long as the broadening factors are independent, but fails when the operation of one broadening factor affects the operation of another, as, for example, occurs in non-linear chromatography. In nearly all the literature of the subject, the conditions are such that Eq. (5.1) is valid. Its use is discussed by Klinkenberg and Sjenitzer (*1*) *inter alios.*

The expressions for the variances due to each broadening factor each contain a number of terms and parameters describing the column variables, so that the column variables can be related to the criteria of quality of the column through the specification of the broadening factors. The broadening factors to be discussed are:

(1) Non-zero rate of longitudinal diffusion of the vapour in the gas phase.
(2) Factors depending on the geometry of the column packing.
(3) Non-infinite rate of equilibration of the vapour with the stationary phase.
(4) Non-linearity of isotherms.
(5) Non-zero concentration of vapour in the gas phase.
(6) Unsharp input distribution of vapour.
(7) Non-zero time constant of the recording system.

Complementary to these are the column variables which affect the column performance either directly or through their effect on one or more of the broadening factors listed above:

(1) Column length (l).
(2) Flow rate ($\dot{V}$ or u).
(3) Partition coefficient (β).
(4) Mass of stationary phase per unit length of column (m).
(5) Pore volume per unit length of column (a).
(6) Temperature (T).
(7) Carrier gas.
(8) Size and shape of particles of column packing.
(9) Column diameter.
(10) Pressure drop across the column (P_i/P_o).
(11) Mass of vapour (w).

Sections 5.2 to 5.8 give the theory of the broadening factors. Following this, the effect of each of the column variables is discussed in Sections 5.9 to 5.20, using the broadening factors as the basis of discussion.

The actual broadening of a peak is measured by the standard deviation, σ, rather than by the variance, σ^2, so that it is apparent from Eq. (5.1) that the broadening produced by several broadening factors operating together is less than the sum of the broadenings produced by each, since

$$\sqrt{\textstyle\sum_i \sigma_i^2} < \textstyle\sum_i \sigma_i. \tag{5.2}$$

This is reasonable. A molecule of vapour slowed down relative to the mean on account of the operation of one broadening factor may well be speeded up by the operation of another, and vice versa, so that the total broadening is not as great as would be calculated by simple addition of the standard deviations due to each factor.

Equation (5.1) has a very important application in the general design of gas chromatographic equipment, for it shows that the total broadening produced by the operation of several broadening factors together is very much dominated by the factor giving the largest individual broadening. Consider, for example, two broadening factors which individually would contribute standard deviations of 10 and 2 cc. The broadening produced by both together is $\sqrt{104} = 10.2$ cc, so that even though the major broadening factor is only 5 times the minor, it contributes 98% to the total broadening, and the effect of the minor broadening factor is virtually negligible. In practical chromatography, this observation implies that in order to improve the over-all performance, it is more important to reduce the largest broadening factor than any other, and given that at least some broadening is inevitable, it is best to design and operate an apparatus so that all broadening factors are more or less equal. When a good column is used in bad conditions, it is the badness of the conditions that determines the performance, not the excellence of the column, and when a bad column is used in good conditions, it is the badness of the column and not the excellence of the conditions that determines the performance.

The reader who is primarily interested in the practical features of column design and operation but not in the theoretical background can omit Sections 5.2 to 5.6 inclusive and assume the results quoted in Section 5.9.

5.2. Broadening Due to Longitudinal Diffusion in the Gas Phase

A narrow and concentrated zone of vapour, such as is introduced into the beginning of a column, in time diffuses into a wider and less concentrated zone. This diffusion occurs whether the zone is stationary or being eluted through the column, and we shall assume here that the diffusion is the same in either case. The effect of this longitudinal diffusion on a zone as it is eluted through the column is shown in Fig. 5.1.

To calculate the variance produced by longitudinal diffusion, we make use of the assumption that the elution of the vapour does not affect the diffusion by adopting a length coordinate, w, the units of which are the

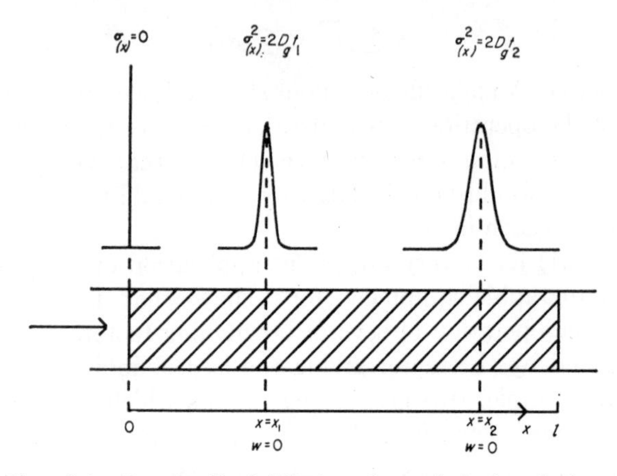

FIG. 5.1. Longitudinal diffusion of a peak during elution.

same as those of x, but the zero of which is always at the peak maximum, as indicated in Fig. 5.1. We assume that the diffusion obeys the one-dimensional diffusion equation,

$$D_g \frac{\partial^2 c}{\partial w^2} = \frac{\partial c}{\partial t}, \tag{5.3}$$

where D_g is the diffusion coefficient of the vapour in the carrier gas, and c, t, and w are as previously defined. The boundary condition for an initial delta-function distribution is

$$t = 0, \qquad c = \delta(w). \tag{5.4}$$

The solution to Eqs. (5.3) and (5.4) is

$$c(w, t) = \frac{1}{2\sqrt{\pi D_g t}} \exp\left(-w^2/4D_g t\right). \tag{5.5}$$

By comparison with Eq. (4.16), it is seen that $c(w, t)$ is a Gaussian function of w with a mean at $w = 0$ and a variance of

$$\sigma^2_{(x)} = \sigma^2_{(w)} = 2D_g t. \tag{5.6}$$

This equation for the diffusional spread of a sharp zone in one dimension is well known, and is sometimes referred to as Einstein's law of diffusion.

Equation (5.6) applies only to the portion of the vapour in the gas phase. An exactly similar equation applies in principle to the portion of the vapour dissolved in the stationary phase, as has been recognised, for example, by Khan (*2*). It appears, however, that longitudinal diffusion in the stationary phase, though it must inevitably occur to some extent, is always small enough to be negligible in comparison with other broadening effects. Since, therefore, only diffusion in the vapour phase is significant, the variance produced on the total sample of vapour is given by Eq. (5.6) multiplied by the proportion of vapour in the gas phase, which is $1/(1 + k)$, where k is as in Chapter 2.

Van Deemter, Zuiderweg, and Klinkenberg (*3*) have also considered the fact that the diffusion path available to the molecules of vapour is not given exactly by the coordinate x or w, since this fails to take into account the curves and twists in the diffusion paths introduced by the presence of the packing. Since the diffusion path is longer than is given by the coordinate x or w, the longitudinal diffusion is less than that anticipated by Eq. (5.6). If the ratio of the straight path to the average real path is called the "Tortuosity," γ, then the variance produced by the diffusion is equal to that calculated for the straight path multiplied by the tortuosity, which is a number always less than unity.

Applying the corrections for tortuosity and for the fact that longitudinal diffusion operates only on $1/(1 + k)$ of the vapour, Eq. (5.6) becomes:

$$\sigma^2_{(x)} = \frac{2D_g\gamma t}{1 + k} = \frac{2D_g\gamma V}{\dot{V}(1 + k)} = 2D_g\gamma \frac{x}{u} \tag{5.7}$$

where the other forms of writing are derived using the equations of Chapter 2. In volume units, the variance is:

$$\sigma^2_{(V)} = \frac{2D_g\gamma a(a + m\beta)V}{\dot{V}}. \tag{5.8}$$

It should be noted that the broadening produced in an initially sharp peak by longitudinal diffusion is symmetrical, so that the formulae given in Chapter 2 for retention volume and retention time are unaffected by this source of diffusion so long as measurements are made to the peak maximum.

5.3. Broadening Factors Dependent on the Geometry of Packing

In an ideal column, the input distribution is unaffected during the elution by the shape either of the particles of packing or of the column. In real packed columns, broadening occurs on account of the geometry of the column, though it is not always possible either in theory or practice to dissociate purely geometrical considerations from those which also involve diffusion.

Probably the most important geometrical factor, which applies with packed columns only, is the process in which the average speed of elution of a zone is different in different interstices of the packing. The specification of this in a form suitable for calculation is difficult, and has not yet been fully worked out. One may distinguish at least three general causes for the dispersion of elution speeds in the column:

(1) A dispersion of speeds in the interstices on account of the difference in size of different interstices, so that a molecule of carrier gas sometimes finds itself in a large interstice where the gas moves slowly and sometimes in a small interstice where the gas moves fast.

(2) A dispersion of speeds in the interstices because of differences in the viscous resistances of different paths through the packing.

(3) A dispersion of speeds of vapour molecules independent of the dispersion of carrier gas speed because of statistical fluctuations in the value of k in different interstices.

No specific analysis of any of these has been given, but their general effect on the broadening of an input distribution has been studied by Klinkenberg and Sjenitzer (*1*). These authors assume that the standard deviation of the transit time of a molecule of vapour crossing a cross section of the column the width of which is of the order of the average particle diameter, d_p, is proportional to the mean time of passage, d_p/u, where u is the average linear flow rate. Thus the variance in the average time of passage across d_p is given by:

$$(\sigma^2_{(t)})_{d_p} = 2\lambda \left(\frac{d_p}{u}\right)^2, \tag{5.9}$$

where λ is a constant. The variance given by this equation is reproduced in each of the cross sections of thickness d_p, of which there is a total of l/d_p in a column of length l. Hence, combining by Eq. (5.1) the variances given by Eq. (5.9) for all the cross sections in the column, the total variance is:

$$\sigma^2_{(t)} = \frac{l}{d_p}(\sigma^2_{(t)})_{d_p} = \frac{2\lambda l d_p}{u^2}. \tag{5.10}$$

This may be converted into length units for the case that the mean of the vapour distribution is at the end of the column,

$$\sigma^2_{(x=l)} = 2\lambda l d_p = 2\lambda d_p u t_m, \tag{5.11}$$

or to volume units, using Eq. (2.10),

$$\sigma^2_{(V)} = 2\lambda l d_p(a + m\beta)^2. \tag{5.12}$$

All the quantities in Eqs. (5.10)–(5.12) are known or knowable except for the constant λ which describes the dispersion occurring across d_p. Klinkenberg and Sjenitzer quote for this a few values obtained from experimentally measured variances. Klinkenberg has found a value of $\lambda = 2$ to 3 for beds of sand of 120 mesh. Values quoted from other work are $\lambda = 1.1$ for Raschig rings, and another value of 1.8. Data reported by Keulemans and Kwantes (*34*) obtained from gas chromatographic measurements suggest that the value of λ is greater the smaller the particles of packing. Thus, it varies from 8 for particles between 200 and 400 mesh to about unity for particles of 20 to 40 mesh.

The shape of the distribution resulting from the treatment leading to Eqs. (5.10)–(5.12) is easily shown to be Gaussian so long as $l \gg d_p$, which condition is usually satisfied. Comparison of the extreme right-hand side of Eqs. (5.11) and Eq. (5.6) suggests that the geometrical broadening described here is exactly analogous in effect to a longitudinal diffusion with a diffusion coefficient of

$$D = \lambda d_p u. \tag{5.13}$$

The regimens leading to the operation of Eqs. (5.10)–(5.12) have frequently been called "Eddy Diffusion." The use of this term, however, has been frequently criticised since the process causing the broadening is not a diffusion. A more descriptive term, "Anastomosis," has been used by Golay, the word being borrowed from physiology, where it refers to the complicated interconnections of blood capillaries.

The treatment of geometrical factors given above is incomplete, and indeed is not very informative, for ignorance of the broadening they produce is merely replaced by ignorance of a coefficient, λ. The value of the above treatment, therefore, depends on the invariance of λ. There is little doubt that λ is a function of particle size, and it is reasonable to suppose that the more regular the packing, the smaller is the value of λ (Section 5.17). Of greater interest is the variation of λ with the average velocity, u; this can be examined in gas chromatographic experiments by a technique described in Section 5.10. The evidence is mixed. Thus in one set of experiments, Gluekauf (*4*) has shown that, in effect, λ is a function of u, but in other experiments in different circumstances (*5*) he found that λ was independent of u. Again, experiments by Bohemen and Purnell (*6*) and by Littlewood (*7*) suggest that, in effect, λ is a function of u. Giddings (*8*) has remarked on these inconsistencies, and has suggested that, in addition to the general causes of dispersion such as are suggested at the beginning of this section, there is also a process in which vapour at different concentrations in adjacent interstices on account of anastomosis can also diffuse laterally. According to Giddings, this leads to Eq. (5.11) being replaced by an equation of the form:

$$\sigma^2_{(x)} = \frac{2xu}{Ku + K'} \tag{5.14}$$

in which the dispersion becomes smaller the slower the flow. The derivation of this equation, however, has been criticised by Klinkenberg and Sjenitzer (*9*), and indeed it seems unreasonable that the dispersion due to anastomosis should be completely removed in the limiting case of zero flow. It is clear that this topic, which has considerable relevance especially in the design of preparative columns, is incompletely worked out.

In much current practice, columns are coiled into helices in order to save space. This results in the gas path along the inside being smaller than that along the outside, and thus contributes a variance to the peak. It has been studied theoretically by Giddings (*10*), who finds that, if it is assumed that the coiling has no effect on the homogeneity or permeability of the packing, the broadening is given by:

$$\sigma^2_{(x)} = \frac{7uxr^4}{48R^2D_g}, \tag{5.15}$$

where r is the radius of the column and R is the radius of the helix into which the column is wound. With ordinary analytical columns, in which $r \ll R$ and r is small, the effect is small, but with wide columns, e.g., preparative columns, even a single right-angled bend may produce a very large variance, and render useless any other precautions taken to secure a small total variance.

5.4. Broadening Due to Non-Instantaneous Equilibration of Vapour

(a) *Qualitative Explanation*

In linear chromatography, which is to be assumed in all the following discussion, the ideal equation $q = \beta c$ should be replaced by

$$q = \beta c f(t), \tag{5.16}$$

where $f(t)$ is some function attaining the value of unity only when the time t is large, since, in a real column, the vapour does not equilibrate instantaneously. The way in which the operation of Eq. (5.16) leads to peak broadening is illustrated in Fig. 5.2, in which the column is idealised as in Fig. 1.1, and a peak produced as a result of the ideal equation $q = \beta c$ is compared with the peak produced as a result of Eq. (5.16). In ideal chromatography, the ratio q/c is constant at every point inside the zone of vapour, so that the distributions in each phase are similar in shape, and differ only in the factor β along the ordinates. In non-ideal linear chromatography, however, q/c is no longer constant. As soon as the front profile of the zone in the gas phase meets a clean region of stationary phase, vapour starts to dissolve, but equilibrium is not reached at once, so that in the front profile the ratio q/c is less than β, and as a result undissolved vapour in the gas phase moves further along the column than it would in the ideal case. At the rear profile of the zone, the reverse happens; as the zone in the gas phase

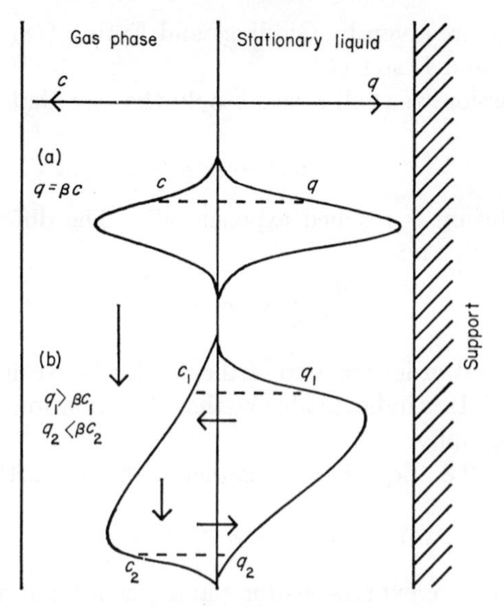

FIG. 5.2. Comparison of (a) peak shapes in ideal chromatography with (b) those broadened by non-instantaneous equilibration of the vapour with the stationary phase.

moves along, vapour leaves the stationary phase to try to maintain equilibrium, but cannot do so instantaneously, so that $q/c > \beta$, and vapour remains in the stationary phase longer than it would have done had the column been ideal. Throughout the zone, the vapour is always trying to keep up with equilibrium, but can never quite do so before the zone in the gas phase has moved on. The result of this on the shape of the peaks is illustrated in the figure, where it is seen that the different conditions in the two profiles require that the peaks are asymmetrical as shown, and broader than in the ideal case.

(b) *Quantitative Theory*

The quantitative study of broadening due to slow equilibrium, or finite rate of mass transfer, is similar in kind to the calculation given in Section 2.3 in which the equation of the chromatogram is obtained from the conservation equation, a relation between q and c, and the initial conditions. In linear non-ideal chromatography, the only difference is the substitution of Eq. (5.16) for Eq. (2.5). The problem has been studied by many authors, including Gluekauf (*11*), Lapidus and Amundsen (*12*), Klinkenberg and Sjenitzer (*1*), Thomas (*13*), and with special reference to gas chromatography by van Deemter, Zuiderweg and Klinkenberg (*3*), Golay (*14*,*15*), Young (*16*), and Funk and Houghton (*17*). Similar results obtained by the stochastic theory are given by Giddings and Eyring (*18*) and by Beynon, Clough, Crooks, and Lester (*19*).

In this discussion we shall consider only the case that Eq. (5.16) takes the form

$$q = \beta c(1 + K'e^{-Kt}), \tag{5.17}$$

in which equilibrium is reached exponentially. The differential equation corresponding to this is:

$$\frac{dq}{dt} = K(\beta c - q), \tag{5.18}$$

and describes a first order reaction of the vapour between the phases with a rate constant K. It is indicated below that this equation generally applies in gas chromatography.

As in Section 2.3, Eq. (5.18), together with Eq. (2.4) and the initial conditions:

$$q(0, x) = 0, \qquad c(V, 0) = \delta(V) \tag{5.19}$$

may be solved to give expressions for c and q as a function of any two of the variables x, t, and V. The solutions for c and q are:

$$c(V, x) = \frac{K}{\dot{V}}\left(\frac{m\beta x}{V - ax}\right)^{1/2} I_1\left\{2\frac{K}{\dot{V}}[m\beta x(V - ax)]^{1/2}\right\}$$
$$\exp\left[-\frac{K}{\dot{V}}(m\beta x - ax + V)\right] + \exp\left(-\frac{K}{\dot{V}}m\beta x\right)\delta(V - ax) \tag{5.20}$$

and

$$q(V, x) = \frac{\beta K}{\dot{V}} I_0\left\{2\frac{K}{\dot{V}}[m\beta x(V - ax)]^{1/2}\right\}$$
$$\exp\left[-\frac{K}{\dot{V}}(m\beta x - ax + V)\right], \tag{5.21}$$

where, in addition to the symbols used in Chapter 2, $I_0(z)$ and $I_1(z)$ are the Bessel functions of the zeroth and first order of purely imaginary argument iz, and are tabulated in many sources, e.g., "Handbook of Chemistry and Physics" (*20*).

The second term in Eq. (5.20) represents the original input distribution swept through the column at the same speed as the carrier gas, and decaying exponentially. The rate of decay is normally so great that this term is negligible after the first few millimetres of the column, and the term will not be considered further.

When the argument of the Bessel functions in Eqs. (5.20) and (5.21) is large,

$$I_n(z) \approx \frac{e^z}{\sqrt{2\pi z}}, \tag{5.22}$$

which holds within about 1% or less for $z > 10$. If this approximation is substituted into the first term of Eq. (5.20),

$$c(V, x) \approx \frac{K^{1/2}}{\sqrt{4\pi\dot{V}}} \cdot \frac{(m\beta x)^{1/4}}{(V - ax)^{3/4}} \exp\left[-\frac{K}{\dot{V}}(\sqrt{m\beta x} - \sqrt{V - ax})^2\right]. \tag{5.23}$$

The equation of the chromatogram of a peak emerging from a column of length l is $c(V)$ for $x = l$. In this case, the two terms in the exponent in Eq. (5.23) are equal when $V = V_R^0$ from Eq. (2.11). The equation for the chromatogram may therefore be written:

$$c(V) \approx \frac{K^{1/2}}{\sqrt{4\pi\dot{V}}} \cdot \frac{(V_R^0 - V_M)^{1/4}}{(V - V_M)^{3/4}} \exp\left[-\frac{K}{\dot{V}}(\sqrt{V_R^0 - V_M} - \sqrt{V - V_M})^2\right]. \tag{5.24}$$

If it is now assumed that the effective total width of the peak is only a small fraction of its retention, so that we need consider the chromatogram only in the region where $V_R^0 - V$ is small compared to V_R^0, the approximation:

$$(\sqrt{z} - \sqrt{z + \Delta z})^2 \approx \frac{(\Delta z)^2}{4z} \tag{5.25}$$

may be substituted in Eq. (5.24), yielding:

$$c(V) \approx \frac{K^{1/2}}{\sqrt{4\pi\dot{V}V'}} \exp\left(-\frac{K(V_R^0 - V)^2}{4\dot{V}V'}\right). \tag{5.26}$$

Comparison with Eq. (4.19) shows that this is the equation of a Gaussian curve with a variance of

$$\sigma^2_{(V)} = \frac{2\dot{V}V'}{K}, \tag{5.27}$$

and a mean of V_R^0. Thus, in conditions in which approximations (5.22) and (5.25) are valid, the result of the finite rate of mass-transfer is to broaden the delta-function input distribution into an approximately Gaussian distribution with the same mean as if the broadening factor were absent. In these conditions, therefore, retention volumes remain unaffected. In length units, the variance is

$$\sigma^2_{(x)} = \frac{2kux}{(1 + k)^2 K}, \tag{5.28}$$

where k is as in Chapter 2, u is the linear flow rate, and x is the position of the mean.

It is apparent from Eq. (5.26) that the broadening is appreciable even when the asymmetry is not, for otherwise it would not be possible to make approximations giving a finite variance belonging to a symmetrical distribution.

(c) *Specification of the Rate Constant, K*

There are several ways in which a non-infinite rate constant in Eq. (5.18) may be conceived, of which three will be considered here:

(1) Slow diffusion of vapour in the stationary phase.
(2) Slow diffusion of vapour in the gas phase.
(3) A process akin to chemical reaction at the interface of the phases.

These three are illustrated in Figs. 5.3a, b, and c, and all three together in Fig. 5.3d.

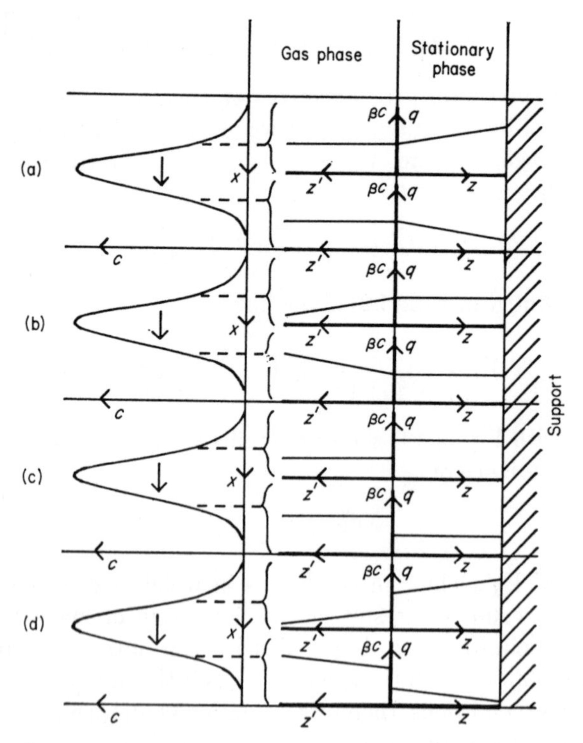

FIG. 5.3. Concentrations of vapour as a function of a coordinate in cross sections of the gas phase and the stationary phase in the front and rear profiles of peaks for various possible causes of non-equilibrium: (a) Non-instantaneous diffusion through the stationary phase. (b) Non-instantaneous diffusion through the gas phase. (c) Discontinuity in chemical potential at the surface of the stationary phase. (d): (a), (b), and (c) operating together.

(d) *Slow Diffusion in the Stationary Phase*

A finite time is required for vapour in the stationary phase to diffuse to and from the interface between the phases. When this is the only factor, $q = \beta c$ at the interface, but within the stationary phase there is a concentration gradient in which the concentration is too small in the front profile and too large in the rear profile of a peak, as shown in Fig. 5.3a.

It may be shown that the effect of slow diffusion within the stationary phase is equivalent to a first order reaction at the surface, so that Eq. (5.18) holds (*3*). The rate constant, K, may be seen intuitively to be proportional to the area of the surface, A, the diffusion coefficient of the vapour in the stationary phase, D_l, and inversely proportional to the thickness of the liquid layer, d_f. Furthermore, since the larger the volume of the stationary phase per unit length of column (m/ρ), the more vapour must diffuse to increase the average concentration a given amount, the rate constant is also inversely proportional to this. Thus, the expression for K is:

$$K \propto \frac{\rho A D_l}{m d_f}. \tag{5.29}$$

The constant of proportionality has been assumed by van Deemter, Zuiderweg, and Klinkenberg (*3*) to be the constant which is obtained if the rate constant is determined by diffusion into an even layer of stationary phase of constant thickness d_f; in this case the constant is $\pi^2/4$. The authors use this constant, at the same time recognising that it applies only to an ideal case, since in a real packed column, the thickness of stationary phase is by no means constant. With this value of the constant, and also making use of the fact that if d_f is assumed constant,

$$A d_f = m/\rho, \tag{5.30}$$

then the value of the rate constant is given by:

$$K = \frac{\pi^2}{4}\frac{D_l}{d_f^2}. \tag{5.31}$$

Thus the variance due to the operation of slow diffusion in the stationary phase is:

$$\sigma^2_{(V)} = \frac{8}{\pi^2} \cdot \frac{d_f^2 \dot{V} V'}{D_l}, \tag{5.32}$$

or

$$\sigma^2_{(x)} = \frac{8}{\pi^2} \cdot \frac{d_f^2 u}{D_l} \cdot \frac{kx}{(1+k)^2}. \tag{5.33}$$

(e) *Slow Diffusion of the Vapour in the Gas Phase*

A finite time is required for vapour molecules in the middle of the carrier gas stream to diffuse to the surface of the stationary phase, as illustrated in Fig. 5.3b. The problem is more complicated than in the previous case, since, in addition to the lateral diffusion, the characteristics of viscous flow are such that gas streams in different parts of the cross section of the gas phase are moving at different speeds. It is shown below that the slow diffusion of the vapour in the gas phase usually only produces a significant variance on a peak in the case of capillary columns, where the geometry is particularly simple, and in this case exact equations for the variance can be calculated. With packed columns, approximate equations can be given; these are discussed in Section 5.19.

In the case of a cylindrical tube such as a capillary column, the problem of determining the magnitude of the dispersion in the vapour phase can be regarded in three successive steps, the final result applying to real capillary columns:

(1) Dispersion because of the viscous flow in a tube without stationary phase.

(2) Dispersion also considering a stationary phase in which equilibrium is instantaneous.

(3) Dispersion also considering a stationary phase in which equilibrium is non-instantaneous.

The first of these has been considered by Taylor (*21*) for cylindrical tubes and by Aris (*22*) for tubes of arbitrary cross section. The dispersion caused by viscous flow in cylindrical tubes can be explained as follows. Vapour in the tube flows faster in the centre than at the outside, so that if we imagine a distribution of vapour initially constant across the tube, the action of the flow of gas is to move the centre of the distribution further along the tube than the outside; a contour of constant concentration initially planar is distorted by the flow into a paraboloid, as shown in Fig. 5.4.

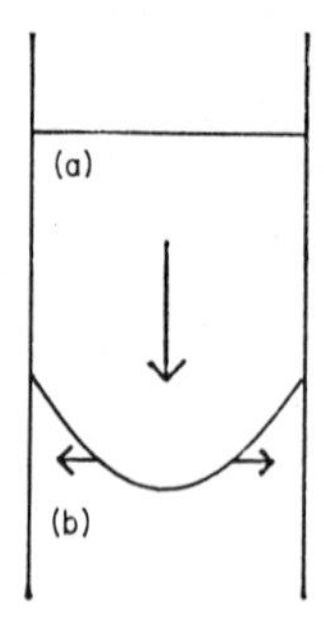

FIG. 5.4. Flow and diffusion in a cylindrical tube. An initially planar concentration contour as at (a) is distorted by viscous flow into the paraboloid (b). If the contour is in a region with more concentrated vapour behind it, lateral diffusion occurs as indicated by the horizontal arrows. If the contour is in a region with less concentrated vapour behind it, lateral diffusion occurs against the arrows.

This process, if allowed to continue undisturbed, would produce a very large variance in an initially compact distribution averaged across the tube, but the dispersion is reduced by the action of lateral diffusion, by which regions of great concentration in the centre of the tube in the front profile diffuse into regions of small concentration at the edges, and regions of great concentration at the edges of the tube in the rear profile diffuse into regions of small concentration at the centre. If the rate of lateral diffusion (considered independently of longitudinal diffusion) is fast compared to the flow of gas, the dispersion due to viscous flow is nullified. Taylor has calculated that the dispersion for cylindrical tubes of radius r is

$$\sigma^2_{(x)} = \frac{r^2ux}{24D_g} \tag{5.34}$$

where u is the average linear flow rate, and Golay, also giving the above result, finds that the dispersion for rectangular tubes with sides z and $y (y \gg z)$ is

$$\sigma^2_{(x)} = \frac{4z^2ux}{105D_g}. \tag{5.35}$$

Golay has considered the next two stages of the argument. In the case that there is a retentive stationary phase in which equilibrium is instantaneous, the variance produced in cylindrical columns is

$$\sigma^2_{(x)} = \frac{1 + 6k + 11k^2}{(1 + k)^2} \cdot \frac{r^2ux}{24D_g} \tag{5.36}$$

and in flat rectangular columns is

$$\sigma^2_{(x)} = \frac{1 + 6k + 51k^2/2}{(1 + k)^2} \cdot \frac{4z^2ux}{105D_g}. \tag{5.37}$$

In these equations, the expressions in k have their smallest values when $k = 0$ indicating that the retentive stationary phase increases the variances due to viscous flow.

Finally, Golay (*15*) has considered the additional effect of slow diffusion in the stationary phase, and finds that it adds a further variance independently of lateral diffusion in the gas phase, in accord with Eq. (5.1). In the case of cylindrical tubes, this variance is

$$\sigma^2_{(x)} = \frac{k^3}{6(1 + k)^2} \cdot \frac{r^2ux}{\iota\alpha^2D}, \tag{5.38}$$

where α is the partition coefficient defined by Eq. (3.1). This equation becomes identical with Eq. (5.33) after suitable transformation, with the constant $8/\pi^2$ replaced by the constant $\frac{2}{3}$. The variance for flat rectangular tubes is

$$\sigma^2_{(x)} = \frac{2k^3}{3(1 + k)^2} \cdot \frac{z^2ux}{\alpha^2D_\iota}. \tag{5.39}$$

(f) Processes Equivalent to Chemical Reaction at the Interface

There is little, if any, experimental evidence in gas chromatography for the effect of a discontinuity in chemical potential at the interface between the phases, though experience in other fields of science suggests that such a discontinuity must be present. Khan (*2*) has proposed that the interfacial resistance can be accounted for in gas chromatography by assuming a first order reaction at the surface, as described by Eq. (5.18), in which the rate constant is given by:

$$K = \frac{Ak_2}{a_2}, \tag{5.40}$$

where k_2 is the rate constant for the desorption of the vapour from the stationary phase, a_2 is (proportional to) the area of the column cross section occupied by the stationary phase, and A is the surface area of stationary phase per unit length of column. A similar term, proposed to account for possible non-instantaneous diffusion of vapour through a stagnant film of gas on the surface of the stationary phase, has been given by Jones [see Kieselbach (*23*)].

(g) Comparison of Magnitudes of Different Variances

The relative magnitudes of the variances produced by lateral diffusion in each phase of a capillary column can be demonstrated by dividing Eq. (5.36) by Eq. (5.38) to give:

$$\frac{\sigma^2_{(x)g}}{\sigma^2_{(x)l}} = \frac{3}{48} \cdot \frac{r^2}{d_f^2} \cdot \frac{D_l}{D_g} \cdot \frac{1 + 6k + 11k^2}{k}, \tag{5.41}$$

where the additional subscripts to the variances refer to gas and liquid phase. The corresponding equation for packed columns cannot be specified exactly, but may be assumed to have the same form with different constants, d_f being interpreted as an average, and r being replaced by half the average interstice dimension.

When k is of the order of unity, as is common in capillary columns operated for rapid analysis or for optimum resolution per second (Section 5.14), the orders of magnitudes of quantities in Eq. (5.41) can be seen by simplifying it to the approximation:

$$\frac{\sigma^2_{(x)g}}{\sigma^2_{(x)l}} \approx \frac{r^2}{d_f^2} \cdot \frac{D_l}{D_g}. \tag{5.42}$$

Values of D_g are of the order of 10^{-2} to 10^{-1} cm^2/second in most carrier gases; values of D_l for the sort of vapours and the sort of stationary liquids used in gas chromatography have been little studied, but the evidence is that they are of the order of 10^{-7} to 10^{-6} cm^2/second, decreasing with increase in the viscosity of the solvent. Thus the ratio D_l/D_g is of the order of 10^{-5}. In capillary columns, d_f is small compared to r in order to minimise σ and for other reasons discussed in other parts of this chapter, and therefore the ratio of r^2/d_f^2 is large. In much current usage, d_f is of the order of the wavelength of light, e.g., 10^{-5} to 10^{-4} cm (0.1 to 1μ), and r is of the order of 10^{-1} cm, so that the ratio is of the order of 10^3. In these circumstances, therefore, Eq. (5.42) shows that $\sigma_g^2 \approx 10\sigma_l^2$, and that diffusion in the gas phase is the more important. For large values of k, Eq. (5.41) shows that the relative importance of gas diffusion becomes still greater. This is shown for capillary columns by Desty and Goldup (*24*), who find that the variance due to mass transfer increases with increase in retention volume. This subject is discussed further in Sections 5.12 to 5.14.

With packed columns, the circumstances may be different, especially when the packing contains much stationary phase. It is found in practice that on most common porous packings with of the order of 10% by weight of stationary phase, d_f is of the order of 10^{-3} cm, while r interpreted as half the average linear dimension of an interstice is of the order of 10^{-2} cm. In this case, the ratio r^2/d_f^2 is only of the order of 10^2, so that for $k \approx 1$, $\sigma_g^2 \approx 10^{-3}\sigma_l^2$, and virtually all the dispersion of the peak is caused by diffusion in the stationary phase. These considerations led van Deemter *et al.* (*3*) to ignore diffusion in the gas phase. When, however, packed columns are made with small proportions of stationary phase and operated with such large values of β that k is large in spite of the small value of m, the circumstances may be such that gaseous diffusion in packed columns is no longer negligible, as is shown in results given by Kieselbach (*23*).

(*h*) *The Range of Validity of Approximations* (*5.22*) *and* (*5.25*).

When Approximations (5.22) and (5.25) fail, the peaks are not Gaussian and the equations given for the variances also fail.

Transformation of the argument of the Bessel function in Eq. (5.20) for the case that $x = l$ yields:

$$z \approx 2Kkt_M, \tag{5.43}$$

where t_M is the gas hold-up time. For packed columns, use of the typical figures given in Section 5.4(g) together with Eq. (5.31) shows that K is of the order of 10^{-1} to 10^0 second^{-1}. In much current practice, t_M is of the order of 10 to 100 seconds, depending on the column length and the flow rate, so that it is apparent from Eq. (5.43) that with short columns, fast flow rates, and/or small values of k, z may well be less than 10, so that there are conditions in common use in which Approximation (5.22) may be invalid.

With capillary columns, K is much larger; if it is assumed that σ_g provides the only significant peak dispersion due to mass-transfer, use of typical figures together with Eqs. (5.28) and (5.36) show that K is of the order of 10 to 10^2 second^{-1}. On the other hand, very much smaller values of k are commonly used with capillary columns, e.g., $k = 0.05$ is not unreasonable. In these circumstances also, therefore, Approximation (5.22) may be invalid.

Similar considerations will also show that Approximation (5.25) is also invalid for peaks with small values of k. The result is that either with excessively small values of k, or with large linear flow rates, or with columns in which, for one reason or another, K is excessively large, the corresponding peaks are unsymmetrical with sharp front profiles. This observation is commonplace in gas chromatography, and, though it may sometimes be due to other causes, e.g., a sluggish recording system, there are many cases where it is not. In these circumstances, retention times measured to peak maxima fail to obey the equations of Chapter 2, and retention volumes calculated from such retention times do not have their characteristic invariance.

5.5. Effect of the Linearity of Isotherms on Broadening

Calculations of peak shapes and variances in non-ideal gas chromatography with a non-linear isotherm equivalent to those of the previous sections have not been made because of the mathematical complexity. If a particular non-linear isotherm is specified, however, the system of differential equations defining the chromatography can be set up, and these can be solved numerically, if not analytically. Funk and Houghton (*17*) have demonstrated this using a digital computer with the isotherm:

$$c = K_1 qP + K_2 q^2 P^2, \tag{5.44}$$

where P is the total pressure and K_1 and K_2 are constants.

The case of non-linear ideal chromatography has been considered by DeVault (*25*). Imagine a zone of vapour with any form of input distribution, e.g., a Gaussian distribution, and consider the chromatography of this in a column in which the vapour has a Langmuir-type isotherm (Fig. 1.6). The front of the front profile of the distribution is at a small concentration, and will start to be eluted through the column at a speed determined by the initial slope of the isotherm. Regions of greater concentration, however, move more rapidly, thus leading to unsymmetrical peaks as described in Section 2.10. If the curvature of the isotherm is considerable, or the column is of sufficient length, the difference in speeds of the front profile and the maximum may be such as would make the peak maximum overtake the front profile, if such a situation were possible or had any meaning. In the case of an ideal column, DeVault shows that the peak maximum crowds up on the front profile until the front profile eventually becomes infinitely sharp, and the equation of the chromatogram contains a discontinuity. This discontinuity moves through the column at a speed determined by the isotherm and the height of the discontinuity, while the rear profile, the concentration in which is always small, moves at a slower speed determined by the initial slope of the isotherm. A similar argument applies in the case of the anti-Langmuir isotherm, the discontinuity now being in the rear profile. In either case, the sharp profile moves at a different speed to the diffuse profile with the result that, though the column is ideal, the zone broadens during its elution. This contrasts with the case of ideal chromatography with a linear isotherm.

In practice, the above processes applying to ideal columns are modified by anastomosis, diffusion, and non-instantaneous equilibrium, with the result that the discontinuity becomes diffuse, and after a certain period of elution a steady state is set up on which, on the one hand, the column is trying to produce a discontinuity on account of the curvature of the isotherm, and on the other hand, diffusional and rate processes are tending to make the sharp profile more diffuse. If the elution takes longer than is required to establish the steady state, as is common, additional length to the column does not affect the shape of the sharp front, but, of course, increases the diffuseness of the diffuse front. This is seen clearly in Fig. 3.18, where, in the first three peaks, the elution is too fast and the isotherms

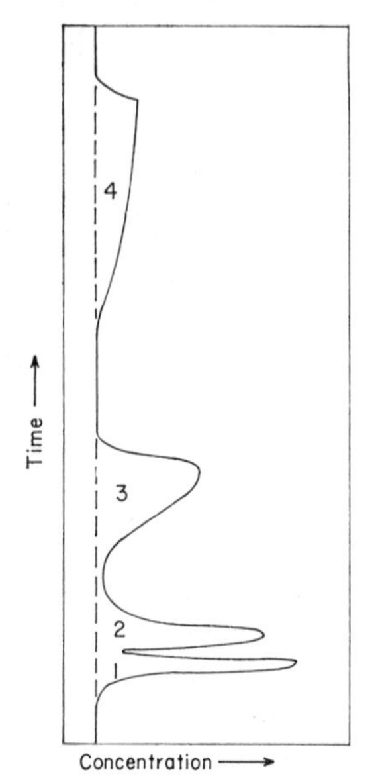

FIG. 5.5. Chromatogram illustrating steady-state sharp rear profiles to peaks eluted from columns with very curved anti-Langmuir type isotherms. After James and Phillips (*26*). Methyl, ethyl, *n*-propyl, and *n*-butyl acetates on tricresyl phosphate at 56°C.

are insufficiently curved for the front profile to reach the steady state, the fourth peak is intermediate, and, with the fifth peak, there is a front profile the width of which is determined solely by diffusion, together with a long diffuse rear profile. Exactly the same occurs for anti-Langmuir isotherms, as is illustrated in Fig. 5.5 (*26*).

5.6. Broadening Due to the Concentration of Vapour in the Gas Phase

When the concentration of vapour within the peak is large, the effect is similar in kind to that produced by a Langmuir type isotherm, for the carrier gas velocity within the peak is greater than elsewhere, with the result that the peak maximum is carried forward with respect to the outside regions of the peak. The effect of the vapour concentration on elution and saturation profiles has been studied by Bosanquet and Morgan (*27*) and by Bosanquet (*28*), as described in Section 2.10.

Bosanquet (*28*) has presented experimental results for the sharpness of saturation and elution fronts in the form of values of

$$S = \frac{\pm (t_{90} - t_{10})}{t_{50}}, \tag{5.45}$$

where the t's are elution times measured to the point where the front is at a concentration level the percentage of saturation of which is indicated by the subscript (Fig. 5.6). Values of S for elution and saturation profiles

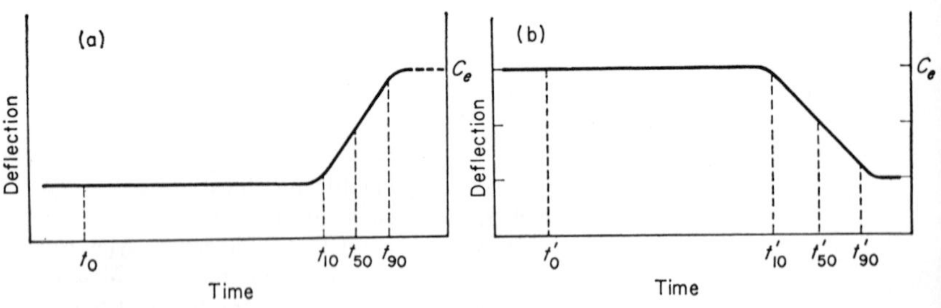

Fig. 5.6. Saturation (a) and elution (b) curves showing t_{10}, t_{50}, and t_{90}. Bosanquet and Morgan (*27*).

for various values of the saturation concentration are given in Table 5.1. In order to appreciate the significance of the figures in ordinary gas chromatography, a peak may be regarded as adjacent saturation and elution profiles, so that the sum of the S values for elution and saturation fronts is equivalent to the peak width. It is seen that when the concentration

TABLE 5.1

EXPERIMENTAL *S*-VALUES OF SATURATION AND ELUTION FRONTS FOR DIFFERENT VAPOUR CONCENTRATIONS[a]

Concentration of vapour (%)	*S* for saturation front	*S* of elution front	Sum of *S*-values of each front
0			0.204
3	0.081	0.125	0.206
5	0.070	0.148	0.218
7	0.061	0.165	0.226
9	0.054	0.184	0.238
20	0.035	0.37	0.41
30	0.027	0.66	0.69

[a] From Bosanquet (*28*).

is small, the widths of elution and saturation fronts differ but little, but as the concentration rises, the saturation fronts become sharper, and the elution fronts more diffuse. The significant observation is, however, that in all cases the sum of the two profiles increases with increasing concentration, so that the finite vapour concentration leads to a net broadening.

A further source of broadening which increases with vapour concentration is caused by ordinary non-linearity in partition chromatography. This happens particularly in cases in which activity coefficients at infinite dilution are considerably greater than unity. The plot of P_2 against x_2 for these is given by line *FD* in Fig. 3.2. If this plot is turned on its side, it

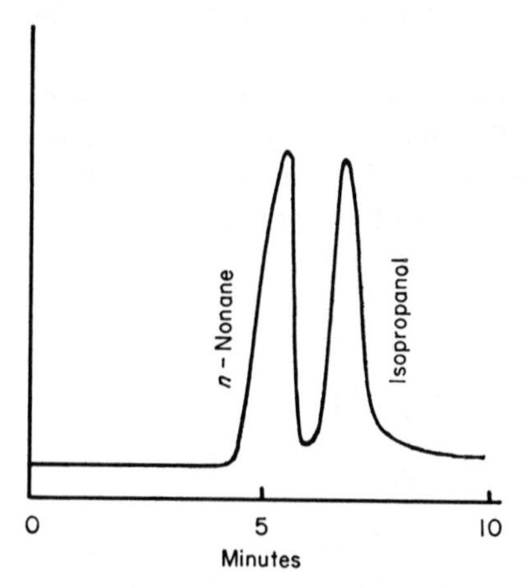

FIG. 5.7. Chromatogram of *n*-nonane and isopropanol on polyethylene glycol 1500 at 70°C, illustrating the asymmetry resulting from a large activity coefficient.

becomes the isotherm of the vapour, the P axis representing the concentration in the vapour phase, and the x axis representing that in the solvent phase. Comparison with Fig. 1.7 shows that the curve is of the anti-Langmuir type, so that peaks have diffuse front profiles and sharp rear profiles. The operation of the effect is shown in Fig. 5.7, which shows a chromatogram of n-nonane (b.p. 151°C) and isopropanol (b.p. 81°C) on polyethylene glycol. Both have comparable retention volumes, but the n-nonane has a large activity coefficient, and shows considerable asymmetry, while the isopropanol has a small activity coefficient, and is symmetrical.

5.7. Broadening Due to the Input Distribution of the Vapour

So far the discussion has assumed that the sample is introduced to the input to the column in an infinitely sharp zone. In practice this is impossible, since the zone of vapour occupies a finite volume at least equal to the volume of pure vapour at the inlet pressure, and usually greater because of dilution with the carrier gas. As discussed in Section 2.9, two extreme input distributions are: (1) a plug of gas of constant concentration (Fig. 2.6a); (2) a distribution of great initial concentration, subsequently falling exponentially (Fig. 2.6b). Of these, the first results when the sample injector has a finite volume equal to the volume of the plug which is completely swept out without mixing by one such volume of carrier gas; the second results when the vapour and the carrier gas can mix freely in the sample injector, so that it requires more than one passage of carrier gas to clean the sample injector cavity. In practice, the actual distribution usually lies between these.

For practical purposes, it is important to know the effect of the volume of the input distribution on the column performance. This may be done as follows. Let the input distribution have a variance σ_I^2, let the column produce a variance of σ_C^2, and let the variance of a peak produced by the column on the input distribution have a variance of σ_T^2, all in volume units. Then, by Eq. (5.1):

$$\sigma_T^2 = \sigma_C^2 + \sigma_I^2. \tag{5.46}$$

Substituting for σ_C^2 with Eq. (4.15),

$$\sigma_T^2 = \sigma_I^2 + \frac{(V_R^0)^2}{\mathfrak{N}}, \tag{5.47}$$

where $\mathfrak{N}$ is the true plate-number of the column. If σ_I^2 is known, therefore, the variance of the resulting peak may be determined.

In practice, a plate-number resulting from the column and input distribution combined would be measured from the chromatogram by the equation:

$$\mathfrak{N}' = \frac{(V_R{}^0)^2}{\sigma_T{}^2}, \tag{5.48}$$

where $\mathfrak{N}'$ is a phenomenological quantity less than $\mathfrak{N}$. If this is substituted into Eq. (5.47), the result is:

$$\mathfrak{N}' = \mathfrak{N} \cdot \frac{(V_R{}^0)^2}{\mathfrak{N}\sigma_I{}^2 + (V_R{}^0)^2}. \tag{5.49}$$

This shows clearly the effect of the input distribution on the performance of the apparatus as a whole. As $\sigma_I \to 0$, $\mathfrak{N}' \to \mathfrak{N}$; as σ_I increases, $\mathfrak{N}'$ decreases, until when σ_I is sufficiently large that $\mathfrak{N}\sigma_I{}^2 \gg (V_R{}^0)^2$, $\mathfrak{N}'$ is inversely proportional to the variance of the input distribution.

Further light may be thrown on Eq. (5.49) by dividing the right-hand side by $(V_R{}^0)^2$, resubstituting the left-hand side in Eq. (5.48), and rearranging, to give:

$$\frac{\sigma_T}{V_R{}^0/\sqrt{\mathfrak{N}}} = \left[\frac{\sigma_I{}^2}{(V_R{}^0)^2/\mathfrak{N}} + 1\right]^{1/2}. \tag{5.50}$$

If the right-hand side of this is plotted against $\sigma_I\sqrt{\mathfrak{N}}/V_R{}^0$ (Fig. 5.8), the result is independent of the true plate-number of the column or the retention volume of the vapour. When σ_I is small in relation to $V_R{}^0/\sqrt{\mathfrak{N}}$, $\sigma_T = V_R{}^0/\sqrt{\mathfrak{N}}$, which is its smallest value. As σ_I rises in relation to

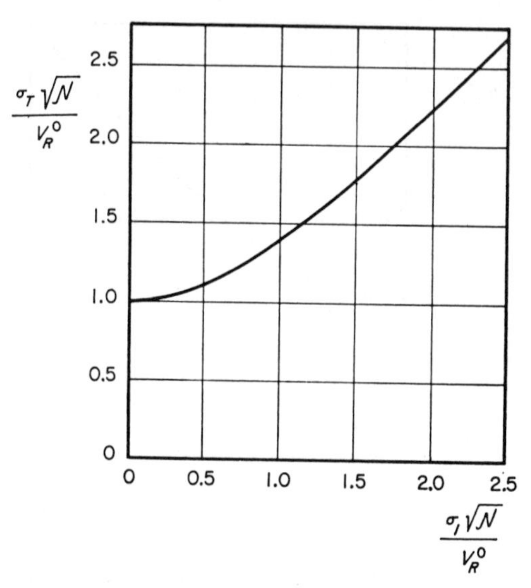

FIG. 5.8. Plot of $\sigma_T\sqrt{\mathfrak{N}}/V_R{}^0$ against $\sigma_I\sqrt{\mathfrak{N}}/V_R{}^0$ according to Eq. (5.50).

$V_R{}^0/\sqrt{\mathfrak{N}}$, σ_T rises compared to $V_R{}^0/\sqrt{\mathfrak{N}}$. It is seen from the curve that if

$$\sigma_I < \approx 0.2 \frac{V_R{}^0}{\sqrt{\mathfrak{N}}} = 0.2\sigma_C, \tag{5.51}$$

then the effect of the input distribution on the performance is negligible. In the case of plug flow in which the volume of the plug is V_I,

$$\sigma_I = V_I/3, \tag{5.52}$$

so that Inequality (5.51) becomes:

$$V_I < \approx 0.6 \frac{V_R{}^0}{\sqrt{\mathfrak{N}}}. \tag{5.53}$$

This equation was calculated in this connection by van Deemter, Zuiderweg, and Klinkenberg (*3*), and has been frequently quoted. It should be noted that there is no special significance in the factor 0.6 (the above authors, in fact, quote 0.5), which is merely a coefficient providing a threshold below which the effect of the input distribution is less than a certain amount.

The above treatment, though simple, suffers from the defect that σ_T is hard to specify when the effect of the sample injector is so bad that the resulting peak is appreciably flat-topped. This is avoided in the more complicated treatment given by van Deemter *et al.* (*3*), who use the quantity M as constructed in Fig. 4.5 in place of σ_T, and plot $M\sqrt{\mathfrak{N}}/V_R{}^0$ against $V_I\sqrt{\mathfrak{N}}/V_R{}^0$ in place of Fig. 5.8 (Fig. 5.9). It is observed that the plots are

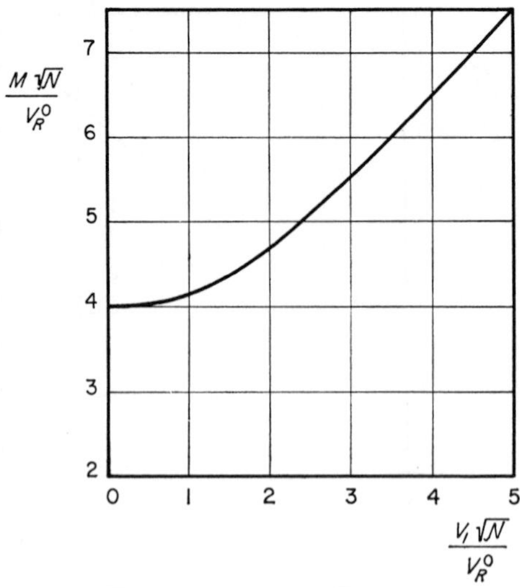

FIG. 5.9. Plot of $M\sqrt{\mathfrak{N}}/V_R{}^0$ against $V_I\sqrt{\mathfrak{N}}/V_R{}^0$ according to van Deemter, Zuiderweg, and Klinkenberg (*3*).

virtually identical apart from the scales, and give exactly the same information in slightly different ways.

5.8. Broadening Due to the Time Constant of the Detecting System

The possibility of a time lag between the true effluent concentration in the detector and the indication of this concentration by the recorder is a factor in the chain of events between the introduction of a sample and the measurement of the results, although it is not really a broadening factor produced by the chromatographic process. For example, in Fig. 5.10, the peak which should appear as in (a) may appear as in (b) or (c), in which the lag in the recording system causes too small a reading when the concentration is rising and too large a reading when the concentration is falling. In gas chromatography, we are interested in the effect of this lag on three

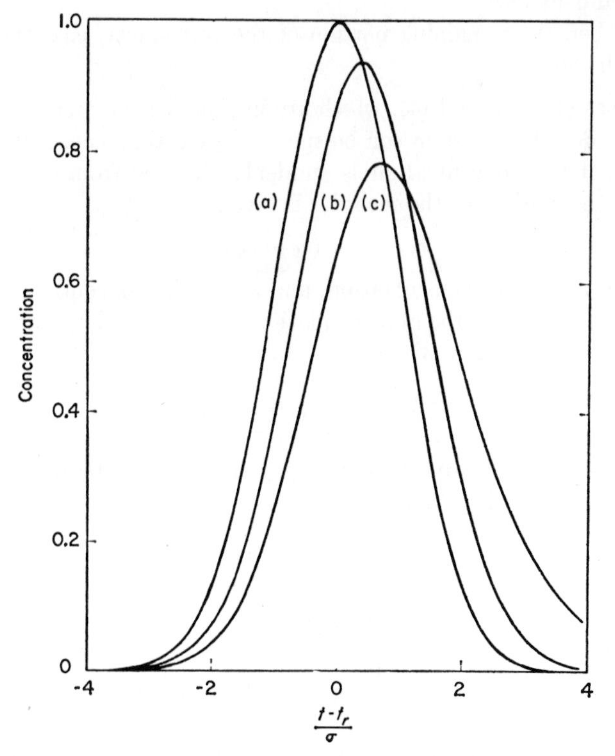

Fig. 5.10. (a) Plot of a Gaussian peak $[c(t)]$ emerging from a column. (b), (c) Plots of $z(t)$ for $k/\sigma = 0.4, 1.0$. From Schmauch (*29*).

parameters of the chromatogram, (a) the position of the peak maximum, (b) the variance, and (c) the peak area, for quantitative analysis. Aspects of the problem have been studied by Schmauch (*29*) and by Johnson and Stross (*30*).

Lag between effluent concentration and its registration can arise in several ways, e.g.:

(1) Non-zero detector volume in which complete mixing occurs (*29,30*). The detector takes time to fill and to empty, during which periods the concentration in the detector lags behind that emerging from the column.

(2) Non-zero detector volume in which different parts of the sensing element of the detector sense different regions of the volume of the detector, not all of which can contain vapour at the true effluent concentration (*29*). This applies, for example, to catharometers consisting of wires coaxially in a tube carrying the effluent and (presumably) to gas density balances.

(3) When the sensing element of the detector is fed by diffusion, as when it is placed in a short side-arm leading from the tube carrying the column effluent (*29*).

(4) When the remaining portion of the transducer, e.g., the recorder, is sluggish (*30*).

In cases (1), (3), and (4), which are in practice the most common, the lag in the detecting system can be specified by a time constant, k, defined such that if the concentration is suddenly changed from a value c_0 to c_1 at $t = 0$, the reading of the recorder is given by

$$c_1 - c = (c_1 - c_0)e^{-t/k}. \tag{5.54}$$

If $c(t)$ is the effluent concentration, and $z(t)$ is the concentration recorded by a detector obeying the above equation, then $z(t)$ and $c(t)$ are related by the usual first order equation,

$$\frac{dz(t)}{dt} = \frac{1}{k}(c(t) - z(t)). \tag{5.55}$$

Making use of the condition that in practice, $z(t) = c(t)$ when $t = 0$, the general solution to Eq. (5.55) is:

$$z(t) = \frac{e^{-t/k}}{k}\int c(t)e^{t/k}\,dt. \tag{5.56}$$

In the case that the effluent appears as a Gaussian distribution, $c(t)$ can be written:

$$c(t) = \frac{A}{\sigma\sqrt{2\pi}}\exp\left[-(t_R - t)^2/2\sigma^2\right] \tag{5.57}$$

and Eq. (5.57) substituted into Eq. (5.56) gives an explicit equation for $z(t)$. This cannot be expressed analytically, but $z(t)$ may be plotted with the aid of tables of the error function, or may be expanded as a series. Curves for $z(t)$ as a function of $(t_R - t)/\sigma$ for two values of k/σ are given in Fig. 5.10 (*29*). It is apparent from Eq. (5.55) that the maximum of all such curves lies on $c(t)$.

The effect of the detector time constant on the maximum of the recorded peak is indicated in Fig. 5.10. When, for a given peak, $k \ll \sigma$, it may be shown by expansion of Eqs. (5.56) and (5.57) that the apparent added retention time is approximately equal to k, the time constant of the recording system. The above condition usually holds in practice; if it does not, then the effect of the detector lag can be found only by calculation.

The effect of the lag of the detecting system on the apparent variance of a peak is most easily assessed using Eq. (5.1). The detector lag superimposes a broadening process described by an exponential curve [Eq. (5.54)] on the real effluent distribution. The variance due to this is easily shown to be equal to k^2. Thus, if the variance of the real distribution is σ^2 and that of the recorded distribution is σ'^2, then

$$\sigma'^2 = \sigma^2 + k^2. \qquad 3)$$

The effect of the detector lag on the peak area is very simply described—there is none, for the areas of $z(t)$ and $c(t)$ are equal. Thus quantitative analysis is not affected by the lag.

5.9. Equations for Plate-Height

Having now described the broadening factors and the variances they produce, we now start to discuss the effect of individual column variables on the column performance, the resolution, and the time of analysis. Since column performances are normally expressed in terms of plate-heights or plate-numbers, we give below a summary of the relations between variances expressed in different units, and the relation of the variances to H and $\mathfrak{N}$, using Eq. (4.15) and the equations of Chapter 2:

$$\sigma_{(V)} = (a + m\beta)\sigma_{(x)} = a(1 + k)\sigma_{(x)} = \dot{V}\sigma_{(t)} = ua\sigma_{(t)}, \qquad (5.59)$$

$$(1 + k)\sigma_{(x)} = u\sigma_{(t)}, \qquad (5.60)$$

$$\frac{\sigma^2_{(V)}}{(V_R{}^0)^2} = \frac{H}{l} = \frac{1}{\mathfrak{N}}, \qquad (5.61)$$

$$\frac{\sigma^2_{(x)}}{x} = H = \frac{l}{\mathfrak{N}}. \qquad (5.62)$$

It is apparent from Eqs. (5.61) and (5.62) that the plate-height is proportional to the peak variance, so that Eq. (5.1) implies that each broadening factor may be regarded as adding a term to H. This idea is used in the classical equations given below.

It is usual to add together the variances due to the column itself, but to exclude those due to other parts of the apparatus and those due to non-linearity, etc., for which no precise equations can be given. In packed columns, the principal variances are those due to anastomosis, longitudinal diffusion, and slow diffusion in the stationary phase, the variances for which are given by Eqs. (5.7), (5.11), and (5.33). If these are added according to Eq. (5.1), and the total variance substituted in Eq. (5.62), the result is:

$$H = 2\lambda d_p + \frac{2\gamma D_g}{u} + \frac{8}{\pi^2} \cdot \frac{d_f^2}{D_l} \cdot \frac{k}{(1+k)^2}. \tag{5.63}$$

This equation was first given by van Deemter, Zuiderweg, and Klinkenberg (*3*), and has since become well known, usually carrying van Deemter's name. The equation is extensively used in the discussion given below. Several sets of experiments have shown that, though this equation is approximately true, there are circumstances in which it fails, and there have been several attempts at producing revised equations (*2,6,23,31*). The need to revise the first term was referred to in Section 5.3; the need for additional terms due to lateral diffusion in the gas phase and possible discontinuity at the surface were considered in Section 5.4. Such extra terms, however, are better considered separately, and for explaining the observed behaviour of packed columns, Eq. (5.63) may usually be left unmodified.

In capillary columns, anastomosis is absent, while longitudinal diffusion in the gas phase and lateral diffusion in both phases may be important. The three variances are given by Eq. (5.11) substituting unit tortuosity, Eq. (5.36), and Eq. (5.38). Together with Eqs. (5.1) and (5.62) these yield:

$$H = \frac{2D_g}{u} + \frac{1 + 6k + 11k^2}{24(1+k)^2} \cdot \frac{ur^2}{D_g} + \frac{k^3}{6(1+k)^2} \cdot \frac{ur^2}{\alpha^2 D_l}. \tag{5.64}$$

This equation is given by Golay (*15*), and often carries his name.

5.10. Effect of Column Length on Performance

It may be seen from any of the equations given for σ in the preceding sections that $\sigma_{(x)}^2 \propto x$, and therefore that H is a constant and independent of the length of the column. This justifies the use of the idea of theoretical plates. It is shown in Section 5.19, however, that H is only constant throughout the column or independent of the column length when the pressure drop across the column is small. The result is that usually the plate-number is rather less than proportion to its length. For example,

DeWet and Pretorius (*32*) find that a packed column of 500-cm length has the equivalent of 2404 plates, and that a similarly constructed column of 5000-cm length operated similarly has the equivalent of 17,605 plates, which is considerably less than 10 times as many as the shorter column. Few workers have investigated the relation between $\mathfrak{N}$ and l in circumstances where the pressure drop is not significant, possibly because the linear relation is considered axiomatic. Scott (*33*), however, shows that $\mathfrak{N} \propto l$ at least up to $\mathfrak{N} = 20{,}000$, $l = 50$ feet if the ratio of inlet to outlet pressure is reduced by means of an outlet choke (Section 5.16).

In connection with column length, it should be emphasised that though the column performance is measured by $\mathfrak{N}$, the resolution (column properties other than length being constant) is proportional to $\sqrt{\mathfrak{N}}$, so that the resolution is proportional to the square root of the length. Thus, double the resolution requires four times the length.

5.11. Effect of Flow Rate on Performance

The carrier gas flow rate has a large effect on the performance of a column, and this variable has been extensively studied.

(a) *Packed Columns*

The first term of the van Deemter equation, Eq. (5.63), does not include the flow rate, the second term contains it in the denominator, and the third term contains it in the numerator. Thus, for a general discussion of the effect of flow rate, the equation can be simplified to:

$$H = A + \frac{B}{u} + Cu, \tag{5.65}$$

where

$$A = 2\lambda d_p, \tag{5.66}$$

$$B = 2\gamma D_g, \tag{5.67}$$

and

$$C = \frac{8}{\pi^2} \cdot \frac{k}{(1+k)^2} \cdot \frac{d_f^2}{D_l}, \tag{5.68}$$

and are in principle not functions of flow rate. Equation (5.65) was first given by Keulemans and Kwantes (*34*). It is the equation of a hyperbola, the general shape of the positive part of which is shown in Fig. 5.11. The curve has a minimum in the H.E.T.P. when

$$H = A + 2\sqrt{BC} \tag{5.69}$$

at a flow rate of

$$u = \sqrt{B/C}. \tag{5.70}$$

For best column performance in a given column, this flow rate is an optimum. It is apparent that longitudinal diffusion is important at slow flow rates, when the vapour resides for a long time in the column, while non-equilibrium is important at fast flow rates, in which case there is little time for equilibration before the zone has passed on. It can be seen that C matters at fast flow rates, B matters at slow flow rates, and all matter at or near the optimum flow rate.

Experimental curves of H.E.T.P. as a function of flow rate have been given by many authors (*6,33–36*) and the general shape of such curves is that of Fig. 5.11. Typical experimental curves are shown in Fig. 5.12 (*7*).

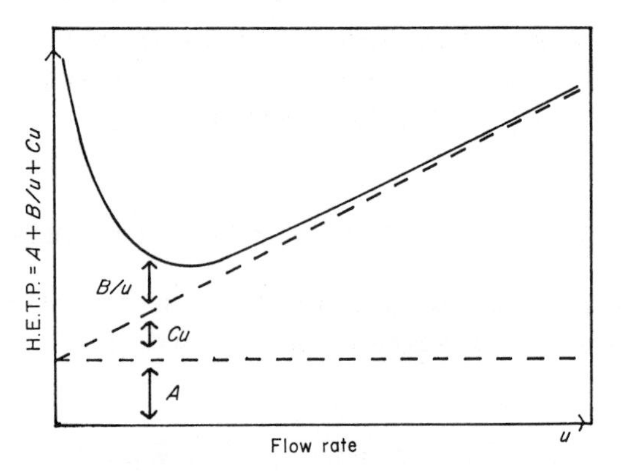

FIG. 5.11. Theoretical plot of Eq. (5.65).

In some cases in the literature, a curve described by Eq. (5.65) has been fitted to the experimental points instead of the experimental points being used to define the form of the curve. There are, however, a few sets of results in which the accuracy of the equation is examined. Kieselbach (*23*) has fitted data to a form of Eq. (5.65) in which the C term contains several variances, and has evaluated the constants from many measurements using the least squares technique, and reports that the fit is good. Similarly, Littlewood (*7*) reports that the residuals obtained on fitting Eq. (5.65) to experimental data are random, indicating that Eq. (5.65) is at least as accurate as his experiments. Bohemen and Purnell (*6*), using columns with firebrick as the support, find that Eq. (5.65) gives a good fit with the experimental points in most circumstances, but, in certain circumstances, the parameter A has a negative value; Littlewood finds a similar result if the pressure drop across the column is considered in calculating the parameters (Section 5.19). Negative values of any contribution to the plate-height are unreasonable, and this result has been interpreted by Bohemen and Purnell as evidence that A is not truly independent of flow,

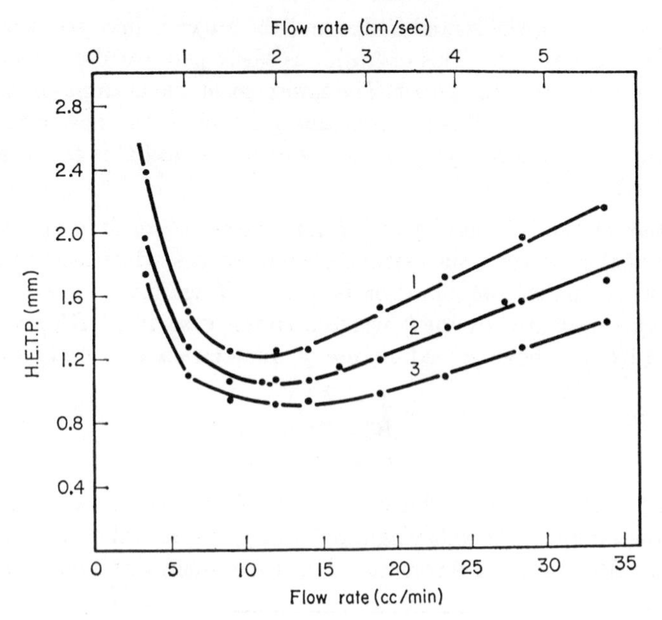

FIG. 5.12. Experimental curves illustrating Eq. (3.65). 1, 2-methyl pentane; 2, *n*-heptane; 3, *n*-octane. From Littlewood (7).

as is discussed in Section 5.3. Other authors, however, find reasonable values for A, so that we may conclude that Eq. (5.65) should better be expressed

$$H = (A + f(u)) + \frac{B}{u} + Cu, \tag{5.71}$$

where $f(u)$ is an unspecified function depending on the packing, and may or may not be small.

Equation (5.65) is useful in the discussion of column design for two reasons: (a) it gives a concise description of the variation of efficiency with flow rate, and (b) it can be used to eliminate the flow rate as a variable, so that the discussion of the other column variables can be made entirely in terms of the parameters A, B, and C, subject to the limitations of the equation discussed above. In order to determine values of A, B, and C from experimental data, it is necessary to determine plate-heights (Section 4.5) as a function of flow rate. The parameters may then be conveniently obtained by standard methods of numerical analysis or by a graphical technique. A suitable graphical technique is:

> Plot H against u (Fig. 5.11). Construct the asymptote to the curve at fast flow rates by placing a transparent straight edge in the approximate position of the asymptote, and adjusting it until the vertical

distance between the straight edge and the curve is inversely proportional to the flow rate. This operation is easily performed if the plot is made on finely squared paper. The intercept of the asymptote on the ordinate $u = 0$ is A, B is the constant product of the flow rate and the distance between asymptote and the curve, and C is the slope of the asymptote.

Alternative methods involve plotting Hu against u^2, or H/u against $1/u$, but both of these involve the extrapolation of curves, which is an uncertain procedure. A further simplification is to plot H against $\dot{V}$, since it is the latter that is measured by the flowmeter. In this case, if A^*, B^*, and C^* are measured by the above procedure, use of the relation $\dot{V} = au$ gives:

$$\begin{aligned} A &= A^* \\ B &= B^*/a \\ C &= C^*a. \end{aligned} \tag{5.72}$$

Values of A, B, and C differ widely according to the design and operation of the columns. The following tabulation gives the orders of magnitude of the quantities for packed columns of the type commonly used in analysis:

A	$\approx$ 0–1 mm
B	$\approx$ 10 mm²/second
C	$\approx$ 0.001–0.01 second
$H_{\min}$	$\approx$ 0.5–2 mm
u_{opt}	$\approx$ 1–10 cm/second

(b) Capillary Columns

The principal difference between capillary columns and packed columns with respect to H.E.T.P. as a function of u is the absence of the A term and the uncertainty in interpreting it. For capillary columns, the equivalent of Eq. (5.65) is derived from Eq. (5.64), and is:

$$H = \frac{B}{u} + Cu, \tag{5.73}$$

where C contains the terms giving the effect of lateral diffusion in both phases and of interfacial resistance to mass transfer if this factor is appreciable. This equation gives a similar plot to that of Fig. 5.11, with $A = 0$. Many examples are given by Desty and Goldup (*24*).

There is special interest in this equation in the case that the layer of stationary phase is thin enough that the term for diffusion in the stationary phase is negligible, so that

$$H = \frac{2D_g}{u} + \frac{1 + 6k + 11k^2}{24(1 + k)^2} \cdot \frac{ur^2}{D_g}. \tag{5.74}$$

From this, it is easily found (*37*) that when k is small,

$$\begin{aligned} H_{\min} &= 0.57r \qquad (0.57 = \sqrt{1/3}), \\ u_{\text{opt}} &= 6.9D_g/r \qquad (6.9 = \sqrt{48}), \end{aligned} \tag{5.75}$$

and when k is large,

$$\begin{aligned} H_{\min} &= 1.9r \qquad (1.9 = \sqrt{11/3}), \\ u_{\text{opt}} &= 2.1D_g/r \qquad (2.1 = \sqrt{48/11}). \end{aligned} \tag{5.76}$$

If the above assumption is justified, as is discussed in Section 5.4(d), typical values for a capillary column of 1 mm diameter would be

$$H_{\min} \approx 0.2 - 1 \text{ mm},$$
$$u_{\text{opt}} \approx 5 - 10 \text{ cm/second},$$

and these figures appear to be typical of current practice.

(*c*) *Other Broadening Factors Dependent on Flow Rate*

The variance due to the detector can be divided into two parts, that due to the time required to sweep out the volume of the detector cavity (σ_D), and that required for the transducer to respond (σ_T). It is apparent that

$$\sigma_{(t)D} \propto \frac{1}{\dot{V}}, \qquad \sigma_{(t)T} = \text{const},$$

and

$$\sigma_{(V)D} = \text{const}, \qquad \sigma_{(V)T} \propto \dot{V}. \tag{5.77}$$

Therefore, for peaks that come through in a fast *time* on account of a fast flow rate, the variance due to the transducer is of primary importance, but for peaks which come through in a small *volume*, whether the flow rate be slow or fast, the variance due to the detector volume is of primary importance.

5.12. Effect of Partition Coefficient on Performance

(*a*) *Packed Columns*

The partition coefficient affects the performance of packed columns largely through its effect on the parameter C of Eq. (5.65). There is a small effect on B, since in general the larger the partition coefficient, the more complex the vapour molecule, and the smallèr the value of D_g. This effect is rarely significant, however, since it is small in any case, and flow rates are commonly greater than optimum, so that the contribution of the B term to H is small.

The expression for C, Eq. (5.68), contains the partition coefficient explicitly in the form

$$\frac{k}{(1+k)^2}, \equiv \frac{a/m \cdot \beta}{(a/m+\beta)^2}. \tag{5.78}$$

The expression has a maximum when $k = 1$, tends to zero as k tends to zero, and tends to $1/k$ as k becomes large. In packed columns, k is generally considerably greater than unity (see Section 2.4), so that because of the above expression, C decreases with increase in partition coefficient.

Expression (5.78), however, does not express the whole of the dependence of C on the partition coefficient, for the diffusion coefficient D_l declines with increase in the size of vapour molecules. Since D_l is on the denominator of the expression for C, the larger the vapour molecules, the larger is C on account of this effect, and, since large molecules have large partition coefficients, the change in D_l opposes the explicit effect of the change in β. It appears from experiment that k usually increases more rapidly than the diffusion coefficient decreases when β increases, so that the net result is that C decreases with an increase in retention volume, though not as fast as suggested by expression (5.78). Hence the commonly observed result that in packed columns, the larger the retention volume, the smaller the plate-height, particularly at fast flow rates. This is illustrated in Fig. 5.12, and in more detail by Littlewood's results shown in Table 5.2. It is seen that, as the retention volume rises, the value of C

TABLE 5.2

VALUES OF C, k, AND $C(1+k)^2/k = d_f^2/D_l$ FOR VARIOUS VAPOURS ON A COLUMN OF TRICRESYL PHOSPHATE PACKED ON GLASS BEADS AT 60°C[a]

Vapour	C (seconds)	k	d_f^2/D_l (seconds)
Carbon dioxide	0.00	0.00	—
cis-2-Butene	0.013	0.19	0.067
2-Methyl pentane	0.035	1.16	0.14
n-Heptane	0.024	3.81	0.14
n-Octane	0.021	8.92	0.23
Toluene	0.009	23.3	0.23
p-Xylene	0.009	53.7	0.48

[a] From Littlewood (7).

declines; the effect of the diffusion is shown by dividing the quantity $k/(1+k)^2$ out of C, so that the residue is proportional to d_f^2/D_l. This quantity is seen to increase with increasing retention volume, corresponding

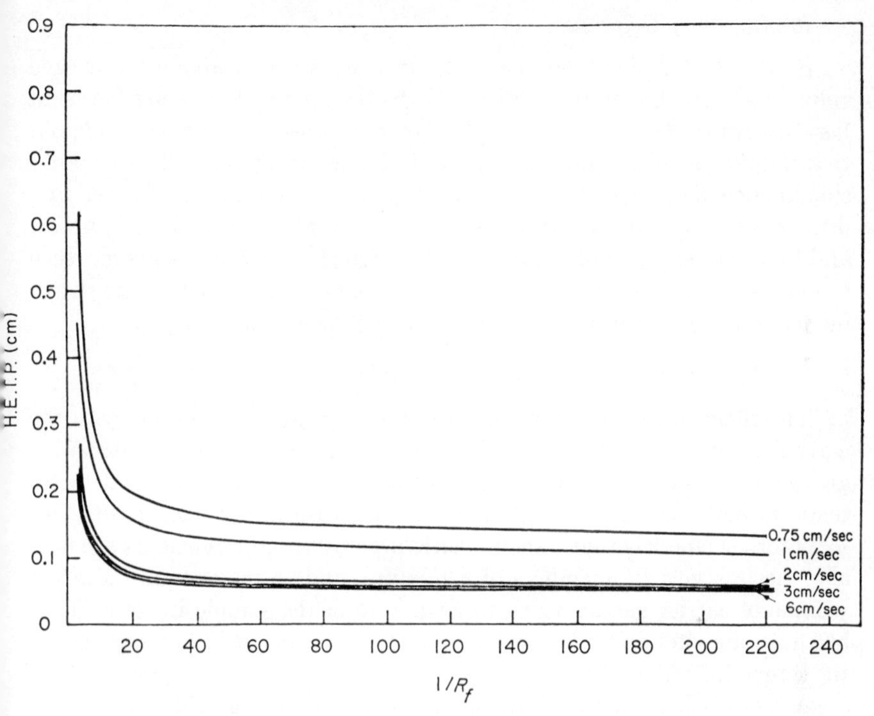

FIG. 5.13. Plot of plate-height against $1 + k$, with flow rate as parameter. From Desty, Godfrey, and Harbourn (*36*).

to a decrease in the diffusion coefficient. Desty, Godfrey, and Harbourn (*36*) have plotted H against k for various flow rates (Fig. 5.13) and find that as k rises, H falls until it approaches a limiting value asymptotically, at which stage the C term is presumably negligible. The figure shows that the limiting plate-height at large values of k decreases with increasing flow rate, indicating the effect of the B term at slow flow rates.

When $k < 1$, $k/(1 + k)^2$ increases with k, and so does C. This can be seen clearly from the first three results of Table 5.2. Clearly, $C = 0$ for carbon dioxide, which is not dissolved at all. After this, C rises to a maximum for 2-methyl pentane, for which $k \approx 1$, and then falls off as described above. The way in which the values of C change when $k \approx 1$ is also shown very clearly in the results of Keulemans and Kwantes (*34*), who have performed experiments in which m, rather than β, was progressively reduced (Section 5.13). When m is large, so that $k > 1$ for all vapours, the plate-number of butane is greater than that of propane, but when m is small, so that $k < 1$, that of propane is greater than that of butane at fast flow rates.

(b) Capillary Columns

Study of Eq. (5.64) on the same lines as are used above for packed columns shows that if gas diffusion is the dominant broadening factor at fast flow rates, then the plate-height should increase with increase in k, but that if diffusion in the stationary phase is dominant, then capillary columns should show the same characteristics as packed columns. The former conditions have been demonstrated in practice by Scott and Hazeldean (*38*) and by Desty and Goldup (*24*), both sets of authors giving results in which C increases as k increases. In this case, families of curves such as are shown for packed columns in Fig. 5.12 are reversed, as in Fig. 5.14.

(c) Partition Coefficient and Other Broadening Factors

The effect of the detector time constant on peaks eluted quickly in the early part of the chromatogram is greater than that on those eluted with greater $\sigma_{(t)}$ in the later parts of the chromatogram. In this way, the detector tends to make H appear to decline with increase in partition coefficient.

Another factor is that vapours with large partition coefficients are usually the less volatile members of a mixture, and so may require a larger volume of carrier gas in which to evaporate in the sample injector. This, however, does not affect H as a function of β, since $\sigma_{(V)}$ is in any case larger the larger the value of β.

A less obvious factor of frequent occurrence is that substances with large retention volumes tend to have non-linear isotherms, especially when their activity coefficients are considerably greater than unity. This produces asymmetrical peaks together with an increase in plate-height, as described in Section 5.5. The effect can be reduced by reducing the sample size

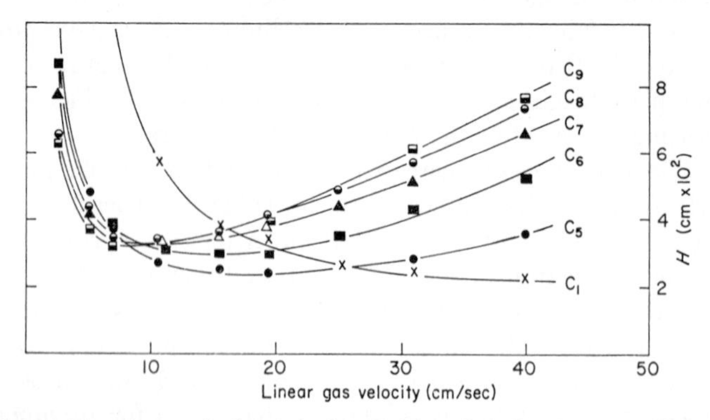

FIG. 5.14. Experimental plots of plate-height of peaks due to n-alkanes against linear gas velocity in a capillary column (75°C). Note that in contrast to the similar plot of Fig. 5.12, the greater the retention of the vapour, the larger the plate-height at large flow rates. From Desty and Goldup (*24*). $C_x = n - C_xH_{2x+2}$.

(Section 5.20), increasing the temperature (Section 5.15), or by choosing a different stationary phase (Section 3.9).

5.13. Effect of the Proportion of Stationary Phase on Performance

For a given support, the weight of stationary phase per centimetre of column (m) affects the column performance through its effect on C of Eq. (5.65), which contains the quantity m explicitly [expression (5.78)], and also implicitly in d_f, the average thickness of the stationary phase layer. In the circumstance that $k \gg 1$, the part of C containing m explicitly reduces to approximately $1/k$. At the same time it appears that d_f is roughly proportional to m, so that from Eq. (5.68), the net result is that $C \propto m$ approximately.

The improvement in performance with decrease in m has been reported many times. Keulemans and Kwantes (*34*) present a series of plots of H versus u for columns in which the proportion by weight of stationary phase varies from 5 to 45%, and these show progressively steeper slopes on the fast flow side of the minimum as m increases. Similar results are given by Duffield and Rogers (*39*), whose graph of H as a function of u with m as parameter is shown in Fig. 5.15. Several authors have pointed out the advantage of using small values of m in the construction of columns with small plate-height, and Scott (*33*), and Cheshire and Scott (*35*) amongst others have constructed packed columns with large plate-numbers the prime feature of which is a small value of m. Thus, with a value of m cor-

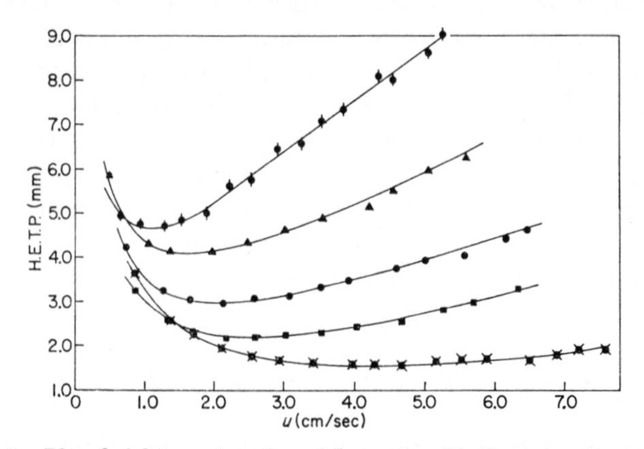

Fig. 5.15. Plate height as a function of flow rate with the proportion of stationary phase as parameter. From Duffield and Rogers (*39*). 2,3-Dimethylbutane on polyethylene glycol 400 at 25°C. ⧫, 50% w/w P.E.G.; ▲, 43%; ●, 34%; ■, 25%; ✕, 18%.

responding to 5% by weight of stationary phase on diatomaceous earth, a 20-foot column gives 12,000 plates, and a 50-foot column gives 30,000 plates for a vapour with a sufficiently large value of k operated at optimum flow rate.

An advantage of the use of small values of m is that C is small, so that flow rates may be increased without much loss in performance, and so analyses may be performed more rapidly. This property has commonly been recognised, but if m is reduced below a certain value, though performance increases, resolution does not, as is described in the following section.

Apart from the considerations of the next section, there are certain drawbacks to using small proportions of stationary phase which may make it desirable to sacrifice the smaller plate-height obtained thereby. As has been pointed out by Scott (*33*) and by Golay (*40*), if m is reduced, the sample size must be reduced in proportion to avoid raising the concentrations of solute in either phase. This may necessitate samples being so small that a very sensitive detector is necessary, or that important trace components are missed. Scott (*33*) in the columns referred to, restricts the sample size to 5 to 15 mg. From Littlewood's experiments on glass bead columns, the plate-number begins to fall if the sample size is increased beyond about 25 μg (Section 5.20).

A further drawback to columns with small quantities of stationary phase is that, if a small weight of stationary phase is removed by evaporation, the proportion so removed is comparatively large, and there is a significant change in retention volumes. Thus, columns with small values of m tend to have short working lives.

Yet another drawback is associated with the fact that the supports of packed columns are rarely completely inert, and, if m is small, the adsorptive properties of the support are comparable with the retention produced by the solvent. This factor is discussed fully in Section 6.3.

In conditions in which mass transfer is largely determined by diffusion in the gas phase, and when k is large, the second term of Eq. (5.64) is dominant, and is independent of k and therefore of m. In these circumstances, therefore, C is nearly independent of the proportion of stationary phase, as is shown for capillary columns by Desty and Goldup (*24*).

5.14. Effect of k on Resolution and Analysis Time

We have described in the previous two sections how the column performance generally increases with increase in β and decrease in m. Large values of β associated with ordinary values of m, however, cause large values of k, and with ordinary flow rates cause excessive retention times. Also, small values of m associated with ordinary values of β cause small values of k, with the result that the column resolution may suffer even when the performance is good, as described in Section 4.7. Thus when retention time and resolution must be considered in addition to column performance, the considerations of the previous sections require enlarging. The matter is discussed most easily by choosing k as an independent variable.

(a) *Effect of k on Resolution*

The resolution defined by Eq. (4.38) contains k explicitly in Eq. (4.43), in the form:

$$R \propto \frac{k}{1+k}. \tag{5.79}$$

Thus, if the relative retention and the plate-number remain constant, R is more or less constant and nearly equal to its greatest value when k is large, but becomes smaller as k declines. Because of this, therefore, it is desirable to use conditions in which k is large, e.g., low temperature, large value of m, and large value of β. This inevitably implies long analysis time.

Ordinary packed columns usually operate with relatively large values of k, and capillary columns operate with small values of k. Purnell (*41,42*) has pointed out that the whole advantage of the enormous plate-numbers given by capillary columns may be lost if they are operated in conditions in which k is fractional. This may be seen by comparing the analyses on a capillary and on a packed column of a mixture with a wide range of values of β, using the typical values of k quoted in Section 2.4, i.e.,

Capillary	$k = 0.2$ to 20
Packed	$k = 2$ to 200.

The effect of k on the resolution operates only on the very fastest peaks in the case of the packed column. On the capillary column, the effect of k on slow peaks is again small, but on fast peaks, however, the effect is such that most of the advantage of the large plate-number is lost. For example, with a vapour which gives $k = 0.2$ on a capillary column and $k = 2$ on a packed column, the capillary column must have $(2/3)/(0.2/1.2)^2 = 16$ times as many plates in order to provide the same resolution. In many chromatograms shown in the literature, the value of k for rapid peaks is even less than 0.2, with the result that, for these peaks, the resolution on a column capable of hundreds of thousands of plates may be poorer than that on quite a short packed column having only of the order of 1000 plates. The operation of k on resolution independently of plate-number is shown in Fig. 5.16, in which are constructed the chromatograms of a mixture of two close vapours with small values of β and two close vapours with large

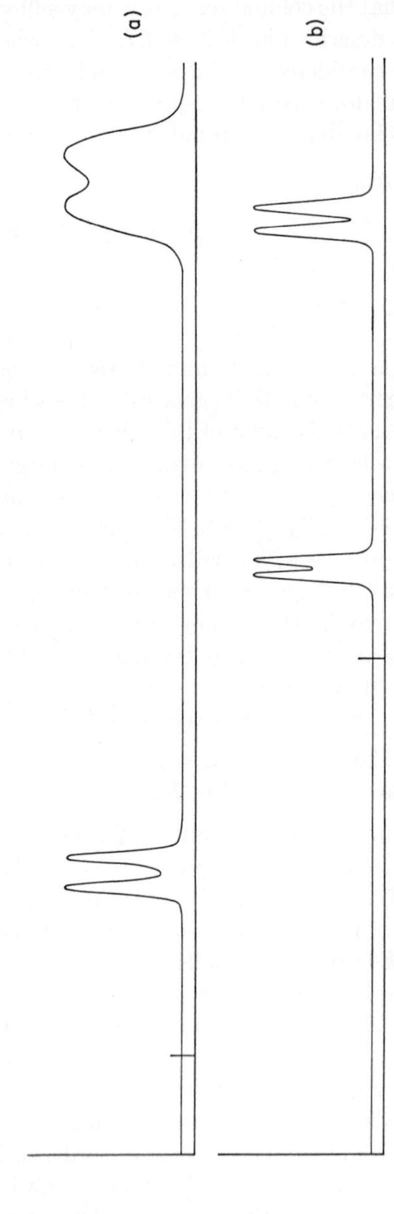

FIG. 5.16. Chromatograms of two close volatile vapours and two close less volatile vapours, (a) on a column of relatively poor performance but operating at large values of k, (b) on a column of relatively good performance, but operating at small values of k. The chromatograms have been constructed as for the separation of 1-pentene, n-pentane, 2-methylhexane, and 2,3-dimethylpentane, (a) on a column with 2000 plates, $k = 2$ for n-pentane, (b) on a column with 20,000 plates, $k = 0.2$ for n-pentane. The vertical line on each chromatogram represents the position of an air peak, i.e., $k = 0$.

values of β (a) on a column with large m but relatively small plate-number, which separates the volatile pair but not the involatile pair, and (b) on a column such as a capillary column, which separates the involatile pair but not the volatile pair. Actual chromatograms in which the operation of this effect can be seen are given by Scott (*43*).

(*b*) *Effect of k on Analysis Time*

According to the principles considered so far, the analysis time can be made arbitrarily small by any of several ways, e.g., increasing the flow rate, reducing m, or reducing β by raising the temperature. In all such cases, however, reduction in analysis time less than a certain threshold results in loss of resolution. It is therefore more appropriate to consider analysis time in relation to the resolution as a function of other variables. For example, Loyd, Ayers, and Karasek (*44*) consider the quotient R_{23}/t, where t is the retention time of either of two close components 2 and 3; this is the amount of resolution produced per unit time. Golay (*45*), and, in effect, Purnell and Quinn (*46*) consider R^2/t, which is more invariant. Apart from considerations of invariance, any such function may be considered, depending on the relative importance of R and t. The quantity R^n/t^m for any positive values of n and m as a function of k always has a maximum or greatest value at a specific value of k.

If, in Eq. (4.43), R is divided by the retention time, t, the result is:

$$\frac{R_{23}}{t} = (r_{23} - 1) \cdot \frac{k}{(1+k)^2} \cdot \frac{\sqrt{\mathfrak{N}}}{t_M}, \tag{5.80}$$

where t_M is the gas hold-up time. Loyd *et al.* assume that $\mathfrak{N}$ is independent of k, and from the above equation they find that R/t has a maximum value when $k = 1$. When k increases greater than unity, the retention time increases faster than the improvement in resolution; when k decreases less than unity, the loss of resolution more than outweighs the gain in retention time.

The assumption made above that $\mathfrak{N}$ is independent of k is unreasonable, as is apparent from Section 5.12. Golay (*45*), Purnell and Quinn (*46*), Scott and Hazeldean (*38*), and others have considered equations also containing assumed relations between $\mathfrak{N}$ and k.

Purnell and Quinn have assumed that, when conditions are optimised for R and t, the flow rate is in all cases so fast that the only significant term in Eq. (5.65) is the C term. Substituting $H = Cu$, together with Eqs. (2.16), (2.19), and (4.13), Eq. (4.43) becomes:

$$\frac{R_{23}^2}{t} = (r_{23} - 1)^2 \cdot \frac{k^2}{4C(1+k)^3}. \tag{5.81}$$

If C is regarded as a constant, R_{23}^2/t has a maximum at $k = 2$, from which the time required for an analysis is

$$t = \frac{27CR_{23}^2}{(r_{23} - 1)^2}. \tag{5.82}$$

(In their discussion, Purnell and Quinn have chosen to discuss one particular value of $R_{23}/(r_{23} - 1)$ throughout.)

The assumption that C is constant, however, is invalid; the only circumstances where it may apply are at large values of k, when C is determined by mass-transfer in the gas phase, and this is inconsistent with $k = 2$. For discussion, C may be regarded as the sum of terms due to slow mass-transfer in each phase, so that Eq. (5.81) becomes:

$$\frac{t(r_{23} - 1)^2}{R_{23}^2} = \frac{4(1 + k)^3}{k^2} (C_g + C_l). \tag{5.83}$$

Purnell and Quinn (*46*), and Scott and Hazeldean (*38*) have substituted the expressions from Eq. (5.64) into this to give:

$$\frac{t(r_{23} - 1)^2}{R_{23}^2} = \frac{4(1 + k)^3 r^2}{k^2} \left\{\frac{1 + 6k + 11k^2}{24(1 + k)^2 D_g} + \frac{k^3}{6(1 + k)^2 \alpha^2 D_l}\right\}, \tag{5.84}$$

assuming that this equation applies exactly to cylindrical capillary columns and at least approximately to packed columns, for which the first term in the bracket differs in detail but not in kind. It is seen from that that the optimum value of k is also a function of α, which determines the relative importance of each term. Further analysis of equations such as these is straightforward (*38,46*). Purnell and Quinn find that when α is large, k has an optimum value close to 2, and that for values of k greater than the optimum, the ratio t/R_{23}^2 increases but slowly. When α is small, the optimum value of k is also small, e.g., $k \approx 0.1$ when $\alpha \approx 10$, but, as a result of these excessively small optimum values of k, the corresponding minimum value of t/R_{23}^2 is very much larger, and furthermore the minimum is deeper, so that the ratio t/R_{23}^2 increases rapidly as k departs from the optimum value. On all counts, therefore, it is recommended that for optimum values of t/R_{23}^2, the partition coefficient should be as large as practical. Using these principles in connection with packed columns, Purnell and Quinn show chromatograms of C_1 to C_4 hydrocarbons made in 20 seconds, and, with capillary columns, similar chromatograms need only occupy times of the order of 1 second or less.

5.15. Effect of Temperature on Performance

Temperature affects column performances largely on account of the C term in Eq. (5.65), but there is a small effect on B on account of the change in D_g with temperature. This increases slightly with increase in temperature; usually $D_g \propto T^{0.3}$ to $T^{0.5}$, so that B increases similarly.

Change of temperature affects performance principally through the change that it causes in the partition coefficient. With packed columns, as the temperature is reduced, the partition coefficient increases, and hence the value of C decreases as described in Section 5.12, thus improving the performance. Operating against this is the fact that as the temperature decreases, the diffusion coefficient D_l also decreases, thus tending to increase the value of C. In most practice, it appears that the effect of the increase in partition coefficient easily outweighs the effect of the increase in diffusion coefficient, so that performances improve as the temperature lowers. This is reasonable on theoretical grounds, for the changes in partition coefficient and in diffusion coefficient with temperature are both processes described by an equation of the form of Eq. (3.55), and the heat of solution of the vapour is always greater than the activation energy of diffusion.

With capillary columns, decrease in the value of k may improve the performance if gas diffusion is the dominant factor in mass transfer, as is illustrated by Fig. 5.14. In this case, increase in temperature should improve the performance both on this account, and on account of the change

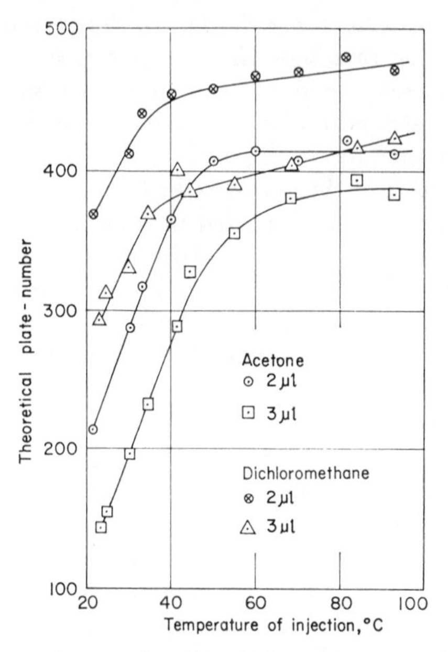

FIG. 5.17. Plate-number as a function of the temperature of the sample injector, with sample as parameter. From Pollard and Hardy (47).

in diffusion coefficient. Desty and Goldup (*24*) present results that show that for a given vapour the value of C decreases considerably with increase in temperature, but that for a given partition coefficient, the changes in performance are small, and probably dominated only by the comparatively small temperature coefficients of diffusion.

In a few cases (*7,39*), it is reported that performances on packed columns also increase with increase in temperature. Littlewood (*7*) finds this with columns using glass beads as support, and has suggested that an increase in temperature causes a decrease in the surface tension of the stationary liquid, which therefore spreads more evenly over the surface of the beads, leading to a decrease in d_f.

The influence of the temperature of the sample injector on the efficiency of a gas-chromatograph has been studied by Pollard and Hardy (*47*), who have plotted the effective plate-height against the introducer temperature (Fig. 5.17). When the temperature of the introducer is below the boiling point of the sample, the input distribution is broadened because of the time taken for the sample to evaporate and the volume of carrier gas required to contain the vapour. As the temperature of the sample injector rises, the plate-number rises, till at a high enough temperature the value of the plate-number becomes nearly constant, at which stage the variance due to the input distribution has become small compared to the broadening produced by the column. The authors observe that the larger the sample, the worse is the broadening due to a cool sample injector, since evaporation takes longer, and more gas is required to contain the vapour. With preparative columns, sample injectors require special design to enable evaporation to occur rapidly (Section 6.6).

General recognition of the above effect has led to the recommendation that sample injectors should be heated to a temperature higher than that of the column by means of a "Flash Heater." The exact temperature is found only by experience, but probably it need not be more than 50°C higher than the column temperature. Note that it is more reasonable to relate the temperature of the sample injector to the temperature of the column rather than to the boiling points of the components of the mixtures to be analysed, since, though it is true that the higher the boiling point of the vapour the greater will be the broadening in a cool sample injector, this extra broadening is swamped by the column broadening if the column temperature is also low.

In cases where vapours have non-linear isotherms on partition columns, the column temperature may have a dominant influence on the performance through its effect on the non-linearity. If there is an anti-Langmuir type non-linearity caused through the variation of a large activity coefficient with concentration (Section 5.6), the non-linearity frequently becomes less

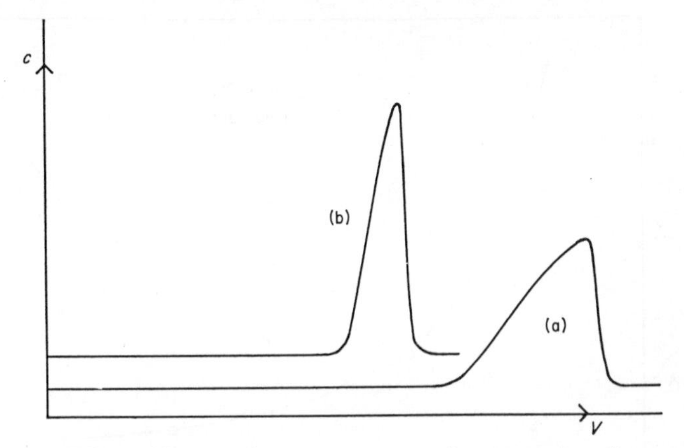

FIG. 5.18. Effect of increase in temperature on the asymmetry of an overloaded peak. (a) 0.03 cc propyl acetate on a silicone column at 56°C. (b) 0.03 cc propyl acetate on the same column at 77°C (Littlewood, unpublished).

at higher temperatures, since large activity coefficients tend to decrease with increase in temperature, just as most solubilities rise with temperature. An example of this effect is shown in Fig. 5.18, which gives the chromatograms of a sample of *n*-propyl acetate at 56°C and at 77°C. It is apparent that the asymmetry is less at the higher temperature, as is confirmed by the plate-numbers, which are 210 at 56°C and 530 at 77°C.

5.16. EFFECT OF CARRIER GAS ON PERFORMANCE AND SPEED

In packed columns in which m is sufficiently large that the effect of lateral diffusion in the gas phase is negligible, the carrier gas affects the performance through its effect on the parameter B of Eq. (5.63), since the lighter and smaller the molecules of the carrier gas, the greater is the diffusion coefficient of vapours within it. Thus, at fast flow rates, where B is only a minor factor in determining the plate-height, the carrier gas has little effect on the performance, while at slow or optimum flow rates, where B is a major factor, the heavier the carrier gas, the better the performance. This is well shown by results given by Bohemen and Purnell (*6*), who give plots of plate-height against flow rate for the same vapour on the same column, but using different carrier gases (Fig. 5.19). The heavy gases nitrogen and argon give much smaller plate-heights at slow flow rates than does hydrogen, while at faster flow rates, the performances approach each other. Values of B for hydrogen and for nitrogen are not exactly in the ratio of the diffusion coefficients of the vapour in the two gases because of the inaccuracy of Eq. (5.65).

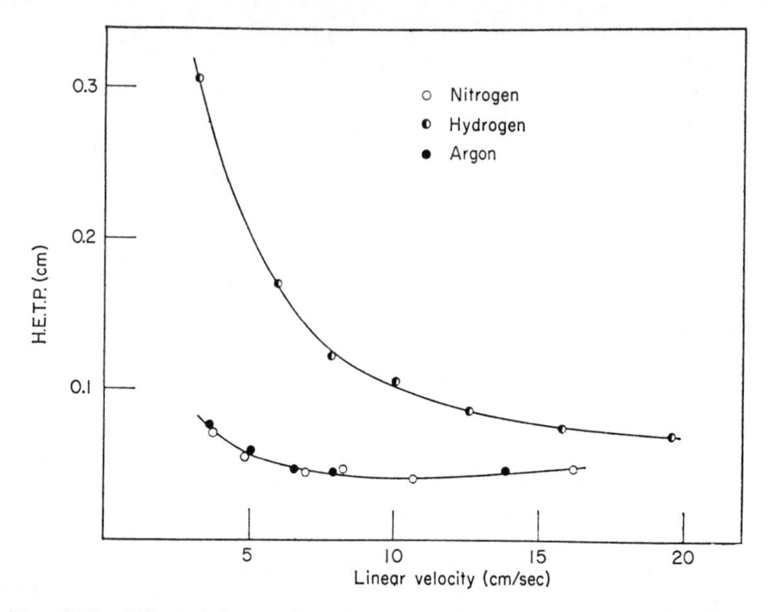

FIG. 5.19. Effect of change of carrier gas on column performance at slow flow rates. The plots of plate-height against flow rate are made in similar conditions apart from change in the carrier gas. From Bohemen and Purnell (*6*).

Scott (*33*) has operated columns at pressures up to 200 lb/in.^{2} by placing a choke at the column outlet and using a high inlet pressure. Such a procedure has two beneficial effects on the performance, (a) since the viscosity of a gas is independent of its pressure, it reduces the pressure ratio across the column (Section 5.19), and (b) it increases the density of the carrier gas, thus reducing the diffusion coefficient of vapours within it. By this means a column which gives a plate-height of 0.56 mm when run with its outlet at asmospheric pressure, gives a plate-height of 0.4 mm at an elevated pressure. Though the use of high-pressure carrier gases may be more desirable from the point of view of performance, it also has the effect that the molar concentrations of the vapours are reduced, so that the detector must be correspondingly more sensitive. In the same way, columns operated at a reduced pressure suffer from an increased value of B, but the sensitivity of the detector need not be so great. As in many other fields of analysis, a choice must be made between resolving power and sensitivity.

If in ordinary analysis with packed columns the flow rate is well above the optimum value, the performance should not be a very serious criterion in the choice of a carrier gas. There are usually, however, other criteria, e.g., detector response, fire hazard, etc., which limit or determine the choice.

When lateral diffusion in the gas phase is also a significant broadening factor, as in capillary columns, the parameter C of Eq. (5.65) is also affected by the choice of carrier gas. Change of the carrier gas changes B and C in opposite directions, a lighter carrier gas increasing B but decreasing C. If the time of equilibration of the vapour with the stationary phase is small compared to the time of diffusion across the thickness of the gas-layer, the product BC is constant, so that, from Eq. (5.69), the carrier gas does not affect the minimum plate-height, but, from Eq. (5.70), the use of a lighter carrier gas causes an increase in the optimum flow rate. If the conditions are such that the above argument applies, therefore, analysis times may be reduced without loss of resolution by using a light carrier gas, e.g., hydrogen. These observations acquire more significance when discussed in connection with the pressure drop across the column in Section 5.19.

5.17. Particle Size and Shape

The effect of the particle size and shape on the performance of packed columns is complicated, and theoretical systematisation of the experimental results is difficult. However, in a general way, the observed behaviour can be more or less classified in terms of the effect of the particle size and shape on the three parameters A, B, and C of Eq. (5.65), all of which are affected.

(a) *Effect on A*

The larger the size of the particles of the support, the larger A should be, by Eq. (5.66). Furthermore, the ultimate plate-height cannot be less than the height of the interstices between the particles, for it seems likely that complete mixing occurs in these, and that the interstices effectively constitute real theoretical plates in the sense defined in Section 4.1. From these considerations A should increase with increase in the particle size of the support, and when the particle size is relatively large, this conclusion appears to be correct. Thus Keulemans and Kwantes (*34*) find that $A = 1$ mm for a 30- to 50-sieve fraction of kieselguhr ($d_p \approx 0.4$ mm), and $A = 2$ mm for a 20- to 30-sieve fraction ($d_p \approx 0.7$ mm). Desty, Godfrey, and Harbourn (*36*) give a plot of A against particle size for kieselguhr and for firebrick packings, each with two different proportions of stationary phase (Fig. 5.20). With both kinds of packing, A increases with increase in particle size, though the variation is more regular in the case of firebrick.

The other factor in the theoretical expression for A is the constant λ, which describes the evenness of packing. Keulemans and Kwantes (*34*) have pointed out that the finer the packing, the more difficult it is to obtain regularity, and have suggested that, when the particles are very fine, the increase in λ may exceed the decrease in d_p, so that there is an optimum

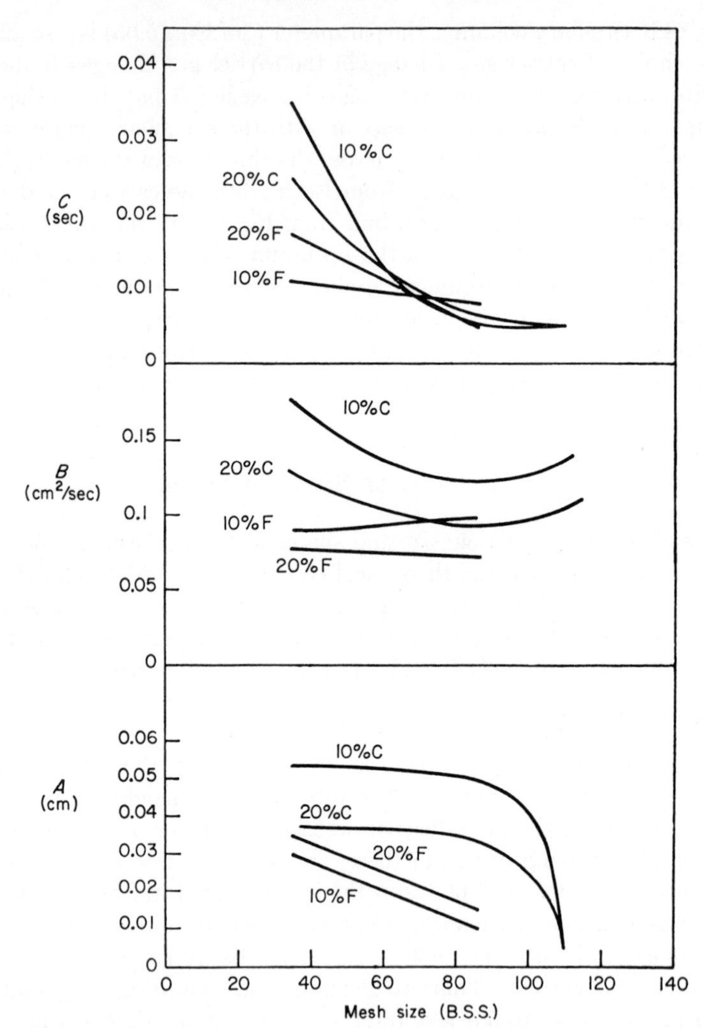

FIG. 5.20. Plots of A, B, and C of Eq. (5.65) against mesh size of packing particles for 10 and 20% stationary phase by weight on Celite diatomaceous earth (C) and on ground firebrick (F). From Desty, Godfrey, and Harbourn (*36*).

particle size for which A is a minimum. Keulemans and Kwantes refer to work by van Deemter *et al.* (*3*) in which the values of A obtained with kieselguhr of 0.04 mm average diameter and with firebrick of 0.25 mm average diameter are approximately the same. In contrast to this, both Desty, Godfrey, and Harbourn (*36*), and Bohemen and Purnell (*6*) find that A decreases with decrease in particle size down to the smallest sizes used [120 mesh (*36*) and 150 mesh (*6*)], though the values of A for the smaller particle sizes in the work of the latter authors are negative, and may have a different significance. Several such comparisons may be made from the results of various authors, and they are not always consistent. Consistency of results between operators in the packing of columns is likely to be poor, especially with materials such as firebrick and kieselguhr, for packing methods differ in detail from operator to operator, and the exact performance of a column is rather sensitive to the technique of packing.

(*b*) *Effect on B*

The effect of the column packing on the longitudinal gas diffusion term should be small, for the over-all rate of diffusion depends only on the cross-sectional area of gas phase over which it can occur, and not on the way in which the cross-sectional area is distributed. Desty, Godfrey, and Harbourn (*36*) have given values of B as a function of mesh size (Fig. 5.20). On the firebrick supports, B is almost independent of particle size, though on kieselguhr supports there is considerable variation. The latter suggests deviations from the van Deemter equation, and similar variations of B with particle size found by Bohemen and Purnell (*6*), using Sil-O-Cel as a support, were interpreted in this way.

(*c*) *Effect on C*

The effect of the particle size of the support on C is the simplest to consider. For non-porous particles, the larger the particles, the smaller the surface area of the packing, and thus the thicker the surface film d_f. Thus, the larger the particles, the greater is C, and the poorer the performance at fast flow rates. Desty, Godfrey, and Harbourn (*36*) give a graph illustrating this (Fig. 5.20). Kieselguhr, the particles of which are relatively non-porous, behaves exactly as described, with C dropping threefold when the particle size is divided by 3. When the particles are porous, however, increase in particle size does not necessarily cause a significant decrease in surface area, and thus does not necessitate an increase in the film thickness except in the case that m is so large that all the pores are filled. This is probably the explanation of the results presented in the figure for firebrick, for which C depends much less on particle size, especially for the smaller value of m.

The importance of the uniformity of particle size has been considered by Bohemen and Purnell (*6*), who have plotted plate-height against flow rate for several mixtures each containing different proportions of two particle sizes of Sil-O-Cel. Values of C obtained from the plots are greater for some mixtures than for either pure grade of support, indicating that the inhomogeneity appears to affect the C term. Measurements of the A and B terms gave erratic results, however, with negative values of A in some instances, and the authors do not draw any very definite conclusions.

5.18. Effect of Column Diameter on Performance

The variation of performance with column diameter depends on the way in which a column is packed, for which there is no reproducible standard (Section 6.1). The result is that different workers produce widely different results which cannot be correlated. Nearly all the data pertains to packed columns.

If the column diameter is not less than approximately 2 or 3 mm, the general trend is for the plate-height to increase with increase in the column diameter. Most workers find that between about 3 mm and about 30 mm the rise in plate-height is small. For example, Dimbat, Porter, and Stross (*48*) find that a sixfold increase in column diameter requires only a 50% increase in column length to maintain the same plate-number at the same linear flow rate, using firebrick as a packing support. This is confirmed by Carle and Johns (*49*, ref. *1*), who find that the plate-height increases but slowly with diameter up to a diameter of about 15 mm, but more rapidly thereafter, and by Baker, Norlin, Zinn, and Wall (*50*), who find a virtually constant plate-height in columns of up to 13 mm diameter.

The variation of performance with diameter in large packed columns suitable for preparative gas chromatography has been studied by Huyten, Beersum, and Rijnders (*49*), who have used columns of 3 and 10 inches diameter in which they have investigated the variation of gas velocity and the radial diffusivity across the column. For the gas velocity profile, a stream of carrier gas containing ammonia was passed up the vertical column and through an even layer of support carrying acid which rested on the top; after a given time, a cutter cut this layer into concentric rings which were extracted separately and analysed by titration. From this, the amount of ammonia in each ring gave the gas velocity at different regions across the column. A similar procedure was used for studying radial diffusion, the difference being that the ammonia was introduced by a jet at the centre of the inlet end of the column.

The authors carried out sets of experiments for different methods of column packing. In all cases, they obtained the result that the gas velocity is greater at the edges than at the centre, the amount varying between 20 and 50%. Some methods of packing gave smaller plate-heights than others, as is evident from Table 6.5. It is not possible to correlate the velocity distribution with the plate-height for different methods of packing, because different methods of packing produce different packing densities, which influence radial and longitudinal diffusion. In the above authors' experiments, the method of packing which produces the smallest plate-height also produces the largest velocity gradient.

The effect of column diameter in capillary columns is considered in Sections 5.11(b) and 5.19(c).

5.19. Effect of Pressure Drop across the Column on Performance and Analysis Time

(a) *Qualitative Considerations*

When the ratio of pressures across the column is considerably greater than unity, there is a velocity gradient in the column, and, since the plate-height is a function of the flow rate, equivalent theoretical plates in different parts of the column have different heights. The measured plate-height is therefore an average value. The velocity gradient can be minimised by the use of coarse packings, short columns, or slow flow rates, but all these involve loss in performance, and for a good performance an appreciable pressure drop is necessary. As columns become longer, the effect of the pressure drop becomes greater, and in the limit, further addition to the column length may not add to the plate-number. At this stage, an ultimate limit to the performance of a column of given design is reached.

Even if the pressure ratio is relatively large, correct choice of outlet flow rate can minimise the deleterious effect of the velocity gradient, for, when the pressure ratio is large, the velocity distribution in the column is such that most of the velocity gradient is near the outlet (Fig. 2.4). Thus, if the pressure ratio is large, it is best to arrange that the inlet flow rate is at or near the optimum value, and, in these circumstances, most of the column is operating near the optimum flow rate, with only the outlet end operating inefficiently. In a sense, the last part of the column acts as a choke, the purpose of which is to maintain a large inlet pressure, in much the same way as the actual chokes used by Scott (*33*)(Section 5.16).

(b) *Modification of the van Deemter Equation*

In this subsection, we describe the effect of the pressure drop in a column on the measured plate-height, mainly following Giddings *et al.* (*31*) and Golay (*15*).

When there is a pressure drop across the column, the plate-height as given by Eq. (5.65) becomes a function of x, the position of the plate in the column:

$$H(x) = A + \frac{B}{u(x)} + Cu(x). \tag{5.85}$$

This can be simplified by making use of the fact that D_g, the diffusion coefficient of the vapour in the gas, is inversely proportional to the pressure, so that

$$D_{g(o)}P_o = D_gP, \tag{5.86}$$

where $D_{g(o)}$ and P_o are the values at the column outlet. This equation, together with Eqs. (2.18), (2.22), and (5.67), gives:

$$H(x) = A + \frac{B_o}{u_o} + Cu(x), \tag{5.87}$$

where B_o is the value relevant at the outlet. The B term in the equation is thus independent of x. The greater the pressure, the slower the gas, and therefore the more time there is for longitudinal diffusion. However, the diffusion coefficient is proportionately smaller, and these two factors exactly cancel each other.

The measured plate-number is defined by:

$$\mathfrak{N} = \frac{V^2}{\sigma^2_{(V)}} = \frac{t^2}{\sigma^2_{(t)}}. \tag{5.88}$$

When there is a pressure drop, however, $\mathfrak{N}$ defined in this way is not equal to l/H, for H is not constant. Let us define a new phenomenological quantity, $\mathfrak{H}$, such that

$$\mathfrak{H} = \frac{l}{\mathfrak{N}} = \frac{l\sigma^2_{(t=t_R)}}{t_R{}^2} = \frac{l(1+k)^2\sigma^2_{(x=l)}}{u_o{}^2t_R{}^2}, \tag{5.89}$$

where the last form of writing follows from Eq. (5.60). We shall now find an equation for $\mathfrak{H}$ [Eq. (5.95)] equivalent to Eq. (5.65) for H.

The variance $\sigma^2_{(x)}$ is given as a function of x alone by Eq. (5.62). Differentiation of this gives:

$$\frac{\partial(\sigma^2_{(x)})}{\partial x} = H(x), \tag{5.90}$$

which applies at any point in the column. The variance is also a function of the pressure, for as the peak moves along the column into regions of smaller pressure, it expands. The dependence of the variance on the pressure alone may be specified by $\partial(\sigma^2_{(x)})/\partial(P^2)$, which is given by:

$$\frac{\partial(\sigma^2_{(x)})}{\partial(P^2)} = -\frac{\sigma^2_{(x)}}{P^2}, \tag{5.91}$$

since by Boyle's law $\sigma_{(x)}$ is inversely proportional to the pressure. The total differential $d(\sigma^2_{(x)})/dx$ is obtained from Eqs. (5.90) and (5.91):

$$\frac{d(\sigma^2_{(x)})}{dx} = H(x) - \frac{\sigma^2_{(x)}}{P^2} \cdot \frac{d(P^2)}{dx}, \tag{5.92}$$

and reference to Eq. (2.24) shows that $d(P^2)/dx$ is constant. The solution to Eq. (5.92) for the case of a sharp input distribution, the peak from which is just being eluted from a column of length l, is:

$$\sigma^2_{(x=l)} = \frac{1}{P_o^2} \int_0 P^2(x) H(x)\, dx. \tag{5.93}$$

This may be substituted in the extreme right-hand side of Eq. (5.89), and the retention time, t_R, is given by Eq. (2.33). The result is:

$$\mathcal{H} = \frac{j^2}{l P_o^2} \int_0^l P^2(x) H(x)\, dx, \tag{5.94}$$

where j is given by Eq. (2.35). The integral may be evaluated substituting for P^2 by Eq. (2.27) and for H by Eq. (5.87). The result is that

$$\mathcal{H} = \left(A + \frac{B}{u_o}\right) g(P_i, P_o) + jCu_o, \tag{5.95}$$

where

$$g(P_i, P_o) = \frac{9\{(P_i/P_o)^4 - 1\}\{(P_i/P_o)^2 - 1\}}{8\{(P_i/P_o)^3 - 1\}^2}, \tag{5.96}$$

which varies monotonically between unity when $P_i = P_o$ and 9/8 when $P_i/P_o \to \infty$. Equations (5.95) and (5.96) are given by Giddings (*31*).

By differentiating Eq. (5.95) with respect to u_o, using the equations of Section 2.5 to give the relation of P_i and u_o, and setting the result equal to zero, the optimum value of u_o and the minimum value of $\mathcal{H}$ may be found. The equations show that the minimum value of $\mathcal{H}$ is always greater than the minimum value of H as given by Eq. (5.69) except in the limiting case that $P_i = P_o$. Thus, the effect of the pressure drop is always deleterious to the performance of the column, and it is desirable to design columns so as to minimise the pressure drop per plate. This adds a fourth criterion of quality to the three given at the beginning of Section 5.1, and the theory of it is considered below.

(c) *The Design of Columns with Regard to the Effect of Pressure Drop–Performance Index*

We have assumed so far that the best possible column by which all others are compared is the ideal column, in which broadening factors are absent. Such a column is impossible in practice, but it is also impossible in principle, for a column must have a finite channel for the passage of gas; diffusion across this cannot occur instantaneously, and if diffusion occurs across it, diffusion must also occur along it. We consider, therefore, the *Best Possible Real Column* (B.P.R. column), which allows longitudinal and lateral diffusion in the gas phase, but does not suffer from anastomosis or slow mass transfer in or into the stationary phase. The plate-height in a cylindrical column with these characteristics is given by the first two terms of Eq. (5.64).

There is another reason why a column as defined above is the best possible. Substitution of Eq. (5.86) into the first two terms of Eq. (5.64) gives:

$$H = \frac{2D_{g(o)}}{u_o} + \frac{u_o r^2 f(k)}{D_{g(o)}}, \tag{5.97}$$

where

$$f(k) = \frac{1}{24} \cdot \frac{1 + 6k + 11k^2}{(1 + k)^2}, \tag{5.98}$$

from which it is seen that H is independent of x, and is independent of the pressure drop across the column. Hence $\mathcal{H}$ has its smallest value, and the pressure drop has the least possible deleterious effect on the performance. In this case,

$$H_{\min} = 2\sqrt{2} \cdot r\sqrt{f(k)}. \tag{5.99}$$

In contrast to an ideal column, a B.P.R. column has three finite quantities:

(1) peaks with a non-zero variance,
(2) a non-zero time of analysis,
(3) a non-zero pressure drop.

All these quantities are zero in the ideal column, and are essentially undesirable, but in a real column none can be avoided, and any attempt to reduce one of them by changing the operating or design variables in any conceivable way always results in an increase of one of the others, as the reader may check. It appears, therefore, that there is a positive function of (1), (2), and (3) which has a minimum but non-zero value for a B.P.R. column operating optimally and which is greater for every other real column. Such a function has been sought by Golay (*14,15,40,45*), from whom the following treatment is derived.

The value of $\mathcal{H}$ in terms of $H_{\min}$ and the pressure drop for a B.P.R. column is given by Eq. (5.94), which becomes:

$$\mathcal{H} = \frac{j^2}{lP_o^2} \int_0^l P^2(x) H_{\min}\, dx = \frac{j^2 H_{\min}}{lP_o^2} \int_0^l P^2(x)\, dx. \tag{5.100}$$

The second form of writing results from the fact that for this column, H is not a function of x. Substituting Eq. (2.27) and integrating, this becomes:

$$\mathcal{H} = gH_{\min} = 2\sqrt{2} \cdot gr\sqrt{f(k)}, \tag{5.101}$$

so that, at worst, $\mathcal{H}$ is no greater than $9H/8$, and the difference between $\mathcal{H}$ and H can be regarded as due solely to the operation of expansion of the peak as described by Eq. (5.91). The radius of the tube in Eq. (5.101) can be converted into quantities relevant in the specification of (1), (2), and (3) above by the equation for the flow of a compressible gas of viscosity η through a cylindrical tube of radius r and length l, which is:

$$u_o = \frac{r^2(P_i^2 - P_o^2)}{16 l \eta P_o}. \tag{5.102}$$

If r is eliminated between Eqs. (5.101) and (5.102), and u_o is substituted by Eqs. (2.17) and (2.33), the result is:

$$\lambda = \frac{\mathcal{H}^2}{64 l^2} \cdot \frac{t_M}{f(k)} \cdot \frac{16(P_i^3 - P_o^3)^3}{27(P_i^4 - P_o^4)^2} = \frac{1}{64 \mathfrak{N}^2} \cdot \frac{t_M}{f(k)} \cdot \frac{16(P_i^3 - P_o^3)^3}{27(P_i^4 - P_o^4)^2}. \tag{5.103}$$

This is the required equation relating performance ($\mathfrak{N}^2$), analysis time ($\propto t_M$), and pressure drop. If the equation is written in the form:

$$1 = \frac{1}{64\eta} \cdot \frac{1}{\mathfrak{N}^2} \cdot \frac{t_M}{f(k)} \cdot \frac{16(P_i^3 - P_o^3)^3}{27(P_i^4 - P_o^4)^2}, \tag{5.104}$$

then the right-hand side is invariant for a B.P.R. column operating optimally, and is independent of the length of the column. Golay has called this expression the "Specific Performance Index," which is identically equal to unity for a B.P.R. column, but is greater than unity for all others. As laid out in Eq. (5.104), the first factor is a constant and the following three factors are the functions of (1), (2), and (3) referred to above.

The smaller the value of the Specific Performance Index (S.P.I.) for a real column, the smaller will be the increase in average plate-height at optimum flow rate when the column is lengthened to such a degree that the pressure ratio becomes large. The specific performance index is a phenomenological quantity, and its purpose is to indicate the performance of the column with regard to the quantities (1), (2), and (3) given above. It does not contain in its specification any mechanism or process by which a specific performance index is in fact greater than unity.

The expression for the S.P.I. given in Eq. (5.104) applies only to cylindrical capillary columns. There is no exact equivalent equation for packed columns, since there is no exact form equivalent to $f(k)$, but according to Golay, the following quantity is equivalent to $f(k)$ within about 50% for any packed column:

$$C_k = \frac{1}{48}\left(1 + \frac{15k}{1+k}\right). \tag{5.105}$$

In order to simplify the use of the idea of S.P.I. in practice, the rather complicated function of P_i and P_o in Eq. (5.104) may be replaced by $P_i - P_o$ for relatively small pressure ratios without much error. If, in addition, the $\mathfrak{N}^2$ in Eq. (5.104) is substituted in Eq. (4.27), and $f(k)$ is replaced by $C(k)$ defined in Eq. (5.105), the result is:

$$\tfrac{1}{3}\, 2^{12}(\log_e 2)^2\eta = \frac{t_M(\omega_{1/2})^4(P_i - P_o)}{t_R^3(t_R - 15t_M/16)}. \qquad (5.106)$$

Golay has pointed out that the viscosities of all common carrier gases other than hydrogen are more or less similar within the limits of the approximations already made, and have such a value that the right-hand side of Eq. (5.106) has the approximate value of 0.1 poise. Equation (5.106) applies in principle to a packed B.P.R. column, and Golay has suggested that the value of the right-hand side calculated from experimental measurements on a particular column may be used as a measure of its performance in the same way as with the more precise S.P.I. Thus the right-hand side of Eq. (5.106) is called the "Performance Index." Values for the performance indices for a number of packed columns are given in Table 5.3, from which

TABLE 5.3

PERFORMANCE INDICES OF PACKED COLUMNS

Description of column		Performance index	Reference
0.5 μl of benzene, nitrogen carrier gas, in a column of 20% w/w P.E.G. 400 on Sil-O-Cel at 47°C. Mesh size:	20–30	48	(*6*)
	30–40	72	(*6*)
	40–50	83	(*6*)
	50–60	82	(*6*)
	90–100	114	(*6*)
	100–150	120	(*6*)
25 μg of *o*-xylene, nitrogen carrier gas, in a column of 1% w/w tricresyl phosphate on 0.1-mm-diameter glass beads:	at 100°C	73	(*7*)
	at 80°C	65	(*7*)
2-methyl pentane as above at 100°C		880	(*7*)
o-xylene, argon carrier gas, in a column of 2½% w/w Apiezon oil on 110 to 120 mesh firebrick, operated at 200 lb/sq in. inlet pressure, $P_i/P_o = 1.2$.		5.5	(*33*)

it is seen that performance indices found in practice are usually of the order of 1000 times greater than that for a B.P.R. packed column.

The performance indices of capillary columns are much smaller than those of packed columns, being of the order of unity rather than of the order of 10. This is partly because of their greater permeability, and partly because anastomosis is absent. The result is that the pressure drop per plate is very much smaller, and, even though the plate-height in capillary columns is not smaller than that in packed columns, very large plate-numbers can be attained by using very great lengths without having excessive pressure drops. Thus capillary columns of up to a mile long and having as many as 10^6 theoretical plates have been constructed, whereas packed columns usually require excessive pressure drops when they are longer than about 50 feet or have more than 20,000 to 30,000 plates. With packed columns, Bohemen and Purnell (*6*) find that the larger the particles of packing, the smaller the performance index, and that therefore columns in which the particles of packing are large may usefully be made very long in order to obtain a large number of plates.

In calculating performance indices, it should be remembered that since its units are those of poises, i.e., dyne second/cm^2, the units of the pressure difference across the column are dyne/cm^2. The conversion factor between cm Hg and dyne/cm^2 is:

$$1 \text{ cm Hg} = 13{,}332 \text{ dynes/cm}^2.$$

5.20. Effect of Mass of Sample on Performance

In most cases, the greater the mass of sample chromatographed, the smaller the performance of the apparatus. For example, Bohemen and Purnell (*6*) have plotted the apparent plate-height of a column against sample size, and obtain straight-line plots for each component of a mixture (Fig. 5.21). There is no definite reason for the linearity, and such a relation is not always found; most workers, however, agree on the sign of the slope of the lines.

Sample size affects the column performance mainly through the effect of the input distribution of vapour (Section 5.7), the volume of vapour in the gas phase, and the non-linearity of isotherms (Section 5.5).

The sample size can affect the input distribution in two ways, firstly, because the sample produces a finite volume of vapour, and secondly because if the sample is a liquid, it requires a finite time to evaporate. The second is a technological problem which may be effectively solved for analytical columns by using a heated sample injector, as described in Section 5.15.

The effect of the finite volume of vapour on performance as a function of other column variables has been studied by DeWet and Pretorius (*51*). The results may be interpreted simply in terms of Fig. 5.9 and equations from Section 5.7, using the premise that σ_I^2 is proportional to the mass of sample.

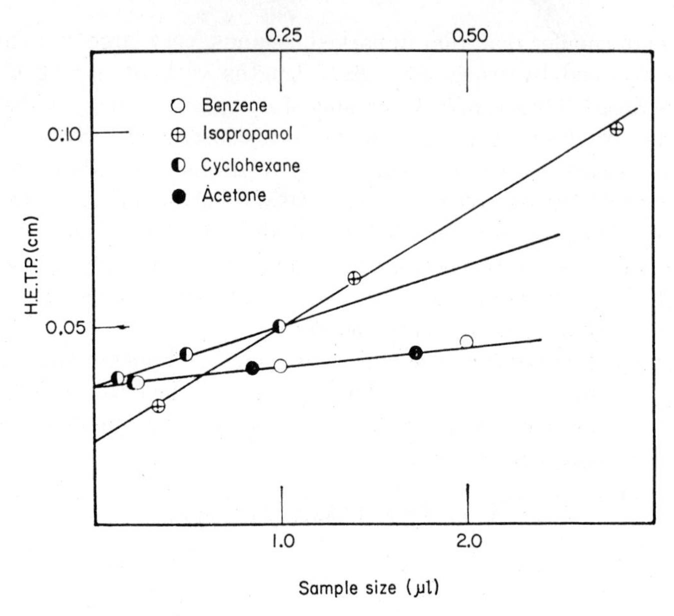

FIG. 5.21. Plot of plate-height against sample size for various vapours. Lower scale for isopropanol, upper scale for the other vapours. From Bohemen and Purnell (*6*).

(*a*) *Effect of the Proportion of Stationary Phase on the Variation of Performance with Sample Size*

With a small sample, performance is best when the proportion of stationary phase is small. However, the smaller the proportion of stationary phase, the smaller the retention volume. From Fig. 5.9, the smaller the retention volume, the smaller the threshold value of σ_I less than which broadening due to sample size is negligible. Hence, with a small proportion of stationary phase, performance falls sharply with increase in sample. With a large proportion of stationary phase, however, though the plate-number for small samples is smaller, retention volumes are larger, so that the threshold for σ_I is larger, and performance does not fall so rapidly with increase in sample size. This argument is illustrated in Fig. 5.22 by the results of DeWet and Pretorius.

(*b*) *Effect of Partition Coefficient on the Variation of Performance with Sample Size*

The greater the partition coefficient of a vapour, the larger is V_R, and hence, as above, the smaller the effect of quantity. This is illustrated from the results of DeWet and Pretorius in Fig. 5.23 for benzene and toluene.

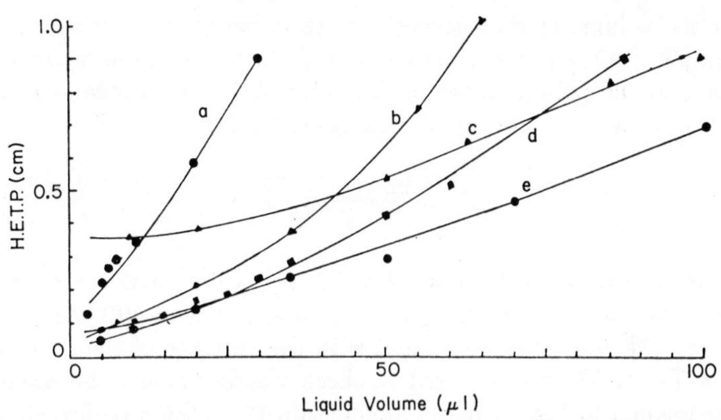

FIG. 5.22. Plot of plate-height against sample size with proportion of stationary phase as parameter. With small values of m, the plate-height with small samples is small, but it increases rapidly with increase in sample. With large values of m, the variation of plate-height with sample is much less steep. (a) 10% w/w stationary liquid; (b) 20%; (c) 44.5%; (d) 25%; (e) 35%. From DeWet and Pretorius (*51*).

(c) *Effect of the Plate-Number of the Column on the Variation of Performance with Sample Size*

Again making use of Fig. 5.9, the larger the plate-number, $\mathfrak{N}$, the smaller the threshold of sample size greater than which sample size causes the performance to deteriorate, and the greater the proportional deterioration produced by a given sample.

If it is assumed that all the broadening due to sa nle size is accounted

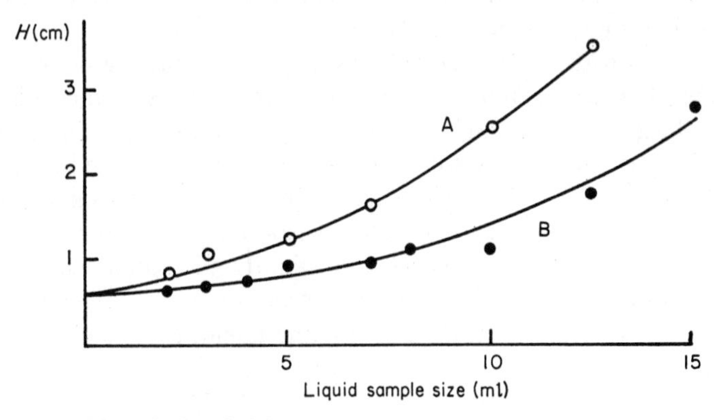

FIG. 5.23. Plot of plate-height against sample size with partition coefficient as parameter: (A) benzene, (B) toluene. The latter, having the greater retention volume, gives peaks the plate-height equivalent to which increases more slowly with increase in sample. After DeWet and Pretorius (*51*).

for by the volume of the vapour, a relation between the broadening and the sample size is easily calculable in terms of the retention volume of the vapour and the plate-number of the column. If the sample of molecular weight M weighs w mg, then its volume at t°C is:

$$V_I = \frac{22.4w(t + 273)}{273M}, \tag{5.107}$$

which, for quantities of the order of milligrams will normally be of the order of cubic centimetres. For example, 5 mg of n-hexane at 40°C has a volume of 1.5 cc. This may then be related with the variance of the peak by Fig. 5.9b, or Eq. (5.53) may be used to check whether or not the sample size is large enough to have a material effect on the column performance. For example, in a column of 2000 plates in which n-hexane has $V_R = 500$, the threshold value of V_I according to Eq. (5.53) is 11 cc, so that the threshold sample size is between 30 and 40 mg.

Whereas the above effect of sample size can be accurately assessed, other effects cannot. The way in which the results of DeWet and Pretorius agree with their theoretical predictions based on the premise that only the vapour volume is relevant suggests that, in their circumstances, other effects are small. DeWet and Pretorius, however, have aimed more at testing the theory than at attempting to separate the maximum sample sizes in a given column; for example, their vapours were usually diluted with carrier gas to prevent their concentration becoming too great. When large samples are put into a column, broadening due to their concentration and due to non-linear isotherms inevitably occurs. Such further discussion as is possible is given in Section 6.6.

An exception to the general rule given at the beginning of this section is given by Bethea and Smutz (*52*), who have reported experiments in which the plate-height shows a minimum when expressed as a function of sample size; with large samples, performance declines with increase in sample as described above, but with very small samples, the performance declines with *decrease* in sample. The probable reason for this is that the authors used column of which the supports were slightly adsorptive, and when the sample was small enough that the adsorption was not completely masked by solution of the sample in the partitioning liquid, excessively broadened peaks were obtained.

References

1. Klinkenberg, A., and Sjenitzer, F., *Chem. Eng. Sci.* **5**, 258 (1956).
2. Khan, M. A., *Nature* **186**, 800 (1960).
3. Van Deemter, J. J., Zuiderweg, F. J., and Klinkenberg, A., *Chem. Eng. Sci.* **5**, 271 (1956).

4. Gluekauf, E., *in* "Vapour Phase Chromatography," Proceedings of the First Symposium, London, May, 1956 (D. H. Desty, ed.), p. 30. Academic Press, New York, 1957.
5. Gluekauf, E., *in* "Gas Chromatography 1958," Proceedings of the Second Symposium, Amsterdam, May, 1958 (D. H. Desty, ed.), p. 33. Academic Press, New York, 1958.
6. Bohemen, J., and Purnell, J. H., *in* "Gas Chromatography 1958," Proceedings of the Second Symposium, Amsterdam, May, 1958 (D. H. Desty, ed.), p. 6. Academic Press New York, 1958.
7. Littlewood, A. B., *in* "Gas Chromatography 1958," Proceedings of the Second Symposium, Amsterdam, May, 1958 (D. H. Desty, ed.), p. 23. Academic Press, New York, 1958.
8. Giddings, J. C., *Nature* **184**, 357 (1959).
9. Klinkenberg, A., and Sjenitzer, F., *Nature* **187**, 1023 (1960).
10. Giddings, J. C., *J. Chromatog.* **3**, 520 (1960).
11. Gluekauf, E., Barker, K. H., and Kitt, G. P., *Discussions Faraday Soc.* **7**, 199 (1949).
12. Lapidus, L., and Amundsen, N. R., *J. Phys. Chem.* **56**, 984 (1954).
13. Thomas, H. C., *Ann. N.Y. Acad. Sci.* **49**, 161 (1948).
14. Golay, M. J. E., *Anal. Chem.* **29**, 928 (1957).
15. Golay, M. J. E., *in* "Gas Chromatography 1958," Proceedings of the Second Symposium, Amsterdam, May, 1958 (D. H. Desty, ed.), p. 36. Academic Press, New York, 1958.
16. Young, J. F., *in* "Gas Chromatography," I.S.A. Symposium, 1957 (V. J. Coates, H. J. Noebels, and I. S. Fagerson, eds.), p. 15. Academic Press, New York, 1958.
17. Funk, J. E., and Houghton, G., *Nature* **188**, 389 (1960).
18. Giddings, J. C., and Eyring, H., *J. Phys. Chem.* **59**, 416 (1955).
19. Beynon, J. H., Clough, S., Crookes, D. A., and Lester, G. R., *Trans. Faraday Soc.* **54**, 705 (1958).
20. "Handbook of Chemistry and Physics." Chemical Rubber Publ., Cleveland, Ohio, published annually.
21. Taylor, G., *Proc. Roy. Soc.* **A219**, 186 (1953).
22. Aris, R., *Proc. Roy. Soc.* **A235**, 67 (1956).
23. Kieselbach, R., *Anal. Chem.* **32**, 880 (1960).
24. Desty, D. H., and Goldup, A., Third Symposium on Gas Chromatography, Edinburgh, June, 1960, Paper No. 11 (Preprint).
25. DeVault, D., *J. Am. Chem. Soc.* **65**, 532 (1943).
26. James, D. H., and Phillips, C. S. G., *J. Chem. Soc.* p. 1066 (1954).
27. Bosanquet, C. H., and Morgan, G. O., *in* "Vapour Phase Chromatography," Proceedings of the First Symposium, London, May, 1956 (D. H. Desty, ed.), p. 35. Academic Press, New York, 1957.
28. Bosanquet, C. H., *in* "Gas Chromatography 1958," Proceedings of the Second Symposium, Amsterdam, May, 1958 (D. H. Desty, ed.), p. 107. Academic Press, New York, 1958.
29. Schmauch, L. J., *Anal. Chem.* **31**, 225 (1959).
30. Johnson, H. W., and Stross, F. H., *Anal. Chem.* **31**, 357 (1959).
31. Giddings, J. C., Seager, S. L., Stucki, L. R., and Stewart, G. H., *Anal. Chem.* **32**, 867 (1960).
32. DeWet, W. J., and Pretorius, V., *Anal. Chem.* **32**, 1396 (1960).
33. Scott, R. P. W., *in* "Gas Chromatography 1958," Proceedings of the Second Symposium, Amsterdam, May, 1958 (D. H. Desty, ed.), p. 189. Academic Press, New York, 1958.

34. Keulemans, A. I. M., and Kwantes, A., *in* "Vapour Phase Chromatography," Proceedings of the First Symposium, London, May, 1956 (D. H. Desty, ed.), p. 15. Academic Press, New York, 1957.
35. Cheshire, J. D., and Scott, R. P. W., *J. Inst. Petroleum* **44,** 74 (1958).
36. Desty, D. H., Godfrey, F. M., and Harbourn, C. L. A., *in* "Gas Chromatography 1958," Proceedings of the Second Symposium, Amsterdam, May, 1958 (D. H. Desty, ed.), p. 200. Academic Press, New York, 1958.
37. Desty, D. H., Goldup, A., and Whyman, B. H. F., *J. Inst. Petroleum* **45,** 287 (1959).
38. Scott, R. P. W., and Hazeldean, G. S. F., Third Symposium on Gas Chromatography, Edinburgh, June, 1960, Paper No. 10 (Preprint).
39. Duffield, J. J., and Rogers, L. H., *Anal. Chem.* **32,** 340 (1960).
40. Golay, M. J. E., *in* "Gas Chromatography," I.S.A. Symposium, 1957 (V. J. Coates, H. J. Noebels, and I. S. Fagerson, eds.), p. 1. Academic Press, New York, 1958.
41. Purnell, J. H., *Nature* **184,** 2004 (1959).
42. Purnell, J. H., *J. Chem. Soc.* p. 1268 (1960).
43. Scott, R. P. W., Third Symposium on Gas Chromatography, Edinburgh, June, 1960, Discussion.
44. Loyd, R. J., Ayers, B. O., and Karasek, F. W., *Anal. Chem.* **32,** 698 (1960).
45. Golay, M. J. E., *Nature* **182,** 1146 (1958).
46. Purnell, F. H., and Quinn, C. P., Third Symposium on Gas Chromatography, Edinburgh, June, 1960, Paper No. 12 (Preprint).
47. Pollard, F. H., and Hardy, C. J., *Chem. & Ind.* (*London*) p. 1145 (1955).
48. Dimbat, M., Porter, P. E., and Stross, F. H., *Anal. Chem.* **28,** 290 (1956).
49. Huyten, F. H., Beersum, W. van, and Rijnders, G. W. A., Third Symposium on Gas Chromatography, Edinburgh, June, 1960, Paper No. 15 (Preprint).
50. Baker, W. J., Norlin, H. L., Zinn, T. L., and Wall, R. F., *Am. Chem. Soc., Div. Petrol. Chem., Preprints* **2,** No. 4, D43 (1957).
51. DeWet, W. J., and Pretorius, V., *Anal. Chem.* **32,** 169 (1960).
52. Bethea, R. M., and Smutz, M., *Anal. Chem.* **31,** 1211 (1959).

Chapter 6

The Preparation and Use of Columns

6.1. Preparation of Packed Columns

The packing material in a partition column is a mixture of a support and a stationary liquid. This mixture is packed into the column tube, and then the column is pre-conditioned. Adsorbents for use in adsorption columns usually require some kind of treatment before packing (Section 3.9). All these operations require as much art as science, and it is not possible to describe exact techniques by which workers could reproduce similar columns. General instructions for column packing, however, are standard, and are described below.

(*a*) *Supports*

Table 6.1 lists in rough order of importance the supports that have been used in chromatography; the great majority of work has been done using the first two. Relevant notes on the supports are given below.

TABLE 6.1

Gas Chromatographic Supports

Support	Reference
Diatomaceous earth	*1* and many others; for reviews, see *2*, *3*
Crushed firebrick	*4* and many others
Glass beads	*5*, *6*, *7*
Glass powder	*8*, *9*, *10*
Metal helices	*11*, *12*
Sodium chloride	*9*, *10*, *13*, *14*
Mixed salts contained in domestic detergent	*15*, *16*, *17*
Powdered Teflon	*18*, *19*
Carborundum	*20*
Sintered glass wafers	*21*
Crushed white tile	*22*

Kieselguhr was used by James and Martin (*1*) in their original work on gas partition chromatography. They used a commercial calcined and extracted brand, Celite (Johns Manville Company) of Californian origin, which is the most commonly used brand of all the kieselguhrs. This product is largely used as a filter aid in industrial filtration, as a white filler in paper, etc., and as a component of thermal insulation material. Only the larger size grades are used in gas chromatography; the size distribution is listed in Table 6.2 (*3*). Kieselguhr is largely composed of silica, but contains small quantities of other oxides (Table 6.3), which have an important

TABLE 6.2

SIZE DISTRIBUTION OF CELITES[a]

Size (μ)	Celite 503 %	Celite 535 %	Celite 545 %
>40	12.0	17.5	24.0
40–20	25.5	32.0	52.0
20–10	29.0	32.0	18.5
10–6	19.5	16.0	4.5
6–2	13.5	2.5	1.0
>2	0.5	—	—
Surface area (m^2/g)	8	7	6

[a] From Cummins (*3*).

TABLE 6.3

COMPOSITION OF CALCINED DIATOMACEOUS EARTH[a]

SiO_2	91.0%
Al_2O_3	4.6
Fe_2O_3	1.9
CaO	1.4
MgO	0.4
Volatile	0.3
Other	0.4

[a] From Hull *et al.* (*2*).

effect on its use as a support (Section 6.3). It may absorb up to about 40% by weight of stationary liquid without becoming unduly sticky, but with such a proportion, it is not freely flowing.

Several proprietary brands of ground firebrick suitable for gas chromatography are available. Firebrick can hold a larger proportion of stationary phase than kieselguhr without becoming sticky, and material with up to

40% of liquid is freely flowing. This is a great advantage over kieselguhr in the rapid manufacture of columns. It has the drawback that its mechanical strength is smaller than that of Celite, so that its granules are rather easily reduced to fine powder. There is little to choose between firebrick and kieselguhr on grounds of plate-height (*23*), though at sizes below about 60 mesh B.S.S., firebrick gives considerably smaller values of C than kieselguhr (Section 5.17).

Glass beads are manufactured in sizes down to at least 0.1 mm diameter, and the smaller sizes are used in gas chromatography. Glass powder is different in that its particles are not spherical; it is familiar in the laboratory for the manufacture of sintered glass apparatus. The maximum proportion by weight of stationary liquid on beads of about 0.1 mm diameter is about 2 to 3%. This is very much smaller than for kieselguhr or firebrick, but since the packing density of glass beads is about 8 times that for kieselguhr and 4 times that for firebrick, the disparity in volume proportions is very much less. The surface area of glass beads is of the order of 0.1 m^2/g, which is much smaller than that of kieselguhr or firebrick, though, again, on account of the difference in packing densities, the ratio of surface area of support to weight of stationary liquid on glass beads is comparable with that on kieselguhr or firebrick.

Metal helices are normally used for packing distillation columns. They have a restricted use in gas chromatography, since they have practically no adsorptive properties. They are too openly packed and hold too little stationary liquid for common use.

Desty and Harbourn (*16*) have used a commercial domestic detergent as a column packing, in which case, the partitioning agent is the alkylaryl sulfonate, and the support is the mixture of inorganic salts composing the remainder of the product. Decora and Dineen (*17*) have extracted the organic detergents from domestic detergent, and have used the granular residue as a convenient support for any other stationary liquid phase. This material is very absorptive, and can contain up to 70% by weight of liquid before becoming sticky.

(*b*) *Preparation of Column Material*

Most powdered supports contain fines which are deleterious to column efficiency (Section 5.17), and which should be removed before use, e.g., by sedimentation. Thus, kieselguhr may be stirred up with ample water, allowed to settle for 3 minutes (*24*), after which the water containing suspended fines is decanted. This operation may be combined with any wet chemical treatment which may be required (Section 6.3). The support may be then dried in an oven, usually at 110° to 200°C.

The blending of the support and the stationary liquid is an important operation which must be done carefully if the resulting column is to perform well. It is also important that the proportion of support to liquid is accurately known, so that if the weight of material packed into a column is known, the weight of stationary liquid may be calculated, and all the advantages accruing from knowledge of specific retention volumes may be used. Four methods of blending may be recognised.

(1) *Slurrying.* The support is weighed out, and a sufficient quantity of volatile solvent in which the stationary liquid is miscible or at least soluble is added to make a slurry. The stationary liquid is added, and the slurry is continuously stirred while the solvent is evaporated, e.g., in a stream of hot air. When the solvent is substantially all removed, the column material is shaken for some time, e.g., half an hour. This method, or some variant of it, is most commonly used.

(2) *Simple mixing.* This method was originally used by James and Martin. The support is weighed out, the correct quantity of stationary liquid is weighed in by difference, and the mixture is shaken for a long period, e.g., 8 hours.

(3) *Spraying.* It has been suggested that a more even distribution of stationary liquid may be made by spraying it on to the support through an atomiser, but there is no evidence that this method has definite advantages.

(4) *Impregnation in a column.* Smith (*25*) recommends the following procedure as an alternative to (1) in order to eliminate the possibility of unevenness due to irregular evaporation. Pack the dry support into a column (not the chromatographic column), and through this allow a solution of the stationary liquid in a volatile solvent to percolate until the concentration of the liquid emerging from the end of the column is the same as that entering at the beginning; this may be seen, for example, by mixing emerging and entering fluids and observing presence or absence of mixing striae. When entering and emerging concentrations are similar, there is a uniform concentration along the column. The column is then extruded, and the solvent evaporated. The weight of stationary phase incorporated in this manner is given by the product of the pore volume of the column and the concentration of the solution.

It is scarcely possible to compare the over-all merits of these methods. In the hands of Baker, Lee, and Wall, at least, different methods produce similar results (*26*).

(*c*) *Packing the Column*

Packing materials composed of adsorbents, of partition liquids on firebrick, or of small proportions of liquids on kieselguhr are completely freely flowing, and may be poured into the column tube. Packing materials with large (e.g., > 20%) proportions of liquid on kieselguhr, and most of those using other less porous supports, are more or less sticky, and require assistance in bedding down into a column. The flow of sticky material into the column tube is accelerated by vibrating the column, e.g., by holding the column against a rapidly rotating spindle one segment of which has been cut away, or against a domestic massage vibrator. In addition, it is often desirable to tamp the packing down into the tube with a close-fitting rod. Experience in such tamping enables one to judge and reproduce the packing density with reasonable accuracy. The intensity of vibration is also a relevant factor. Too weak a vibration is insufficient for the sticky particles to bed down evenly. With too strong a vibration, the amplitude of the motion in the particles is so great that the packing expands. There is thus an optimum, which is normally found by experience. The above phenomenon has been confirmed and studied in connection with the packing of powders by Macrae *et al.* (*27*).

(*d*) *Conditioning of the Column*

A newly packed column invariably contains small quantities of residual solvent from the preparation of packing material, together with water condensed from the atmosphere and other volatile contaminants; these may be removed by heating the column in a stream of carrier gas in a gas-chromatographic apparatus until the base-line remains steady. Cooper *et al.* (*28*) then continue heating the column until the base-line begins to drift again due to volatilisation of stationary liquid, in order to determine the maximum operating temperature of the column. The final weight of a column should be recorded after a preliminary heat-treatment to remove superfluous volatiles, which may otherwise lead to appreciable error in calculating the mass of stationary liquid. Littlewood (*6*) has found that the efficiency of a column (using glass beads) may be improved by heating a new column in the absence of a stream of carrier gas up to a temperature where the stationary phase is appreciably volatile. The stationary liquid is held by surface tension around points of contact of particles of support, and, since all its surfaces are concave, it tends to equilibrate itself so that all surfaces have the same curvature. If the support is carefully size-graded, this has the result that each point of contact holds the same amount of liquid, thus producing less randomness in the distribution of stationary liquid.

6.2. Preparation of Capillary Columns

Capillary columns have been constructed of copper, stainless steel (*29*), glass (*30,31*), and nylon (*32*); of these, copper is liable to deleterious oxidation if used at high temperatures (*33*), and nylon has a slight retention for some compounds, e.g., higher aromatic hydrocarbons, but not paraffins (*32*). Stainless steel is less frangible than glass, although coils of fine glass tube are remarkably resilient. Capillary columns are invariably used in coils; Desty, Haresnape, and Whyman (*34*) have described a simple machine for constructing uniform coils of fine glass tube, in which 4- to 6-mm glass tubing is fed by rollers into a furnace from which it is drawn at 50 times the speed into a semicircular metal tube heated to the softening point of the glass. It emerges from this as the required helix. Glass or metal capillaries may be used up to at least 250°C. The maximum temperature of nylon columns is between 100° and 180°C, depending on the kind of nylon.

The coating of stationary liquids for capillary columns must be very thin and very uniform. Two methods of application have been developed.

(1) Fill the capillary completely with a solution of the stationary liquid in a volatile solvent, close one end, and feed the capillary steadily into a furnace so as to evaporate the solvent. In this procedure, all the stationary liquid in the column is applied to the walls, and a simple calculation enables the required film thickness to be related with the concentration of the solution. Golay has used a 1% solution in methyl chloride, with a furnace at 100°C (*29*).

(2) Fill the capillary completely with a solution of the stationary liquid in a volatile solvent, and then blow it out by applying pressure at one end of the column. Evaporate the remainder of the solvent by blowing gas through the column for a further period, e.g., 1 hour. In this procedure, most of the stationary liquid which was in the column is blown out, leaving only that contained in the solution wetting the walls. Thus, a larger concentration of stationary liquid is required than for method (1), and it is not possible to calculate the layer thickness from the concentration of the solution. Current practice uses solutions of about 10% stationary liquid (*31,32,35*). A 20% solution, as used by Dijkstra and Goey (*36*), is probably too concentrated.

From Sections 5.4 and 5.14, it is seen that the thickness of the stationary liquid should not be greater than about 1/300th of the tube diameter, and, from Sections 4.7 and 5.14, the desirability of large values of k implies that the film thickness should not be unnecessarily small. With capillary columns of diameter about 0.01 inch, therefore, the film thickness should be neither very much greater nor very much less than 0.00003 inch, which is approximately 1μ. The above procedures secure approximately correct film thickness. Dijkstra and Goey (*36*) report a film thickness of 5μ, which is clearly too great and does not enable capillary columns to be used to their best advantage.

Many workers have found that capillary columns work much more satisfactorily when coated with non-polar stationary phases than when coated with polar stationary phases; with the latter the plate-height may well be several centimetres. Though this fact is generally familiar, published data on the poor performance of polar capillary columns is not unnaturally sparse. The point is well illustrated, however, by comparison of the excellent chromatograms of fatty acid esters obtained by Lipsky *et al.* (*37*) on Apiezon L capillaries with the same authors' mediocre chromatogram taken on a capillary coated with diethylene glycol glutarate polyester (Section 11.6).

6.3. Reactivity of Supports in Packed Columns

Ideally, the support in a packed column is inert; but, in practice it may cause chemical reaction of the vapours either between themselves or with the stationary liquid, it may produce tailing, or it may influence retention volumes. All these effects are generally attributed to the adsorptive properties of the support; the reactions are caused through heterogeneous catalysis, the tailing through superimposition of the usual asymmetrical peak shape produced on adsorbents, and the change in retention volumes through the addition of the adsorption to the partition. It should be recalled that the supports mainly used in gas partition chromatography are largely composed of silica, which, when activated, is also used as an adsorbent in gas adsorption chromatography.

The adsorptive properties of various supports have been studied by several workers (*38–40*). The relevance of the adsorption is clearly shown in Fig. 6.1, which shows the chromatogram of a mixture of the five hexane alkanes taken on a column of pure Celite kieselguhr at 0°C (*38*). Similar

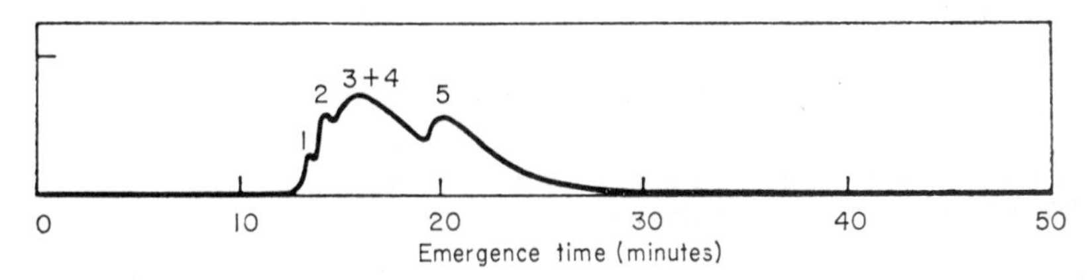

Fig. 6.1. Chromatogram of a mixture of the hexanes on a column of pure Celite kieselguhr at 0°C. Eggertsen and Knight (*38*). 1, 2,2-Dimethylbutane; 2, 2,3-dimethylbutane; 3, 2-methylpentane; 4, 3-methylpentane; 5, *n*-hexane.

results are obtained by Bens (*39*). Purnell, however, has tried to correlate the retention produced by adsorption alone on a particular support with the extra retention found on a partition column using that support, and has found that the adsorption measured on the pure support is in general insufficient to account for its influence on the retention volumes (*40*). This anomaly remains unexplained. Furthermore, Purnell finds that the adsorption isotherms of solutes on supports are virtually linear up to about 5% concentration of vapour. This is normally not exceeded inside chromatographic peaks, so that the explanation of tailing as the sum of partition and adsorption is suspect.

Of the common supports, there is fairly general agreement that firebrick is more adsorptive than Celite (see, e.g., discussion to reference *23*). Firebrick is generally brown in colour, and it has been thought that brown firebricks, presumably containing much iron, are more adsorptive than colourless samples. Hishta, Messerly, and Reschke (*7*) consider that glass beads are much less adsorptive than either kieselguhr or firebrick, but this is not universal experience, and, as indicated in Section 6.1, there is no obvious reason why it should be so; for example, Naves (*9,10*) finds that glass powder used as a support causes the catalytic isomerisation of terpenes.

The choice of support has much more effect on the chromatography of polar compounds than on that of less reactive compounds such as hydrocarbons. Thus, petroleum hydrocarbons can normally be analysed on all but the most adsorptive columns, which would produce bad tailing of other compounds. This is illustrated by Fig. 6.2, which shows two peaks taken

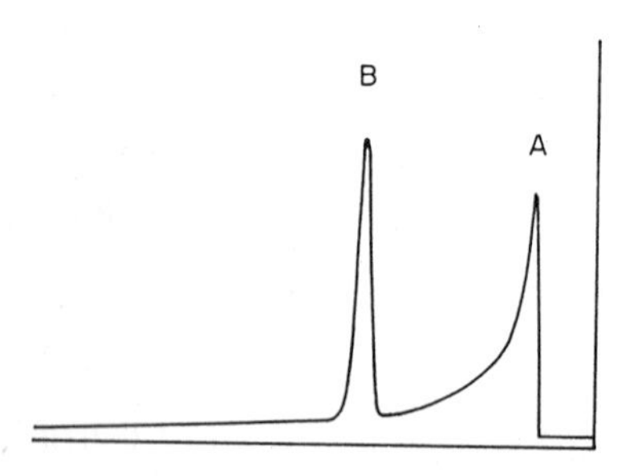

FIG. 6.2. Peaks due to ethanol (A) and octane (B) taken from a chromatogram made on a column of silicone 550 on 42 to 50 mesh firebrick, temperature 130°C. Redrawn from Johns (*41*), omitting peaks due to other components.

from a chromatogram (*41*) run on a column of silicone 550 fluid on kieselguhr. The hydrocarbon peak is narrower than the alcohol peak, even though its retention volume is more than twice as great. The effect of the adsorption of the support diminishes when the stationary liquid is itself polar.

There are two reasons for this; first, that the stationary liquid saturates the active sites of the support as described below, and second, that polar substances are more soluble in polar stationary liquids, so that the relative importance of the adsorption in the total retention is smaller.

An interesting effect of the tailing influence of the support is reported by Baker, Lee, and Wall (*26*). With either firebrick or kieselguhr, the plate-height shows a minimum as a function of the proportion of stationary liquid applied to the support. At a concentration greater than the minimum, the plate-height rises as usual with increase in the proportion of stationary phase (Section 5.13); at concentrations smaller than the minimum, the broadening produced through the influence of adsorption presumably outweighs the further reduction in plate-height because of the reduction of the thickness of the liquid layer. This observation is consistent with the variation of plate-height with sample size found by Bethea and Smutz (Section 5.20).

The influence of the adsorptive properties of the support on retention

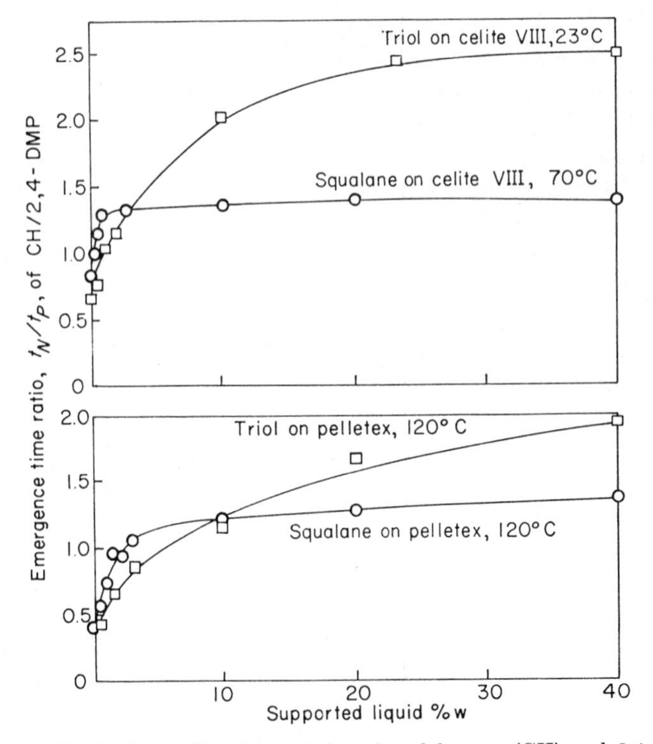

FIG. 6.3. Ratio of retention times, t_N/t_P, of cyclohexane (CH) and 2,4-dimethylpentane (2,4-DMP) as a function of proportion of stationary phase for Triol and squalane on Celite and Pelletex. Eggertsen and Knight (*38*).

volumes has been investigated for alkanes and naphthenes by Eggertsen and Knight (*38*). On some pure adsorbents, including silica and carbon, naphthenes have greater activity coefficients than alkanes, and on nearly all partitioning liquids, alkanes have greater activity coefficients than naphthenes. Thus, the authors have investigated the relative activity coefficients of the two groups of compounds as a function of the proportion of stationary liquid applied to a kieselguhr support. As examples, they have chosen cyclohexane and 2:4-dimethylpentane, which have virtually identical vapour pressures, so that retention times are in inverse ratio to activity coefficients [Eq. (3.64)]. When the proportion of stationary liquid is small or zero, the naphthene appears first, but, as the proportion increases, it is selectively retained till, at greater proportions, the alkane appears first. This is shown in Fig. 6.3 by plotting the ratio of the retention times, $t_{\text{naphthene}}/t_{\text{paraffin}}$, as a function of the proportion of stationary liquid on the adsorbent. It is seen that both on Celite and on charcoal (Pelletex) the components change their order of elution at a given concentration of stationary liquid, as is shown by the plots crossing the ordinate $t_N/t_P = 1$. When squalane is used as stationary phase, the concentration at which the partition swamps the adsorption is smaller than when a polar stationary liquid, e.g., Triol, is used, since the hydrocarbons are much more soluble in the former. It will be noted that an adsorptive kieselguhr column with a very small proportion of squalane acts similarly to the squalane-Pelletex columns described in Sections 3.11 and 11.3. They differ in that the adsorptive capacity of kieselguhr is very small, so that, though the selective acceleration of the naphthenes might otherwise be useful, the over-all retention is very small.

It is apparent that the adsorptive properties of supports are nearly always undesirable. Cures may be put in four categories:

(1) Enveloping the support, e.g., by silver metal.
(2) Temporary removal of adsorption sites.
(3) Permanent removal of adsorption sites.
(4) Saturation of adsorption sites.

(1) Ormerod and Scott (*42*) have coated a support made of firebrick by silvering it in the same way as mirrors are silvered, using the Rochelle salt process, in which a solution of ammoniacal silver nitrate and Rochelle salt containing the firebrick is slowly warmed. This process is repeated until the support has gained between 40 and 100% of its weight in silver. Microscopic examination shows that the silver forms a coherent layer over the particles of support, and the treated support may then be mixed with stationary liquid in the usual way. The treatment of the support can make a great difference in the chromatography of polar compounds, especially

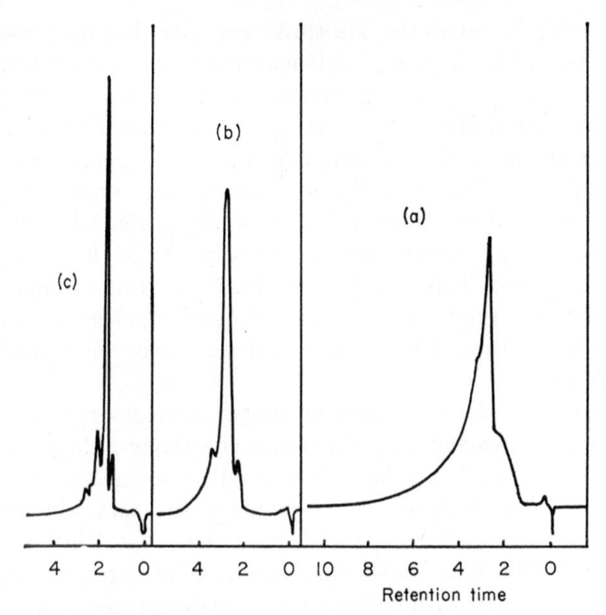

FIG. 6.4. Chromatograms of impure methylcyclohexanol on Apiezon grease L, 15% w/w on uncoated Sil-O-Cel brick dust. After Ormerod and Scott (*42*). (a) Uncoated brick dust, (b) silver coated brick dust, 3.9:10, Ag:brick, (c) silver coated brick dust, 9.5:10, Ag:brick.

using non-polar stationary phases, as is shown in Fig. 6.4. A drawback of this method is that sulfur compounds and amines attack the silver. The authors' attempts to prepare corresponding gold-treated supports failed.

(2) It is commonly accepted that the adsorption sites on siliceous supports consist of Si—OH groups, together with Al—OH and Fe—OH groups where the other elements are present. These are acidic, and indeed, the reactions caused by supports, e.g., isomerisation of olefins and terpenes, and the dehydrogenation of alcohols, are all acid-catalysed reactions. Thus several workers have tried the effect of various kinds of alkali pre-treatment to the support. For example, Holmgren (*43*) reports that alcohol dehydrogenation may be prevented by using a suppport which has merely been treated with sodium carbonate solution for 10 minutes. Mitzner and Jacobs (*44*) find that this treatment reduces chemical reactivity, but does not eliminate it. They find also that alcohol dehydrogenation may occur on capillary columns prepared in untreated tubing, but that, if the tubing is rinsed out with detergent solution, followed by caustic potash, rinsing water, methanol, acetone, chloroform, and benzene, the reactivity is removed.

Other workers have pre-treated supports with acid. According to

Purnell (*40*), this increases the adsorptive capacity, but it is possible that vigorous treatment with strong acids may leach out surface alumina and iron, thus removing many adsorption sites. Thus, Villalobos (*18*) finds that tailing in analyses of $H_2S—SO_2—NH_3$ mixtures is reduced by acid treatment, and Kirkland (*45*) finds that tailing of polar compounds on kieselguhr may be reduced by slurrying the kieselguhr with concentrated hydrochloric acid, followed by alkali and water washing. Zlatkis *et al.* (*46*) find it advantageous to pre-treat firebrick or kieselguhr with hot aqua regia for a considerable period. This detaches "peninsulars" from the main body of large particles, thus producing a mixture of roughly spherical granules and fines; the latter are then elutriated out, and the former are neutralised with alkali before use.

(3) Since many adsorption sites on supports are associated with —OH groups, a chemical reagent for such groups effectively reduces the adsorption. The methylchlorsilanes have been used by several workers for this purpose, since they replace —OH groups with inert Me—Si groups, Horning, Moscatelli, and Sweeley (*47*) pack the support into a tube, and pass dimethyldichlorsilane vapour in a stream of nitrogen through it. The support is then treated with methanol, removed from the tube, and dried, after which it is ready for the preparation of the column packing, as described in Section 6.1. They find that this technique is effective in preventing tailing of peaks on polyester stationary liquids.

The use of dimethyldichlorsilane may be criticised, since it is difunctional, with the result that, if it reacts with only one active site, one active halogen atom remains. Purnell (*40*) has found that a more satisfactory method of pre-treatment for the removal of adsorption is to reflux the support in a 5% solution of hexamethyl disilazane, $Me_3SiNHSiMe_3$, in petroleum pentane. This has the advantages that the labile hydrogens are replaced by the monofunctional Me_3Si-group, and the reagent is easier to handle than methylchlorsilanes. The extent of reaction may be studied by monitoring the ammonia which is produced.

Not all the adsorption is removed by reaction with methylsilane groups, however thorough the treatment. This suggests that not all the adsorption is associated with OH groups. Purnell finds that any adsorptive capacity remaining after the hexamethyl disilazane treatment may be removed by method (4) below, using 0.1% w/w polyethylene glycol.

(4) The active sites in adsorptive supports may be effectively incapacitated by saturating them with a non-volatile compound, which in general may be any compound of similar chemical type to the vapours the adsorption of which is required to be inhibited. An example of this procedure appears in James and Martin's original paper on gas partition chromatography (*1*), where the separations of mixtures of fatty acids on silicone

columns were much improved by the incorporation of 5% stearic acid into the stationary liquid. Another example is given by Johns (*41*), who shows that the addition of 2% of any of several polar compounds, e.g., oleic acid, polyethylene glycol, long-chain amine, to silicone or firebrick support will inhibit the tailing of alcohols and esters. The effect of polyethylene glycol is shown in Fig. 6.5.

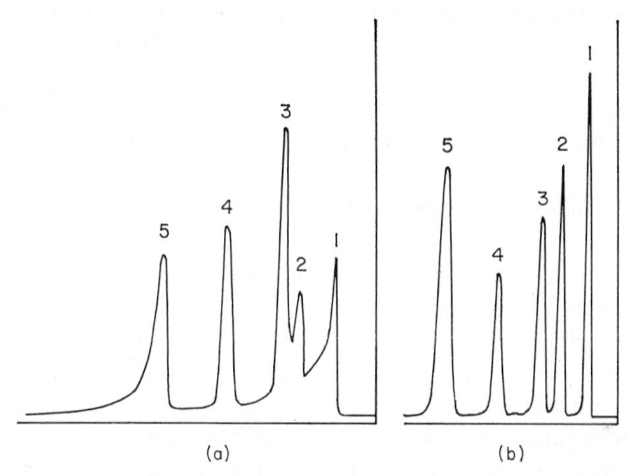

FIG. 6.5. Chromatograms on: (a) silicone 550 on 42 to 50 mesh firebrick, (b) the same, plus 2% w/w polyethylene glycol 600. After Johns (*41*). 1, Ethanol; 2, methyl ethyl ketone; 3, carbon tetrachloride; 4, octane; 5, butyl acetate.

Johns (*41*) also shows that in the chromatography of a polar vapour on a non-polar stationary liquid on an adsorptive support, previous samples of the vapour can effectively condition the column against tailing, so that separations improve with use. It is a comparatively frequent observation that in routine analyses the first one or two analyses are in error; a probable reason is that some components are almost irreversibly adsorbed, and only when such adsorption is saturated will successive runs become reproducible.

6.4. USE OF TWO STATIONARY LIQUIDS

In a mixture of more than two substances, it often happens that one pair of components overlaps when chromatographed on one stationary liquid, and that a different pair of components overlaps when it is chromatographed on another stationary liquid. It is clear that all components could be resolved by running the mixture first on a column of one stationary liquid, and then on a column of the other. This is occasionally necessary, but it is time-consuming, and it is common practice where possible to combine the two stationary phases in such a way that all components are resolved. For example, in a mixture of ethane, ethene, propane, and propene (Section 11.2) the alkanes may be separated from the alkenes with a column of silver nitrate in glycol, and the C_2's may be separated from the C_3's with a column of tri-isobutylene. A column of tri-isobutylene and silver nitrate-glycol used together, however, can separate all four components, and, with careful choice of the proportions of each stationary phase, does not cause any other overlaps. Many examples of this procedure appear in Chapter 11.

The use of two stationary liquids is generally most effective when they are of different chemical type. They may be used together in three different ways:

(1) Series columns each packed with material made with one stationary liquid.

(2) One column packed with an intimate mixture of separate packings each made with one stationary liquid.

(3) One column with a packing made from a mixture of the stationary liquids.

If no interaction occurs between the stationary liquids and if the pressure drop across columns in series is small, the retention volumes for vapours on a composite column may be presumed to be the sum of the retention volumes on each stationary liquid. Thus, if superscripts ‡ and † are used for each of two stationary liquids, the retention volume of a vapour is given by

$$V_R{}^0 = (V_R{}^0)^{\dagger} + (V_R{}^0)^{\ddagger} = V_M{}^{\dagger} + W^{\dagger}\beta^{\dagger} + V_M{}^{\ddagger} + W^{\ddagger}\beta^{\ddagger}, \qquad (6.1)$$

using the symbols of Chapter 2. When both the stationary liquids are contained in the same column, $V_M{}^{\dagger} = V_M{}^{\ddagger}$. Note that relative retention times on a composite column cannot be calculated directly from relative retention times on each component stationary liquid of the column.

Using Eqs. (2.14), (2.41), and (2.42), Eq. (6.1) becomes:

$$\frac{V_R{}'}{W^{\dagger} + W^{\ddagger}} = \frac{W^{\dagger}}{W^{\dagger} + W^{\ddagger}}(\beta^{\dagger} - \beta^{\ddagger}) + \beta^{\ddagger}. \qquad (6.2)$$

The right-hand side of this is a kind of specific retention volume for the composite column, without any correction for pressure drop (for which, see below), and the equation shows that it is a linear function of $W^{\dagger}/(W^{\dagger} + W^{\ddagger})$, which is the proportion by weight of one of the stationary liquids. Thus, a plot of the modified specific retention volume defined above, or of the corresponding retention time obtained by dividing by the flow rate, against the proportion of one of the stationary liquids should give a straight line. This has been indicated specifically by Primavesi (*48*),

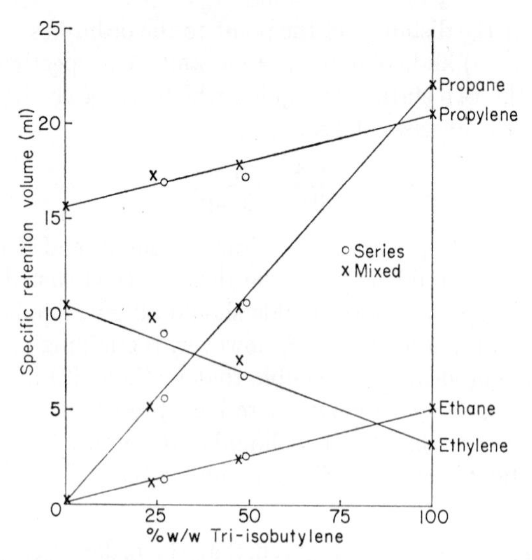

FIG. 6.6. Specific retention volumes of solutes on either series or mixed column materials as a function of the proportion of one column material. Primavesi (*48*). *Solutes:* ethylene, ethane, propylene, propane. *Solvents:* triisobutylene, ethylene glycol—silver nitrate.

using the case of ethane, ethene, propane, and propene quoted above (Fig 6.6). Such a plot gives one straight line for each component of the vapour mixture, and the value of the abscissa for which there is adequate vertical distance between all pairs of lines gives the proportions of stationary liquids for which a good separation of all the components may be secured.

In a complex mixture of vapours for which there are different overlaps on each of two pure stationary phases, a random choice of proportions of the two stationary liquids for use in a composite column may lead to a column which gives further overlaps, as indeed has often been found. This suggests that the kind of plot given in Fig. 6.6 may be generally useful in choosing proportions of stationary liquids for a composite column. A satisfactory procedure, the theory for which merely involves Eq. (6.2), is as follows:

> Run chromatograms of the mixture on each of two columns containing known weights ($M^{\dagger}$ and $M^{\ddagger}$) of different stationary liquids. Mark the adjusted retention volumes (or retention times if the flow rates are equal) of each component of each chromatogram on each of two parallel ordinates. Join the marks of each component on each ordinate by a straight line. Choose a point (A) on the abscissa joining the two ordinates such that there is adequate vertical distance between all pairs of

lines. Then, if the distances of the point to the ordinates corresponding to the column (†) and column (‡) are $a^\dagger$ and $a^\ddagger$, respectively, the proportions of the two stationary liquids which will give the separations indicated at the abscissa A are:

$$\frac{W^\dagger}{W^\ddagger} = \frac{M^\dagger a^\ddagger}{M^\ddagger a^\dagger}.$$

If the pressure drop across the column is small, and if the mixture of the two stationary liquids is ideal, the three methods listed above for the combination of two stationary liquids should all give similar results. This is confirmed by McFadden (*49*). If, however, the mixing of the stationary liquids is very non-ideal, it is possible that methods (2) and (3) may give different results from (1), though there is at present no evidence for this. In the extreme case that the two liquids are immiscible, as in Fig. 6.6, methods (1) and (2) should still give similar results, as is confirmed by Primavesi.

It has frequently been observed that the order of elution of components from series columns is changed if the columns are reversed. No systematic study of this phenomenon has been published, but a simple theoretical argument shows that it will inevitably occur if the pressure drop across the columns is not small. The arrangement is illustrated in Fig. 6.7; let † refer to the first column, and let ‡ refer to the second; let symbols be as in Chapter 2. The retention time in the first column is:

$$t_{21}^\dagger = \{V_M{}^\dagger + W^\dagger\beta^\dagger\} j\left(\frac{P_2}{P_1}\right) \Big/ \dot{V}_1, \tag{6.3}$$

where $j(P_2/P_1)$ is the pressure correction factor between P_2 and P_1. The unknown quantity $\dot{V}_1$ is related to the measurable quantity $\dot{V}_o$ by the equation:

$$\dot{V}_1 = \dot{V}_o \cdot \frac{P_o}{P_1}. \tag{6.4}$$

The retention time in the second column is given by

$$t_{1o}^\ddagger = (V_M{}^\ddagger + W^\ddagger\beta^\ddagger) j\left(\frac{P_1}{P_o}\right) \Big/ \dot{V}_o. \tag{6.5}$$

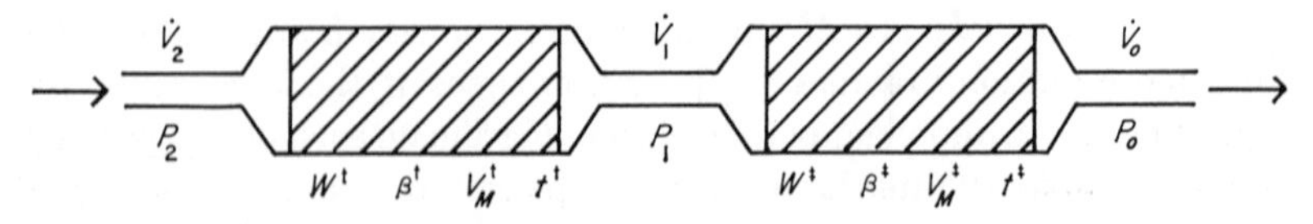

FIG. 6.7. Specification of symbols for the discussion of series columns with pressure drop.

The total retention time is given by the sum of Eq. (6.5) and the product of Eqs. (6.3) and (6.4):

$$t = t_{21}^{\dagger} + t_{1o}^{\ddagger} = \left\{(V_M{\dagger} + W{\dagger}\beta{\dagger})j\left(\frac{P_2}{P_1}\right) \cdot \frac{P_1}{P_o} + (V_M{\ddagger} + W{\ddagger}\beta{\ddagger})j\left(\frac{P_1}{P_o}\right)\right\}\frac{1}{\dot{V}_o}. \quad (6.6)$$

If, for simplicity, it is assumed that the columns have similar permeabilities and dead volumes, interchanging the columns does not affect P_1, and the total retention time is:

$$t = t_{21}^{\ddagger} + t_{1o}^{\dagger} = \left\{(V_M{\ddagger} + W{\ddagger}\beta{\ddagger})j\left(\frac{P_2}{P_1}\right) \cdot \frac{P_1}{P_o} + (V_M{\ddagger} + W{\dagger}\beta{\dagger})j\left(\frac{P_1}{P_o}\right)\right\}\frac{1}{\dot{V}_o}. \quad (6.7)$$

Equations (6.6) and (6.7) are *not* identical except when $W{\dagger}\beta{\dagger} = W{\ddagger}\beta{\ddagger}$, and in practice this is most unlikely, since the columns have almost certainly been chosen so that $\beta{\dagger} \neq \beta{\ddagger}$. What has happened is that everything in the first column is P_1/P_o times slower than in the second column, so that a large retention in the first column has a greater effect on the over-all retention time than a similarly large retention in the second. Hence vapours that are largely retained by the first column and not by the second will come through faster when the columns are interchanged, and vapours that are largely retained by the second column and not by the first will come through more slowly on interchange.

6.5. Programmed Temperature Operation

When chromatographing a mixture of large boiling range on a column at constant temperature, the first peaks to be eluted are very high and narrow, and the last peaks are eluted as long and shallow zones after an inconveniently long retention time. The first and last peaks are also liable to give erroneous quantitative analyses; the first on account of the difficulty in measuring an area of such long boundary and the possibility of the concentration being such that the detector is non-linear; the last because of the incorporation of much noise into the peak. These drawbacks may all be overcome by increasing the temperature of the column in the course of the run, so that the initial temperature is low enough to produce reasonable shapes for the initial peaks, and the final temperature is high enough to allow the elution of the last peaks at reasonable speed. The contrast between a constant temperature run and a run with continuously

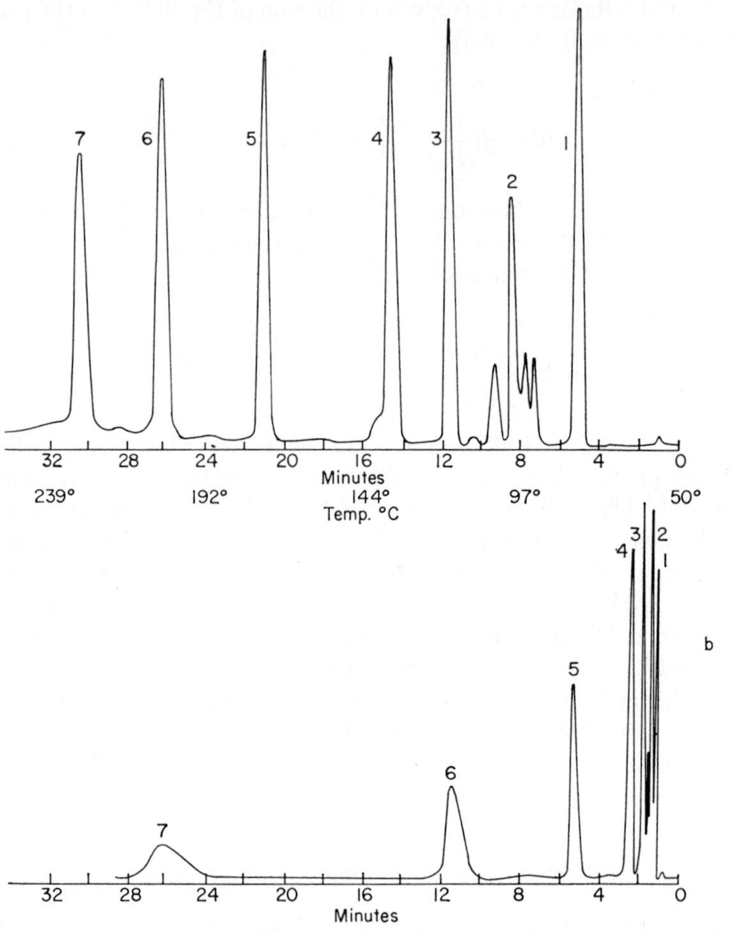

FIG. 6.8. To illustrate the effect of temperature programming. (a) Chromatogram of a hydrocarbon mixture on a temperature programmed column. (b) The same mixture chromatographed at 168°C. Nogare and Bennett (*50*). 1, Pentane; 2, hexane; 3, heptane; 4, 1-octene; 5, decane; 6, 1-dodecene; 7, 1-tetradecene.

increasing temperature is shown clearly in Fig. 6.8, from Nogare and Bennett (*50*).

The column temperature may be increased during a run in any of three ways:

(1) discontinuously either with or without interruption of the gas flow during the heating periods,

(2) continuously in an uncontrolled manner (*49,51–57*),

(3) continuously with a linear relation between temperature and time (*50,58–60*).

The method of heating is referred to as the "Programme," even though such a title is rather pretentious in some applications, and the technique is called "Programmed Temperature" operation.

(1) *Discontinuous heating.* The column is heated between the appearance of the more volatile and the less volatile components of interest. This simple method has been used regularly in applications of gas chromatography since its early days, and several examples appear in Chapter 11. It has not been made the subject of specific study.

(2) *Uncontrolled continuous heating.* In this technique, the detector is run in a separate thermostat at a temperature greater than that of the column at its hottest, and the column is heated continuously from the time the sample is introduced. In most examples of this technique, the column is contained in a furnace which is heated electrically with a constant voltage input. As the temperature rises, the rate of heat loss and also the resistance of the heating elements increase, so that the rate of increase of temperature falls. This is shown by Harrison *et al.* (*52*). If, however, the furnace is well lagged and the range of the temperature programme is not too great, the rate of rise in temperature may well be nearly linear, as was found by Griffiths, James, and Phillips (*51*). Much of the utility of programmed temperature operation is lost if as much time is taken by the furnace in cooling down for a new run as is saved in operation by its use. Thus, in practice it is necessary to use a furnace of small heat capacity, as for example is described by Roper (*61*).

(3) *Linear temperature programming.* Temperature programmed operation is most useful when the column is heated linearly at a reproducible rate. This may be done by controlling the temperature of the furnace with a standard commercial temperature controller in which the thermostatted temperature is continuously adjustable, and by linearly varying the latter, for example by driving the control with a geared-down serve-motor (*50*). Another method which is in effect the same as the above broken down into its component units is given by Harrison *et al.* (*52*).

Ideas on retention volumes, retention times, and column performances all need modification in considering chromatograms from programmed temperature columns. The most noticeable feature of chromatograms of homologous series is that, so long as the partition coefficient at the emergence temperature is large, the retention time is approximately proportional to the carbon number. This is clearly seen from Fig. 6.8; it is illustrated for a number of heating rates in Fig. 6.9 (*59*), which shows a plot of the retention time against homolog number for a homologous series. Two interpretations follow, each leading to a comparison of performances in programmed temperature operation with those in isothermal operation.

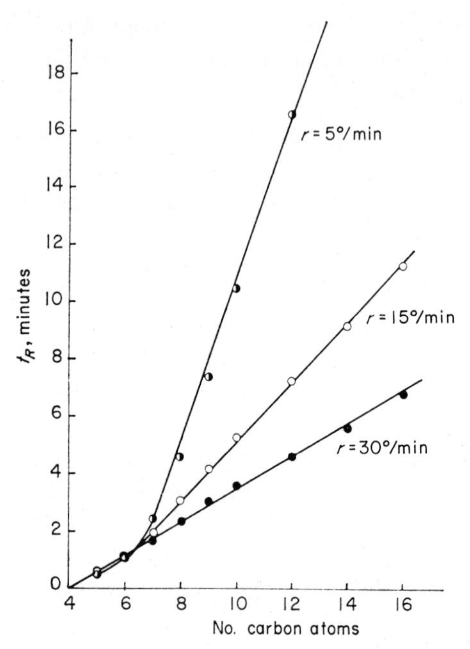

FIG. 6.9. Plots of retention time, t_R, against carbon number for various heating rates, r. Nogare and Langlois (*59*).

(1) If the number of theoretical plates is defined phenomenologically by any of the methods given in Section 4.5, then the chromatogram of Fig. 6.8a shows that the number of plates so defined rises rapidly with retention time. If it is assumed that all peaks are equally wide, then

$$\mathfrak{N} \propto t^2; \qquad \sqrt{\mathfrak{N}} \propto t. \tag{6.8}$$

The other factor in determining separation is the relative retention, which again, if regarded phenomenologically, is the ratio of retention times. It is observed that substances of which the retentions are in a constant time *ratio* on isothermal columns produce peaks with an approximately constant time *difference* on linear programmed temperature columns. Thus, if $1 + x_{23}$ is the phenomenological relative retention of two close components, then

$$x_{23} = \frac{t_3 - t_2}{t_2} = \frac{\text{const}}{t_2}, \tag{6.9}$$

i.e., the phenomenological relative retention is inversely proportional to the retention time. If we now multiply Eqs. (6.8) and (6.9), then the resolution, given by $x\sqrt{\mathfrak{N}}$ [Eq. (4.39)], is seen to be independent of t, and therefore unaffected by the increase of the phenomenological plate-number with retention time. The conclusion is that the resolution of a column is not appreciably affected by temperature programming.

(2) Habgood and Harris (*60*) argue that since a peak moves through most of the column when the column temperature is close to the emergence temperature (see below), the number of plates in the column is virtually given by:

$$\mathfrak{N} = 16\left(\frac{(t)_{T_R}}{M_{(t)}}\right)^2, \tag{6.10}$$

where $(t)_{T_R}$ is the retention time for the vapour in the same column used isothermally at the temperature at which the vapour emerges, T_R (emergence temperature), and $M_{(t)}$ is as defined in Eq. (4.28), expressed in time units. The quantity $(t)_{T_R}$ may be calculated from the emergence temperature, and from log $(t) - 1/T$ plots, as described in Section 3.6. It appears that $(t)_{T_R}$ is virtually independent of T_R, so that the number of plates calculated on this basis is more or less constant. Since in this case retention volumes of different close vapours are compared isothermally, the temperature programme does not affect the calculated relative retention, and so has little effect on the resolution of two vapours.

Both these arguments neglect the relatively small changes in plate-height with temperature and rétention volume. The conclusion is that temperature programming does not grossly affect the resolution, and this

TABLE 6.4

PLATE-HEIGHTS IN A COLUMN RUN WITH A LINEAR TEMPERATURE PROGRAMME COMPARED WITH THOSE IN THE SAME COLUMN RUN ISOTHERMALLY AT THE EMERGENCE TEMPERATURE[a]

Vapour: hexane
Parameters: heating rate and flow rate

Flow rate (ml/minute)	Heating rate (°C/minute)	T_R (°C)	Plate-height (cm)	
			Programmed	Isothermal
125	1.66	40	0.45	0.49
118	3.7	49	0.48	0.40
44	1.58	52	0.27	0.19
45	3.6	66	0.21	0.21
17	1.65	71	0.22	0.27
17	3.7	92	0.22	0.28
24	9.1	111	0.26	0.27
17	13.4	158	0.56	0.47
17	20	166	0.42	0.51

[a] See Habgood and Harris (*60*).

is illustrated in Table 6.4, which shows plate-heights in programmed runs compared with plate-heights run isothermally at the emergence temperature (*60*).

The calculation of retention times in programmed temperature operation involves the integration of the continuously changing speed of the zone of a vapour during its elution. In linear programmed operation, the temperature T at time t is given by

$$T = T_0 + rt, \tag{6.11}$$

where T_0 is the temperature at the start of the run and the heating rate. The change in temperature can cause alteration of several column parameters:

(1) the partition coefficient,
(2) the gas flow rate in the column,
(3) the pressure ratio,

of which, the first is by far the largest. All three factors have been taken into account by dal Nogare and Langlois (*59*) in the calculation of the retention time. The result is a complicated integral with a large number of parameters which can only be integrated numerically, for which purpose the authors use a digital computer.

Since the effect of temperature on the partition coefficient greatly exceeds the effect on the flow or the pressure drop, no great error is introduced into the calculations if the effects of (2) and (3) above are neglected. In this case, retention times in temperature programmed runs can be treated either graphically, by a method of Habgood and Harris (*60*), or analytically, as has been done by Giddings (*62*).

Habgood and Harris use the equation:

$$\int_{T_0}^{T_R} \frac{dT}{(V)_T} = \frac{r}{\dot{V}}, \tag{6.12}$$

where T_R is the emergence temperature, related with the retention, t_R, by Eq. (6.11), and $(V)_T$ is the retention volume at a temperature T; this equation is easily derived from equations given below. The authors plot $1/(V)_T$ against T, either empirically, or by replotting known $\log (V)_T$ versus $1/T$ plots, and by measuring the areas of these plots between T_0 and T, the integral of Eq. (6.12) may be plotted as a function of T_R. The value of T_R for a given vapour is then given by the abscissa on such a plot corresponding to an ordinate of the known value of $r/\dot{V}$. Finally, the retention time is obtained from Eq. (6.11).

The essential difficulty in deriving an analytical expression for t_R lies in the fact that the integral involved can only be expressed exactly as a power series. However, a simple approximate formula may be derived as follows.

The partition coefficient, β, may be expressed as a function of temperature by Eq. (3.54), which on integration becomes:

$$\beta = CTe^{\Delta H/RT}, \tag{6.13}$$

where C is an integration constant. The basic approximation is that $\Delta H/RT$ is always sufficiently large that $d\beta/dT$ is dominated by the exponential term, so that in Eq. (6.13), the T outside the exponential may be replaced by a constant. In this case, C may be replaced by $e^{\Delta S/R}$, where ΔS is the entropy of solution, and is treated as if independent of temperature.

From Eq. (2.17) and the definition of R_F, the speed of a zone through the column, u_v, is:

$$u_v = \frac{u}{1+k} = \frac{u}{1+k'e^X}, \tag{6.14}$$

where $k' = (We^{\Delta S/R})/V_M$ and $X = \Delta H/RT$. The distance travelled along the column by a zone is $\int u_v\,dt$, so that, if the length of the column is l, then the retention time, t_R, is given by:

$$l = \int_0^{t_R} u_v\,dt. \tag{6.15}$$

Substituting Eq. (6.14), and changing the variable of integration from t to T by Eq. (6.11),

$$l = \frac{u}{r}\int_{T_0}^{T_R} \frac{dT}{1+k'e^X}. \tag{6.16}$$

In most application of programmed temperature chromatography, $k \gg 1$, so that $1 + k \approx k$, and this becomes

$$\frac{lrk'}{u} = \int_{T_0}^{T_R} e^{-X}\,dT. \tag{6.17}$$

This may be integrating using the approximation mentioned above, by dividing the right-hand side of Eq. (6.17) inside the integral by a function of T which makes it immediately integrable, and multiplying the right-hand side by the constant value of the same function at a temperature intermediate between T_0 and T_R. By the nature of the approximation, the choice of the intermediate temperature is not critical. Giddings (*62*) chooses such a value that, on performing the integration, the result is:

$$\frac{Rrlk'}{u\,\Delta H} = \frac{e^{-X_R}}{(X_R-1)^2} - \frac{e^{-X_0}}{(X_0-1)^2}. \tag{6.18}$$

If T_R is considerably greater than T_0, the second term may be neglected, and

$$\frac{Rrlk'}{u\,\Delta H} = \frac{e^{-X_R}}{(X_R + 1)^2}. \tag{6.19}$$

In this equation, $T_R = \Delta H/RX_R$, and all the quantities on the left-hand side are known or knowable. Thus, T_R may be computed numerically.

The significance of Eq. (6.19) may be demonstrated by using the rather gross approximation that unity may be neglected in comparison with X_R, so that the equation becomes, after rearrangement:

$$T_R = \frac{-\Delta H/R}{\ln\left\{\dfrac{rlk'\,\Delta H}{RuT_R^2}\right\}}. \tag{6.20}$$

Let z equal the argument of the logarithm. The behaviour of Eq. (6.20) is apparent when it is recalled that $d(\ln z)/dz = 1/z$, so that the larger z is, the smaller the variation of the logarithm with change of any of the quantities composing z. Thus, when z is large,

$$T_R \propto -\Delta H. \tag{6.21}$$

Hence, when z is large, a plot of retention time or emergence temperature against heat of solution should be linear. Successive homologs have constant increments to ΔH, as described in Section 3.6, so that the linear plot of emergence temperature against carbon number shown in Fig. 6.9 is explained. If z is to be large, the column length, heating rate, retention volume, and heat of solution must be adequately large, and the flow rate must not be too large. The specific effect of ΔH is seen from Fig. 6.9; when this falls below a certain value, its linear relation with emergence temperature fails. Increase in flow rate, reduction in heating rate and in retention volume, and decrease in column length all contribute to performing the whole elution in conditions that there is insufficient temperature rise between introduction and emergence. It is clear that in this case Eq. (6.20) must inevitably fail, for the elution approaches isothermal elution, in which case the usual logarithmic relation between retention time and heat of solution must inevitably supervene.

The linear relation between T_R or t_R and homolog number is approximate even though z is large, partly because of the approximations involved in calculating Eq. (6.20), partly because successive increments in ΔH for homologs are a function of temperature, and partly because of the temperature dependence of flow rate and pressure ratio. In particular, especially with constant mass-flow rate, the time between successive homologs declines with increase in homolog number.

The approximate proportionality of ΔH and T_R may be interpreted in a manner which shows the nature of programmed temperature chromatography. The approximate constancy of $\Delta H/T_R$ recalls Trouton's law [Eq.

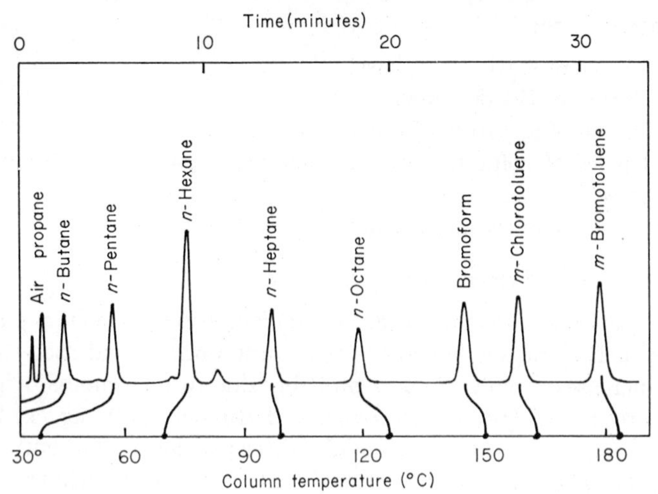

FIG. 6.10. Linear temperature programmed chromatogram illustrating that vapours may emerge at temperatures close to their normal boiling points. After Habgood and Harris (*60*).

(3.34)] for boiling points. In programmed temperature chromatography in conditions that z is large, vapours spend the great majority of their residence time in the first few per cent of the column, and only when the temperature comes within a few degrees of T_R do they begin to move appreciably through the column, which they do at a rapidly increasing rate on account of the large value of $d\beta/dT$. Vapours may, therefore, be described as evaporating out of the column at a temperature T_R in the same way that vapours in a distillation column boil out at their boiling point; and both processes obey Trouton's law. The analogy between programmed temperature chromatography and boiling is shown clearly in a chromatogram given by Habgood and Harris (*60*) (Fig. 6.10) in which vapours chromatographed on a column in which differences in activity coefficients are small all emerge at temperatures close to their boiling points.

6.6. Preparative Columns

Many workers have scaled up analytical gas chromatography for the preparation of small pure samples. The scaling up introduces a number of new problems. The general effect is that, as the quantity increases, the column performance declines; this may be analysed under three headings:

(a) Change in performance with diameter (Section 5.18).
(b) Change in performance with sample size (Section 5.20).
(c) Change in input distribution with sample size (Section 5.7).

Other aspects are:

(d) Choice of stationary phase.
(e) Design of the detector.
(f) Design of apparatus for collecting products.
(g) Choice of column materials and carrier gas, especially as regards price.
(h) Adaptation for automatic batchwise operation.

(*a*) *Change in Performance with Diameter*

As described in Section 5.18, no problem arises for columns of up to about ½ inch diameter, but above that most workers find that the plate-height increases rapidly. This is probably due to unevenness of packing, and the results of Huyten, Beersum, and Rijnders (*63*) suggest that the unevenness usually takes the form of tighter packing at the centre than at the outside. These authors have found that the mode of packing is critical, as is shown in Table 6.5, but there is no obvious logic behind the results.

TABLE 6.5

EFFECT OF PACKING METHOD AND MESH SIZE ON COLUMN PERFORMANCE[a]

Column length: 1 m
Column diameter: 3 inches
Carrier gas: 385 litres/hour
Sample: 1 ml *n*-pentane

Temperature: 22°C
Packing: 30/100 w/w silicone oil MC 200/200 on Sil-O-Cel

Mode of packing	Mesh size (B.S.S.)	Mean plate-number
Pouring	30–40	250
Pouring followed by gentle beating	30–40	120
Vibration	30–40	220
Beating	30–40	330
Beating together with a filling speed of 20 g/minute	30–40	500
Vibration plus beating	30–40	400
Vibration plus beating	50–80	315
Vibration plus beating	20–70	300

[a] See Huyten *et al.* (*63*).

Since the result which gives the smallest plate-height also gives the largest velocity gradient across the column (*63*), it seems that none of the packing methods listed is ideal.

(*b*) *Change in Performance with Sample Size*

As described in Section 5.20, the larger the sample, the worse the performance. The steepness of the decline in performance with increase in sample is greater when the proportion of stationary phase is smaller, and if it is assumed that a preparative column is to be designed so as to have as large a throughput as possible, the proportion of stationary phase should be large. A large proportion of stationary phase implies a long retention time, so a further conclusion is that the larger the sample, the longer the separation time for a given resolution.

The effect of temperature on the maximum sample size for a given resolution is complicated. Lowering the temperature increases resolution on account of increase in relative retentions (Section 3.6) and on account of decrease in plate-height (Section 5.15), and, with small samples, this is decisive. With large samples, furthermore, the lower the temperature, the longer the retention volume, and, according to Section 5.20, the smaller the effect of quantity. All these arguments, however, may well be upset by the fact that the lower the temperature, the smaller the concentration of vapour at which non-linearity becomes important, as is illustrated in Fig. 5.18. The result is that there is an optimum temperature above which decreases in retention volume, retention ratio, and plate-number are predominant, and below which broadening due to non-linearity is predominant.

(*c*) *Change in Input Distribution with Sample Size*

A considerable amount of heat is required to volatilise a liquid sample. Sample injectors of the type used in analytical work (Section 10.6) cannot usually supply this, and sample injectors designed for preparative work usually consist of a cavity in front of the column packed with metal beads (*45,64*). This may be heated to such a temperature that its heat capacity is sufficient to volatilise all the sample. The sudden creation of vapour produces a large increase in pressure at the head of the column, which may easily cause a reverse flow of carrier gas and vapour into the carrier gas feed line. This may be cured either by heating a region of the feed line (*45*), or by incorporating a non-return valve in the gas line immediately behind the introducer (*65*).

(*d*) *Effect of Stationary Phase*

As is indicated above and in Section 5.20, the partition coefficient should be large in preparative work. This may be achieved by choosing a stationary phase in which components of interest have small activity coefficients; in such circumstances, partition coefficients are large, and furthermore, non-linearity does not occur until fairly large vapour concentrations are reached, so that large samples may be used without peak broadening. There is, however, another consideration working against this. Preparative gas chromatography is presumably only undertaken in cases where there is some good reason against using simpler means, e.g., distillation, and in most applications, it is likely that use is to be made of differences in activity coefficients. Now, when activity coefficients are all small, so that partition coefficients are large, the differences in activity coefficients of different vapours are also small, since activity coefficients less than unity rarely fall below 0.5. Differences in activity coefficients provide the greatest advantage in separating different substances when the activity coefficients are greater than unity, in which case they may span a range from unity to infinity; in these circumstances, however, partition coefficients are small, with consequent peak broadening when quantities are increased. It is, in fact, impossible to make the best of both sets of circumstances. Given that a large sample is to be used in a preparative column, one may either use a stationary phase giving small activity coefficients, with no peak-broadening, but no possibility of using large differences in activity coefficients, *or* one may use a stationary phase giving large activity coefficients, with the advantage of large differences in activity coefficients, but with so much peak broadening that the advantage may well be nullified.

(*e*) *Detector*

In preparative work, the conditions for the detector are very much simpler than for analysis, for the detector is only required to record the presence of components and not to measure them. In most apparatuses, an analytical detector of no special sensitivity is run on a small monitoring stream of carrier gas taken off from the main stream, which passes to the fraction collectors. It is possible, however, to put a detector probe, e.g., a catharometer element, directly in the main gas stream (*66*) with satisfactory results.

(*f*) *Collecting Traps*

It is difficult to trap out vapour completely from a large volume of fast flowing carrier gas. The usual technique is to pass the column effluent into a trap cooled in a suitable coolant, e.g., liquid air, solid carbon dioxide, or ice, according to the volatility of the components. Several workers have found that the efficiency of a simple U- or concentric-tube trap is poor; partly because it requires the rapid transfer of much heat in order to cool the carrier gas sufficiently to condense the vapours, and partly because vapours condense as a fog which is carried through the trap.

Some workers have improved the heat transfer between the coolant and the gas by passing the latter through some sufficiently long tube con-

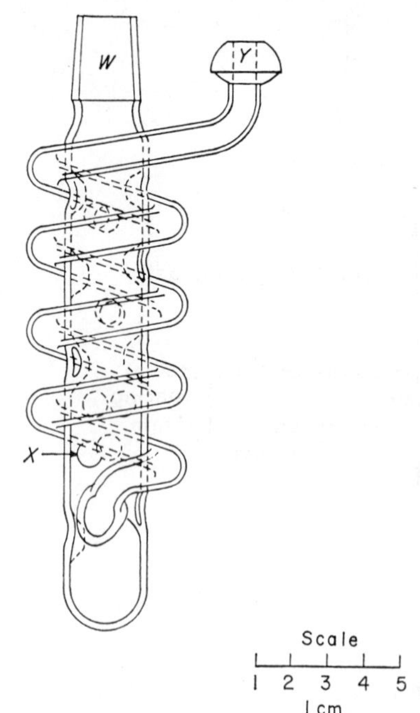

FIG. 6.11. Vapour trap according to Kirkland (*45*). Gas enters through *W*, passes down the tube with indentations *X*, and emerges through *Y*.

tained in the coolant. Thus, Kirkland (*45*) passes the gas through the trap shown in Fig. 6.11, consisting of a central indented tube, where most of the sample collects, and a long helical outlet, where the remainder is condensed. Atkinson and Tuey (*64*) find that condensation efficiency as a function of gas flow rate possesses a minimum; below the minimum, there is sufficient time for the gas to be cooled sufficiently below the dew point, and, above the minimum, the gas flow becomes turbulent, thus producing better heat transfer. All designs using relatively narrow tubes are inapplicable if the vapour is frozen out as a solid which would block the tubes.

The problem of fog formation has been solved by Atkinson and Tuey with an electrostatic precipitator (Fig. 6.12) consisting of two electrodes between which a potential of about 8 kv is applied from a commercial E.H.T. unit. Simpler solutions involve packing the trap with glass wool, or adsorbing the product on alumina, from which it is removed later by heating.

(*g*) *Carrier Gas and Column Material*

The solid supports and liquids used in analytical gas chromatography are frequently expensive, and preparative columns using these materials would be unduly expensive. Most of the cost of the supports is due not to the raw material, but to the preparation, particularly the size-grading. In

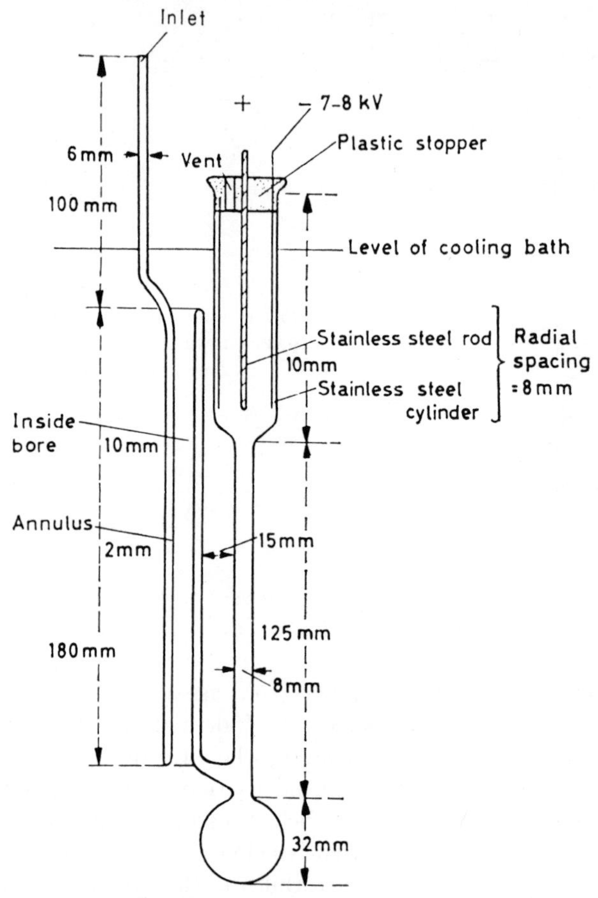

FIG. 6.12. Electrostatic vapour trap according to Atkinson and Tuey (*64*). After condensing the vapour as far as possible in the annular condenser, the remaining fog is precipitated on the two electrodes between which 8 kv is applied.

analytical gas chromatography size-grading is desirable for reducing the plate-height, but, since plate-heights in preparative columns are large for other reasons, elaborate size-grading is unnecessary. This is illustrated, for example, in the last three entries of Table 6.5, where the size-range has negligible effect on the efficiency. Thus, in preparative gas chromatography, cruder supports may be used satisfactorily.

A preparative apparatus passes a large volume of carrier gas, which may be expensive and troublesome if obtained from tanks of compressed gas. Some workers have incorporated apparatus for recycling carrier gas (*65*). Another solution is to use dried and filtered air, which is satisfactory in any circumstances where oxidation does not occur.

(*h*) *Automatic Batchwise Operation*

The amount of material produced in a preparative apparatus may be multiplied by continuous repetition of the same run. Several authors have contrived apparatus to perform such repetitions automatically (*64,67,68*). The apparatus consists of the usual units required for preparative chromatography, together with servo-mechanisms capable of putting a reproducible sample into the column and of switching from one collector to another as zones of product come through. The servo-units are controlled by a programming unit, which may be actuated either by time-cycles or by the chromatographic peaks as they appear in the output of the detector. In the latter scheme, the cycles are upset if the programmer responds to any spurious electrical impulse given by the detector. In the former scheme, the flow rate in the columns is set constant, and the programme is such that the apparatus puts on a sample, switches from one fraction collector to another at times pre-set between each required peak, and repeats the cycle

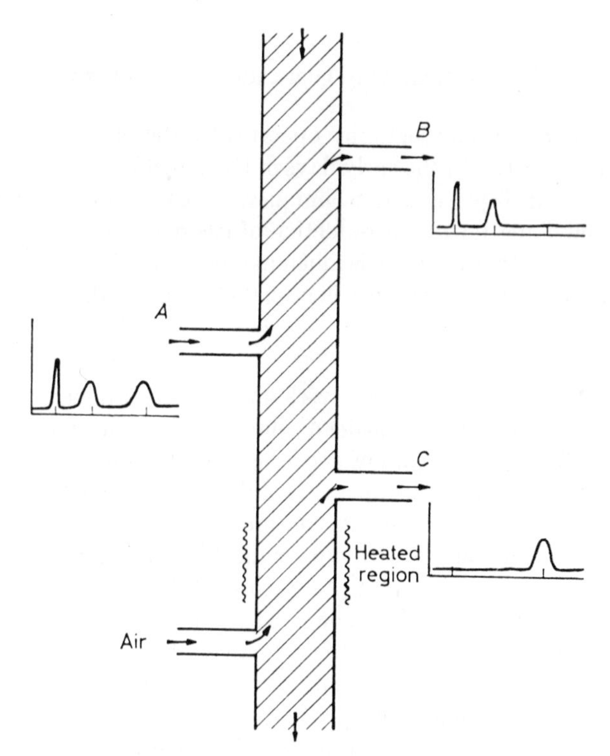

FIG. 6.13. Scheme for continuous chromatography. Scott (*69*). The mixture enters at *A*, and is divided into the more volatile components, which emerge at *B*, and the less volatile components, which emerge at *C*.

after a given time in which all components have appeared. This first scheme is used by all the workers referred to above.

(i) *Continuous Gas Chromatography*

Preparative gas chromatography can be carried out continuously in various ways, but as the method resembles extractive distillation, it is doubtful whether it finds a place in this book. In the technique, column packing is moved down a tube in the opposite direction to a stream of carrier gas by some vibrating device, and the vapour to be separated is fed into the middle. In an arrangement described by Scott (*69*) (Fig. 6.13), the relative speeds of the carrier gas upwards and the column packing downwards are adjusted so that zones of more volatile components move upwards, and are extracted from the emerging carrier gas, while zones of less volatile components move downwards, and are extracted from the column packing by heat, as illustrated. See also Benedek *et al.* (*70*).

6.7. Frontal and Displacement Analyses

Nearly all gas chromatography operates by the elution technique described in Section 1.1. In the early days of the subject, gas chromatography used frontal and displacement techniques, which rapidly fell into almost complete oblivion after the introduction of gas partition chromatography. Though it is clear that their use is much more restricted than that of elution technique, their complete neglect is probably unjustified.

(a) *The Formation of Sharp Fronts*

Frontal and displacement analyses operate on stationary phases with Langmuir-type isotherms. Consider a column packed with such a stationary phase through which a stream of carrier gas passes, and at a given instant the entering carrier gas picks up a constant concentration of vapour which thereafter passes into the column continuously. The stationary phase at the start of the column adsorbs vapour until it is in equilibrium with the vapour; further vapour entering passes through the equilibrated region to clean stationary phase further along the column. This process continues until the vapour breaks through the column at the far end, and the whole column is in equilibrium with the entering vapour stream. This is the basis of the technique for determining adsorption isotherms described in Section 3.11. The above process operates whether the isotherm is Langmuir or linear, but in the case of a Langmuir isotherm the mechanism described in Section 5.5 operates, and excessive diffuseness in the advancing front is nullified by the tendency of regions of greater vapour concentration to move faster through the column. The result is that with Langmuir isotherms the front that breaks through the far end of the column is sharp, however long the column. Also, any vapour in a region behind the front in which the concentration is greater than that in surrounding regions tends to move towards the front, thus levelling out any concentration gradients behind the front. The result is that the concentration of vapour behind the front is constant.

(*b*) *Frontal Analysis*

In frontal analysis, the technique is as above, except that the vapour introduced continuously into the carrier gas stream is the vapour of the mixture to be analysed. In this case, the least adsorbed of the components breaks through first, and appears as a step on the recorder of the detector. Some time later, a further step appears due to the next component, and so on, so that the observed chromatogram appears as a series of steps, as shown by the full line in Fig. 6.14. The first step contains pure vapour of the first species, but the second zone contains vapour both of the second species and the first species, and in general the nth zone contains n species, since vapour of every species is continuously entering the column, and vapours of species in equilibrium with the whole column must necessarily emerge from it. The concentration of a species coming through first in a given step is smaller in all subsequent steps, as indicated by the dotted lines shown in Fig. 6.14, because of the characteristics of the Langmuir isotherm for mixed vapours. The result is that the height of successive steps cannot be used directly as a measure of the concentration of the nth species in the mixture. A study of the theory of the process, however, can yield

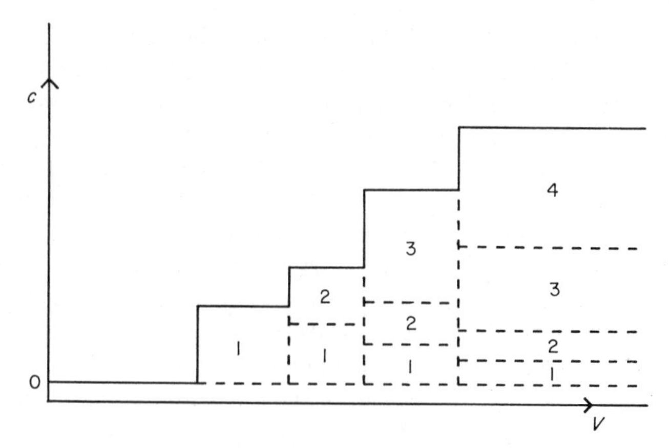

FIG. 6.14. Chromatogram obtained in frontal analysis.

simple equations for the heights of both dotted and full lines of all steps in Fig. 6.14 [Claesson (*71–73*)], so that the frontal technique can be used if required for quantitative analysis. The retention volumes of the fronts in frontal analysis are functions of all the vapour concentrations, and are not significant in identifying vapours qualitatively, as in linear elution chromatography.

A modification of frontal analysis using partition chromatography has been described by Boeke (*74*), who uses an ordinary partition column, through which he passes in a stream of carrier gas a continuous dilute mixture of the vapours to be analysed. If the mixture is sufficiently dilute, the isotherms of different vapours are linear and independent, so that the self-sharpening character of the fronts is absent, but retention volumes still have meaning, and step heights are proportional to the concentration of vapour in the sample stream. Boeke uses a detector which differentiates the stepwise plot of total effluent concentration against volume, and the result has the appearance of an ordinary chromatogram. One of the characteristics of this technique is that the fronts obtained are sharper than elution peaks would be if the same column were used as an elution column, partly because an elution front is equivalent to only half of a peak, and partly because of the vapour concentration effect described in Section 5.6. Thus the differentiated peaks on a vapour flow chromatogram can give phenomenological plate-heights of as little as 0.15 mm in ordinary packed columns, but this is clearly no measure of the resolution of the column, since the column does no resolving. There appears no reason why this apparent great resolving power should not be used purely for analysis of vapours of small relative retention.

(*c*) *Displacement Analysis*

In displacement analysis a discrete sample of the mixture to be analysed is placed at the beginning of a column packed with an adsorbent, and a carrier gas stream containing a constant concentration of a vapour called the "Displacer" more strongly adsorbed than any of the components of the mixture is passed through the column. An approximate explanation of what happens is given below. It inevitably suffers from the difficulty of explaining simultaneous occurrences consecutively.

The components of the mixture start to be eluted through the column, and would normally form a series of unsymmetrical elution zones in the usual way. However, the conditions are chosen so that the front of the displacer moves faster than any of the elution zones. The displacer first reaches the rear profile of the slowest of the zones, and displaces the vapour contained in the profile from the adsorbent. This material is thus pushed forward ahead of the advancing front of displacer, and the zone of vapour

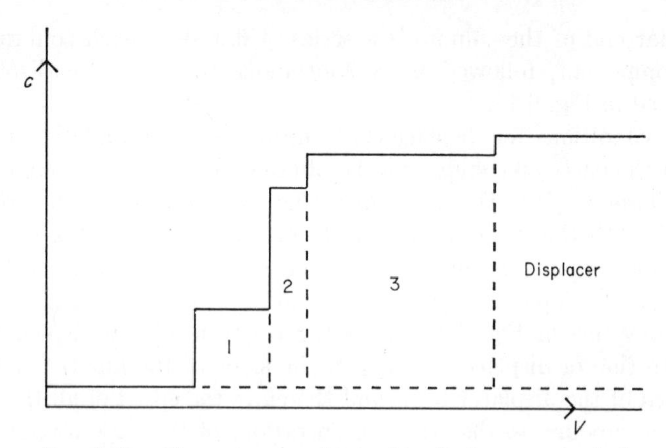

FIG. 6.15. Chromatogram obtained in displacement analysis.

is compressed into a step, which is pushed along by the front of displacer at the displacer's speed. By the same argument as used in Subsection (a), the step consists of a region of column with a constant concentration of vapour in each phase. The step next to the displacer then encounters the rear profile of the next slowest zone, and acts towards that as the displacer did towards it. This process continues, so that the chromatogram obtained

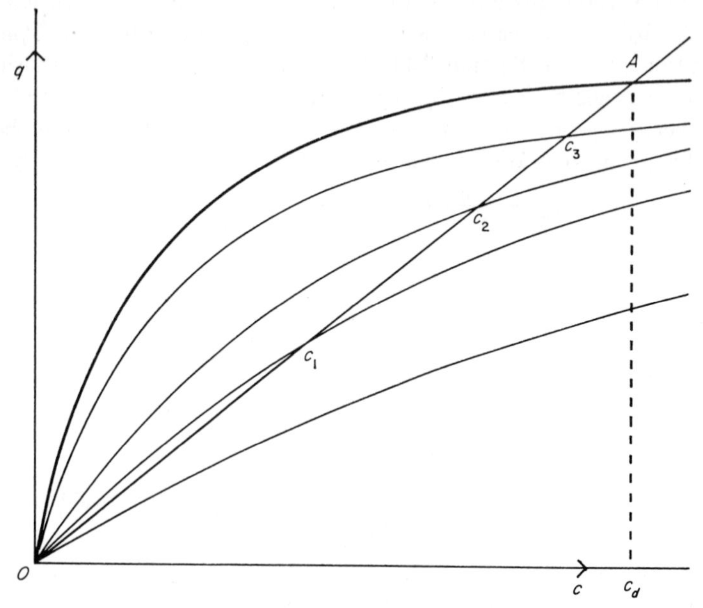

FIG. 6.16. Construction for calculating the conditions for displacement chromatography, and the concentrations of vapours within the steps.

at the far end of the column is a series of flat steps each containing one pure component, followed by a continuous zone of pure displacer, as illustrated in Fig. 6.15.

The conditions for displacement chromatography and the concentrations of the successive steps may be obtained by a construction originally due to Tiselius (*75*). The speed of a zone or a front through a column is determined by the effective value of the ratio q/c, whether this is dependent on or independent of concentration. Thus, on an isotherm, or plot of q against c, the slope of a straight line through the origin defines a speed. The heavy line in Fig. 6.16 shows the isotherm of the displacer. If the concentration of displacer is c_d, then the slope of the line OA determines the speed of the displacer front and therefore the speed of all the zones of displaced vapours, so that the concentrations of the vapours in the zones are given by the points at which the isotherms of the vapours intersect the line OA, i.e., at c_1, c_2, etc. The less strongly the vapour is adsorbed, the shallower is its isotherm and the smaller the concentration at which the speed of the zone equals the speed of the displacer front. Hence, if the units of the abscissa of Fig. 6.16 are the same as those of the ordinate of Fig. 6.15, all the steps of Fig. 6.15 are upwards, as shown.

The explanation is incomplete so far, since no relation is given between the units of concentration for different vapour species, without which any argument involving comparison of isotherms is meaningless. In gas chromatography, such a relation is given by the general properties of physical adsorption given in Section 3.11. Usually, if a number of isotherms are plotted together with c and q expressed in molar units, the initial slopes are inversely proportional to the vapour pressures of the pure liquids, and change in saturation levels between different vapours is very much

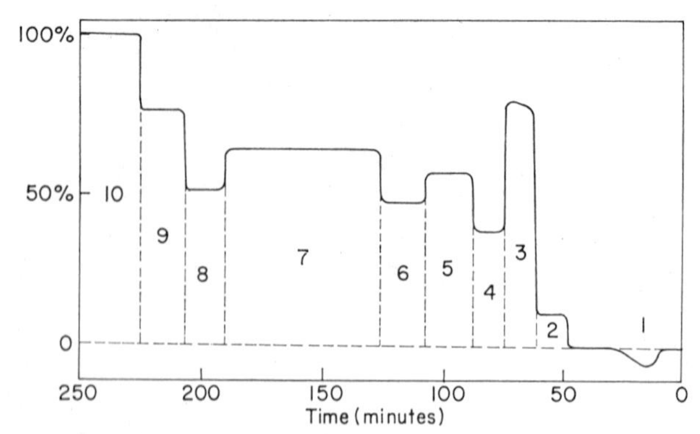

FIG. 6.17. A displacement chromatogram. James and Phillips (*24*). 1, Water; 2, diethyl ether; 3, chloroform; 4, ethyl acetate; 5, thiophen; 6, dioxan; 7, pyridine; 8, butyl acetate; 9, chlorobenzene; 10, bromobenzene (displacer).

smaller than change in initial slope. The result is that the order of elution is at least approximately the order of boiling point, as is seen from the example of displacement chromatogram [James and Phillips (*24*)] given in Fig. 6.17. Some adsorbents, however, are slightly selective, as discussed in Section 3.11.

It is apparent that the chromatogram of Fig. 6.17 does not show a series of ascending steps as predicted for Fig. 5.15. The reason is that the mixture contains some volatile compounds of relatively large molecular weight, and, since the detector gives a response proportional to weight concentration and not mole concentration, the relatively small mole concentration appears magnified for these components. Note also in Fig. 6.17 that water appears as an elution peak, since the initial slope of the isotherm was less than that of the line *OA* in the conditions used.

Displacement analysis cannot be used for qualitative identification, but quantitative identification of components is particularly simple, for the zones of vapour appear as rectangles the area of which is proportional to the weight of vapour.

References

1. James, A. T., and Martin, A. J. P., *Biochem. J.* **50,** 679 (1952).
2. Hull, W. Q., Keel, H., Kenney, J., and Gamson, B. W., *Ind. Eng. Chem.* **45,** 256 (1953).
3. Cummins, A. B., *Ind. Eng. Chem.* **34,** 403 (1942).
4. Keulemans, A. I. M., and Kwantes, A., *in* "Vapour Phase Chromatography," Proceedings of the First Symposium, London, May, 1956 (D. H. Desty, ed.), p. 15. Academic Press, New York, 1957.
5. Callear, A. B., and Cvetanovic, R. J., *Can. J. Chem.* **33,** 1256 (1955).
6. Littlewood, A. B., *in* "Gas Chromatography 1958," Proceedings of the Second Symposium, Amsterdam, May, 1958 (D. H. Desty, ed.), p. 23. Academic Press, New York, 1958.
7. Hishta, C., Messerly, J. P., and Reschke, R. F., *137th Am. Chem. Soc. Meeting, April, 1960.*
8. Liberti, A., Cartoni, G. P., and Pallotta, U., *Ann. chim.* (*Rome*) **48,** 40 (1958).
9. Naves, Y.-R., *J. Soc. Cosmetic Chemists* **9,** 101 (1958).
10. Naves, Y.-R., *Am. Perfumer Aromat.* **71,** 38 (1958).
11. Kwantes, A., and Rijnders, G. W. A., *in* "Gas Chromatography 1958," Proceedings of the Second Symposium, Amsterdam, May, 1958 (D. H. Desty, ed.), p. 125. Academic Press, New York, 1958.
12. Sorensen, I., and Soltoft, P., *Acta Chem. Scand.* **10,** 1673 (1956).
13. Cropper, F. R., and Heywood, A., *Nature* **174,** 1063 (1954).
14. Cropper, F. R., and Heywood, A., *in* "Vapour Phase Chromatography," Proceedings of the First Symposium, London, May, 1956 (D. H. Desty, ed.), p. 316. Academic Press, New York, 1957.
15. Desty, D. H. and Harbourn, C. L. A., *Am. Chem. Soc. Symposium, New York, September, 1957,* p. D157.
16. Desty, D. H., and Harbourn, C. L. A., *Anal. Chem.* **31,** 1965 (1959).

17. Decora, A. W., and Dinneen, C. U., *Anal. Chem.* **32,** 164 (1960).
18. Villalobos, R., *I.S.A. Symposium on Instrumental Methods, Montreal, 1900.*
19. Ellis, J. F., and Iveson, G., *in* "Gas Chromatography 1958," Proceedings of the Second Symposium, Amsterdam, May, 1958 (D. H. Desty, ed.), p. 300. Academic Press, New York, 1958.
20. Sunner, S., Karrman, K. J., and Sunden, V., *Mikrochim. Acta* p. 1144. (1956).
21. Robinson, C. F., U.S. Patent 2,845,136 (1958).
22. Lukes, V., Komers, R., and Herout, V., *J. Chromatog.* **3,** 303 (1960).
23. Desty, D. H., Godfrey, F. M., and Harbourn, C. L. A., *in* "Gas Chromatography 1958," Proceedings of the Second Symposium, Amsterdam, May, 1958 (D. H. Desty, ed.), p. 200. Academic Press, New York, 1958.
24. James, D. H., and Phillips, C. S. G., *J. Chem. Soc.* p. 1600 (1953).
25. Smith, E. D., *Anal. Chem.* **32,** 1049 (1960).
26. Baker, W. J., Lee, E. H., and Wall, R. F., *I.S.A. Second International Symposium, Lansing, Michigan, 1959.*
27. Macrae, J. C., Finlayson, P. C., and Gray, W. A., *Nature* **179,** 1365 (1957).
28. Cooper, J. A., Canter, R., Estes, F. L., and Cast, J. H., *J. Chromatog.* **3,** 87 (1960).
29. Golay, M. J. E., *in* "Gas Chromatography," I.S.A. Symposium, August 1957 (V. J. Coates, H. J. Noebels, and I. S. Fagerson, eds.), p. 1. Academic Press, New York, 1958.
30. Desty, D. H., Goldup, A., and Swanton, W. T., *Nature* **183,** 107 (1959).
31. Desty, D. H., Goldup, A., and Whyman, B. H. F., *J. Inst. Petrol.* **45,** 287 (1959).
32. Scott, R. P. W., *Nature* **183,** 1753 (1959).
33. Condon, R. D., *Anal. Chem.* **31,** 1717 (1959).
34. Desty, D. H., Haresnape, J. H., and Whyman, B. H. F., *Anal. Chem.* **32,** 302 (1960).
35. Zlatkis, A., and Lovelock, J. E., *Anal. Chem.* **31,** 620 (1959).
36. Dijkstra, G., and Goey, J. de, *in* "Gas Chromatography 1958," Proceedings of the Second Symposium, Amsterdam, May, 1958 (D. H. Desty, ed.), p. 56. Academic Press, New York, 1958.
37. Lipsky, S. R., Landowne, R. A., and Lovelock, J. E., *Anal. Chem.* **31,** 852 (1959),
38. Eggertsen, F. T., and Knight, H. S., *Anal. Chem.* **30,** 15 (1958).
39. Bens, E. M., *Pittsburgh Conf. Anal. Chem. and Appl. Spectroscopy, March, 1960.*
40. Purnell, J. H., Informal Symposium on Gas Chromatography (Gas Chromatography Discussion Group), London, April, 1960.
41. Johns, T., *in* "Gas Chromatography," I.S.A. Symposium, August 1957 (V. J. Coates, H. J. Noebels, and I. S. Fagerson, eds.), p. 31. Academic Press, New York, 1958.
42. Ormerod, E. C., and Scott, R. P. W., *J. Chromatog.* **2,** 65 (1959).
43. Holmgren, *in* "Gas Chromatography," I.S.A. Symposium, August, 1957 (V. J. Coates, H. J. Noebels, and I. S. Fagerson, eds.), p. 39. Academic Press, New York, 1958.
44. Mitzner, B. M., and Jacobs, M. H., *137th Am. Chem. Soc. Meeting, Cleveland, Ohio, April, 1960.*
45. Kirkland, J. J., *in* "Gas Chromatography," I.S.A. Symposium, August, 1957 (V. J. Coates, H. J. Noebels, and I. S. Fagerson, eds.), p. 203. Academic Press, New York, 1958.
46. Zlatkis, A., Ling, S., and Kaufman, H. R., *Anal. Chem.* **31,** 945 (1959).
47. Horning, E. C., Moscatelli, E. A., and Sweeley, C. G., *Chem. & Ind. (London)*, p. 751 (1959).
48. Primavesi, G. R., *Nature* **184,** 2010 (1959).
49. McFadden, W. H., *Anal. Chem.* **30,** 479 (1958).

50. dal Nogare, S. D., and Bennett, C. E., *Anal. Chem.* **30,** 1157 (1958).
51. Griffiths, J. H., James, D. H., and Phillips, C. S. G., *Analyst* **77,** 897 (1952).
52. Guild, L. V., Bingham, S., and Aul, F., *in* "Gas Chromatography 1958," Proceedings of the Second Symposium, Amsterdam, May, 1958 (D. H. Desty, ed.), p. 241. Academic Press, New York, 1958.
53. Kogler, H., *Chem. Tech. (Berlin)* **9,** 400 (1957).
54. Greene, S. A., Moberg, M. L., and Wilson, E. M., *Anal. Chem.* **28,** 1369 (1956).
55. Drew, C. M., and McNesby, J. R., *in* "Vapour Phase Chromatography," Proceedings of the First Symposium, London, May, 1956 (D. H. Desty, ed.), p. 213. Academic Press, New York, 1957.
56. Ryce, S. A., and Bryce, W. A., *Anal. Chem.* **29,** 925 (1957).
57. Eggertsen, F. T., Groennings, S., and Holst, J. J., *Anal. Chem.* **32,** 904 (1960).
58. Harrison, G. F., Knight, P., Kelly, R. P., and Heath, M. T., *in* "Gas Chromatography 1958," Proceedings of the Second Symposium, Amsterdam, May, 1958 (D. H. Desty, ed.), p. 216. Academic Press, New York, 1958.
59. dal Nogare, S., and Langlois, W. E., *Anal. Chem.* **32,** 767 (1960).
60. Habgood, H. W., and Harris, W. E., *Anal. Chem.* **32,** 450 (1960).
61. Roper, J. N., Jr., *Anal. Chem.* **32,** 447 (1960).
62. Giddings, J. C., *J. Chromatog.* **4,** 11 (1960).
63. Huyten, F. H., Beersum, W. van, and Rijnders, G. W. A., Third Symposium on Gas Chromatography, Edinburgh, June, 1960, Paper No. 15 (Preprint).
64. Atkinson, E. P., and Tuey, G. P., *in* "Gas Chromatography 1958," Proceedings of the Second Symposium, Amsterdam, May, 1958 (D. H. Desty, ed.), p. 270. Academic Press, New York, 1958.
65. Johns, T., Third Symposium on Gas Chromatography, Edinburgh, June, 1960, Paper No. 16 (Preprint).
66. Patrick, C. R., Informal Symposium on Gas Chromatography (Gas Chromatography Discussion Group), Bristol, September, 1959.
67. Heilbronner, E., Kovats, E., and Simon, W., *Helv. Chim. Acta* **40,** 2410 (1957).
68. Ambrose, D., and Collerson, R. R., *Nature* **177,** 84 (1956).
69. Scott, R. P. W., "Gas Chromatography 1958," Proceedings of the Second Symposium, Amsterdam, May, 1958 (D. H. Desty, ed.), p. 287. Academic Press, New York, 1958.
70. Benedek, P., Szepesy, L., and Szepe, S., "Gas Chromatography," I.S.A. Symposium, August, 1957 (V. J. Coates, H. J. Noebels, and I. S. Fagerson, eds.), p. 225. Academic Press, New York, 1958.
71. Claesson, S., *Arkiv Kemi, Mineral Geol.* **23A,** 1 (1946).
72. Claesson, S., *Ann. N.Y. Acad. Sci.* **49,** 183 (1948).
73. Claesson, S., *Discussions Faraday Soc.* **7,** 34 (1949).
74. Boeke, J., Third Symposium on Gas Chromatography, Edinburgh, June, 1960, Paper No. 7 (Preprint).
75. Tiselius, A., *Arkiv Kemi, Mineral Geol.* **16A,** No. 18 (1943).

Chapter 7

The Use of Detectors for Quantitative Analysis

7.1. Principles of Quantitative Analysis by Gas Chromatography

The quantitative analysis of a sample by gas chromatography depends solely on the performance of the detector and its associated equipment, and not on the column. The basic equation for differential detectors responding to vapour concentration is:

$$w = \int c(V)\, dV, \tag{7.1}$$

where w is the weight of a vapour, $c(V)$ is its concentration expressed as mass per unit volume of gas passing through the detector, and the integration extends over all the gas volume containing significant quantities of vapour.

As previously indicated, the practical measure of the quantity of a vapour is the area, A, of the peak that it produces in a differential detector. This may be expressed as:

$$A = \int y\, dx, \tag{7.2}$$

in which x is a length along the axis proportional to time on the strip-chart of the recorder, and y is the recorder deflection. In the case that $y \propto c$, the detector is said to be *linear*, and we assume here that this condition is true. In normal practice also, $x \propto V$. Thus, by studying the constants of these proportionalities, and substituting them in Eqs. (7.1) and (7.2), an explicit relation between A and w may be derived [Eq. (7.5)], as in the next three paragraphs.

If the reciprocal chart speed, e.g., in minutes/centimetre, is C_1, then

$$t = C_1 x.$$

Also, $V = \dot{V}t$; hence,

$$dV = C_1 \dot{V}\, dx. \tag{7.3}$$

The relation between y and c involves the sensitivity of the detector, for the more sensitive the detector, the larger is y for a given value of c. Numerical specification of the sensitivity is aided by the fact that the output of nearly all practical detectors appears as an electric potential, so that the sensitivity is conveniently measured by the potential change produced by unit concentration of vapour in the gas stream. Dimbat, Porter, and Stross (*1*) have defined a unit of sensitivity which is that of a detector which gives an output of 1 mv for a concentration of 1 mg of vapour per cubic centimetre of carrier gas. The sensitivity of any detector may then be defined in the following units:

$$\text{mv}/(\text{mg}/\text{cm}^3), \qquad \text{i.e.,} \qquad (\text{mv cm}^3)/\text{mg}.$$

This unit may obviously be modified to $(\text{mv cm}^3)/\mu\text{g}$ for more sensitive detectors. In practice, the sensitivities of common designs of ionisation detectors (Chapter 8) are of the order of 1000 $(\text{mv cm}^3)/\mu\text{g}$, and those of thermal conductivity cells (Section 1.2; Chapter 9) are of the order of 1 to 10 $(\text{mv cm}^3)/\mu\text{g}$.

We may now relate c and y in terms of the sensitivity, S, as defined above. If C_2 is the reciprocal of the sensitivity of the recorder alone, i.e., the number of millivolts applied (E_g) per centimetre movement, then

$$E_g = C_2 y.$$

Also, from the definition of S,

$$c = E_g/S,$$

so that

$$c = C_2 y/S. \tag{7.4}$$

Substituting Eqs. (7.3) and (7.4) into Eq. (7.1),

$$w = \int \frac{C_2 y C_1 \dot{V}}{S}\, dx = \frac{C_1 C_2 \dot{V}}{S} \int y\, dx,$$

whence, making use of Eq. (7.2),

$$w = C_1 C_2 \dot{V} (A/S). \tag{7.5}$$

This equation, given by Dimbat, Porter, and Stross, gives the weight of vapour in terms of the peak area A, the detector sensitivity S, and three measurable parameters C_1, C_2, and $\dot{V}$, which are normally constant throughout any chromatographic run, as implied in the derivation.

Equation (7.5) may be modified to suit different circumstances. With detectors the response of which is proportional to the rate of passage of vapour rather than to concentration,

$$w = C_1 C_2 (A/S'), \tag{7.6}$$

where S' is the sensitivity of the detector expressed in units of voltage response per (unit weight per unit time). With ionisation detectors, the sensitivity is better expressed as current response per unit weight per unit time rather than as voltage response, and in this case Eq. (7.6) may be used if C_2 is expressed in terms of meter movement per unit change in current.

In the great majority of applications of gas chromatography, quantitative analysis consists of the determination of relative proportions by weight of components in a mixture, and not the determination of absolute weights of vapour. In normal practice, subject to the restrictions given below, the quantities C_1, C_2, and $\dot{V}$ remain constant throughout the chromatography except as a result of known and measurable changes made by the operator, so that relative weight of two components i and j is given by:

$$\frac{w_i}{w_j} = \frac{A_i/S_i}{A_j/S_j} \tag{7.7}$$

and the proportion by weight of a component i in a mixture is

$$w_i = \frac{A_i/S_i}{\sum_k A_k/S_k}, \tag{7.8}$$

in which the summation includes the peaks due to every component of the mixture. These equations form the basis of quantitative analysis by gas chromatography. Similar equations apply in many other analytical techniques, and are commonplace; details of their use not directly concerned with gas chromatography are not discussed here.

Since quantitative analysis normally consists of the determination of relative weights, it is apparent that it is only necessary to make measurements of relative areas and relative sensitivities; Eq. (7.8) may equally well be written:

$$w_i = \frac{A_i/S_i}{\sum_k A_k/S_k} \times \frac{S_n/A_m}{S_n/A_m} = \frac{A_{im}/S_{in}}{\sum_k A_{km}/S_{kn}}, \tag{7.9}$$

in which A_{im} is the area of the peak due to the component i relative to that due to the component m, and S_{in} is the sensitivity of the vapour i relative to that of the vapour n. The operations necessary in performing an analysis for weight proportions are, therefore:

(1) Determine the sensitivities relative to a single standard of each vapour passing through the detector.

(2) Chromatograph the sample, and measure the relative areas of all the peaks.

(3) Use Eq. (7.9).

In connection with (1), it will be appreciated that the standard need not be a component of the mixture being analysed, and in connection with (2), the areas of peaks may be measured in arbitrary units. Details of the above operations, and of useful variants, are given in the following section.

The use of Eqs. (7.7), (7.8), and (7.9) necessitates that C_1, C_2, and $\dot{V}$ are held constant throughout the run. A fundamental source of error in the control of $\dot{V}$, which, however, is only serious when concentrations of vapour are large, is described by van der Craats (*2*). He finds that the flow rate in the detector is influenced by the vapours themselves in two ways:

(i) As soon as a vapour leaves the column, it is added to the gas volume, thus augmenting the flow rate.

(ii) The viscosity of the gas-mixture composed of vapour and carrier gas differs from that of pure carrier gas, and the flow rate is determined at least in part by the resistance of the column.

A simple calculation shows that the increase in flow rate on account of (i) is given by:

$$70x_{\max}\frac{k}{1+k}\,\%, \tag{7.10}$$

where $x_{\max}$ is the mole fraction of vapour in the peak maximum and k is as in Chapter 2. In practice, $x_{\max}$ is normally less than 0.01, and those peaks for which it is greatest are the early peaks for which $k/(1+k)$ is least. Thus, so long as massive samples are not used, this source of error may be avoided.

The effect of the change in viscosity is not calculable as above, but again, it is only operative for large samples.

It appears also that there are frequently more trivial reasons for inconstancy of the product $C_1C_2\dot{V}$. Thus, control of flow rate to better than 1% is comparatively difficult, and in practice flow rates generally fluctuate by at least this proportion. Also, C_1 may fluctuate if the mechanical link between the roller of the recorder and the synchronous motor driving it is imperfect; it appears that this is comparatively common, and liable to remain unnoticed. The speed of the roller is easily checked with a stopwatch (*3*).

7.2. Technique of Quantitative Analysis

(a) *The Determination of Relative Sensitivities*

Relative sensitivities may occasionally be found in the literature, but in most cases they must be calculated or determined experimentally. The methods of calculation are discussed under each individual detector. Ideally, the sensitivity of a detector should be a simply calculable function of the molecular structure of the molecule of the vapour. Unfortunately, this is not so except in the case of some rather rarely used detectors, e.g., the gas-density balance. With most detectors, the relation between sensitivity and structure is complicated, and investigation of it is incomplete. A very approximate general rule which holds with all common designs of ionisation detector and with catharometers is that the weight sensitivities of organic compounds consisting mainly of carbon, hydrogen, and oxygen are constant if the molecular weight of the compound is greater than a certain value (usually of the order of 100). This rule is generally too inaccurate to be more than a guide to the composition of a mixture; for greater accuracy, various relations between sensitivity and molecular structure are described for each detector in the next three chapters, but at present all such relations are imperfect both in theory and practice.

It is apparent, that, for accurate analysis, relative sensitivities must usually be determined experimentally.

The simplest technique for experimental determination of relative sensitivities is to chromatograph a sample of a mixture of known composition. The relative sensitivity of any two components is then given by Eq. (7.7) rearranged:

$$\frac{S_i}{S_n} = S_{in} = \frac{w_i/A_i}{w_n/A_n}. \tag{7.7}$$

It is convenient to regard the sensitivity of one vapour, e.g., n, as standard, so that $S_{nn} = 1$, and to use Eq. (7.7) on every other vapour i ($i \neq n$), so as to give a series of values of S_{in}.

The analysis of a particular mixture of interest requires that relative sensitivities be known, and the above procedure implies that the qualitative composition of the mixture is known, and that separate samples of its pure components are available. Both of these conditions restrict the quantitative use of gas chromatography, though there is not much indication in the literature that the restriction has so far proved onerous. In the case that only impure samples are available from which to determine relative sensitivities, it is possible to work out an iterative technique by which accurate relative sensitivities can be obtained. The details of this are a matter of general analytical procedure.

(*b*) *Use of Internal Standards*

A common technique, as in many other branches of analysis, is to add an accurately measured weight proportion of a known pure substance to the sample of interest; in gas chromatography, this must be chosen so as not to give a peak which overlaps with any other peak.

The principal advantage in the use of an internal standard in quantitative analysis lies in the implications of the word *every* in connection with the summation of Eq. (7.8). If no internal standard is used, it is necessary to measure the peak due to *every* component of the mixture and to know the relative sensitivity of every component of the mixture. This may be inconvenient, or even impossible, if, for example, the mixture contains involatile components. If, however, a known proportion of internal standard is added to the mixture, absolute weight proportions of individual components may be obtained using Eq. (7.7) and the known value of w for the internal standard.

Another advantage of the internal standard is that its weight proportion may be made approximately equal to that of a component of particular interest, and it may be chosen so that it has a comparatively close retention volume. In this way, errors due either to slight non-linearity of the detector or due to slow drift in the quantities C_1, C_2, or $\dot{V}$ can be minimised.

Lee and Oliver (*4*) have suggested the use of two or more internal standards in certain circumstances. Thus, if two components of interest are separated by a long time on the chromatogram, one internal standard appearing near each component of interest enables errors due to change in sensitivity with time to be eliminated. Also, if two components of interest are present in very unequal proportions, two internal standards in roughly the same proportions enable errors due to non-linearity to be eliminated.

(c) *Analysis by Peak-Height*

In some cases, it is possible to obtain rapid but approximate analyses by assigning a height-sensitivity, defined as peak height per unit weight, to each component, and by using this in Eq. (7.8), heights replacing areas. If all the chromatographic conditions are sufficiently constant, there is no doubt that this method can give results within a few per cent, but the technique is very liable to error. Any process which alters the plate-number of the column alters the ratio of peak area to peak-height, and thus invalidates the analysis. Since changes in the plate-number are a function of nearly every possible variable, this is very liable to happen. In particular, one of the principal variables which alters the area-to-height ratio is the sample size itself (Section 5.20), so that the range of linearity of height measurements is likely to be small.

(d) *The Measurement of Peak Areas*

Areas of peaks may be measured by any of the following methods:

(1) Providing that the peaks are Gaussian, measure the height of the peak, h, and the width at the half-height, $\omega_{1/2}$ (see Fig. 4.4). The area is:

$$A = 0.941 h\omega_{1/2} \qquad [0.941 = 2\sqrt{\ln (2)/\pi}]. \tag{7.11}$$

In relative area measurements, the value of the constant is immaterial.

(2) Providing that the peaks are Gaussian, draw tangents at the points

of inflection, and form a triangle with these and the base line (Fig. 4.5). The area of this triangle, i.e., half the base times its height (A') is related with the area of the peak by:

$$A = 1.032A' \qquad [1.032 = \sqrt{2\pi e}/4]. \tag{7.12}$$

Again, the value of the constant is superfluous in relative area measurements.

(3) By planimetry.

(4) By cutting out and weighing.

Area measurements may be done automatically by integrators, many of which are available commercially and are available for specific use with many commercial gas chromatographs.

(*e*) *The Measurement of Absolute Sensitivities*

Absolute sensitivities can be measured by an experiment in which all quantities other than S in Eqs. (7.5) and (7.6) are measured. With detectors which respond adequately to relatively large samples, such an experiment is straightforward. With sensitive ionisation detectors which cease to be linear at concentrations greater than, e.g., 1 in 10^4, however, any sample that is sufficiently small that its greatest concentration in the detector is less than the allowable maximum is too small to be accurately weighable and accurately introduced into the apparatus. Several convenient methods have been suggested for introducing measurable and reproducible small concentrations into a sensitive detector, of which two are described below.

Lovelock (*5*) uses an exponential decay technique (Fig. 7.1), in which

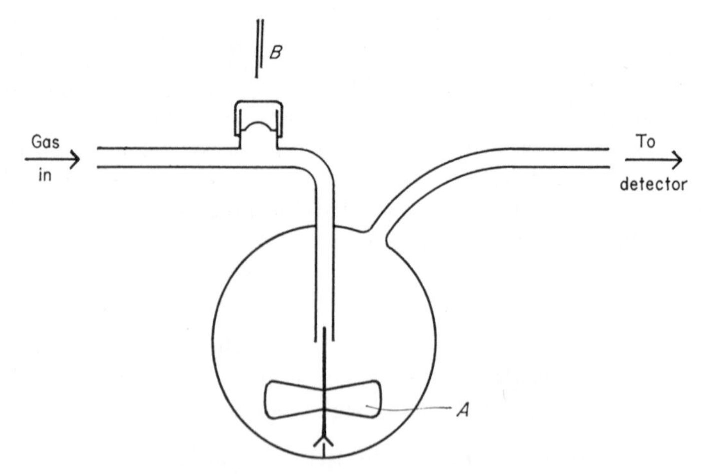

FIG. 7.1. Exponential dilution apparatus for securing a known concentration of dilute vapour. A is a magnetically operated paddle which ensures complete mixing within the flask. The sample is injected at B. After Lovelock (*5*).

the detector is connected directly to the effluent from a large flask through which carrier gas is passing. A sample of the substance of which the sensitivity is to be determined is injected into the flask; this sample is sufficiently large to be accurately measured. It is assumed that complete mixing occurs within the flask, and thus the concentration of vapour in the flask decreases exponentially with a time constant equal to the volume of the flask divided by the flow rate, both of which may be measured. Though the concentration of vapour is probably too large for the detector immediately after the sample is injected, it decreases continuously and calculably, and after a few time constants have passed, the concentration is within the region of linearity of the detector.

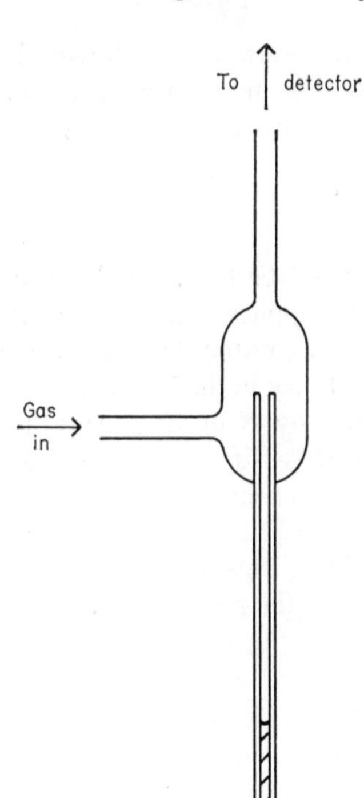

FIG. 7.2. Apparatus for securing a dilute vapour of calculable concentration. After Desty, Goldup, and Geach (*6*).

Desty, Goldup, and Geach (*6*) use a technique in which carrier gas passes over the open end of a length of capillary tube closed at the other end containing the sample, as shown in Fig. 7.2. The vapour of the sample is delivered into the gas stream at a rate which is determined calculably by the diameter of the capillary, the length from the surface of the liquid to the open end of the capillary, and the diffusion coefficient of the vapour of the sample.

7.3. Properties of Detectors

The essential quality of a detector is the sum of a large number of individual properties; we recognise the following as principally relevant in any evaluation: (a) sensitivity, (b) signal-to-noise ratio, (c) drift, (d) linearity, (e) independence of extraneous variables, (f) ease of calibration in terms of known properties, (g) speed of response, (h) chemical inertness, (i) range of application. In addition to these, other considerations such as robustness, price, safety, and the extent to which a detector has already been studied are obviously relevant, but do not require any special discussion.

The above qualities are discussed in general below, and with regard to each detector in the next three chapters. Reviews in English specifically on the general classification of detectors have been given by James (*7*), Boer (*8*), and McWilliam (*9*).

(*a*) *Sensitivity*

It is usually desirable that a detector should be sensitive. Even if a large sensitivity is not required for a particular application, it is comparatively easy to divide a large sensitivity by an accurately known fraction, but it is not possible to multiply a small sensitivity in like manner.

Sensitivities may be specified numerically by S or S' discussed in Section 7.1. A more direct method of specifying sensitivity, which applies only when considerations of noise level (see below) are not involved, is to specify the smallest detectable vapour concentration. This may be done by determining the sensitivity S, and dividing this into the smallest potential change just able to cause movement of the recorder pen.

(*b*) *Signal-to-Noise Ratio*

After sufficient amplification, the output of a detector always shows random variations called "Noise." Since by suitable electronics, the electrical output of a detector can always be multiplied by almost any factor, the sensitivity as described in Subsection (a) above may be made as great as one pleases. This amplification also amplifies inherent noise in the detector, which can obscure peaks due to small quantities of vapour. Thus, the amplitude of the noise is a more important criterion of a detector's ultimate performance than its sensitivity.

The amplitude of the noise, or "Noise Level," is most simply expressed as its average electrical amplitude, e.g., in μv. Dividing the noise by the sensitivity, the result is the vapour concentration which would give a signal equal to the noise. In cases that the noise is visible on the recorder, this figure makes a convenient though crude method of expressing the detector performance, since it does not contain any electrical units, and in many cases is a rough threshold of concentration less than which the detector cannot satisfactorily be used. The ratio of the response of the detector produced by a given concentration of vapour to the noise is called, by analogy with communications technology, the "Signal-to-Noise Ratio." Detector performances are sometimes specified by the vapour concentration which gives some stated signal-to-noise ratio other than unity, e.g., 2.

The specification of noise by a vaguely defined average value is sometimes inadequate, and in some circumstances gives an entirely false idea of the performance of a detector, for the noise may be such that signals in which the signal-to-noise ratio is much less than unity may be significant. This can be seen by the three examples given in Fig. 7.3. In Fig. 7.3a, a

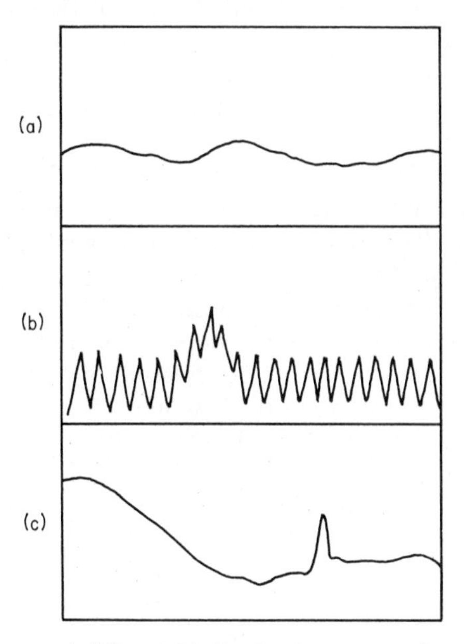

FIG. 7.3. Diagrams of different kinds of noise expressed as plots of amplitude against time.

noisy base line has been drawn, and there are variations in the base line which may or may not be peaks. In these circumstances, which are unfortunately rather common in practice, no signal smaller than the maximum noise can be measured with any degree of confidence in a single run, and the crude specification of noise already given is adequate. In Figs. 7.3b and 7.3c, however, two extreme cases have been drawn in which peaks may be identified with confidence from a single run, even though the signal-to-noise ratio is less than unity. The characteristic of these examples is that the average period of the largest component of the noise is very different from the time occupied by a peak.

Of the two extreme cases shown in Figs. 7.3b and 7.3c, the case in Fig. 7.3c is always a result of instrumental imperfection, but the case in Fig. 7.3b arises in several detectors where there is a high-frequency noise inherent in the operation, for example, ionisation detectors using α-radiation of small intensity such that the number of ionising particles emitted in unit time is small enough that there are significant statistical variations in their number in successive short periods. In these circumstances, the base line averaged over different short periods shows significant deviations from period to period, but if the base line is averaged over longer periods, the deviations become smaller and smaller as the periods over which the averages are taken become longer. If, therefore, the behaviour of the base line over short periods is not relevant in securing information on the chromatogram, nothing is lost by smoothing out the base line by increasing the time constant of the detector. In gas chromatography as used at present, peaks have a longer period than the longest period in which statistical variations are at present considered significant, and detectors in which such statistical fluctuations are inherent use time constants that are as large as possible without producing significant loss of resolution of close peaks.

It should be emphasised that, though the use of a large time constant improves the signal-to-noise ratio, it does not improve the performance of the detector, which in such a case is determined not by the ratio of the signal to the *actual* variations in the base line, but to the *significant* variations in the base line, which are much smaller. If the peak becomes quicker, so that the period occupied by the peak becomes smaller, then the significant deviations in the base line averaged over the peak become greater and the ratio of signal to significant noise becomes smaller. Thus, the relevant factor in judging the detector performance is not the time constant of the detector, but the ratio of the time occupied by a peak to the average period between successive random events, e.g., the evolution of α-particles. In other words, increasing the time constant makes the chromatograms prettier, but not more informative.

The statistical theory of detector noise, including the above qualitative arguments, is given by Johnson and Stross (*10*), who describe a method of determining a "Limit of Detection" which takes into account the factors described above. In this, noise is defined in terms of a "Noise Area," which is a measure of the total error in area produced by noise in a given region of base line at least as great as that occupied by a peak. If the standard deviation of a number of such noise areas is N_s, and the sensitivity of the detector as described in the last subsection is S, then Johnson and Stross propose that the quantity:

$$W = (\text{const} \cdot N_s)/S \tag{7.13}$$

should be called the "Limit of Detection," which is such that, for each of 19 out of 20 similar detectors, W is the least amount of sample for which at least 19 out of 20 trials will produce sample peaks with areas which deviate no more than $\pm 50\%$ from the area they would have if the detector were noiseless. The value of the constant depends on the number of noise areas used in the determination of N_s, e.g., for 24 noise areas it is 5.29. The fact that in most cases N_s is less than individual noise areas corresponds to the fact that significant variations in base line are generally smaller than the actual noise.

(c) Drift

A feature of imperfect detectors is that their base line slowly drifts in the course of time. In principle, drift is a type of very low-frequency noise, and the treatment of Johnson and Stross can include both drift and noise. In practice, however, drift and noise can generally be distinguished, drift being regarded as base line changes the average period of which is greater than that of the time occupied by a chromatogram, whereas noise has an average period less than that occupied by a chromatogram. Commonly, drift and noise are caused differently. No exact means of specifying drift has been given; statistical methods of expression could easily be produced, but to do so would normally be more trouble than the matter is worth. It is, however, very desirable to quote drift in terms of average voltage drift per unit time, e.g., millivolt/hour, and this has occasionally been done (*9*).

(d) Linearity

In order for quantitative analysis to be possible by the methods described in the previous sections, the detector must be linear. Such linearity is always desirable in any physical method of analysis, but not necessary; for example, Beer's law imposes a non-linear relation between response and concentration in spectrophotometry. It appears, however, that all practical quantitative analysis by gas chromatography has used linear detectors.

(e) Independence of Extraneous Variables

Many detectors respond to variables other than a change in concentration of the vapour in the carrier gas; examples are change in flow rate, pressure, temperature, conditions of the electrical supply, etc. Such extraneous response can, of course, be eliminated by keeping all other variables constant, but this may be troublesome and expensive. Independence of extraneous variables, therefore, is a desirable feature of detectors. In practice, it is the lack of such independence on the part of many common detectors that is responsible for much of the noise and the drift, particularly the latter.

(f) Ease of Calibration

Detectors in which the relation between response and concentration is a calculable function of some known molecular property have an advantage over others in that relative sensitivities do not require to be determined experimentally, and that, therefore, it is not necessary to have samples of the components of a mixture of interest.

(g) Speed of Response

This factor is discussed in detail in Section 5.8.

(h) Chemical Inertness

Some detectors destroy the sample in the act of detecting; others preserve it so that separate fractions may be collected. In practice some of the most sensitive detectors destroy the sample, but if a sample is required it has often been found advantageous to make use of the sensitivity of the detector by detecting only a small fraction of the carrier gas stream, and passing the rest into collection apparatus.

(i) Range of Application

Some detectors will detect almost any vapour; others will only detect efficiently certain classes of chemical compound.

References

1. Dimbat, M., Porter, P. E., and Stross, F. H., *Anal. Chem.* **28,** 290 (1956).
2. Van der Craats, F., *in* "Gas Chromatography 1958," Proceedings of the Second Symposium, Amsterdam, May, 1958 (D. H. Desty, ed.), p. 241. Academic Press, New York, 1958.
3. For example, Informal Symposium on Gas Chromatography (Gas Chromatography Discussion Group), London, April, 1959.
4. Lee, E. H., and Oliver, G. D., *Anal. Chem.* **31,** 1925 (1959).
5. Lovelock, J E , *Anal. Chem.* **32,** 162 (1961).
6. Desty, D. H., Goldup, A., and Geach, C. J., Third Symposium on Gas Chromatography, Edinburgh, June, 1960, Paper No. 4 (Preprint).
7. James, A. T., *in* "Vapour Phase Chromatography," Proceedings of the First Symposium, London, May, 1956 (D. H. Desty, ed.), p. 127. Academic Press, New York, 1957.

8. Boer, H., *in* "Vapour Phase Chromatography," Proceedings of the First Symposium, London, May, 1956 (D. H. Desty, ed.), p. 169. Academic Press, New York, 1957.
9. McWilliam, I. G., *J. Appl. Chem.* **9,** 379 (1959).
10. Johnson, H. W., Jr., and Stross, F. H., *Anal. Chem.* **31,** 1206 (1959).

Chapter 8

Ionisation Detectors

8.1. Introduction

In normal conditions gases and vapours emerging from a column are virtually perfect electrical insulators, but if caused to ionise they will conduct. There are great differences, both in kind and degree, in the ease of ionisation of different substances and in the conductivity that ionisation gives to the gas. Thus, the conductivity of an ionised carrier gas almost invariably changes when the gas contains a vapour, and this change may be measured and made the basis of a gas-chromatographic detector. In particular, certain types of ionisation detector have a very small background conductivity for pure carrier gas and show a great rise in conductivity when a vapour enters, so that they give a positive response to a vapour rather than measuring a small change in an already large quantity. This is advantageous in producing little noise and great useful sensitivity.

Ionisation detectors may conveniently be classified by the manner in which the carrier gas is ionised:

(1) *Radiation (Radiological) Detectors*, in which ionisation is produced by ionising radiation, usually α- or β-rays. The following four are in use and will be described, but others are in process of development.

(i) Ionisation Cross-Section Detector.
(ii) Argon Detector.
(iii) Electron Capture Detector.
(iv) Electron Mobility Detector.

(2) *Flame Ionisation Detector*, in which the carrier gas is burned in a flame, which causes ionisation.

(3) *Ionisation Gauge Detector*, in which electrons are obtained by emission from a heated cathode, and these ionise the gas.

(4) *Discharge Detectors*, in which ionisation results from an electrical discharge between two electrodes.

The study of ionised gases has formed a branch of physics for many years, but it has impinged little on chemistry. Much of the principles and theory of ionisation in the following pages will be commonplace to a physicist, yet probably unfamiliar to the chemist. Useful books are those of Townsend (*1*) and von Engel (*2*). Of the different kinds of detector classified above, the argon and flame ionisation detectors at the time of writing (1960) are receiving much more attention than the others. However, the study of ionisation detectors started as recently as 1956, and the subject is still rapidly expanding. It cannot be assumed that these two types of detector are destined to be the only ones to become established.

Detectors in the classes (1) to (4) above will be considered in turn.

8.2. Ionisation by Radiation

Gases become ionised when traversed by "Ionising Radiation," which includes α- and β-rays, ultraviolet radiation, γ-rays and X-rays. In gas chromatography, only the first three are used, the first two being conveniently obtained from suitable sources of radioactive material. For purposes of rough explanation, one may regard α- or β-rays as streams of particles emanating from the source. These traverse the gas, and, after traversing a distance the average length of which is the mean free path, they collide with an atom or molecule of the gas. The rays are emitted from the radioactive material with a large energy, which we may assume to be kinetic; thus they collide so hard with the atom or molecule of gas that they are capable of providing sufficient energy to displace an electron. The reaction is therefore:

$$M \rightarrow M^{+} + \epsilon^{-}$$

The energies with which ionising particles are emitted from radioactive materials are of the order of 10^4 to 10^6 ev, whereas the energy required to ionise singly an atom or molecule is of the order of 10 ev. Thus, after one collision, the ionising particle has lost very little energy, and it can then go on to collide with another atom, produce another ion and electron, and so on until it is finally brought to equilibrium. The progress of an ionising particle in this way can be seen in Wilson Cloud Chamber photographs, which are generally familiar.

Knowledge of the range of ionising radiation is important in connection with health hazard and with the design of ionisation detectors. With α- and β-rays, the range is inversely proportional to the density of the medium and very approximately proportional to the energy of emission of the rays. Because of the first proportionality, the product of range and density is constant for a given energy, so that range is usually quoted in units of cm g/cc, i.e., g/cm^2. For β-rays, the range in these units is very approximately given by (*39*):

$$\text{Range (g/cm}^2) \approx 0.5 \times \text{energy (Mev)}.$$

For example, the range of β-radiation from Sr^{90} (0.54 Mev) in air (0.001 g/cc) is approximately 2.7 metres. The range of α-radiation is much smaller, and normally lies between 3 and 7 cm in air. The ranges of γ- and X-radiation cannot be quoted by formula, since the intensity of a beam declines exponentially with distance. Extinction coefficients are a function both of the wavelength of the radiation and the material through which it passes, but are all such that the distance through air required to halve the radiation intensity is many metres, so that the effective range is greater than those of α- and β-rays.

The greater the amount of ionisation produced in unit volume by the radiation, the greater the specific conductivity of the ionised gas. Of the types of radiation, α-rays produce the greatest density of ionisation, followed by β-rays, followed by γ-rays, which is the inverse order of their ranges; the more frequently the particles collide and produce ions, the shorter the range in which their energy is exhausted. The density of ionisation is also a function of the energy of the radiation. When the energies are less than the ionisation potential, clearly no ionisation occurs at all. At energies greater than this, ions are formed, and as the energy increases to a figure of the order of 100 ev, the ionisation rapidly increases to a maximum. At still greater energies, the ionisation density declines, and this trend continues into the Mev range.

Whereas ions are formed at a rate which depends only on the intensity

TABLE 8.1

SOURCES OF RADIATION

Element	Effective radiation	Radiation energy (Mev)	Half-life (years)	Approximate quantity used in G.C. detectors
Sr^{90}	β	0.54	25	10–100 mC
T (H^3)	β	0.018	12.5	
Kr^{85}	β	0.72	9.4	
		0.54		
Ra^{226}	α^a	4.795	1620	20–100 μC
		5.3		
RaD = Pb^{210}	α^a	5.3	25	

[a] From daughter species, and not from the original element.

of radiation, and is constant at a given pressure and temperature, ions are removed by any of a number of processes, e.g., collision with neutral molecules, at rates depending on and increasing with their concentration. Thus, on applying radiation to a gas, the concentration of ions will rise until the rate of removal of ions equals the rate of creation by the radiation, so that normally there is a stationary concentration of ions, a state which is reached almost instantaneously.

The sources of radiation which have been used in gas-chromatographic ionisation detectors are given in Table 8.1. Note that α-sources may be weaker than β-sources, since the ionisation intensity produced by α-rays is so much greater.

8.3. Conduction of Electricity in Irradiated Gases

The conductivity of an irradiated gas can be measured by placing two electrodes in the gas between which a potential may be applied (Fig. 8.1).

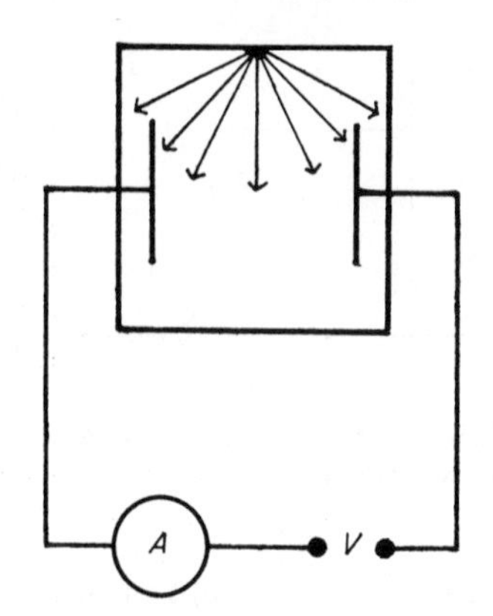

Fig. 8.1. Ionisation chamber.

The current can then be measured. The reactions occurring in the gas may be very complicated; we consider briefly below only those mechanisms which have so far been recognised as being relevant in gas-chromatographic detectors.

(a) *At Small Ion Concentrations*

When the potential is small, positive ions drift in the electric field towards the cathode, and negative electrons towards the anode. When these arrive at their destinations, they discharge, and the result shows as a current. The magnitude of the current is determined by the concentration of charged particles and their speed of drift. As already stated, the concentration is stationary and the speed of drift is proportional to the field, so that if the current is sufficiently small it is proportional to the applied voltage, and the gas obeys Ohm's law (region A, Fig. 8.2). As the applied voltage, and therefore the ion current, increases, the removal of ions by drift to the electrodes augments the removal of ions by other processes, so that the steady-state concentration of ions begins to fall. This causes the current to lag behind the Ohm's law prediction (region B). With more intense fields, ion removal by conduction predominates, until eventually, at sufficiently intense fields, virtually every ion formed is

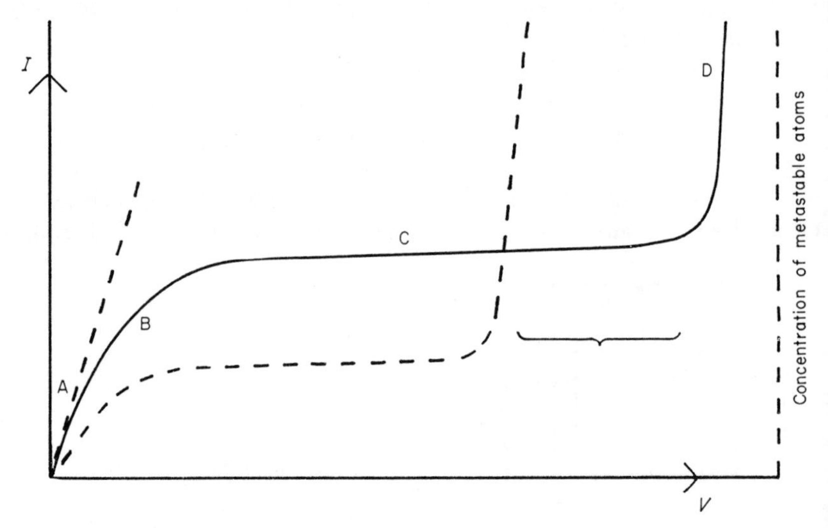

FIG. 8.2. *Full line:* Plot of current against applied voltage in an ionisation chamber. *Dashed line:* Plot of the concentration of metastable argon atoms against applied voltage in a simple argon detector [see Section 8.5(b)].

removed by conduction, so that further increase in the applied voltage produces no further increase in the current (region C). Such a condition is called "saturation." Finally, at still greater voltages, electrons reach sufficient speeds in the course of their drift to ionise further molecules by collision and there is a sharp increase in the current; the eventual result is a spark discharge (region D).

The principal factor determining the voltage range of the region in which saturation occurs is the steady-state ion concentration, for the more ions present in the absence of a field, the longer are regions A and B, whereas the threshold at the high-voltage end of the saturation region is little changed. The steady-state ion concentration is a function of the intensity of the radiation, so the result is that, as this is increased, the saturation region decreases, while regions A and B increase, and region D remains relatively steady. Above a certain threshold radiation intensity, region C disappears, and, since ionisation detectors normally operate in the saturation region, there is a limit to the usable radiation intensity.

(b) At Large Ion Concentrations

If the concentration of ions is not small, a complication derives from the fact that positive ions move more slowly than electrons, so that, in the space near the cathode, there is a large concentration of relatively slow moving positive ions. These form a "Space Charge" close to the cathode. Inside the space charge, the gas is highly conducting, and therefore the field is small. The volume, the strength, and the effect of the space charge all increase with increase in the ion concentration. Space charge effects become appreciable at current densities greater than $\approx 10^{-8}$ amp/cm^2 (*2*).

(c) Non-Uniform Field

The discussion so far tacitly implies parallel plate electrodes. In practical detectors, either approximately coaxial cylindrical or concentric spherical electrodes are often used. This has the result that the field is non-uniform even in the absence of a space charge, and different parts of the gas between the electrodes operate on different parts of the curve of Fig. 8.2. If the ratio of the dimensions of the electrodes is not very large, the only effect at small ionisations is to reduce the range of voltage over which the cell exhibits saturation. At large ionisations, the effects become complicated, but significant observations are (1) that the breakdown potential, i.e., the voltage where the current becomes infinite, is greater when the small electrode is the anode; (2) when the small electrode is the anode, the space charge has a modifying influence on any increase in current produced by increased ionisation.

(d) Electron Capture

Free electrons, particularly those of fairly small energies, may be captured by neutral atoms or molecules, to give negative ions. The negative ions so formed recombine much more readily with positive ions than do free electrons, so that the result of adding a compound with large electron affinity to a gas is to decrease the ionisation current within it. The effectiveness of atoms and molecules in capturing electrons depends very much on molecular structure and composition. Complex molecules, particularly when they contain electronegative elements, or elements or groups with large electron affinity, e.g., the halogens, are much more effective electron capturers than the rare gases.

(e) *Elastic and Inelastic Electron Collisions*

In a gas containing unaccelerated electrons, i.e., with no electric field, the electrons and molecules and atoms of the gas are in thermal equilibrium. As soon as a field is applied, however, the electrons acquire further energy by acceleration in the field, whereas the neutral atoms or molecules retain the same energy. If the gas consists exclusively of rare gas atoms, the collisions between electrons and atoms not producing ionisation or excitation are necessarily elastic, since there is no way in which kinetic energy can be lost during the collision. The result is that since the electron and the atom have very different masses, very little energy is transferred, and the speed of the electron is scarcely changed. If, however, the gas consists of or contains molecules, which possess internal degrees of freedom, their collisions with electrons are inelastic, and much of the excess energy given to the electrons by acceleration in the field is transferred to the gas molecules. After such collisions, the electrons are slowed.

(f) *Ionisation Efficiency*

An important measure of the performance of ionisation detectors in general is their *ionisation efficiency*, which is the ratio of the number of ions or electrons collected by the electrodes to the number of molecules of vapour causing the electrons to be formed. This figure is easily obtained by dividing the total quantity of electricity (coulombs) passed by the cell as a result of the vapour by the product of the number of moles of vapour and the value of the faraday, which is 96,494 coulombs/mole.

8.4. The β-Ray Ionisation Cross-Section Detector

The saturation current, i.e., the level of the plateau of Fig. 8.2, is determined by the number of ions produced per second. Among other things, this depends upon the composition of the gas, for the larger the gas molecules, the larger is the area which they present to the stream of ionising radiation, and the greater the chance that ionisation will occur. This fact is used in the "Cross-Section" detector, described by Boer (*3*) and by Deal, Otvos, Smith, and Zucco (*4,5*). It has been used occasionally since, especially for the detection of permanent gases, but it has been rather overshadowed by the argon detector which was developed from it.

The detector is shown diagrammatically in Fig. 8.3. Essentially, it consists of a cavity through which the column effluent passes, and which is irradiated from a suitable radiation source contained within it. The cavity itself is made of metal, and forms one electrode; the other electrode consists of a metal rod, or other shape, well insulated from the cavity. A constant potential such as to maintain saturation current (region C, Fig. 8.2) is applied across the electrodes. With dimensions of the order of centimetres, this is of the order of 300 volts.

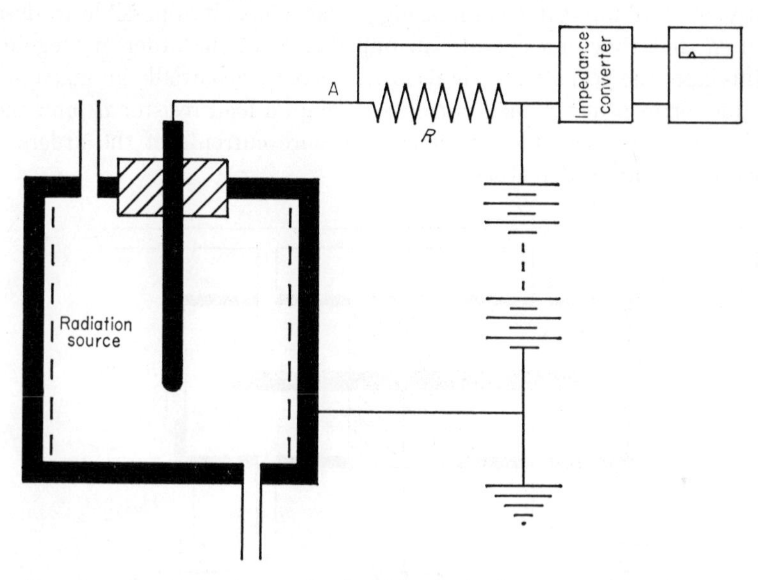

FIG. 8.3. Basic circuit associated with an ionisation cross-section detector.

The remainder of the apparatus is electrical or electronic, and is designed to provide a continuous measure of the current through the cell. Values of the current are of the order of 10^{-8} amp with applied potentials of about 300 volts, so that the cell resistance is of the order of 10^{10} ohms. The measurement of such small currents in large resistances is a specialised branch of physics which is encountered in a number of other connections, e.g., in mass spectrometry, and may be studied independently of gas chromatography. The usual technique is to place in series with the ionisation chamber a resistance (R, Fig. 8.3), the potential across which is measured. For the greatest voltage change per unit change in current, R should equal the resistance of the ionisation chamber, but in most current practice, such a large voltage response is unnecessary, and R may well be a couple of orders of magnitude smaller, e.g., 10^8 ohms. The voltage developed across R is usually measured by an electrometer valve, the output from which is fed via suitable electronics into a recorder. The actual voltage changes at the point A produced by vapours are at least equal to, and usually much greater than the voltage span of a recorder, so that the electronic apparatus does not provide voltage amplification, but rather serves to match the impedances of the ionisation chamber and the recorder. It is thus best called an "Impedance Converter." Most commercial potentiometric recorders include impedance converters as a necessary component in their design. Though in many designs these are intended for relatively small input impedances, e.g., <500 ohms, it is possible to design them so that they can operate on impedances of the order of megohms. In this case, the potentiometric recorder becomes essentially an instrument suitable for measuring small currents through a load resistor R, and there are instruments available which can measure currents of the orders obtained in ionisation detectors.

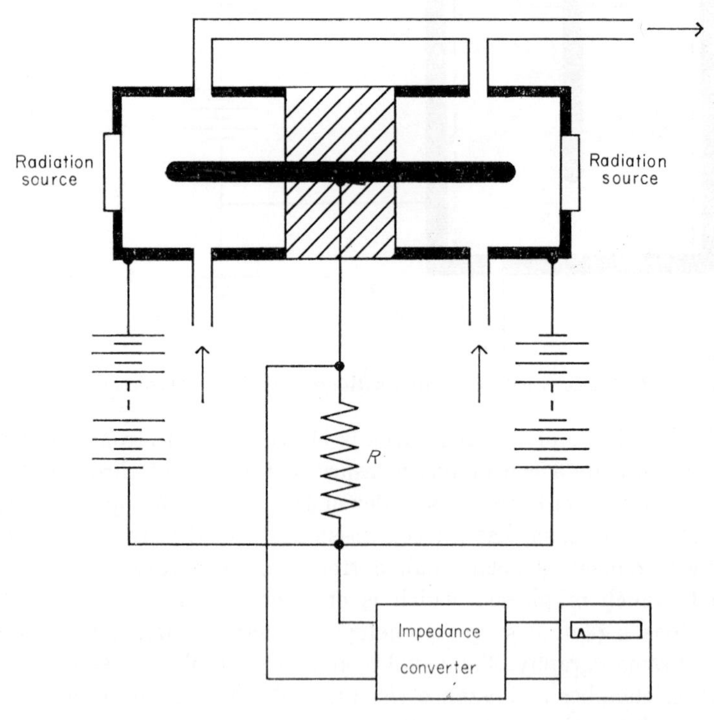

FIG. 8.4. Basic circuit of twin-cell ionisation cross-section detector. After Boer (*3*).

An alternative but similar arrangement is that of Boer (*3*), who uses two opposing ionisation chambers, one passing column effluent, and one passing pure carrier gas, arranged and connected as in Fig. 8.4. This arrangement has the advantage that any changes affecting both cells which might produce drift in one are nullified by the other.

The sensitivity of the ionisation cross-section detectors is determined by the amplification provided by the electronics, and, since it is found in practice that the noise arises from the detector itself and not from the electronics, the useful sensitivity is determined by the signal-to-noise ratio and not by the amplification. A minimum to the noise is provided by the discontinuous nature of the evolution of β-rays from the radioactive source. If N ionising particles are emitted in a time equal to one time constant of the apparatus, the random fluctuations in the current are of the order of $N^{-1/2}$ of the total current. One curie represents 3.7×10^{10} disintegrations per second, so a 10-mC source and 1-second time constant gives $N \approx 10^8$, whence $N^{-1/2} \approx 10^{-4}$. Deal *et al.* (5) claim that the noise found experimentally was of the order expected from the above source. In their detector, the signal equivalent to the noise was produced by a concentration of 0.005 mole % of heptane in nitrogen, so that the detector would give unit signal-to-noise ratio for a concentration change of 1 part in 2×10^4. The noise may be reduced by increasing the intensity of the source, or by increasing the time constant; the first, however, is restricted by practical considerations and by considerations mentioned in the previous section, and the second by whatever resolution is required from the apparatus. Such a sensitivity is small compared to that of many other detectors.

The current is proportional to the concentration of ions, and the latter is proportional to the cross section offered to the radiation by the molecules of gas contained in the cell. The cross section offered by the gas, assumed to be a mixture of carrier gas (g) and a vapour (v), is proportional to the sum of the products of the molar concentrations (c) of the components and their molecular ionisation cross sections (Q). Thus, the current I is given by:

$$I = k'(c_g Q_g + c_v Q_v) = \frac{k}{RT}(p_g Q_g + p_v Q_v), \tag{8.1}$$

where k and k' are apparatus constants, and the second form of writing takes into account variation in temperature, p_g and p_v being partial pressures. Normally, $p_g + p_v$ is a constant, usually atmospheric pressure, P, so that

$$I = \frac{k}{RT}\{(P - p_v)Q_g + p_v Q_v\},$$

whence ΔI, the change in current produced by a partial pressure p_v of vapour, is given by:

$$\Delta I = (k/RT)p_v(Q_v - Q_g), \tag{8.2}$$

and the proportional change in current is given by:

$$\frac{\Delta I}{I_0} = \frac{p_v}{P} \cdot \frac{Q_v - Q_g}{Q_g}. \tag{8.3}$$

Hence the calibration factors connecting response with concentration are proportional to the difference between the ionisation cross sections of carrier and vapour. Ionisation cross sections relative to hydrogen of a number of common gases have been determined, and are given in Table 8.2. Not many ionisation cross sections of the individual organic molecules

TABLE 8.2

HIGH-ENERGY β-RAY IONISATION CROSS SECTIONS OF COMMON GASES RELATIVE TO HYDROGEN

	Relative ionisation cross section for Sr^{90} radiation	
Gas	Observed	Calculated
H_2	1.23	
He	1.64	
Ar	10.9	
N_2	7.04	
O_2	8.55	
CO_2	10.8	
CH_4	7.04	7
C_2H_4	10.7	10.6
C_2H_6	12.7	12.6
C_3H_6	15.7	15.9
C_3H_8	17.8	17.9
C_4H_{10}	23.1	22.8

likely to be encountered in gas chromatography are available, but Otvos and Stevenson (*6*) have shown that they may be obtained by adding together ionisation cross sections of individual atoms in the molecule. Table 8.2 also shows relative ionisation cross sections of some common organic compounds, obtained from data given by Otvos and Stevenson (*6*), and for comparison gives ionisation cross sections calculated on the assumption that C = 3.2 and H = 1 (arbitrary units). The agreement suggests that use of Eq. (8.2) in conjunction with tables such as Table 8.2 would make a satisfactory method of calibrating ionisation cross-section detectors *a priori*. A few results given by Boer (*3*) and by Deal *et al.* (*5*) confirm this, but the relation has not been confirmed for many chemical types.

With regard to the other properties of interest given in Section 7.3, the *linearity* of the detector is adequate. Deal *et al.* (*5*) show that a plot of response against mole fraction may be made at least up to mole fractions of 0.06, and the plot is virtually linear up to 0.01 mole fraction, which is not normally exceeded in analytical gas chromatography. The linearity, together with other features of the performance, may be poor if the design of the cell is such that the space charge is appreciable, or if the field is locally very large, e.g., through using too small a central electrode or leaving sharp edges on any of the metal inside the chamber. Deal *et al.* (*5*) find that the single cell instrument does not produce significant *drift* in ordinary operating conditions; however, any drift due to excessive fluctuations in temperature or pressure, or drift produced through use of a more sensitive unit can be eliminated using the twin-cell arrangement described by Boer (*3*).

The *speed of response* of the cell is determined by its volume, and not by any lag in the change in conductivity. There is no obvious reason why the volume should not be made small enough for use with, e.g., capillary columns, but no such cells have been reported.

The cross-section detector is as versatile as the catharometer, and the few substances which fail to give a response in one carrier gas will respond in another gas. In spite of this versatility, the detector has not been extensively used; the reasons are probably the comparatively low sensitivity, which gives it no advantage over the catharometer, already well established in use and considerably cheaper; and the intensive development of the argon detector. On the other hand, the ancillary apparatus used with the cross-section detector is similar to that used with the argon detector, and furthermore, the cross-section detector can serve purposes that the argon detector cannot. The result is that the cross-section detector is very conveniently substituted for the argon detector, and forms a simple complement to it.

8.5. The Argon Detector

The apparatus for the Argon Ionisation detector, first introduced by Lovelock (*7*), consists of an ionisation chamber basically similar to that for the cross-section detector. The differences are in the details of design, that either argon, neon, or helium must be used as carrier gas, and that the potential applied across the electrodes is much greater, normally between 1000 and 2000 volts. The principle of operation is completely different. Argon has been used most commonly as the carrier gas and has given its name to the detector, but it is not the only usable gas, so that the name is inaccurate, though it is now definitely established.

By slight alterations in the design and operating conditions of the ionisation chamber, different aspects of the complicated processes of ionisation and recombination such as are mentioned in Section 8.3 can be brought into prominence, and the detector can operate usefully in several entirely different ways, as Lovelock (*11*) has emphasised. Often, if the conditions are not correct, it operates in several ways at once, with consequent unreliability, non-linearity, etc., so that careful attention to design and conditions is necessary to obtain full advantage from any one mode of operation.

(*a*) *The Production of Excited Atoms*

In addition to producing ionisation, radiation can interact with atoms or molecules to raise them to an excited state in which the atoms or molecules have more energy than normal, but insufficient to cause them to ionise. The half-lives of the excited atoms of rare gases are very much longer than those of the molecules of other gases, in which the energy is rapidly distributed among internal degrees of freedom, so that their stationary concentration can be relatively large. At atmospheric pressure, half-lives of such states may be of the order of 10^{-4} second, whereas those of the ions are of the order of 10^{-8} second. For this reason, such excited atoms are called "metastable." Unlike ions, they do not contribute to the conductivity of the gas.

The excited atoms of the first three inert gases, He, Ne, and Ar, are

TABLE 8.3

IONISATION AND EXCITATION POTENTIALS

Substance	Ionisation potential (volts)	Excitation potential (volts)
He	24.46	19.8
Ne	21.47	16.6
Ar	15.68	11.6
Kr	13.93	10
H	13.527	
H_2	15.6	7.0
N_2	15.51	6.3
O_2	12.5	
CO	14.1	
CO_2	14.4	
H_2O	12.56	
H_2S	10.42	
CH_4	14.5	
C_2H_6	12.8	
C_6H_6	9.6	
Organic compounds	≈ 11	

of particular interest, for their energies of excitation are greater than the ionisation potentials of most organic compounds, so that a collision between an excited atom and an organic molecule is energetically capable of ionising the latter, and in fact it generally does so. Thus, using argon as an example, the reaction:

$$Ar^* + M \rightarrow Ar + M^+ + \epsilon^-$$

occurs, and the consequent organic ion and the electron contribute to the gas conductivity. Table 8.3 gives excitation and ionisation potentials of the rare gases, and the ionisation potentials of a number of common compounds.

In an irradiated rare gas, the concentration of ions is small, so the electrical conductivity is small, and a comparatively small concentration of organic vapour capable of being ionised by collisions with excited mole-

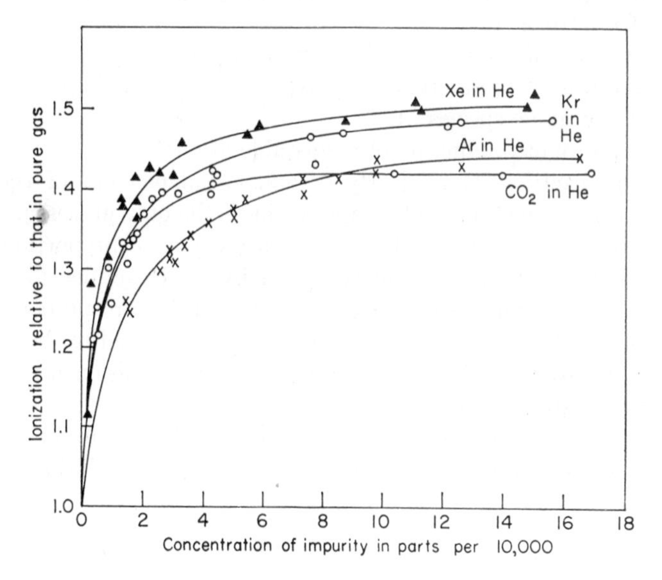

FIG. 8.5. Increase in ionisation produced by an impurity in irradiated helium as a function of the impurity concentration. Jesse and Sadauskis (*8*).

cules causes a large proportional increase in the conductivity. This has been shown for gases in helium irradiated with α-rays in a parallel-plate ionisation chamber by Jesse and Sadauskis (*8*), who plotted the proportional increase in ionisation against the concentration of added trace component (Fig. 8.5). At small concentrations, the increased response is determined by the concentration of the trace component causing it, so that the curve is roughly linear. At large concentrations, the response is determined by the concentration of excited atoms, which is a constant, and thus the curve exhibits saturation.

One can obtain a simple equation for the curves of Fig. 8.5 by considering the relevant kinetics. There are four basic reactions; if Ar is assumed to be the carrier gas, and M is the molecule of a trace component,

$$\begin{aligned} &\mathrm{Ar} + \text{radiation} \rightarrow \mathrm{Ar}^+ + \epsilon^- &(1)\\ &\mathrm{Ar} + \text{radiation} \rightarrow \mathrm{Ar}^* &(2)\\ &\mathrm{Ar}^* + \mathrm{M} \rightarrow \mathrm{Ar} + \mathrm{M}^+ + \epsilon^- &(3)\\ &\mathrm{Ar}^* + \mathrm{Ar} \rightarrow 2\mathrm{Ar} + \text{radiation.} &(4)\end{aligned}$$

In the last case, the radiation will be in the visible and ultraviolet regions. If the potential is such that the cell operates on region C of Fig. 8.2, and if the concentrations of ions and of M are sufficiently small that other reactions may be neglected, then no electrons are lost except at the electrodes, and the current through the cell is proportional to the rate of production of electrons. Let:

e_0 = the rate of production of electrons in pure argon.
e_x = the rate of production of electrons in presence of a mole fraction x of organic species M.
α_0 = the rate of production of metastable atoms.

The rate of reaction (1) is clearly e_0, and is independent of the added vapour. Since in the absence of a vapour, this is the only process producing electrons, the conductivity in the absence of a vapour is proportional to e_0. The rate of reaction (2) is similarly given by α_0. Reactions (3) and (4) are assumed to be bimolecular reactions whose rates are proportional to the molecular collision frequencies, which are proportional to the products of the concentrations of the species multiplied by the collision cross sections and average relative speeds. If :

σ_A, v_A are the cross section and speed of Ar* in collision with Ar,
σ_M, v_M are the cross section and speed of Ar* in collision with M,

then the rates of reactions (3) and (4) are:

$$K\sigma_M v_M x[\mathrm{Ar}^*]$$

and

$$K\sigma_A v_A[\mathrm{Ar}^*],$$

respectively, where square brackets [ ] denote concentration and the constant K includes the other terms in the specification of the collision frequency. [Ar*] is steady at any constant concentration of M, so that the rate of its formation by reaction (2) is equalled by its rate of removal by reactions (3) and (4). Hence

$$\alpha_0 = [\mathrm{Ar}^*]K\{\sigma_A v_A + \sigma_M v_M x\}.$$

When a vapour is present, electrons arise from reaction (3) as well as from reaction (1), so the total current is proportional to the sum of the rates of reactions (1) and (3):

$$e_x = e_0 + K\sigma_M v_M x[\mathrm{Ar}^*] = e_0 + \frac{\sigma_M v_M \alpha_0 x}{\sigma_M v_M x + \sigma_A v_A}, \tag{8.4}$$

the increase in current caused by the vapour being given by the second term. The above equation is more familiar in the form

$$\frac{1}{e_x - e_0} = \frac{\sigma_A v_A}{\sigma_M v_M} \cdot \frac{1}{\alpha_0 x} + \frac{1}{\alpha_0}, \tag{8.5}$$

which was first given by Stern and Vollmer [see Jesse and Sadauskis (*8*)]. This equation should only hold in the conditions given; if the cell operates with large ion currents (in practice, $>10^{-8}$ amp), or in conditions where there are appreciable effects from a space charge, or with large values of M, reactions other than those specified occur, and the situation becomes more complicated.

(*b*) *Ion Multiplication by the Field*

So far, the description applies to cases where the potential between the electrodes is relatively small, so that electrons are not accelerated appreciably by the field. When, however, the field is increased by application of a greater voltage, there comes a stage when the field is such that electrons are sufficiently accelerated between collisions to acquire the energy required to *excite* the rare gas atoms, but do not acquire the energy sufficient to *ionise* them. At such voltages, the number of metastable atoms is much multiplied, but the number of ions remains steady. This is illustrated in Fig. 8.2, which shows, in addition to the curve already discussed, the concentration of metastables as a function of applied potential (dotted line). It is clear that in the region bracketed, where there is a large concentration of metastables but few ions, the effect of an organic vapour described above is very much enhanced, and it is in these circumstances that the simplest form of argon detector operates.

The Stern-Vollmer equation can be extended to cover this case, and the resulting equation is significant in discussing the calibration and linearity of simple argon detectors. The method is exactly as before, but in addition there is the reaction:

$$\mathrm{Ar} + \epsilon^{-*} \rightarrow \mathrm{Ar}^* + \epsilon^-, \tag{5}$$

where ϵ^{-*} is an electron which has been accelerated in the field sufficiently to cause excitation. We shall regard this as a first-order reaction, the rate of which is proportional to the electron concentration. The latter is assumed to be the rate of formation of electrons multiplied by a constant, φ, the value of which depends on the proportion of the electrons the energy of which is sufficient to cause reaction (5). This in turn depends on the field strength, the temperature, the pressure, and other variables. We now list the rates of the five reactions:

Reaction	Rate
(1)	e_0
(2)	α_0
(3)	$K\sigma_M v_M x[Ar^*]$
(4)	$K\sigma_A v_A[Ar^*]$
(5)	$\varphi e_x = \varphi\{e_0 + K\sigma_M v_M x[Ar^*]\}$.

As previously, there is a stationary value of [Ar*], which is generated by reactions (2) and (5), and is removed by reactions (3) and (4). Hence,

$$\alpha_0 + \varphi\{e_0 + K\sigma_M v_M x[Ar^*]\} = [Ar^*]K\{\sigma_A v_A + \sigma_M v_M x\},$$

whence,

$$e_x = e_0 + K\sigma_M v_M x[Ar^*] = e_0 + \frac{\sigma_M v_M x(\alpha_0 + \varphi e_0)}{\sigma_M v_M x(1 - \varphi) + \sigma_A v_A}$$

and the increase in current caused by the vapour is:

$$e_x - e_0 = \frac{\sigma_M v_M x(\alpha_0 + \varphi e_0)}{\sigma_M v_M x(1 - \varphi) + \sigma_A v_A}, \tag{8.6}$$

which equation may be compared with (8.4). Lovelock has suggested that φ is of the form:

$$\varphi = ae^{b(V - V_0)}, \tag{8.7}$$

where V is the voltage applied to the cell, V_0 is a threshold voltage, and a and b are positive constants (*11,38*).

When φ is zero Eq. (8.6) becomes the same as Eq. (8.4), as expected. When φ is less than unity, examination of the equation shows that the response per unit concentration is somewhat greater at all concentrations, but that the increase in current caused by a vapour still exhibits saturation at high concentrations, as when $\varphi = 0$. When φ is unity the detector is, in principle, linear throughout its concentration range; this is confirmed in practice (*7*). When φ is greater than unity, examination of Eq. (8.6) shows that the response increases faster than linearly with concentration, and that there is a finite concentration at which the response is infinite; that is, the detector sparks. The physical interpretation of this is that when the concentration x reaches a certain value, very many electrons are produced by reaction (3). These produce so large a number of metastable atoms by reaction (5) that they cannot all be removed by reaction (4). The remainder increase the rate of reaction (3), thus further increasing the rate of reaction (5), and so on, so that an infinite catastrophe occurs.

(c) The Simple Argon Detector

The simple argon detector is designed to take advantage of electron multiplication by the field, but not to use other effects, such as space charge, electron capture, etc., described below. This instrument was first described by Lovelock (*7*). Ideally, the cell should employ parallel-plate electrodes so as to produce a uniform field, but, in practice, the cell normally consists of one electrode inserted in a metal cavity which forms the other electrode, and, so long as the central electrode is not too small, the field is not sufficiently inhomogeneous to cause complications. The basis of a suitable design is that shown in Fig. 8.3. Satisfactory cells have been constructed using an automobile spark plug as the central electrode, soldering a small circular metal plate on the electrode in order to increase its size (*9*). Lovelock (*10*) has used a rod inside a metal cavity exactly as indicated in Fig. 8.3. Dimensions are conveniently such that the cell volume is of the order of 1 to 10 cc. Lovelock recommends that the diameter of the central electrode is approximately 2 mm, smaller values producing too inhomogeneous a field, larger values requiring too large an applied potential for convenience.

The behaviour of the simple argon detector at ion currents less than about 10^{-7} amp is described adequately by Eqs. (8.6) and (8.7). The percentage change in current as a function of proportion to a vapour, with applied voltage as a parameter, is shown in Fig. 8.6. At low voltages, when

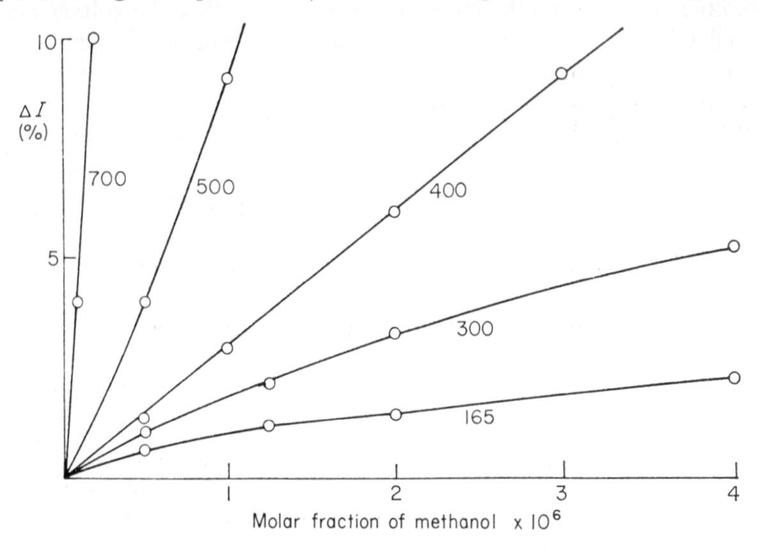

Fig. 8.6. Increase in ionisation current as a function of the concentration of an added vapour (methanol) in a simple argon detector with applied voltage as parameter. Lovelock (*7*).

$\varphi < 1$, the increase in current is linear at very small concentrations, but reaches saturation at larger concentrations. At one specific voltage, which is 400 volts in the example shown, the detector is linear, and it is presumed that $\varphi = 1$. At greater voltages, the current increases extra-linearly with concentration of vapour, and in some cells breakdown may occur at a threshold vapour concentration, as anticipated by Eq. (8.6), even though it is not quantitatively applicable.

It is apparent either from the equations or from Fig. 8.6 that the sensitivity is enormously dependent on the applied voltage. When this is small, the sensitivity is small, but the detector may be used up to a more less large vapour concentration; when the applied voltage is large, the sensitivity becomes very great, but there is the possibility of breakdown and other effects if the vapour concentration is large. The chief virtue of the argon detector is that it is capable of very great sensitivity, and, for this, it is operated at such a voltage that $\varphi \approx 10^3$–10^4, so that every primary electron produced by the radiation creates as many as 10^4 more by acceleration in the field.

When φ is large, the detector is very non-linear. This can be largely corrected by a "Linearising Resistance" in series with the detector, usually of the order of 10^9 to 10^{10} ohms. When a vapour enters the cell, the current rises, and without the linearising resistance, would rise extra-linearly. However, with a suitable series resistance, as soon as the current increases, the voltage drop across the resistance increases, so that the voltage across the cell falls, causing a drop in the value of φ, whence the extra-linear part of the current increase may be prevented. The best value of the linearising resistance must be found empirically.

With the simple argon detector, the background current equivalent to the primary ionisation is usually about 10^{-8} amp, and the maximum current at which the response is approximately linear, using a linearising resistance, is about 10^{-7} amp. At currents greater than this, no single linearising resistance can maintain even approximate linearity at all vapour concentrations.

The ionisation efficiency of the simple argon detector is about 0.1%.

(d) *Effects of Geometry and Space Charge; Micro-Argon Detector*

In the case that the anode is small compared to the cathode, as in a cell which consists of a small anode placed in a large cavity forming the cathode, the field in the neighbourhood of the anode is intense, and the field in the neighbourhood of the cathode is small. Positive ions moving slowly towards the cathode soon leave the intense field around the anode, and enter a region of small field, which will augment their natural sluggishness described in Section 8.3(c). The result is that in these circumstances a strong space charge is formed around the cathode.

When a detector is constructed in this way, the space charge and the inhomogeneity of the field cause it to behave very differently from the simple detector. The first difference is that the field is only sufficiently intense to produce metastable atoms by collision with accelerated electrons in the immediate neighbourhood of the small electrode, and since metastable ions produced in this manner vastly outnumber those produced by collision with primary ionising radiation, the detector will only respond to vapour in this region. Hence, however large the cell cavity, the effective detector volume is located within a few diameters of the small electrode. Such a detector has been described by Lovelock (*10,11*), and may be called the micro-argon detector.

A diagram of a micro-argon detector is given in Fig. 8.7. The central electrode is hollow, and carries the gas to be analysed, which is thus delivered straight into the region of high field. In order to prevent back-diffusion of vapour already recorded from the main volume of the cell into the effective region around the small electrode, vapour leaving this region is at once swept out of the cell by an auxiliary stream of carrier gas, conventionally referred to as the *scavenger* gas. It is found in practice that the flow of scavenger gas must be laminar throughout the cell, and it is necessary to distribute the flow of incoming gas by means of some kind of baffle, e.g., of gauze, as shown in the figure.

The performance of the micro-argon detector is modified in other ways also. In the case that the central electrode is the anode, an increase in the current causes a change in the space charge, such that there is a decrease in the field immediately around the anode. This causes reduction in φ. Thus, the space charge fulfills the same purpose as a linearising resistance, and, if the geometry of the space charge is correct, then no such external resistance is required. Lovelock has found that the relation of the space charge to the anode can be easily controlled in a cell consisting of coaxial cylindrical electrodes by moving the central anode in and out of the cell along its axis. It is found in practice that the space charge is such as to give linearity if the end of the anode is several millimetres beyond the end of the cathode and well away from the source of radiation, as shown. Since the linearity depends on the space charge, the magnitude of which is a function of the primary ion concentration, it is necessary that the standing ion current be maintained at a sufficient value. In practice, with cells of the order of 1 to 10 cc total volume, a current of not less than 10^{-8} amp is necessary.

The small effective volume of the micro-argon detector recommends its use for capillary columns, where not only great sensitivity but also small detector volume is required. Such detectors are finding increasing application for this purpose. In a recent modification, the "Triode Detector" (*10*), a third electrode in the form of a ring coaxial with the other two inside the cavity serves to collect the positive ions produced from

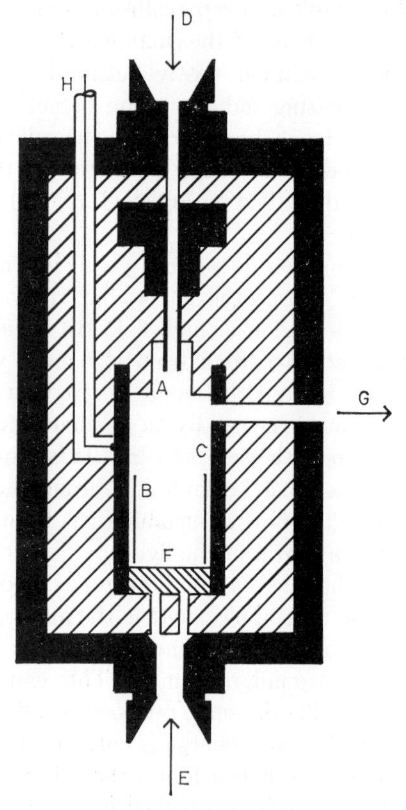

FIG. 8.7. Micro-argon detector. After Wiseman (*40*). A, Anode; B, radiation source; C, cathode; D, inlet from column; E, inlet for scavenger gas; F, baffle for scavenger gas; G, common outlet; H, insulated lead to cathode.

reaction of vapour molecules with excited argon atoms, but nothing else, so that there is little or no background current when there is no vapour present.

The ionisation efficiency of the micro-argon detector is larger than that of the simple argon detector, and may be as great as 1% (*10*).

(*e*) *Auxiliary Electronic Apparatus*

The electronics associated with any form of the argon detector is similar to that used with the cross-section detector, and consists merely of apparatus required to measure currents of the order of 10^{-8} to 10^{-7} amp with as great an accuracy as possible. The basic circuit generally employed is illustrated in Fig. 8.8. A large negative potential from a suitable stabilised source is applied to the cathode of the cell. The current through the cell passes through a load resistor in the anode circuit, and the voltage across this is measured by an electrometer tube. The background current obtained in pure carrier gas is normally "Backed Off," for example, by applying a suitable potential to the grid of the electrometer tube via

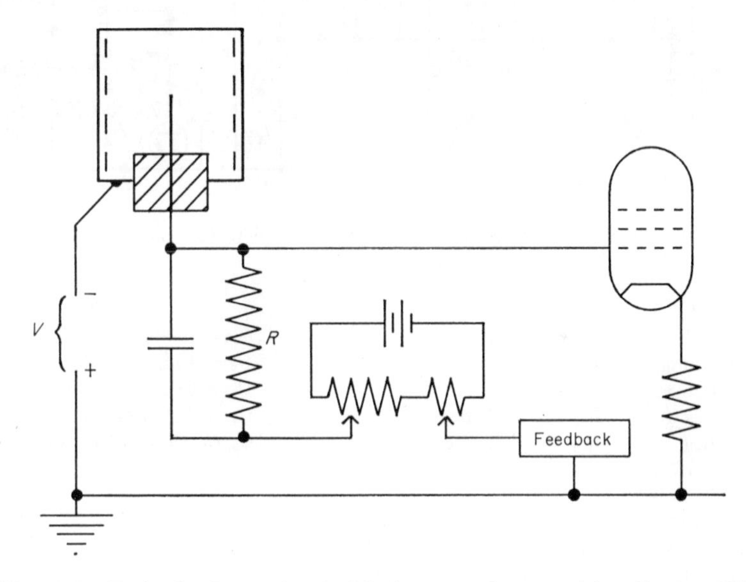

FIG. 8.8. Basic circuit associated with the argon detector. After Condon, Scholly, and Averill (*12*).

a potential divider across a battery, as shown in Fig. 8.8 (*12*), or by other electronic means (as in Fig. 8.9). With currents of the order of 10^{-8} amp, the load resistor is of the order of 10^8 to 10^9 ohms, so that the voltage developed across it is of the order of 1 to 10 volts.

A circuit suitable for operation of a moving-coil recording milliammeter as used by Lovelock *et al.* (*9*) is shown in Fig. 8.9, but it should be emphasised that the design of impedance converters such as these is a specialised task, and requires more information, knowledge, and experience than is conveyed merely by a circuit diagram.

It should be remembered that the load resistance also constitutes a linearising resistance, so that very large load resistances may have an appreciable effect on the linearity of the detector.

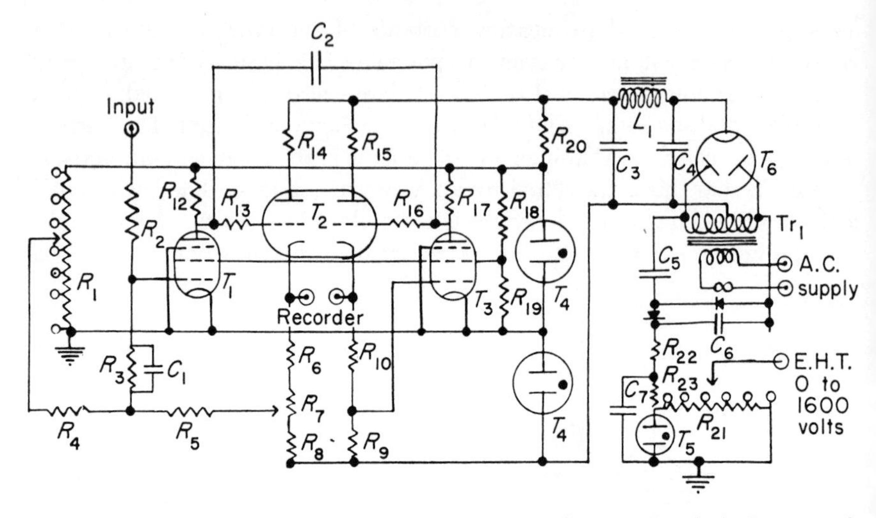

FIG. 8.9. Typical circuit associated with an argon detector. Lovelock, James, and Piper (*9*).

Resistors		*Capacitors*
$R_1 = 6 \times 10$ k	$R_{18} = 150$ k	$C_1 = 1000\ \mu\mu$f
$R_2 = 2000$ meg	$R_{19} = 250$ k	$C_2 = 4\ \mu$f, 400 volts
$R_3 = 500$ meg	$R_{20} = 3.9$ k	$C_3 = 32\ \mu$f, 400 volts
$R_4 = 4$ meg	$R_{21} = 5 \times 5$ meg	$C_4 = 8\ \mu$f, 400 volts
$R_5 = 1$ meg	$R_{22}, R_{23} = 2$ meg	$C_5, C_6, C_7 = 0.1\ \mu$f, 2000 volts
$R_6, R_{10} = 4.7$ k		
$R_7 = 500$ ohms		
$R_8, R_9 = 10$ k		
$R_{12}, R_{17} = 500$ k	$L_1 = 10$ hy. inductance 50 ma	
$R_{13}, R_{16} = 1$ meg	Tr$_1$ = 300-0-300 volt transformer	

(*f*) *Sensitivity and Noise*

The limiting factor to the sensitivity is the signal-to-noise ratio, and not the electrical response in volts, which has normally to be attenuated and not amplified.

The response is essentially change in the current through the cell, and we may consider sensitivity in terms of this. As with the cross-section detector, the minimum noise level is determined by random fluctuations in the current caused by the discontinuous nature of the radiation so that, for example, with sources of ≈ 10 mC and a time constant of 1 second, the noise is $\approx 0.005\%$ of the total (see Section 8.4). The difference between the argon detector and the cross-section detector, however, is that the change in current produced by the same concentration of vapour is very much greater, so that, though the noise is the same, the signal-to-noise ratio is much greater. With the cross-section detector, a concentration of 1 part in 10,000 of, for example, *n*-butane in argon would cause a proportional increase of:

$$10^{-4} \times \frac{10.9 + 23.1}{10.9} = 0.031\%$$

in the current (figures from Table 8.2). With the argon detector, the corresponding percentage increase would be of the order of 10 to 100%, depending on the applied voltage (see, for example, the percentage increases in current caused by methanol given in Fig. 8.6).

Simple argon detectors, the effective volume of which is that of the whole cavity, give a response proportional to concentration, and thus sensitivity is expressible as the minimum detectable concentration. Lovelock (*10*) quotes a figure of 4×10^{-11} g/ml, which, for a substance of molecular weight of 100 is a mole fraction of 10^{-8}. Condon *et al.* (*12*) quote a figure of 1.5×10^{-10} g/ml for a signal-to-noise ratio of 2:1 for propane. A very rough guide is that one molecule of vapour per million of argon produces $\approx$1% increase in current in a normally operating detector.

With micro-argon detectors, in which the column effluent flows from a small anode (Fig. 8.7), the response is proportional to the quantity of vapour flowing out per second, so that if the flow rate were doubled, the same concentration of vapour would give twice the response. Lovelock (*10*) quotes a figure minimum detectable rate of vapour flow of 4×10^{-13} g/second for a detector such as shown in Fig. 8.7, and 2×10^{-14} g/second for the triode detector. These figures may be converted into the equivalent concentrations in grams per millilitre by dividing by the flow rate in millilitres per second. Using Lovelock's figures, this gives 1.2×10^{-12} and 6×10^{-14} g/ml for the cases quoted above.

It will be appreciated that these sensitivities are very great indeed, and such detectors should be used when the greatest sensitivities are required.

(*g*) *Drift*

Base line drift in argon detectors may result from poor design or operation, but is not an inherent nuisance. The operation of the instrument depends on the accurate measurement of a large resistance, and ordinary precautions relevant to such measurements must be made. Thus, voltages supplied to the impedance converter should be stabilised, and the impedance converter should be allowed to reach a steady state before operation. Precautions against leakage across surfaces, particularly as a result of moisture, should be taken. Probably the commonest source of drift, which is scarcely the fault of the detector, is due to slow changes in the concentration of inevitable contaminants in the carrier gas stream, especially those due to the slow volatilisation or decomposition of the stationary phase.

(*h*) *Linearity*

The simple argon detector operating at large electron multiplication factors is essentially a non-linear detector; linearity is secured by the introduction of a linearising resistance, but it is clear that even in the conditions where Eq. (8.6) holds, one adjustable parameter can scarcely correct for non-linearity which results from the large number of constants contained in the equations. The result is that if a plot of response against concentration for the simple argon detector is compared with that for many other detectors *on the same concentration scale*, the argon detector will appear very non-linear. Such a comparison, however, is deceptive, for it neglects the fact that the argon detector can register much smaller concentrations than many others, so that though the maximum concentration at which it is approximately linear is small, the dynamic range between the limit of detection and the threshold of significant non-linearity is of the same order as that of other detectors.

Lovelock (*10*) quotes an upper concentration limit of 1 molecule in 2000 for the simple argon detector, above which the linearity is poor. With an ultimate limit of detection of about 10^{-8} mole fraction, this gives a dynamic range of a little more than 10^4. With micro-argon detectors, the dynamic range is greater, partly because of their greater sensitivity, and possibly because the linearising by the space-charge effect is more effective than that produced by an external resistance.

When vapour concentrations become large, reactions not considered in Section 8.5(c) become significant. In particular, the added vapour causes electrons to lose energy by inelastic collision as described in Section 8.3(e), with the result that there are fewer electrons with sufficient energy to cause excitation. Also, capture of electrons by the vapour molecules as described in Section 8.3(d) increases exponentially with the vapour concentration. The result is that at comparatively large vapour concentrations the current reaches a maximum and at still greater concentrations it declines. Clearly, in the limiting case of 100% vapour, the current is determined by the ionisation cross section of the vapour alone, and electron multiplication by the field is absent. The kinetics of processes at large vapour concentration is complicated, but the observation is commonplace. Figure 8.10 shows a plot of response against concentration of butane in argon, obtained by replotting the record obtained from an exponential dilution experiment on semi-log paper [Wiseman (*40*)].

The relative importance of inelastic collisions, electron capture, and the mechanisms already described depends also on the chemical nature of the vapour; if this is a ready electron acceptor, as when it contains electronegative atoms, e.g., the halogens, then electron capture becomes predominant at much smaller concentrations. In some detectors, carbon tetrachloride will give negative peaks whereas hydrocarbons give posi-

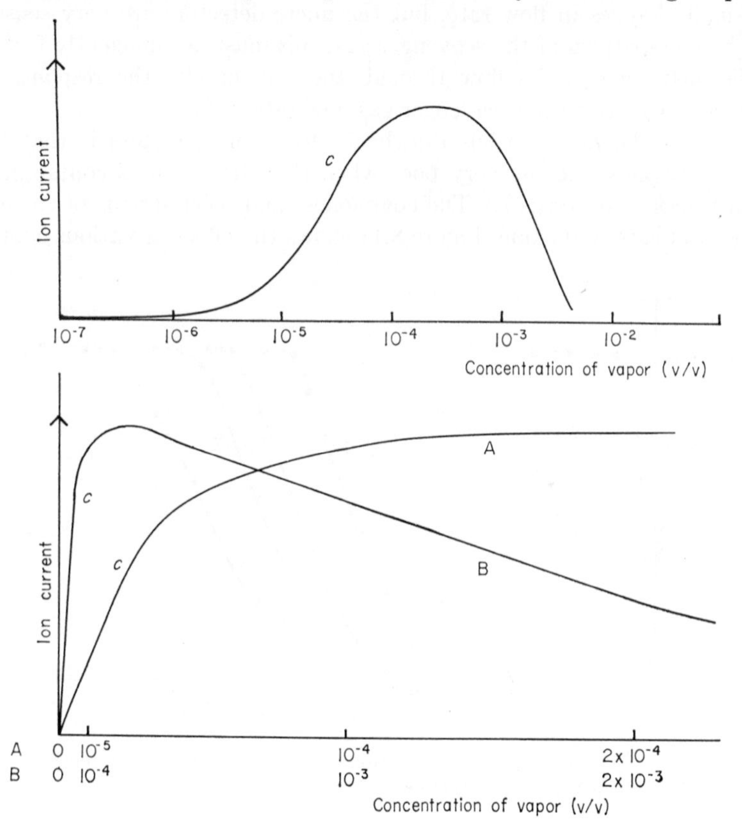

FIG. 8.10 Plot of ionisation current against concentration of butane in an argon detector, using large concentrations of butane. Wiseman (*40*). Point *c* indicates the upper concentration limit of approximate linearity. *Upper:* Traced from experimental record of response produced by vapour from an exponential dilution apparatus—logarithmic concentration scale. *Lower:* The same plotted on (A) large linear scale, (B) small linear scale.

tive peaks. In other detectors, however, halogenates may be caused to give positive peaks, and it is apparent that the behaviour of such compounds also depends on the detector geometry in a manner as yet uncertain.

(*i*) *Independence of Extraneous Variables*

Small changes in temperature or pressure have little effect on the base line. Increase in temperature or decrease in pressure, however, increases the mean free path of electrons, so that a larger number acquire excitation energy before collision; this leads to an increase in φ. Thus, if the sensitivity is to remain the same, the applied voltage should be reduced in order to compensate. The simple detector is relatively insensitive to small changes in flow rate, but the micro-detectors are very sensitive to the flow-pattern of the scavenger gas; this must be sufficiently fast and sufficiently even in its flow through the cell, or else the response will become sensitive to the scavenger gas flow rate (*10*).

One of the most serious drawbacks to argon detectors is that their sensitivity may become very poor when the carrier gas is contaminated with traces of other gases. The commonest and most serious of these are water and carbon dioxide. Figure 8.11 shows the effect of various contam-

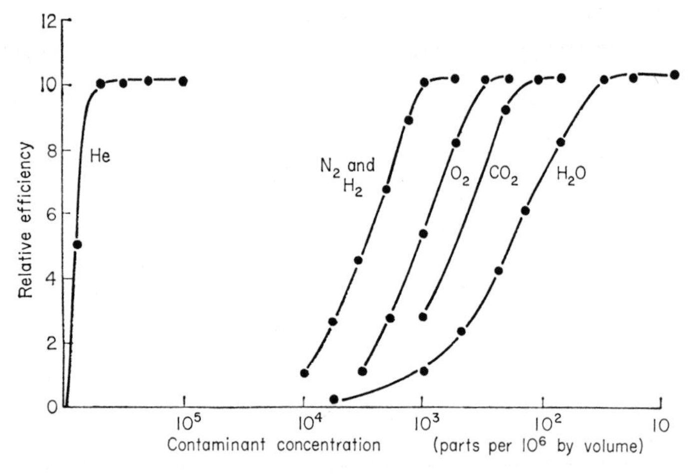

FIG. 8.11. Plot of the effect of contaminant gases in argon on the sensitivity of a simple argon detector. Lovelock (*11*).

inants on the sensitivity as a function of mole fraction. Argon obtained from commercial tanks of gas may well contain water vapour, and a vapour trap filled with magnesium perchlorate, charcoal, or molecular sieve at dry-ice temperature should be included in the gas-feed.

(*j*) *Calibration*

According to Eq. (8.6), when the concentration is small enough that the detector is substantially linear, the sensitivity is proportional to $\sigma_M v_M$, the product of the cross section and velocity of metastables with respect to the vapour. The relative velocities are easily calculable by elementary kinetic theory to be $(M_M^{-1} + M_A^{-1})^{1/2}$, so that the sensitivities should be proportional to:

$$\sigma_M \left(\frac{1}{M_M} + \frac{1}{M_A}\right)^{1/2}. \qquad (8.8)$$

Lovelock (7) has investigated this assuming that the collision cross section is given by the square of the sum of the radii of the argon and the vapour, and the radius of the vapour molecules is given by $(3M/4d)^{1/3}$, where d is the density of the liquid or solid. On this basis, a theoretical calibration curve as shown by the solid line in Fig. 8.12 is obtained, and the points

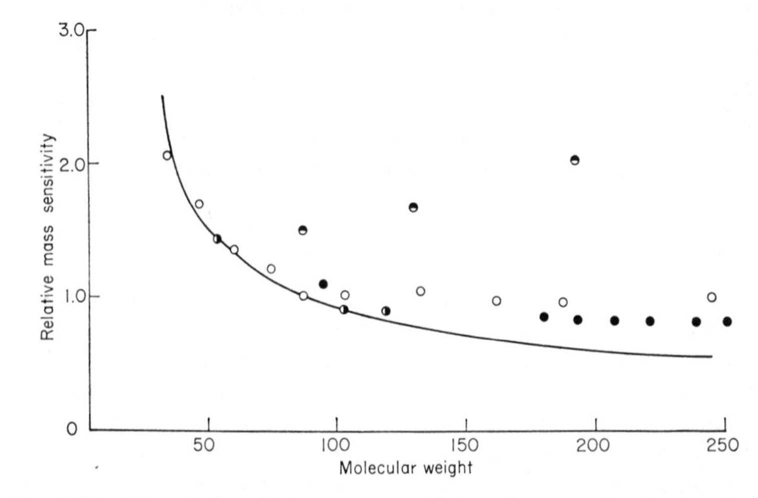

FIG. 8.12. Plot of the relative mass sensitivity of vapours in the simple argon detector as a function of their molecular weight. Lovelock (7). *Full line,* theoretical line; ○, *n*-primary alcohols; ●, *n*-primary fatty acid methyl esters; ◑, ketones and ethers; ◓, aromatics.

show the accuracy of the calculation. The conclusion is that the above method of calculation is fairly satisfactory for many compounds, but is unusable for chemical types such as aromatics.

Lovelock's results, and also results of several other workers, confirm that the weight sensitivity of compounds of high molecular weight which are largely paraffinic, e.g., higher fatty acid esters, petroleum products above about C_8, etc., is nearly constant. However, below about $C_6 - C_8$, weight sensitivities exhibit significant variations. These have not so far been studied in detail.

(*k*) *Chemical Inertness*

Since the ionisation efficiency of current argon detectors is only of the order of 1%, 99% of the sample is unchanged in passage through the cell. With such a sensitive detector, though, vapours are not normally recovered, since the quantity recovered would be too small to be useful.

(*l*) *Range of Application*

The detector will give a sensitive response only to substances which can be ionised by excited molecules. When argon is the carrier gas, this includes nearly all organic compounds and many inorganic compounds, but excludes the following: H_2, N_2, O_2, CO_2, CO, $(CN)_2$, H_2O, CH_4, fluorocarbons, nitriles. These compounds give weak responses in an argon detector operating at least partially as a cross-section detector (*13,14*), but linearity and performance are unreliable. In addition to these, other compounds with large electron affinity may fail to give normal responses, but much depends on the exact design of the cell, see Subsection (h).

If helium is used as carrier gas, then all the above gases may be detected and measured with the characteristic great sensitivity, but the use of helium is restricted by the necessity for excessive purity, as described below.

Willis (*15*) has described a device by which argon detectors using argon may be used to detect permanent gases. In this, the argon is mixed with a constant trace quantity of an organic vapour, e.g., 1 in 10^6 part of ethylene, which causes a considerable increase in the cell current. When a trace quantity of permanent gas is introduced, the current produced by the ionisation of the ethylene falls, thus giving a measurable response to the inert gas. This device enables the argon detector to be used for as little as 0.5 ppm of hydrogen, oxygen, or methane. This adaptation of the argon detector probably operates largely on account of the mechanism mentioned in Section 8.3(e). Addition of a permanent molecular gas causes a drop in the proportion of electrons sufficiently excited by the field to produce metastable argon atoms, with the result that fewer ionised ethylene molecules are produced, and hence the current is reduced.

(*m*) *The Use of Helium in Argon Detectors*

It is apparent from the figures of Table 8.3 that though excited argon atoms cannot ionise the molecules of permanent gases, those of helium can do so, and indeed, excited helium atoms have sufficient energy to ionise every other molecular species. This suggests the use of helium rather than argon in argon detectors. It is in fact possible to use helium, but its use involves much more difficulty. The basic reason for this is that the complications which cause argon detectors to fail at large vapour concentrations occur at much lower concentrations when helium is used as carrier gas. Thus, whereas the maximum allowable concentration of vapours in argon is about 100 to 500 ppm (see Sections 8.5(h), 8.5(i)), the corresponding figures for helium are much smaller, probably of the order of 10 ppm or less. Furthermore, whereas the air gases do not have a very profound effect on the operation of the detector using argon except at rather large concentrations (Fig. 8.11), in helium, the air gases are ionised, and any appreciable concentration will cause the detector to become overloaded. The net result is that helium may only be used if *extremely* careful precautions are taken to purify it. Apart from the difficulty of taking such precautions, it should be recalled that the vapour pressures of most current stationary phases are at least sufficient to saturate an argon detector using helium.

8.6. Electron Capture Detector

Lovelock and Lipsky (*16*) have described a detector which operates primarily by the electron capture mechanism described in Section 8.3(d). Molecules can capture only slow-moving non-energetic electrons, so in this detector, the applied voltage is of the order of 1 to 50 volts, which is far less than is required to produce any electron multiplication. Any carrier gas may be used (e.g., nitrogen or hydrogen), so long as it is not itself a compound with large electron affinity.

A plot of the current against applied voltage at small fields (i.e., regions A and B of Fig. 8.2) for an irradiated gas both pure and with electron capturing impurities is shown in Fig. 8.13. With pure gas, the curve is as described in Section 8.3(a). With electron capturing impurities,

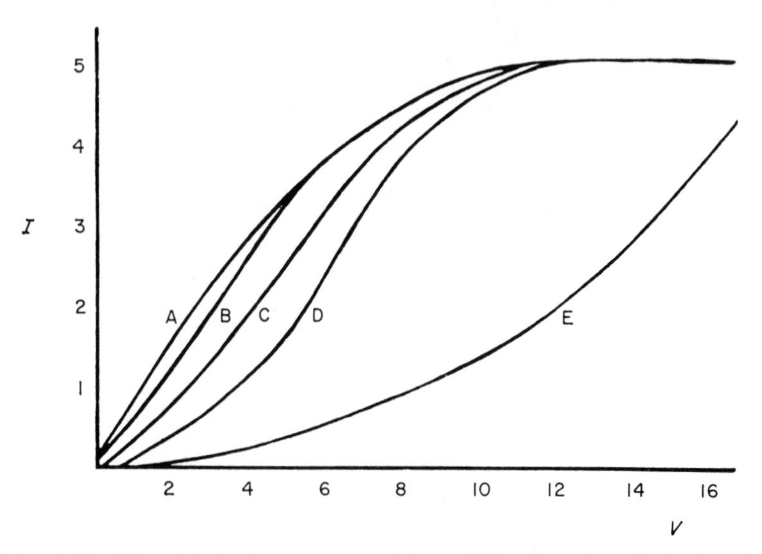

Fig. 8.13. Plot of ionisation current against applied voltage in an ionisation chamber containing pure nitrogen (curve A), and nitrogen containing a: B, hydrocarbon; C, ester; D, alcohol; E, halogenated hydrocarbon. Lovelock and Lipsky (*16*).

the current at a given voltage is smaller so that a zone of electron capturing vapour coming through the detector appears as a drop in the current, which may be measured and recorded.

In an ionisation chamber used at small fields, with a permanent gas as carrier, and with complex electron capturing molecules as the vapour, there are always two processes causing the vapour to change the ionisation current: (1) the electron capturing effect tending to reduce the current, (2) the cross-section effect of Section 8.4; tending to increase it, since the vapour molecules all have larger cross sections than the carrier molecules. The relative magnitude of these two depends on the molecular ionisation

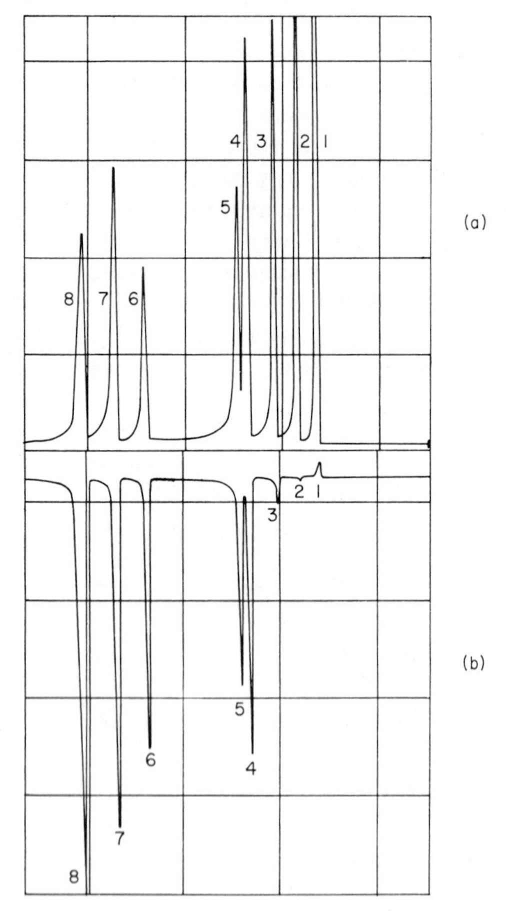

FIG. 8.14. Chromatograms of (1) cyclohexane, (2) fluorobenzene, (3) chlorobenzene, (4) *m*- and *p*-dichlorobenzene, (5) *o*-dichlorobenzene, (6) 1,3,5-trichlorobenzene, (7) 1,2,4-trichlorobenzene, and (8) 1,2,3-trichlorobenzene from an argon detector (a) and from an electron capture detector (b). Lovelock (*41*).

cross section, on the one hand, and the affinity of the molecule for electrons and the electron speed, on the other. The electron affinity of molecules is very sensitive to their composition, so that molecules of similar size but different chemical type can give different responses in an electron capture detector. Since also the electron capture process diminishes the greater the field, molecules of different chemical classes lose their ability to capture electrons one after the other in order of electron affinity as the field is increased. These properties clearly form the basis of a method for the qualitative identification of the effluent peaks from a chromatographic column.

The greater the electron affinity of a group in a molecule, the larger the field in which electrons may still be captured. Thus, hydrocarbons, which have small electron affinities, cause an increase in ionisation current except at voltages less than about 2 volts. Halogenated compounds, compounds containing carbonyl groups, etc., cause decrease in the ionisation currents at much greater applied voltages, e.g., up to about 20 volts. The use of the detector for qualitative identification of different chemical classes is shown in Fig. 8.14, which shows two chromatograms, one taken with an argon detector (a) and one taken with an electron capture detector (b). Chromatogram (b) shows a small positive response for the only hydrocarbon in the mixture, nil response for a fluorinated compound, and negative responses for chlorinated compounds, the response increasing with the number of chlorine atoms in the molecule.

Since the use of the electron capture detector as a qualitative tool depends on the magnitude of the field in the cell, its qualitative resolving power is greater the more uniform the field. Thus, the electron capture detector should employ an ionisation chamber with plane parallel electrodes (*4*), and the ion current should be very small ($\approx 10^{-9}$ amp) in order to prevent the formation of an appreciable space charge.

8.7. Electron Mobility Detector

Lovelock (*42*) has described a detector in which the primary mechanism is the effect on the mobility of accelerated electrons in a rare gas produced by the introduction of any gas possessing internal degrees of freedom. In this detector, the carrier gas is argon, and the cell is a parallel-plate design using a radiation source of small range, e.g., tritium or an α-emitter located near the anode. A pulsed potential of about 50 to 100 volts at a frequency variable between about 0.1 and 1 Mc/second is applied between the electrodes. When pure carrier gas is passing, the electrons produced by ionisation are moving at great speed, and the duration of the pulse is insufficient for them to be sufficiently deflected to arrive at the electrodes before the end of the pulse. Thus, the ionisation current is very small ($\approx 10^{-10}$ amp). When a molecular vapour enters, the electrons are slowed down as described in Section 8.3(e), and after this, they may be deflected sufficiently during a pulse to be collected. The result is an increase in the ionisation current, which is recorded.

The pulse frequency below which the pulse is long enough for electrons to be collected depends on the extent to which they are slowed by the inelastic collisions, and this appears to depend on the molecular complexity of the vapour. Thus, the more complex the vapour, the greater may be the frequency of the pulses without a fall in the current, as illustrated in Fig. 8.15, which shows a plot of current against frequency for the same

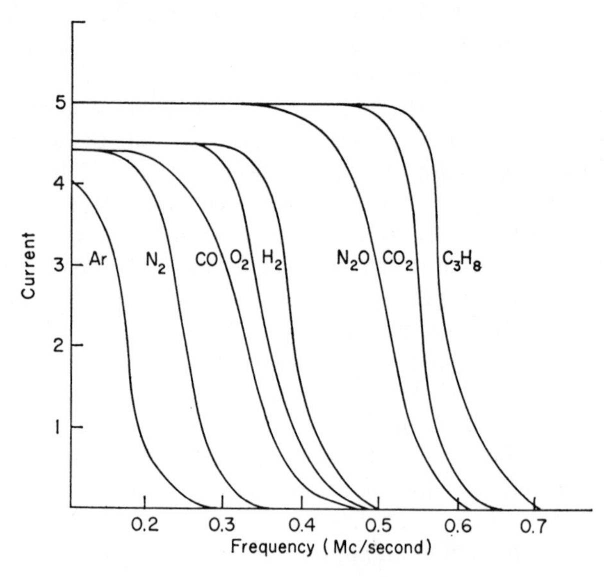

FIG. 8.15. Plot of current against pulse frequency for 0.1% by volume of various vapours in argon in an electron mobility detector. Lovelock (*42*).

concentration of various vapours. It is clear that this technique provides a limited means of qualitative identification of vapours.

Of the detectors described, the electron mobility detector is the least developed, but it is of importance in that it is the only ionisation detector so far described which gives a large response to the permanent gases.

8.8. Flame Ionisation Detector

Gases burning in a flame become sufficiently hot for a small proportion of the molecules to acquire sufficient energy to ionise and so give the flame an electrical conductivity. When an organic vapour enters the flame, the conductivity becomes greater, and the increase in conductivity may be measured and recorded. This is the basis of the hydrogen flame detector (*12,17–25*). At least two reasons have been suggested for the increase in conductivity. One is that the ionisation is purely a result of the high temperature in the flame, and that organic compounds, having smaller ionisation potentials than hydrogen, produce more ions at a given temperature than does hydrogen (*26*). Another is that particles of carbon formed in the flame have a small work function, and thus supply a large number of electrons to the flame (*27*). It is apparent, however, that neither of these explanations is adequate to account for the observed conductivity (*28*), and we shall not discuss the mechanism of the process further. The ionisation efficiency of the hydrogen flame detector is small; it has been quoted as 0.01 to 0.05% (*18*), and in many cases is even smaller than this.

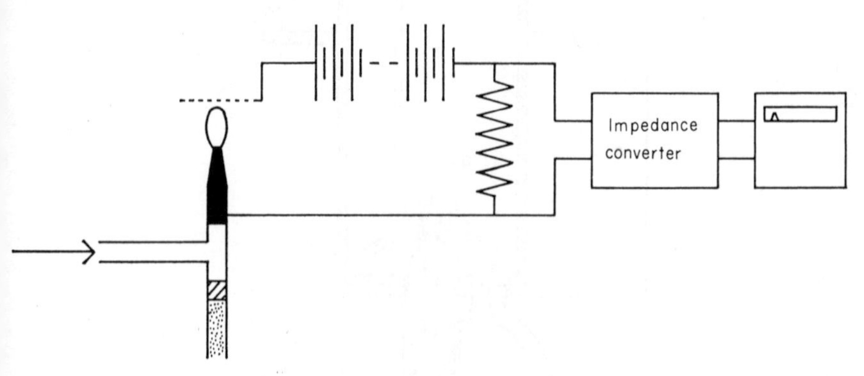

FIG. 8.16. Basic circuit of the flame ionisation detector. If hydrogen is not used as the carrier gas, it may be introduced by the tube indicated with the arrow.

In the detector (Fig. 8.16), the effluent from the column passes into a hydrogen flame, the conductivity of which is measured either between two electrodes (*17*), or, more commonly, between a metal jet and one electrode, as shown in the figure. The simplest arrangement is to use hydrogen as the carrier gas and to burn it at the jet at the column outlet. If, however, hydrogen is not to be used as carrier, the carrier gas may be mixed with sufficient hydrogen for the mixture to burn.

(*a*) *Design and Operation*

The variation of current with voltage applied across the electrodes in general is as outlined in Section 8.3(a). When the applied voltage is small (<5 volts/cm), the flame obeys Ohm's law in that the current is determined by the rate of migration of ions, which is proportional to the field. When the applied voltage is greater, all available ions arrive at the electrodes, so that further increase in voltage does not increase the current; this region of saturation holds from about 10 volts/cm up to at least several hundred volts/cm (*12,24*). At still higher voltages, the result is a rapid increase in current followed by a discharge. Hydrogen flame detectors are operated in the saturation region, and the voltage applied to the electrodes is usually 200–300 volts. Desty *et al.* have studied the influence

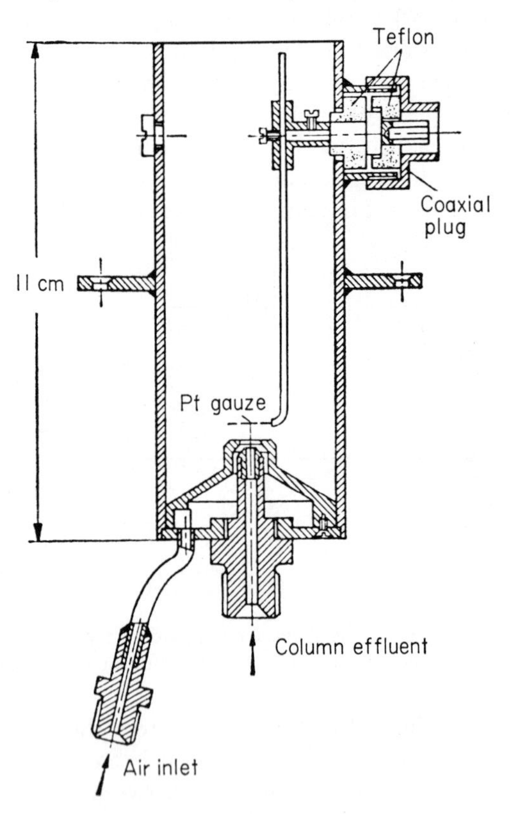

FIG. 8.17. Flame ionisation detector according to Ongkiehong (*24*).

of interelectrode distance and electrode shape on the voltage-current plot for the case of conduction between the jet and a single electrode (*25*), and the general conclusion is that, though there are minor differences in the shape of the curves before saturation is reached, these geometrical factors are remarkably uncritical. Only two factors appear to affect the design from this point of view. If a negative electrode becomes too hot, it may emit thermal electrons which raise the background conductivity, and raise the noise. This may happen if a small metal jet of low heat capacity is used as one electrode, or if an electrode is too far into the flame. The second factor is that electrodes should not be too far away from the flame, or the ions will recombine before reaching it, so that currents will be too small.

Of the several designs of detector of which details have been published, all appear to give comparable performances, emphasising that design characteristics are not very critical. In all designs, the flame and the electrode or electrodes are screened by some kind of chimney through the

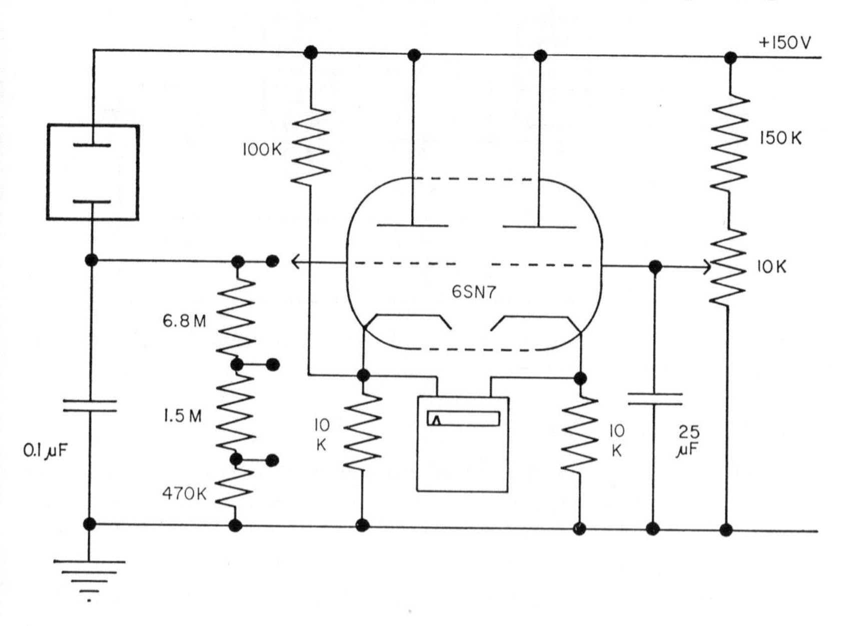

FIG. 8.18. Circuit associated with the flame ionisation detector by Harley, Nel, and Pretorius (*17*).

base of which a supply of air is fed. The chimney is best constructed of metal, which serves to provide electrostatic screening of the electrodes as well as performing its principal function as a draught shield. The flame is extremely sensitive to fine dust particles which may enter it, so the air feeding the flame should be efficiently filtered, e.g., through glass wool (*19*,*20*). The design of Ongkiehong (*24*) is shown in Fig. 8.17.

The resistance of the hydrogen flame is of the order of 10^{14} ohms, and the current through the cell varies from of the order of 10^{-12} amp background current to about 10^{-7} amp on maximum signal. Thus the techniques for measuring the current are very similar to those used with the argon detector, except that no high-voltage supply is necessary. Figure 8.18 shows a simple circuit used by Harley, Nel, and Pretorius (*17*).

Figure 8.19 shows the circuit of McWilliam and Dewar (*19*) with a twin-flame arrangement. In addition, the circuit shown in Fig. 8.9 may be used, with obvious alterations to the voltage supply.

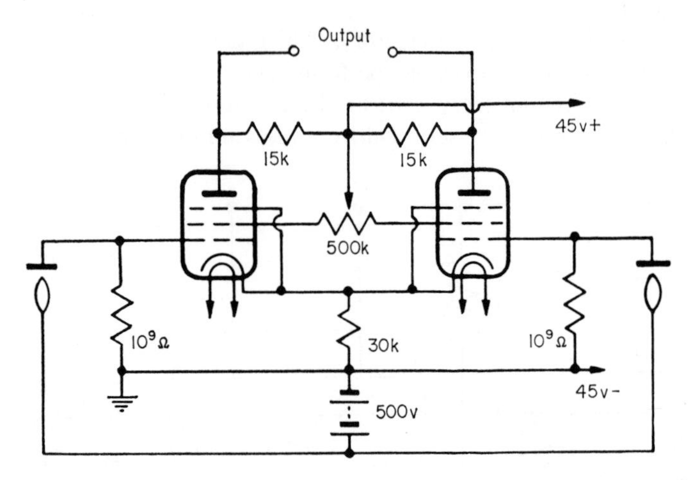

FIG. 8.19. Circuit used with a twin-flame ionisation detector by McWilliam and Dewar (*19*).

(*b*) *Sensitivity and Noise*

Different authors using different designs of detector give remarkably similar figures for the limit of detection, i.e., the concentration equivalent to the noise. This limit appears to be about 1 in 10^9 molar for substances in hydrogen (*20,24,25*). As with the argon detector, the response is best expressed in terms of the mass flow of vapour rather than its concentration, so as to be able to calculate a response for detectors in which hydrogen is mixed with non-combustible carrier gas before the flame, in which case considerable dilution of the vapour occurs before it is detected.

The number of ions produced in the time of a time constant of the order of 1 second is sufficiently large that statistical variations in this number do not contribute to the noise. The background current produced by the pure hydrogen flame, however, is proportional to the flow rate of hydrogen, and thus variations in the flow rate appear as background noise and, in practice, it appears that this factor determines the noise (*24*). By a simple calculation, Ongkiehong (*24*) gives the following relation between the vapour concentration equivalent to the noise produced by uneven flow:

$$\Delta = d \cdot \frac{S_h}{S} \cdot \frac{F_h}{F_g}, \tag{8.9}$$

where Δ = vapour concentration equivalent to noise.
S = response of vapour (amp g^{-1}second = coulomb/g).
S_h = response of pure hydrogen (amp g^{-1}second) calculated from background current of pure hydrogen flame.
F_h = hydrogen flow rate.
F_g = carrier gas flow rate; = F_h if hydrogen is carrier gas and no mixture is made.
d = flow fluctuation as proportion of total flow.

It is the fact that $S \gg S_h$, as described above, that enables large signal-to-noise ratios to be obtained with the hydrogen flame detector. The figure of a noise level equivalent to 10^{-9} M quoted at the beginning of this sub-section was derived from the above equation by Ongkiehong (*24*) assuming $d = 0.001$, i.e., control of the flow to 0.1%.

(*c*) *Linearity*

The hydrogen flame detector appears to behave linearly over a large range, probably from the limit of detection to a vapour mole fraction of about 0.5%. McWilliam and Dewar (*19*) show straightline plots of peak area against mass for a variety of compounds; Desty, Goldup, and Geach (*25*) show a linear plot of the *log* of the current response *versus* the *log* of the mass flow rate over a 100-fold range of the latter. The accuracy of the linearity, however, has not been determined. The dynamic range extends from the limit of detection at a concentration of about 10^{-9} M to a maximum concentration of about 5×10^{-3} M (*28*). This gives a dynamic range of about 10^6.

(*d*) *Independence of Extraneous Variables*

It is, of course, necessary to protect the flame from draughts, but this is normally done by a shield which is an integral part of the apparatus. The effect of change in flow rate has already been considered, and it is necessary to employ an efficient flow control if a large signal-to-noise ratio is required. Apart from these considerations, other variables, e.g., ambient temperature and pressure, have little effect on the detector.

(*e*) *Calibration*

From the few data available on the calibration of hydrogen flame detectors, it is apparent that with organic compounds, there is a general tendency for molar response (e.g., measured in coulombs per mole) to increase with increasing carbon number, so that with hydrocarbons the weight response is approximately steady. From results of Desty, Goldup, and Geach (*25*) such a rule is only good to some 30%, for they find that molar response of 2:2:4-trimethylpentane is 30% greater than that for ethylbenzene, and 15% greater than that for *n*-octane, all C_8 molecules. The responses of oxygenated compounds do not appear to follow any simple rule, but Ongkiehong (*24*) finds that the response is approximately proportional to a "Carbon Number" calculated as the number of carbon atoms remaining after as many CO_2 groups as possible have been split off.

The net conclusion is that at present no simple relation sufficiently accurate to be of use exists between structure and response. Furthermore, since the mechanism of the ionisation process is complex, no adequate theoretical survey of the subject has been made.

(*f*) *Range of Application*

The hydrogen flame detector responds to all compounds containing CH groups, but fails to respond to a number of common inorganic compounds. A list of such compounds is given by Condon *et al.* (*12*), and is reproduced below:

Rare gases	Silicon tetrachloride
Oxides of nitrogen	Silicon tetrafluoride
Hydrogen	Trichlorosilane
Oxygen	Hydrogen sulfide
Nitrogen	Sulfur dioxide
Oxides of carbon	Carbonyl sulfide
Ammonia	Carbon disulfide
Water	

The lack of response to water and the air gases is useful in that these need not be removed from the carrier gas or from samples when they are not components of interest. Unlike the argon detector, the flame ionisation detector does not lose its sensitivity in the presence of these contaminants.

8.9. Ionisation Gauge Detector

Electrons are produced from a heated filament, and these may be accelerated by a field so that they acquire sufficient energy to ionise gas in their path. This fact is familiar from the vacuum ionisation gauge, which uses the current so produced to measure small gas pressures. Ryce and Bryce (*29,30*) have modified a standard vacuum ionisation gauge to act as a detector in gas chromatography (Fig. 8.20). An adjustable leak enables a small fraction of the effluent to pass into an ionisation gauge (type RCA 1949). The gas in the ionisation gauge is continuously pumped out through a needle valve set so that the pressure in the gauge has a steady value of the order of 1 mm. In operation, helium is used as the carrier gas, the grid of the gauge is set at approximately +18 volts relative to the filament, and the plate is set at about −20 volts negative so as to collect any positive ions formed. The ionisation potential of helium is 24.5, so that when no vapour is passing through, the electrons do not have sufficient energy to ionise the helium, and there is no current at the plate. As soon as an organic vapour enters, however, its molecules will be ionised by 18-volt electrons, so that there is a plate current. The plate current is measured by an impedance converter similar to those already described in previous sections and the output is applied to a strip-chart recorder.

The sensitivity of the detector is greater the larger the grid potential,

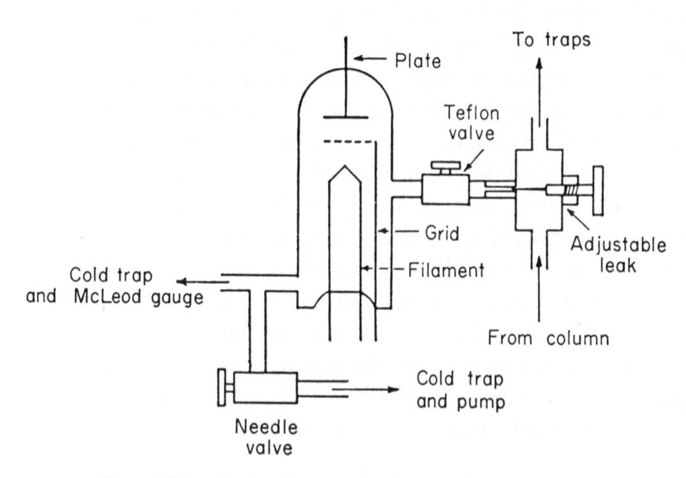

Fig. 8.20. Ionisation gauge. Ryce and Bryce (*30*).

but in the design of Ryce and Bryce, grid potentials above 18 volts produce undesirable ionisation of the helium since some of the electrons emitted by the filament have sufficient thermal energy for the total energy (including the 18 ev supplied by the field) to exceed the ionisation potential of the helium. This effect can be somewhat diminished by reducing the temperature of the filament, but a modification by Hinkle *et al.* (*31*) enables grid voltages of 23.5 volts to be used without ionisation of the helium. The modification employs a short D.C. filament from which the electron stream is collimated so that only electrons of very small thermal energy are exposed to the field.

Figures for the sensitivity and noise have been given. Ryce and Bryce report a sensitivity of 32500 cc mv/mg with no visible noise for a gauge pressure of 0.7 mm, with a grid potential of 15 volts, together with a limit of detection of 5×10^{-11} moles. Since no noise is visible, this clearly is not the ultimate sensitivity of the instrument. Probably the factor most responsible for the noise is fluctuation of the grid potential, which should be controlled as well as possible. Hinkle *et al.* (*31*) regulate this to 0.01% with useful improvement in the noise level.

The response of the detector is proportional to the pressure of gas in the gauge from 0.02 to 1.5 mm (*30*) and when operated in this region, it responds linearly with concentration of organic vapour (*32*). Hinkle *et al.* (*31*) find that the greatest range of linearity is secured by operating the detector at such a pressure that the gas flow through the detector is by molecular flow, i.e., that the mean free path of the gas molecules is at least as large as the dimensions of the electrodes. This is secured in the region of 2 mμ (0.002 mm) or less. The dynamic range has not been reported.

One of the advantages of this detector is that it is little affected by temperature, flow rate through the column, or external pressure. Thus it can be used effectively with programmed temperature operation of the column without danger of drift. The emission of electrons from the filament is somewhat affected by contaminants in the carrier gas, particularly oxygen. Thus, helium should be purified by passage through charcoal or molecular sieve cooled in liquid nitrogen before use. Mercury vapour from the vacuum system also inhibits the ionisation efficiency (*30*).

The speed of response of the detector to a change in composition is almost instantaneous. The detector is large, but since it operates at a low gas pressure, the volume of gas emerging from the column at or near 1 atmosphere required to fill it is very small, so the effective volume of the detector is very small. Hinkle *et al.* report that only 0.5 cc atm/minute is required. Thus, in spite of its large actual volume, the detector is rapid, and will work on small gas flow rates without producing peak broadening. For this reason it is suitable for use with capillary columns, in which case the whole throughput of the column could be bled through the leak into the detector without the use of the sampler illustrated in Fig. 8.20.

The detector will respond to all substances of which the ionisation potential is less than that of the carrier gas; with a helium carrier gas, this includes everything. Thus, its use is universal. Its largest drawback is that it does not operate at atmospheric pressure and requires a vacuum pump as ancillary equipment.

8.10. Discharge Detectors

Several ionisation detectors have been described in which ionisation is produced by a gas discharge between two cold electrodes. There are many possible variants, and several have been tried. None of these detectors is in common use at present, however, and it appears that all have defects that no development work has so far overcome.

(*a*) *Glow Discharge*

If a high voltage is passed between two electrodes contained in a gas at between about 0.1 to 10 mm, a glow discharge is established. After the discharge is started, the voltage may be reduced, and the discharge is maintained; such discharges are familiar in neon signs. One of their characteristics is that at certain pressures, the voltage across the discharge is almost independent of pressure or current—the independence of the latter is used in voltage control tubes—but depends markedly on the composition of the gas. This fact has been made the basis of a detector by Harley and Pretorius (*33*), and, following them, by Pitkethly (*34,35*), and by Basson, DeWet, Nel, and Pretorius (*36*).

Pitkethly (*35*) uses a domestic neon lamp (Phillips SBC 200/260) modified so that effluent from the column can be passed over the electrodes (Fig. 8.21) as a detector. This is used, together with a similar lamp used

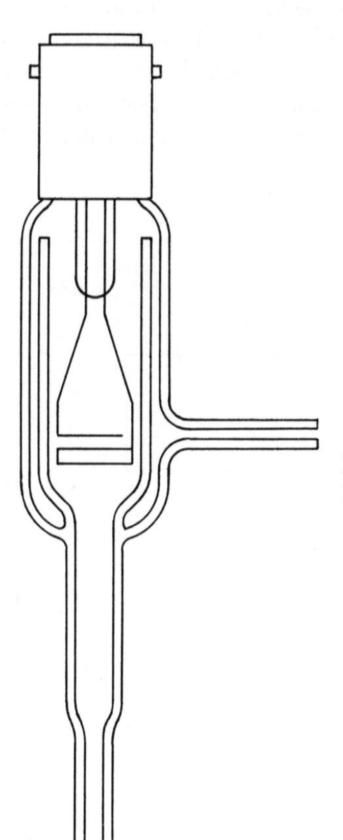

FIG. 8.21. Adaptation of a domestic neon lamp for use as a discharge detector. After Pitkethly (*35*).

as a reference, in a simple electronic circuit recording changes in potential across the lamp. The lamp is run at between 3 and 5 mm pressure, with a current of 1.5 ma, in which conditions the voltage across it is maintained at 220 volts in the absence of a vapour. When a vapour comes through, the voltage changes; the auther quotes 0.3 volt change for a concentration of 1 μg/litre. This gives a sensitivity of 3×10^8 mv cc/mg at a pressure which is about 1/100th of atmospheric. The noise level is about 10 mv, so that the concentration equivalent to the noise is of the order of $\frac{1}{3} \times 10^{-10}$ g/cc. For substances of molecular weight about 100, and an operating pressure in the region of 1/100 atmospheric, this converts to a mole fraction of about 10^{-6}. Note that while the concentration equivalent to the noise is small in units of weight/volume of carrier gas, the minimum mole fraction concentration is comparatively large, since the detector operates at low carrier gas pressure.

The detector is moderately linear over a dynamic range of at least 10^3, but the accuracy of the linearity is uncertain. Pitkethly has studied the response for various hydrocarbons, and finds that both the molar and the weight responses increase with increasing carbon number. There does not appear to be any simple relation by which the response may be calculated.

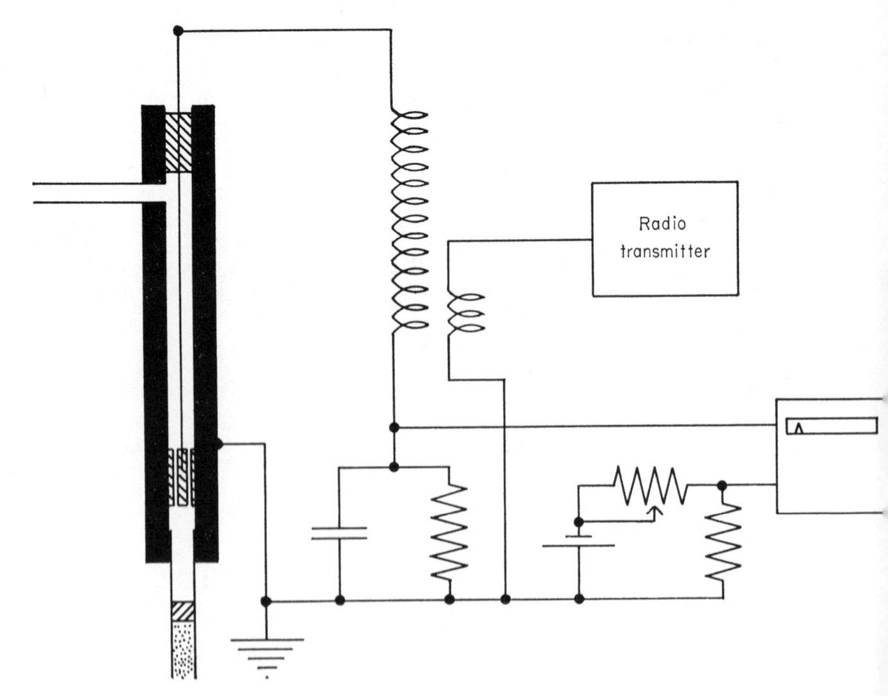

FIG. 8.22. Radio frequency discharge detector. After Karmen and Bowman (37).

A defect of such discharge detectors is that the cathode is liable to "Sputter," i.e., the metal is removed and deposited on other parts of the cavity. The tendency to do this depends on the material of the electrodes. Pitkethly found that the iron used in the commercial neon tubes was best in this respect. Basson *et al.* (*36*) find platinum satisfactory.

(*b*) *R.F. Discharge*

Karmen and Bowman (*37*) have based a detector on the fact that when an R.F. discharge occurs between two electrodes between which the field is diverging a D.C. potential appears between the electrodes, and that the D.C. potential is sensitive to the composition of the gas through which the discharge is passing. The cell (Fig. 8.22) consists of a cylindrical cavity forming one electrode, coaxial with which is wire, diameter 0.02 inch, forming the other electrode. The electrodes are fed by a radio transmitter operating at a frequency of about 40 Mc, and the D.C. potential developed between the electrodes is measured by a recorder, coupled with a circuit to back off the constant portion of the potential.

The sensitivity of this detector is reported by the authors to be 1.6×10^5 mv cc/mg for methyl laurate, with a noise level of 0.05 mv. This would give a concentration equivalent to the noise of 3×10^{-7} mg/cc. This would be 3×10^{-12} mole/cc for a substance of molecular weight about 100, and would correspond to a mole fraction of about 10^{-7}. Note that this discharge detector works at atmospheric pressure, so that no vacuum pump is required.

(*c*) *Spark Discharge*

Lovelock (*38*) has suggested a detector which uses the fact that the threshold potential between two points above which a spark occurs depends

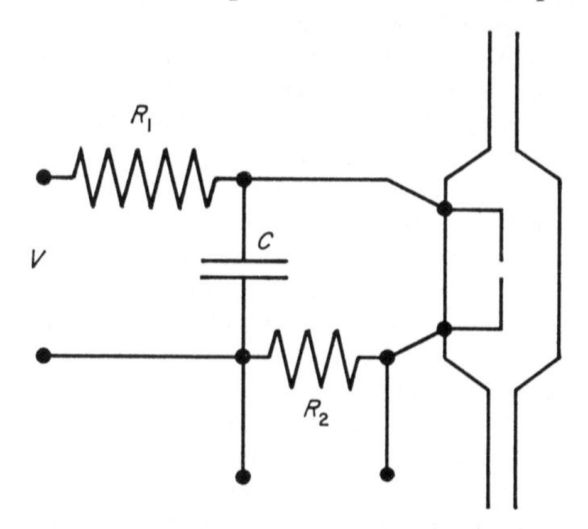

FIG. 8.23. Spark discharge detector. After Lovelock (*38*).

on the composition of the gas between the points. This could be done using the circuit of Fig. 8.23. The voltage V is just less than that required to cause a spark in the carrier gas, so that, in the absence of vapour, no spark occurs. When a vapour appears, the threshold potential for sparking is lowered, so that a spark occurs, and discharges the condenser C, until the voltage falls sufficiently low for the spark discharge to cease. The potential on C then builds up through the large resistance R_1 until the voltage is great enough for a new spark. In this way, the frequency of sparking is proportional to (or at least a monotonic function of) the vapour concentration, and can be measured by the frequency of pulses across R_2. When this device is used with argon as carrier gas, it operates according to much the same principles as the simple argon detector, and the relation between breakdown voltage and concentration of added vapour is roughly determined by Eqs. (8.6) and (8.7).

References

1. Townsend, J. S., "Electrons in Gases," Hutchinson, London, 1947.
2. Von Engel, A., "Ionized Gases," Oxford Univ. Press, London and New York, 1955.
3. Boer, H., *in* "Vapour Phase Chromatography," Proceedings of the First Symposium, London, May, 1956 (D. H. Desty, ed.), p. 169 ff. Academic Press, New York, 1957.
4. Deal, C. H., Otvos, J. W., Smith, V. N., and Zucco, P. S., *129th Am. Chem. Soc. Meeting, Dallas, Texas, April, 1956.*
5. Deal, C. H., Otvos, J. W., Smith, V. N., and Zucco, P. S., *Anal. Chem.* **28,** 1958 (1956).
6. Otvos, J. W., and Stevenson, D. P., *J. Am. Chem. Soc.* **78,** 546 (1956).
7. Lovelock, J. E., *J. Chromatog.* **1,** 35 (1958).
8. Jesse, W. P., and Sadauskis, J., *Phys. Rev.* **100,** 1755 (1955).
9. Lovelock, J. E., James, A. T., and Piper, E. A., *Ann. N.Y. Acad. Sci.* **72,** 720 (1959).
10. Lovelock, J. E., Third Symposium on Gas Chromatography, Edinburgh, June, 1960, Paper No. 2 (Preprint).
11. Lovelock, J. E., *Nature* **182,** 1663 (1958).
12. Condon, R. D., Scholly, P. R., and Averill, W., Third Symposium on Gas Chromatography, Edinburgh, June, 1960, Paper No. 3 (Preprint).
13. Chmielowski, J., and Isaac, C. G., *Nature* **183,** 1120 (1959).
14. Graven, W. M., *Anal. Chem.* **31,** 1197 (1959).
15. Willis, V., *Nature* **184,** 894 (1959).
16. Lovelock, J. E., and Lipsky, S. R., *J. Am. Chem. Soc.* **82,** 431 (1960).
17. Harley, J., Nel, W., and Pretorius, V., *Nature* **181,** 177 (1958).
18. McWilliam, I. G., and Dewar, R. A., *Nature* **181,** 760 (1958).
19. McWilliam, I. G., and Dewar, R. A., *in* "Gas Chromatography 1958," Proceedings of the Second Symposium, Amsterdam, May, 1958 (D. H. Desty, ed.), p. 142 ff. Academic Press, New York, 1958.
20. Thompson, A. E., *J. Chromatog.* **2,** 148 (1959).
21. Ettre, L. S., and Claudy, H. N., Symposium on Gas Chromatography, Chemical Institute of Canada, Toronto, February, 1960.
22. Andreatch, A. G., and Feinland, R., Pittsburgh Conference on Analytical Chemistry, etc., March, 1960.

23. Arndt, R. R., Nel, W. J., and Pretorius, V., *J. S. African Chem. Inst.* **12,** 62 (1959).
24. Ongkiehong, L., Third Symposium on Gas Chromatography, Edinburgh, June, 1960, Paper No. 1 (Preprint).
25. Desty, D. H., Goldup, A., and Geach, C. J., Third Symposium on Gas Chromatography, Edinburgh, June, 1960, Paper No. 4 (Preprint).
26. Saha, M., *Proc. Roy. Soc.* **A99,** 135 (1921).
27. Stern, O., see B. Lewis and G. von Elbe, "Combustion Flames and Explosions," 2nd ed., p. 558. Academic Press, New York, 1961.
28. Third Symposium on Gas Chromatography, Edinburgh, June, 1960, Discussion.
29. Ryce, S. A., and Bryce, W. A., *Nature* **179,** 541 (1957).
30. Ryce, S. A., and Bryce, W. A., *Can. J. Chem.* **35,** 1293 (1957).
31. Hinkle, E. A., Tucker, H. C., Wall, R. F., and Combs, J. F., *in* "Gas Chromatography," 2nd International I.S.A. Symposium, June, 1959 (H. J. Noebels, R. F. Wall, and N. Brenner, eds.), p. 55. Academic Press, New York, 1961.
32. Guild, L. V., Lloyd, M. I., and Aul, F., *in* "Gas Chromatography," 2nd International I.S.A. Symposium, June, 1959 (H. J. Noebels, R. F. Wall, and N. Brenner, eds.), p. 91. Academic Press, New York, 1961.
33. Harley, J., and Pretorius, V., *Nature* **178,** 1244 (1957).
34. Pitkethly, R. C., *132nd Am. Chem. Soc. Meeting, New York, September, 1957.*
35. Pitkethly, R. C., *Anal. Chem.* **30,** 1309 (1958).
36. Basson, R. A., DeWet, C. R., Nel, W., and Pretorius, V., *J. S. African Chem. Inst.* **12,** 62 (1959).
37. Karmen, A., and Bowman, R. L., *Ann. N.Y. Acad. Sci.* **72,** 714 (1959).
38. Lovelock. J. E., *Nature* **181,** 1460 (1958).
39. Hine, G. J., and Brownell, G. L., "Radiation Dosimetry," p. 106. Academic Press, New York, 1956.
40. Wiseman, W. A., Private communication, 1960.
41. Lovelock, J. E., *Anal. Chem.* **33,** 162 (1961).
42. Lovelock, J. E., *Nature* **187,** 49 (1960).

Chapter 9

Thermal Conductivity Detectors

9.1. Introduction

The *Thermal Conductivity Detector*, or *Catharometer*,* is designed to measure continuously the thermal conductivity of the column effluent. Catharometers have been hitherto the most commonly used detectors in gas chromatography, but the use of ionisation detectors is increasing and only ionisation detectors can be used for measurement of samples smaller than about 10^{-7} to 10^{-8} g. When extreme sensitivity is not required, catharometers and ionisation detectors are more or less comparable; the choice between them is either immaterial, or dependent on some special property of one or the other, e.g., the fact that catharometers respond more simply to permanent gases.

The instrument (Fig. 9.1) consists of a cavity, A, containing the gas of which the thermal conductivity is to be measured; in the continuous measurement of a flowing gas, the gas may go either through the cavity as shown, or past it, so that the cavity is fed by diffusion (Fig. 9.11). The walls of the cavity are held at a constant temperature, and the cavity contains an electrically heated *hot element*, B, of either metal or semiconductor material. With a constant current in the hot element, the rate of production of heat is constant, and this heat must be dissipated, largely by conduction through the gas. The presence of a vapour changes the thermal conductivity of the gas, so that a different temperature gradient is necessary to maintain the required rate of dissipation, and therefore the hot element changes temperature. The temperature of the hot element is measured as if it were a resistance thermometer; change in temperature produces change in resistance, which is measured by including it as one arm of a Wheatstone's bridge circuit. It is almost universal practice to

* The thermal conductivity cell was first introduced by Shakespear (*1*), who called it a "Katharometer," but in accord with modern practice in spelling words derived from the Greek κατα, it is spelt here with a "C."

have two such cells forming adjacent arms of a Wheatstone's bridge, one carrying column effluent, and one carrying pure carrier gas; this procedure enables instrumental drift to be considerably reduced.

In most catharometers, the resistances of the hot elements and the other arms of the bridge are smaller than the maximum input impedance of potentiometric recorders, so that the galvanometer of the bridge may be replaced directly by such a recorder, and the continuous record of the out-of-balance E.M.F. of the bridge forms the chromatogram.

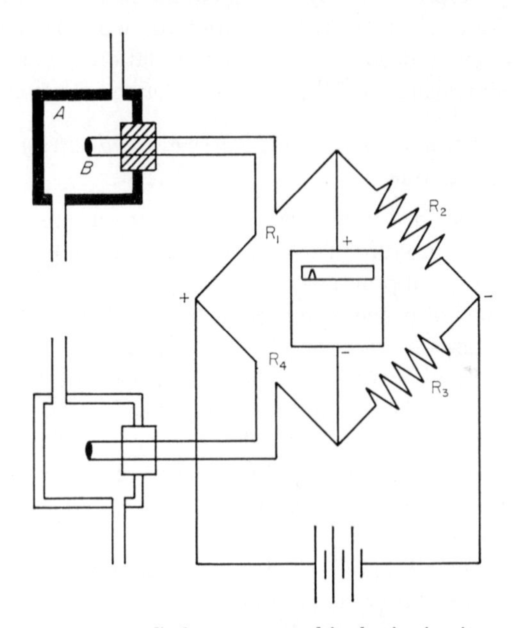

FIG. 9.1. Catharometer and its basic circuit.

The catharometer was first used in gas chromatography by Claesson (*2*) in the early days of gas adsorption chromatography, and has been used regularly ever since. General accounts of catharometry are given in a book by Daynes (*3*) (1933) and in an article by Weaver (*4*) (1951).

9.2. THEORY OF CATHAROMETRY

The chain of events between the arrival of a vapour in the catharometer cell and the change in out-of-balance E.M.F. recorded on the meter may be regarded as a succession of four more or less independent relations:

(a) a relation between the concentration of vapour in the carrier gas and the change in thermal conductivity which it produces,

(b) a relation between the change in thermal conductivity and the change in temperature produced in the hot element,

(c) a relation between the change in temperature and the change in resistance of the hot element,

(d) a relation between the change in resistance of the hot element and the change in E.M.F. across the meter.

To a first approximation these may be considered independently, and the theory may be presented by giving equations for each and combining them. Of the four relations, (b), (c), and (d) may be worked out with complete accuracy; indeed, (c) is trivial. Relation (a), however, can be specified only approximately. We now consider the relations in turn.

(*a*) *The Effect of a Vapour on the Thermal Conductivity of the Carrier Gas*

This may be specified numerically by $\partial\lambda_{12}/\partial x_2$, where λ_{12} is the thermal conductivity of the mixture of carrier and vapour, and x_2 is mole fraction of vapour. In nearly all practical cases it is negative, so that presence of a vapour causes the hot element to become hotter. The study of the thermal conductivity of gases is a section of the study of gas transport properties, which also includes viscosity, diffusion, and thermal diffusion. This is part of the kinetic theory of gases and may be studied on two levels of sophistication, namely,

(1) elementary theory, using the concept of "Mean Free Path" of molecules between collisions and of fixed collision diameters, and ignoring all but head-on collisions,

(2) detailed theory based on the calculations of Chapman and of Enskog, for which the primary source is the book of Chapman and Cowling (*5*); other references include books by Hirschfelder, Curtiss, and Bird (*6*) and (as an introduction) Kennard (*7*).

Several formulae for $\partial\lambda_{12}/\partial x_2$ have been proposed, both as a result of experiment and by calculation. The simplest possible formula for the thermal conductivity of a binary mixture assumes a linear relation between thermal conductivity and mole fraction:

$$\lambda_{12} = x_1\lambda_1 + x_2\lambda_2 = \lambda_1 + x_2(\lambda_2 - \lambda_1), \tag{9.1}$$

whence

$$\partial\lambda_{12}/\partial x_2 = \lambda_2 - \lambda_1, \tag{9.2}$$

where $\lambda_{12}, \lambda_1, \lambda_2$ = thermal conductivities of mixture, carrier, and vapour, respectively.

x_1, x_2 = mole fractions of carrier and vapour, respectively.

Such a relation has been assumed or implied by several authors on gas chromatographic catharometry, but it has no justification either in theory or in practice. It is possible to find binary mixtures for which it is approximately true, but this is coincidence. For mixtures of which the molecules have different weights, shapes, and sizes, as in gas chromatographic catharometry, Eq. (9.2) is not even approximately true.

An equation for the thermal conductivity of binary mixtures based on elementary kinetic theory has been given by Wassiljewa (*8*), and has been used by Lindsay and Bromley (*9*):

$$\lambda_{12} = \frac{\lambda_1}{1 + A(x_2/x_1)} + \frac{\lambda_2}{1 + B(x_1/x_2)}, \tag{9.3}$$

where

$$A = \left(\frac{\sigma_1 + \sigma_2}{2\sigma_1}\right)^2 \left(\frac{M_1 + M_2}{2M_2}\right)^{1/2} \tag{9.3a}$$

$$B = \left(\frac{\sigma_1 + \sigma_2}{2\sigma_2}\right)^2 \left(\frac{M_1 + M_2}{2M_1}\right)^{1/2}, \tag{9.3b}$$

where σ_1, σ_2 = molecular diameters of carrier gas and vapour molecules, respectively.

M_1, M_2 = molecular weights of carrier gas and vapour, respectively.

These equations are moderately successful in satisfying experimental data; and at least they give the extreme points which are often observed in plots of experimental thermal conductivities against molar composition. If A and B in Eq. (9.3) are regarded as parameters and are fitted to experimental values, a good fit is obtained (i.e., small least-squares residues), but the values of A and B obtained are not in accord with Eqs. (9.3a) and (9.3b). Thus, it is legitimate to regard Eq. (9.3) as an adequate two-parameter equation to fit the facts; but the calculation of A and B by Eqs. (9.3a) and (9.3b) has little value except as a general guide.

As applied to gas-chromatographic catharometry, Eq. (9.3) can be simplified by assuming that x_2 is always small, and x_1 is approximately unity. In this case:

$$\lambda_{12} \approx \frac{\lambda_1}{1 + Ax_2} + \frac{\lambda_2}{1 + B/x_2} \approx \lambda_1 (1 - Ax_2) + \frac{\lambda_2 x_2}{B} \tag{9.4}$$

and

$$\frac{\partial \lambda_{12}}{\partial x_2} = \frac{\lambda_2}{B} - A\lambda_1, \tag{9.5}$$

where A and B are to be regarded as arbitrary constants of the order of unity. This equation has no quantitative use, but it is interesting in that it is consistent with the frequent observation that, when using heavy carrier gases, even though $\lambda_2 < \lambda_1$, $\partial\lambda_{12}/\partial x_2$ is positive, resulting in cooling of the hot element and thus producing a reversed peak. In such a case, B is sufficiently small that the first term of Eq. (9.5) exceeds the second.

In the case of heavy carrier gases, elementary theory can go no further without becoming grossly inaccurate, and, to date, detailed theory can provide no manageable equations for the thermal conductivity of mixtures of complex molecules. In the case of vapours in nitrogen or in cases in which the mixture consists of vapours the molecules of which have comparable masses, e.g., helium and hydrogen, the plot of thermal conductivity against molar fraction of vapour often shows a maximum, and van der Craats (*10*) has shown that in at least one case—acetylene in nitrogen—the maximum occurs at the remarkably small vapour concentration of 4%.

In the case of light carrier gases, Littlewood has proposed an application of the equations of the detailed theory (*11*) which illustrates in a particularly simple way the mechanism of heat conduction in the type of binary mixture treated in gas-chromatographic catharometry. If, in the equations given by Chapman and Cowling (*5*) for the thermal conductivity of binary mixtures of gases not possessing internal degrees of freedom, it is assumed:

(1) that x_2 is small,
(2) that $M_2 \gg M_1$,
(3) that the molecules may be regarded as hard spheres,
(4) that the internal structure of vapour molecules has no effect on the validity of the equations other than possibly modifying the collision diameter,

then it can be shown that:

$$\frac{1}{\lambda_1}\frac{\partial \lambda_{12}}{\partial x_2} = -2.30\,\frac{\sigma_{12}^2}{\sigma_1{}^2}, \tag{9.6}$$

where $\sigma_{12} = (\sigma_1 + \sigma_2)/2$. This equation should be true to within a few per cent so long as $M_2 > 20M_1$, and the approximations are valid when helium is used as carrier gas. It illustrates how the vapour acts in changing the thermal conductivity of the carrier. The vapour molecules are large, heavy, and slow, whereas those of the carrier gas are small, light, and fast. Virtually all the heat is carried by the carrier molecules, and the vapour molecules act merely by getting in the way. The fact that they obstruct and thus reduce the thermal conductivity is expressed by the minus sign; the extent of their obstruction is proportional to their effective cross-sectional area, which is $x_2\sigma_{12}^2$.

An equation of similar form to Eq. (9.6) may be obtained from the elementary theory by applying assumptions (1) and (2), together with the necessary result that $\lambda_1 > \lambda_2$, to Eq. (9.5); the difference is that the constant comes to $1/\sqrt{2}$ rather than 2.30.

(b) *The Effect of Thermal Conductivity on the Temperature of the Hot Element*

The temperature distribution of the gas in the cell cavity satisfies the steady-state equation for the conduction of heat,

$$\operatorname{div}(\lambda \operatorname{grad} T) = 0. \tag{9.7}$$

In catharometry, it is probably adequate to assume that λ is independent of temperature if the hot element is not too hot, in which case Eq. (9.7) becomes Laplace's equation:

$$\nabla^2 T = 0. \tag{9.8}$$

In catharometry, the surfaces of the hot element and of the walls of the cavity should each be isothermal. Thus, if T_1 and T_2 are the temperatures of, and $T'(\tau) = 0$ and $T''(\tau) = 0$ are the equations of, the surfaces of the walls and hot element, respectively, where τ represents spatial coordinates, the boundary conditions are:

$$\begin{aligned} T &= T_1 \quad \text{for} \quad T'(\tau) = 0 \\ T &= T_2 \quad \text{for} \quad T''(\tau) = 0. \end{aligned} \tag{9.9}$$

Solutions of Eqs. (9.8) and (9.9) have been extensively studied for many sets of boundary conditions in connection with many kinds of problem. General methods of solution may be found in texts on partial differential equations [e.g., (*12*)] or in texts on any subject in which Laplace's equation is relevant, e.g., electrostatics.

We observe below a general consequence of Eqs. (9.8) and (9.9). If T satisfies Eq. (9.8), then

$$\varphi \equiv (T - T_1)/(T_2 - T_1) \tag{9.10}$$

also satisfies Eq. (9.8), since T_1 and $T_2 - T_1$ are both constants. In terms of φ, the boundary conditions (9.9) become $\varphi = 0$ and $\varphi = 1$, which are independent of T_1 and T_2. Hence, Eqs. (9.8) and (9.9) may be solved to give $(T - T_1)/(T_2 - T_1)$ as a function of the spatial coordinates only, so that at every point in the cavity, $(T - T_1) \propto (T_2 - T_1)$.

In catharometry, the quantity of interest is T_2, and there is the additional condition that the total heat flux through any surface surrounding the hot element is determined by the electrical input. If the resistance of, and the current in, the hot element are R and I, respectively, the total heat flux is I^2R/J, where J is Joule's constant. One may now derive a significant general equation [Eq. (9.15)] for T_2 in terms of the heat flux and the thermal conductivity. If the heat flux at any point in the cavity is $\mathbf{H}$, then, by definition of thermal conductivity,

$$-\lambda \operatorname{grad} T = \mathbf{H}. \tag{9.11}$$

Also

$$\int_s \mathbf{H} \cdot d\mathbf{s} = \frac{I^2R}{J}, \tag{9.12}$$

where the integration is over a surface including the hot element. Hence

$$-\int_s \text{grad } T \cdot d\mathbf{s} = \frac{I^2R}{J\lambda}. \tag{9.13}$$

But

$$\text{grad } T = \text{grad } (T - T_1)$$

$$= (T_2 - T_1) \text{ grad } \frac{T - T_1}{T_2 - T_1} = (T_2 - T_1) \text{ grad } \varphi. \tag{9.14}$$

Hence

$$T_2 - T_1 = I^2R/J\lambda G, \tag{9.15}$$

where

$$G = -\int_s \text{grad } \varphi \cdot d\mathbf{s} \tag{9.16}$$

and is a function of the geometry of the cavity and hot element only.

The function G may be calculated from the geometry of the cell, though the calculation is complex except for simple geometries. Its form for two particularly common cases is given below:

(1) The hot element is a wire of radius r_2 and length l situated coaxially in a tube of radius r_1:

$$G = 2\pi l/\ln (r_1/r_2). \tag{9.17}$$

(2) The hot element is a sphere of radius r_2 situated concentrically in a spherical cavity of radius r_1:

$$G = 4\pi r_1 r_2/(r_1 - r_2). \tag{9.18}$$

A significant approximate generalisation may be made from case (2). When $r_1 \gg r_2$, Eq. (9.18) becomes $G \approx 4\pi r_2$, which is independent of r_1. Thus, if a roughly spherical hot element is small compared with the cavity, the exact shape of the cavity does not much affect the sensitivity of the cell. The physical explanation of this is that, if the heat source is small, the temperature gradient is large only in its immediate neighbourhood.

The required effect of change in λ on T_2 is obtained by differentiation of Eq. (9.15) with respect to λ:

$$\partial T_2/\partial \lambda = -I^2R/JG\lambda^2. \tag{9.19}$$

This equation was given (in effect) by Ray (*13*), and subsequent criticisms of Ray's conclusions (*11,14–17*) do not invalidate it.

The above discussion is sometimes complicated in practice by the dissipation of heat other than by conduction. Other possible sources of heat loss are, in approximate order of magnitude:

(1) loss through mass-transfer, in which hot gas in the neighbourhood of the hot element is swept out in the gas stream (*18*),

(2) loss through thermal conduction in the support of the hot element (*3,19,20*),

(3) loss through convection,

(4) loss through radiation.

To discuss these quantitatively, a heat balance equation may be set up, with the heat input, I^2R/J, on one side, and the sum of all sources of heat loss on the other. Application of Stefan's law shows that at temperatures at least as high as 200°C, radiation contributes less than 0.1% to the total heat dissipation. According to Daynes (*3*), convection is negligible in cavities smaller than about 1 cm linear dimensions. Snowden and Eanes (*20*) report that there is no difference in the power input required to maintain a given temperature in a wire axially placed in a tube of 5 mm diameter whether the tube is vertical or horizontal, thus showing that no appreciable heat is lost by convection. There is the possibility, however, that very slight convection may produce significant noise.

Losses from the first two factors given above may be serious, and have been considered in detail.

Bohemen and Purnell (*18*) have considered the effect of heat loss through mass-transfer in the case of a cell consisting of a heated wire situated axially in a glass tube carrying the column effluent, so that a certain proportion of the heat from the wire is carried out of the cell, and thus is not conducted to the walls of the tube. The heat balance equation in this case is:

$$I^2R/J = G\lambda(T_2 - T_1) + V'C_p\,\Delta T' + S, \qquad (9.20)$$

where G is given by Eq. (9.16), and in addition to symbols already used,

V' = molar flow rate (moles/second) = $273\dot{V}/22{,}400T$ cc/second,

C_p = molar specific heat of carrier gas,

$\Delta T'$ = average temperature difference between entering and departing gas,

S = other sources of heat loss not depending on V', including end effects, free convection, and radiation.

The importance of this equation is that when a vapour enters the cell, not only does λ change, but also C_p changes, so that in cases where the second term of the equation is comparable with the first, the final expression for the response will include the term $\partial C_p/\partial x_2$ in addition to $\partial\lambda_{12}/\partial x_2$. With cells in which the hot element is not in the gas path, there is no doubt that the second term in Eq. (9.20) is negligible, but Bohemen and Purnell conclude that, in the case they consider, the second term may be of the same order of magnitude as the first.

We now derive an equation [Eq. (9.23)] which will demonstrate the effect of heat losses other than thermal conduction on the response of the above design of cell. The response is proportional to the quantity dT_2/dx_2; in the absence of terms other than those due to thermal conduction in the heat balance equation, and assuming the independence of relations (a) and (b) given at the beginning of this section, this is given by the simple product $(dT_2/d\lambda_{12}) \cdot (d\lambda_{12}/dx_2)$. In this case, however, T_2 is a function of both λ_{12} and C_p, so that:

$$\frac{dT_2}{dx_2} = \frac{\partial T_2}{\partial \lambda_{12}} \frac{d\lambda_{12}}{dx_2} + \frac{\partial T_2}{\partial C_p} \frac{dC_p}{dx_2}. \tag{9.21}$$

The quantity $\Delta T'$ is also a function of T_2; Bohemen and Purnell assume that $\Delta T'$ is the difference between the temperature, T_1, of the entering gas and the average temperature of the distribution across the tube as given by Eqs. (9.8) and (9.9), from which:

$$\Delta T' = (T_2 - T_1)/2 \ln (r_2/r_1). \tag{9.22}$$

Assuming this, substitution of Eq. (9.20) into Eq. (9.21) yields:

$$\frac{dT_2}{dx_2} = \frac{-1}{G\left(\lambda_{12} + \frac{\dot{V}' C_p}{4\pi l}\right)^2} \left[\frac{I^2 R}{J} - S\right] \left[\frac{d\lambda_{12}}{dx_2} + \frac{\dot{V}'}{4\pi l} \frac{dC_p}{dx_2}\right]. \tag{9.23}$$

This equation largely summarises the effect of the important forms of heat loss other than thermal conduction. The first square bracket shows that the end losses S have no other effect than to subtract from the effective power input to the cell. The relative importance of thermal conduction and mass-transfer in producing the response is given by the comparative size of the terms in the second square bracket. The greater $\dot{V}'$, or the smaller l, the larger the effect of mass-transfer. In practice, $d\lambda_{12}/dx_2$ is normally negative, as already discussed, but dC_p/dx_2 is normally positive, so that the two terms tend to cancel rather than to reinforce. The effect of the mass-transfer terms on linearity will be considered in Section 9.7.

The relative contributions of thermal conduction through the gas, thermal conduction through the supports, and radiation have been determined by Snowden and Eanes (*20*) for a diffusion-fed cell, in which the mass-transfer effect is absent (Fig. 9.2). They have plotted the temperature of the hot element against power input, both in the presence of a carrier gas (curve A) and in a vacuum so that the gas conductivity is zero (curve B). In the former case, heat is lost by gas conduction, end losses, and radiation; in the latter case, by end losses and radiation only. At low temperatures, the loss by radiation is negligible, so the initial slope of the plot obtained *in vacuo* gives the end losses, which are assumed to be a linear function of the power input (curve C). The method of plotting results in

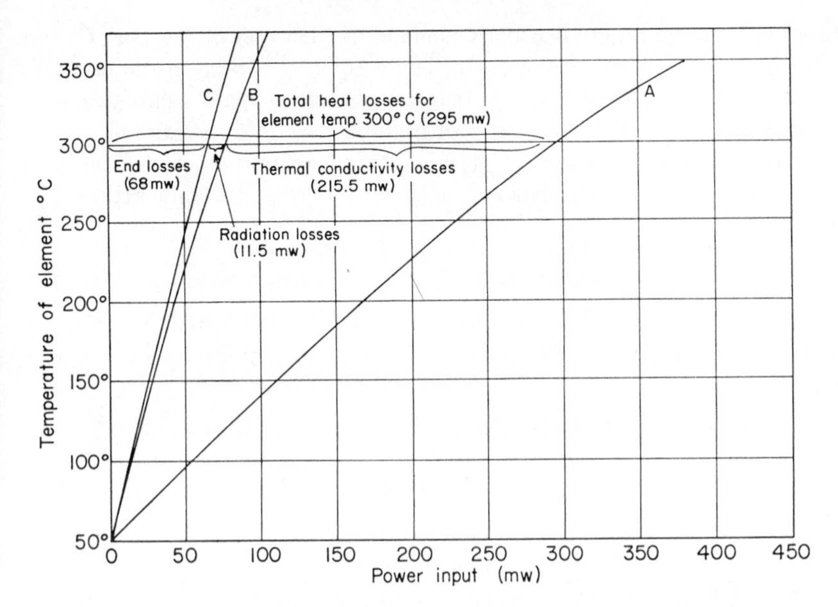

FIG. 9.2. Diagram by Snowden and Eanes (*20*) illustrating relative sizes of heat losses due to conduction through the supports of the hot element (end losses), radiation, and thermal conduction. Cell envelope maintained at 50°C ± 0.02° in oil bath. Curve A, total heat losses expressed in terms of power input (mw) required to maintain the cell element at a given temperature; air flowing through cell at atmospheric pressure at the rate of 200 ml/minute. Curve B, heat losses with cell evacuated to 10^{-4} mm Hg represents sum of radiation and end losses. Curve C, tangent to curve B at element temperature of 50°C represents end losses.

four lines including the vertical axis, the horizontal distances between adjacent pairs of which represent the proportions of heat lost by each of the three causes at any temperature of the hot element.

(c) *Effect of the Temperature of the Hot Element on Its Resistance*

The resistance of the hot element and its temperature are approximately connected by the familiar relation:

$$R = R_0(1 + \alpha T), \tag{9.24}$$

where α is the temperature coefficient of resistance, and is tabulated for many substances in many sources (*21*). On differentiation, this gives:

$$\frac{1}{R_0}\frac{\partial R}{\partial T} = \alpha. \tag{9.25}$$

The above equation may be used provided that the temperature difference of the hot element produced by a vapour is small. If this is not so, account should be taken of the fact that α is not independent of temperature over a large range; it usually changes of the order of 1% per °C, and, over large ranges, the change of resistance with temperature is normally expressed as a power series in T. It is not normal to operate catharometers in such a manner that this source of non-linearity is significant.

Thermistors have negative temperature coefficients of resistance in which the resistance falls exponentially with increase in temperature.

(d) *Effect of the Resistance of the Hot Element on the Out-of-Balance E.M.F. of the Wheatstone's Bridge*

If the resistances of a Wheatstone's bridge are numbered as in Fig. 9.1, and, in addition, we specify the general scheme of symbols in the following manner:

E, I = E.M.F. across the bridge and the total current in it,
E_n, I_n, R_n ($n = 1, 2, 3, 4$, or g) = voltage across, current in, and resistance of R_1, R_2, R_3, R_4, or the galvanometer, then application of Kirchoff's laws gives the equation:

$$I_g = \frac{E(R_2R_4 - R_1R_3)}{R_1R_2R_3 + R_2R_3R_4 + R_3R_4R_1 + R_4R_1R_2 + R_g(R_1 + R_2)(R_3 + R_4)} \tag{9.26}$$

In the usual case that the resistance of the meter is great compared with that of any of the arms, and that the meter responds to E_g rather than to I_g, then E_g is given by:

$$E_g = \frac{E(R_2R_4 - R_1R_3)}{(R_1 + R_2)(R_3 + R_4)} \tag{9.27}$$

if R_g is assumed to be infinite.

In the latter case, the effect on E_g of a change in resistance of the hot element, which we assume to be R_1, is found by differentiating Eq. (9.27) with respect to R_1:

$$\frac{\partial E_g}{\partial R_1} = -\frac{ER_2}{(R_1 + R_2)^2}. \tag{9.28}$$

Of greater practical significance is the change in E_g for a given proportional change in R_1, i.e., $R_1\, \partial E_g/\partial R_1$:

$$R_1 \frac{\partial E_g}{\partial R_1} = -\frac{ER_1R_2}{(R_1 + R_2)^2}. \tag{9.29}$$

Note that this equation is independent of R_3 and R_4, which merely serve to fix the potential of one side of the galvanometer. Thus Eq. (9.28) is true whether or not the bridge is in balance, and thus the sensitivity of a catharometer is not affected if, for example, the base-line is moved from zero to the other side of the galvanometer or recorder scale by adjustment of the "zero set." Bridges are normally run near their balance point for convenience.

In the special case that $R_1 = R_2 = R$, Eq. (9.28) becomes:

$$\partial E_g/\partial R_1 = -E/4R. \tag{9.30}$$

If the sum $R_1 + R_2$ is constrained to be constant, so that the current through the hot element is constant, the ratio of R_1 to R_2 for which $R_1\,\partial E_g/\partial R_1$ is a maximum is easily calculated by differentiation of Eq. (9.28), and the result is that the maximum in the response occurs when $R_1 = R_2$. The special case of Eq. (9.30), therefore, is commonly employed in practice.

(e) Combination of the Four Relations (a) to (d) Discussed Above

The preceding four subsections have provided a set of equations, (9.6), (9.19), (9.25), and (9.29), giving in turn:

$$\frac{\partial \lambda_{12}}{\partial x_2}, \quad \frac{\partial T_2}{\partial \lambda_{12}}, \quad \frac{\partial R_1}{\partial T_2}, \quad \frac{\partial E_g}{\partial x_2}.$$

If all these differentials are independent, all four may be multiplied together to give dE_g/dx_2, which is the reading of the recorder for a given vapour concentration in the cell. Hence, an equation for dE_g/dx_2 may be obtained by multiplying together the above four equations, giving:

$$\frac{dE_g}{dx_2} = -2.30\,\frac{\sigma_{12}^2}{\sigma_1^2} \cdot \frac{I^2R_1}{J\lambda_1 G} \cdot \alpha \cdot \frac{ER_1R_2}{(R_1 + R_2)^2}, \tag{9.31}$$

the symbols of which are all defined in the previous subsections, and the sign of which applies for the polarities given in Fig. 9.1. The units of this equation are *volts/mole-fraction.* By the transformation

$$E_g' = 1000E_g, \qquad c_2 = (M_2/22.4)x_2,$$

where M_2 is the molecular weight of the vapour, they may be turned into mv cc/mg, which are the sensitivity units used by Dimbat, Porter, and Stross (*22*) (Section 7.1). In this case, the sensitivity, S, is given by:

$$S = \frac{dE_g'}{dc_2} = -\frac{K}{M_2} \cdot \frac{\sigma_{12}^2}{\sigma_1^2} \cdot \frac{I^2R}{J\lambda_1 G} \cdot \alpha \cdot \frac{ER_1R_2}{(R_1 + R_2)^2}, \tag{9.32}$$

where K is a constant, and, for the value of the constant given in Eq. (9.31), becomes 5.1×10^4.

All the quantities on the right-hand side of Eq. (9.32) are known and knowable, and thus, in principle, this equation provides for the *a priori* calibration of catharometers. All the arguments leading to the derivation of this equation have been given in the literature, and it is presented here as a convenient summary of the theory of catharometers. It is consistent with the behaviour of the sensitivity of catharometers with change of any of the variables contained in it, as is shown in later sections, but the value of the constant K, though reasonable, as may be shown by substituting typical figures, has no experimental confirmation.

There are several cross-terms resulting in the mutual dependence of the four relations considered at the beginning of this section. Such terms are given by:

(1) the temperature dependence of $\partial\lambda_{12}/\partial x_2$,
(2) the temperature dependence of α,
(3) the change in I_1 on account of the change in R_1,
(4) the change in R_1, which enters as a constant in Eq. (9.19).

All such terms are small and may be neglected if the temperature change in the hot element is sufficiently small. In the case that they are not small, as when $T_2 - T_1$ is large, the catharometer becomes non-linear. The effect of such terms has not been considered in detail.

The temperature of the hot element, T_2, may be determined from Eq. (9.19), but in practice, T_2 is usually a more significant quantity than G, so that it is desirable to be able to measure T_2 without knowledge of G. This may be done by placing an ammeter in series with and a voltmeter in parallel with the hot element, R_1, and plotting E_1/I_1 against I_1, so as to give R_1 as a function of I_1. By extrapolating to $I_1 = 0$, R_1^0, the resistance of R_1 at $T_2 = T_1$ is obtained; at any given current I_1, T_2 is then given by:

$$T_2 - T_1 = (R_1 - R_1^0)/\alpha. \qquad (9.33)$$

From Eq. (9.15), $(T_2 - T_1)$ is proportional to I_1^2; this relation has been confirmed with considerable accuracy in experiments by Bohemen and Purnell (*18*) and by Harvey and Morgan (*23*). As described in the next section, Eq. (9.32) implies that the sensitivity of a catharometer is proportional to I_1^3. Hence the sensitivity is given by:

$$S \propto (T_2 - T_1)^{3/2}. \qquad (9.34)$$

This relation was given by Wiseman (*24*), who has confirmed it in practice, using tungsten and platinum hot elements (*19*).

9.3. Sensitivity

According to the theory given in the last section, the sensitivity of a catharometer is given in mv cc/mg by Eq. (9.32), which may be made the basis for discussion. Until fairly recently, values of S of the order of 100 were considered average, but in fact values of the order of 10^4 may easily be attained (*25*). The sensitivity is determined by the quantities appearing in Eq. (9.32), which will be discussed in turn.

(a) Applied Voltage

According to Eq. (9.32), the sensitivity is proportional to E and to $I_1^2R_1$. If the change in R_1 is small, $I_1^2 \propto E^2$, so that the sensitivity is proportional to E^3. This rule would be expected to apply if all other conditions remain constant. In particular, it should apply in the range of values of E within which the temperature of the hot element is only slightly greater than that of the walls, so that R_1 changes but little and no appreciable change occurs in the relation connecting thermal conductivity with composition. It does not apply with thermistors, for which R_1 changes very rapidly with I_1, except at extremely small currents.

Most experimental studies of the effect of applied voltage on sensitivity use conditions such that the temperature elevation of the hot wire is not small. This has two results; first, the resistance of the hot element changes appreciably, so that in the case of metal elements, for which α is positive, the wattage dissipation is less than proportional to E^2; second, the change in temperature on raising E is sufficient to cause a fall in the value of α. Both these factors operate to reduce the increase in sensitivity with applied voltage, so that in these conditions it is found that $S \propto E^x$, where x is less than 3. Mellor (*26*) presents graphs showing the rapid rise in sensitivity with increase in catharometer current. Harvey and Morgan (*23*) present

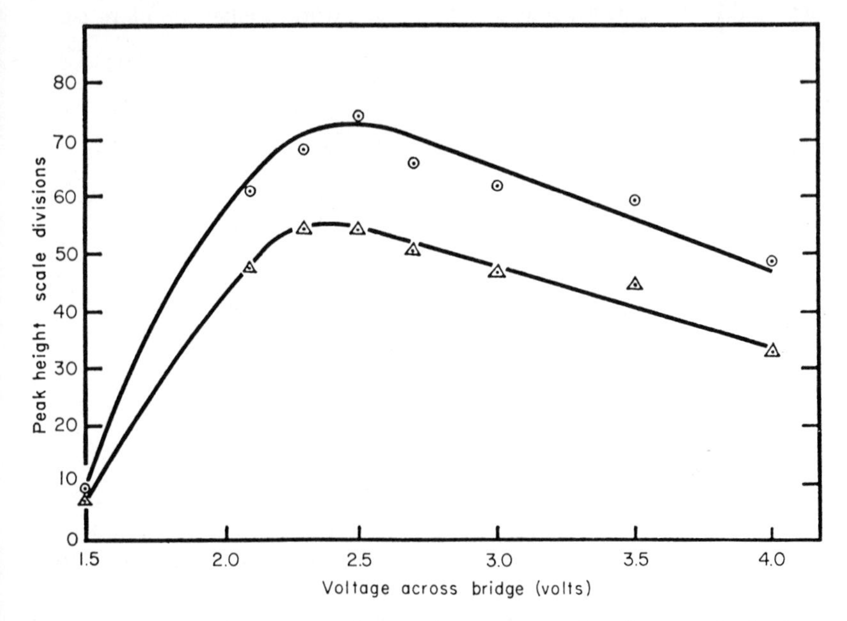

Fig. 9.3. Sensitivity of a thermistor catharometer as a function of applied voltage. Cowan and Stirling (*27*). Curves are for two different vapours in nitrogen as carrier gas.

results which show that, on doubling the current supplied to the bridge, the sensitivity increases by a factor of between 5.5 and 6.5, i.e., $2^{2.46}$ to $2^{2.70}$. In some extreme conditions, the sensitivity varies in a more complex manner with applied voltage, but these conditions are such that for other reasons they should not be used in quantitative gas chromatography. In cases where a heavy carrier gas, e.g., nitrogen, is used as a carrier, a large increase in applied voltage may even produce a reduction of sensitivity, as is shown by Mellor (*26*) and by Bohemen and Purnell (*18*).

The variation of the sensitivity of thermistor cells with applied voltage is complicated, and depends sharply on other variables, especially the carrier gas and the cell temperature. In general, at small applied voltages, the sensitivity rises sharply with increase in applied voltage, as it does for metal wires, but at a certain applied voltage the loss in sensitivity through reduction in R_1 balances the gain from increase in E, so that the sensitivity reaches a maximum; at greater applied voltages the sensitivity declines. This is shown by the results of Cowan and Stirling (*27*) (Fig. 9.3). The voltage of maximum sensitivity increases with increase in the thermal conductivity of the carrier gas.

(*b*) *Temperature Coefficient of Resistance*

The sensitivity of a catharometer is simply proportional to this quantity. Table 9.1 shows values of the temperature coefficients of resistance

TABLE 9.1

TEMPERATURE COEFFICIENTS OF RESISTANCE OF COMMON METALS

Metal	Temp. (°C)	α (°C^{-1})
Copper	20	0.0039
Iron	20	0.0050
Nickel	20	0.006
Platinum	20	0.004
Tungsten	18	0.0045
Brass	18	0.001
Bronze	18	0.0005

of a few common metals at room temperature. When other factors do not interfere, greatest sensitivity is provided by metals with large temperature coefficients, but the table shows that there is little to choose between several common metals. Platinum, tungsten, and nickel are all commonly used. Table 9.1 also shows that the temperature coefficients of resistance of alloys—not ones especially designed for the purpose—are much smaller than those of pure metals. This draws attention to the fact that the temperature coefficient of resistance of a metal may be considerably reduced by even a small proportion of impurity.

The temperature coefficients of thermistors may be as large as $-0.1°C^{-1}$. These coefficients are an order of magnitude larger than those for metals, and thus cells made with thermistors should be an order of magnitude more sensitive than those made with metal wires; as a result, a large number of designs of thermistor cells have been produced. In practice, however, thermistor cells do not always exhibit the expected advantage in sensitivity over cells with metal elements; the reason probably lies in the difference in the values of G as discussed in the next subsection. A further drawback is that the resistance of the hot element is halved for every 10 or 15°C rise in temperature This causes a drop in the power dissipation with increase in temperature [see Section 9.3(e) below], and also, since the resistance changes grossly with temperature, the Wheatstone's bridge can only operate efficiently over a very limited range of temperature. The result is that a cell which is sensitive at one temperature becomes much less sensitive at a higher temperature; furthermore, at a lower temperature its resistance becomes greater than the input impedance of the recorder, so that the latter becomes sluggish. The conclusion is that the value of the temperature coefficient of resistance cannot be considered in isolation in the design of a sensitive catharometer.

(c) *The Apparatus Constant, G*

From Eq. (9.32), the sensitivity is inversely proportional to G, which is a positive function of the size of the hot element. Wiseman (*19*), for example, has shown that in the case of an axial wire, the sensitivity is proportional to the inverse fourth power of the wire radius. The above consideration, however, is generally insufficient, since for a given power dissipation, decrease in G causes an increase in the temperature of the hot element, which is undesirable. If the temperature of the hot element is constrained to be constant, Eq. (9.15) shows that $I_1 \propto G^{1/2}$. Under correct operating conditions, $S \propto I_1^3$. Thus, in the case that G is varied and I is adjusted so as to keep the hot element at a constant temperature,

$$S \propto I^3/G \propto G^{3/2}/G = G^{1/2}. \tag{9.35}$$

Hence, subject to the above constraint, the sensitivity increases with an increase in G, and thus increases the larger the hot element. The thermistors used in catharometry are usually very small so as not to be sluggish [Section 9.9(a)], and this above factor is probably partly responsible for the fact that their sensitivity is not as great as their large temperature coefficient would suggest. Equation (9.35) is implicit in the work of Cowan and Stirling (*27*), where it is considered in greater detail.

(*d*) *Carrier Gas*

The carrier gas can affect the catharometer sensitivity on account of the molecular quantities contributing to $\partial\lambda_{12}/\partial x_2$, and on account of the λ_1^2 of Eq. (9.19). Also, if the temperature of the hot element is constrained to be constant, the carrier gas affects the sensitivity on account of the changes in E and I necessitated by the constraint. It is apparent that a complete discussion of this would be confusing, as is shown by the literature of the subject (*13–17,28*). We consider first the case of a cell in which all the quantities in Eq. (9.32) are constant other than the parameters of the carrier gas. As the thermal conductivity of the carrier gas *falls*, (1) the sensitivity rises on account of the λ_1^2 on the denominator of Eq. (9.32), (2) the sensitivity changes on account of change in $\partial\lambda_{12}/\partial x_2$. The expression given in Eq. (9.6) holds only in the case of light carrier gases, and cannot be used in this discussion. In the catharometry of organic materials, the molecules of vapour are usually heavier and larger than those of the carrier. In general, therefore, the heavier the carrier gas, the more its molecules behave like the vapour molecules, and the smaller is $\partial\lambda_{12}/\partial x_2$. On this account, the heavier the carrier, the smaller the sensitivity.

Ray (*13*) has suggested that whereas according to (1) the sensitivity rises proportionally to λ_1^2 on decreasing the thermal conductivity of the carrier gas, it cannot fall faster than directly proportionally to λ_1 according to (2), so that the net sensitivity should rise with increasing molecular weight of carrier gas. This is confirmed with some vapours in helium and in argon. Ray's argument applies only to vapours which are considerably larger and heavier than the heaviest carrier gas considered. For vapours the molecular weight of which is close to that of the carrier, $\partial\lambda_{12}/\partial x_2$ may be quite small or even zero, and may change rapidly, with possible reversal of sign, as the concentration of vapour increases. In such cases, considerable variation of $\partial\lambda_{12}/\partial x_2$ may occur at mole fractions of vapour not much greater than 0.01.

In the case that the temperature of the hot element is constrained to be constant, considered by Schmauch and Dinerstein (*14*), Eden, Karmen, and Stevenson (*15*), and Fredericks, Dimbat, and Stross (*17*), Eq. (9.15) requires that $I_1^2R_1/J \propto \lambda_1$, so that, in place of the proportionality $\partial T_2/\partial\lambda_{12} \propto 1/\lambda_1^2$ considered above, Eq. (9.15) and the above condition yields $\partial T_2/\partial\lambda_{12} \propto 1/\lambda_1$. The above authors then find that on decreasing the value of λ_1, the sensitivity falls faster on account of changes in $\partial\lambda_{12}/\partial x_2$ than it rises on account of change in $\partial T_2/\partial\lambda_1$. The result is that decrease in the thermal conductivity of the carrier gas causes a large reduction in sensitivity. This is illustrated in Table 9.2 by values from Schmauch and Dinerstein (*14*).

TABLE 9.2

RELATIVE SENSITIVITIES OF A CATHAROMETER IN HELIUM AND NITROGEN, USING CONSTANT T_2

			Response (mv) for $x_2 = 0.01$	
T_2	T_1	Solute	Helium	Nitrogen
100	25	*n*-Hexane	21.2	2.20
100	25	Methanol	11.0	0.45
200	150	Benzene	9.9	0.29
200	150	Cyclohexane	10.8	0.20
200	150	*n*-Hexane	11.5	0.23

The thermal conductivity of a pure gas is given approximately by the equation (*6*):

$$\lambda = K\left(C_v + \frac{9R}{4}\right)\sqrt{\frac{T}{M}} \cdot \frac{1}{\sigma^2}, \tag{9.36}$$

where M = molecular weight,
C_v = molar specific heat at constant volume [cal/(mole °C)],
T = temperature (°K),
R = gas constant [cal/(mole °C)],
σ = collision diameter of molecule (Å),
λ = thermal conductivity (cal cm^{-1} sec^{-1} °C^{-1}),
K = 2.67×10^{-5} for the above units.

More detailed equations are given in the source for the above (*6*). It is apparent from the equation that the larger the molecule, the smaller its thermal conductivity; a short table of thermal conductivities is given in Table 9.3.

In general, heavy carrier gases of small thermal conductivity should not be used for catharometry; a summary of reasons, including those discussed above, is:

(1) Sensitivity comparable with that in light carrier gases can only be obtained by raising $T_2 - T_1$, which is undesirable, and, furthermore, may be ineffective on account of (5) below.

(2) $\partial\lambda_{12}/\partial x_2$ cannot be estimated *a priori*.

(3) $\partial\lambda_{12}/\partial x_2$ becomes small or even zero for vapours which are not very different from the carrier gas in molecular size or shape.

(4) The range of linearity is smaller with heavy carrier gases.

TABLE 9.3

THERMAL CONDUCTIVITIES OF COMMON GASES

Gas	$\lambda \times 10^5$ at 0°C (cal cm^{-1} sec^{-1} °C^{-1})
Helium	34.8
Hydrogen	41.6
Neon	11.1
Air	5.83
Nitrogen	5.81
Argon	3.98
Carbon dioxide	3.52

(5) The change in sensitivity with temperature is more rapid with heavy carrier gases (see Subsection (e) below).

(6) The time constant of the hot element is greater the smaller the thermal conductivity of the carrier gas.

(e) *Temperature*

Increase in catharometer temperature almost invariably causes a decline in the sensitivity. The effect with metal wires is very much less than with thermistors, with which it is so great as to provide a serious drawback in their use. The effect may be analysed as follows.

Effect on α. With metal wires, α decreases slowly with rise in temperature, and this causes a small decrease in sensitivity.

Effect on R_1. In the case of wires, R_1 increases with increase in temperature; if the current I_1 were steady, this would cause an increase in the power dissipation, but generally, catharometers are run with E constant, so that as R_1 increases, I_1 decreases. The effect of temperature on the product $I_1^2R_1$ for constant E clearly depends on the ratio R_1/R_2; if this is small, the power dissipated will increase with increasing temperature, and if it is large, it will decrease. Over limited temperature ranges, the effect is small. In the case of thermistors, the large decrease in R with increase in temperature produces a large drop in the power dissipation. This can be eliminated by making $R_1 > R_2$, so that I_1 increases fast enough to compensate for the drop in R_1, but this has drawbacks; two obvious ones are that the bridge is operating inefficiently, and that a catastrophe may occur if E rises above a certain threshold value, or even if a large concentration of vapour comes through.

Effect of $d\lambda_{12}/dx_2$. In general, this appears to decrease somewhat with increase in temperature, though there are few data. This conclusion is reasonable on the basis of the collision diameter theory, for collision diameters of the complex vapour molecules decrease rapidly with increase in temperature.

9.4. Noise

There is no theoretical lower limit to the noise from catharometers except that resulting from statistical fluctuations in current flow, which is very small, and actual noise results from instrumental imperfections. In the early days of gas-chromatographic catharometry, noise provided a limit to the useful sensitivity. In current good designs, however, noise is generally invisible on potentiometric recorders of 1-mv span, so is smaller than about 5 μv, indicating that the range of catharometers could usefully be improved by amplification of the output.

Sources of noise may be subdivided into electrical and thermal.

(a) *Electrical Noise*

Thermoelectric. The Wheatstone's bridge circuit normally contains several intermetallic junctions, unequal heating of which leads to thermoelectric voltages. The most serious of these are at the leads into the cells, where the temperature may be high, where there may be convection draughts, and where intermetallic connections are likely. Thus, cell leads should be well protected, and preferably, intermetallic junctions should be bunched together in pairs arranged so that thermoelectric voltages cancel.

Temperature Variation in the Fixed Arms of the Bridge. All resistances other than the hot elements should be composed of resistance wire of negligible temperature coefficient, e.g., constantan or manganin. Thermoelectric voltages may also be eliminated by using wire which has both negligible temperature coefficient and small thermoelectric voltages with copper; such wire is commercially available.

Bad Contacts. It is obvious that these produce noise, but it is worth emphasising how good the contacts must be. For example, in a cell with $R_1 = 100$ ohms, $E = 20$ volts, a noise of 5 μv is given by a change in resistance of 0.0001 ohm [Eq. (9.30)].

(b) *Thermal Noise*

Apart from electrical noise, thermal noise results from random variations in the temperature of the hot elements in adjacent arms of the bridge. If again we consider two cells, $R_1 = R_4 = 100$ ohms, $E = 20$ volts, $\alpha = 0.004°C^{-1}$, a noise of 5 μv is provided by random temperature differences of 2.5×10^{-4} °C. Thus, sensitive catharometers should be contained in a thermostat, and should be designed so that there is as good a temperature equality between the two cells as possible. This is normally done by building them into the same metal block.

9.5. Drift

Long-term drift is generally more troublesome than noise in catharometry. Apart from the extraneous causes of drift mentioned in Chapter 7, the most common serious causes of drift in catharometers are slow changes in the temperature of the metal block containing the cells and slow changes in the potential applied to the bridge, which is usually supplied by accumulators. Littlewood (*29*) has described a method by which this drift may be eliminated.

In an "ideal" bridge, in balance, a change in E or T for two cells contained in the same metal block should not change the balance, for if R_1 and R_4 are properly matched, their resistances should each change in the same proportion. In practice, however, this is not quite true, for it is impossible to match two hot elements with sufficient accuracy, and the

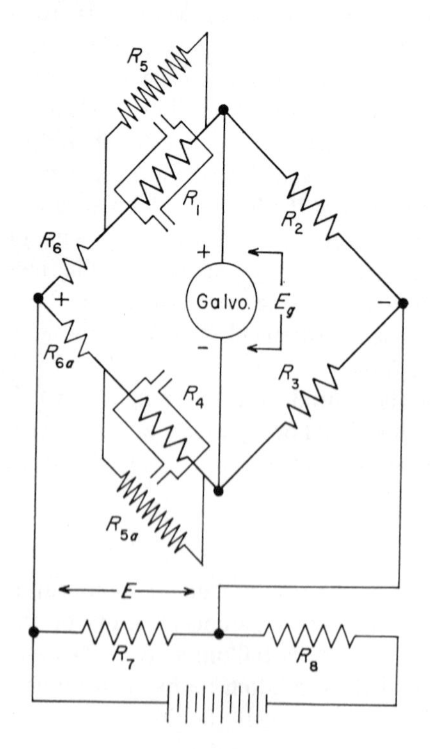

Fig. 9.4. Wheatstone's bridge circuit modified by resistances designed to reduce drift. Littlewood (*29*).

result is that slight changes in E and T cause drift. This drift may be eliminated using a Wheatstone's bridge circuit $R_1 - R_2 - R_3 - R_4$ modified by one or two of the resistances R_5, R_{5a}, R_6, or R_{6a} shown in Fig. 9.4. The operation of these may be explained qualitatively as follows. As T changes, R_1 and R_4 also change. Ideally, the temperature coefficients of resistance of R_1 and R_4 are identical, but in practice, the effect is that the temperature coefficient of one is slightly greater than that of the other. A fixed resistance is therefore placed either in series or in parallel with the hot element which effectively has the greater temperature coefficient, and its value is adjusted until the temperature coefficient of the two together equals that of the other hot element. After this, the net temperature coefficients of each arm of the bridge are identical, and change of temperature does not alter the balance. The same explanation serves for the correction of drift due to changes in E, but the value of the compensating resistance required is not necessarily the same. It is also possible to choose one series and one shunt resistance such that the catharometer does not drift for simultaneous changes in E and T.

The values and positions of the required compensating resistances may be found by the following routine, which is derived merely by use of Ohm's law and the rules of partial differentiation.

(a) To Eliminate Drift due to Changes in T Only

(1) Measure the magnitude of the drift as the quantity $\partial E_g/\partial T_1$ by warming or cooling the cell block slightly, with due regard to the signs as in Fig. 9.4.

(2) Calculate a number a by the formula:

$$a = -\frac{1}{E\alpha}\frac{\partial E_g}{\partial T_1}\frac{(R_1 + R_2)^2}{R_1 R_2}, \tag{9.37}$$

where α is the temperature coefficient of resistance of the hot elements. The quantity a is a measure of the effective difference between the two hot elements. It may be of either sign, but if it is greater than about 0.1, the mismatch is too great for this method to be used.

(3) If a is *positive*, insert $R_5 = R_1/a$ *or* $R_6 = R_1 a$.
If a is *negative*, insert $R_{5a} = -R_4/a$ *or* $R_{6a} = -R_4 a$.

(b) To Eliminate Drift due to Changes in E Only

(1) Measure the magnitude of the drift as the quantity $\partial E_g/\partial E$, with due regard to signs as in Fig. 9.4.

(2) Plot the resistance of a hot element against the voltage applied across it, and from the result determine the quantity $\beta = (1/R_1)\partial R_1/\partial E_1$.

(3) Calculate a number b by the formula:

$$b = -\frac{1}{E\beta} \cdot \frac{\partial E_g}{\partial E} \cdot \frac{(R_1 + R_2)^2}{R_1 R_2}. \tag{9.38}$$

The quantity b has a similar status to a, and the same comments apply.

(4) If b is *positive*, insert $R_5 = R_1/b$ *or* $R_6 = R_1 b/2$.
If b is *negative*, insert $R_{5a} = -R_4/b$ *or* $R_{6a} = -R_4 b/2$.

(c) *To Eliminate Drift due to Changes in E and T*

(1) Measure the drift due to each variable independently.
(2) Calculate a and b.
(3) See Table 9.4.

TABLE 9.4

VALUES AND POSITIONS OF TWO COMPENSATING RESISTANCES

R_5 or R_{5a}	R_6 or R_{6a}	Conditions of applicability
$R_5 = R_1/(2a - b)$	$R_{6a} = R_4(a - b)$	$0 \leqslant a \geqslant b$ or $0 \geqslant 2a \geqslant b$
$R_{5a} = R_4/(b - 2a)$	$R_6 = R_1(b - a)$	$0 \geqslant a \leqslant b$ or $0 \leqslant 2a \leqslant b$
$R_5 = R_1/(2a - b)$	$R_6 = R_1(b - a)$	$0 \leqslant a \leqslant b \leqslant 2a$
$R_{5a} = R_4/(b - 2a)$	$R_{6a} = R_4(a - b)$	$0 \geqslant a \geqslant b \geqslant 2a$

The above routines invariably lead to the correct positions of the compensating resistances, but the calculated values are sometimes not exactly those which give perfect compensation from drift. In practice, the final adjustments are easily made by trial. With metal hot elements, the compensation remains good over a range of 50°C and at least 1 volt; one may even heat a catharometer block over a Bunsen burner and obtain a straight base line. With thermistors, however, the range in which the compensation is adequate is much smaller.

9.6. LINEARITY

If the concentration of vapour is such that Eq. (9.32) holds, and if the cross-terms mentioned in connection with it are negligible, then the catharometer is linear. The causes of non-linearity are complex, however, and it is not possible from existing theory or practice to give a value of x_2 for which the non-linearity at greater values of x_2 is greater than a given amount. General experience is that so long as certain conditions are satisfied and subject to certain exceptions, catharometers are linear within a few per cent up to the greatest mole fractions usually encountered in gas chromatography, but this fact may be obscured by the literature of the subject, which is mainly preoccupied with the exceptions and conditions.

(a) Carrier Gas and Vapour

When the carrier gas and the vapour have comparable molecular dimensions and weights, non-linearity is likely to occur at relatively small vapour concentrations, as is indicated in Section 9.2(a). Thus, for vapours in the C_2 to C_6 region, of which the molecular weight is less than 50 to 100, heavy carrier gases such as nitrogen or argon are likely to cause the vapours to give non-linear responses, and a light carrier gas should be used. This is illustrated in Fig. 9.5, which shows plots of response against molar

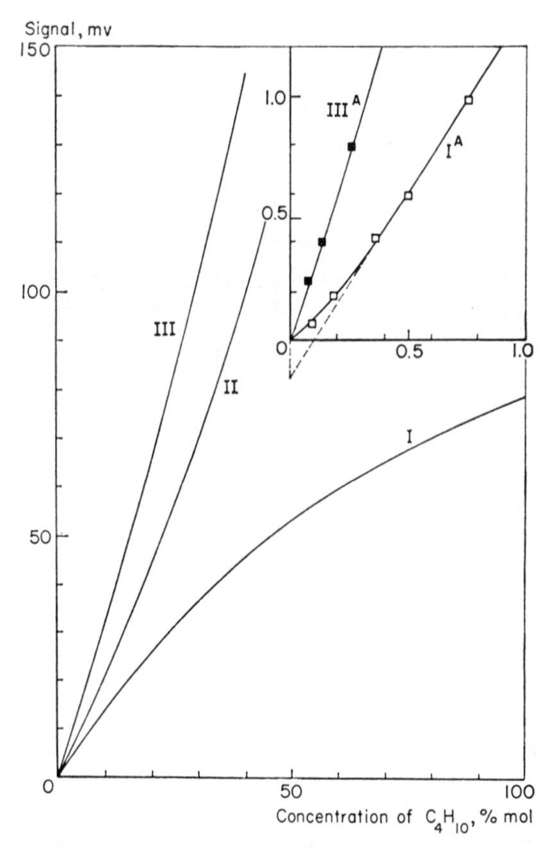

FIG. 9.5. Response of butane in various carrier gases as a function of its concentration. Curve I, *n*-butane in nitrogen; curve II, *n*-butane in hydrogen; curve III, *n*-butane in helium. Cell with Pt wires (diam 20 μ); bridge current, 200 ma. Curves I and III near the origin are magnified in the inset. Van der Craats (*30*).

concentration of butane in nitrogen, helium, and hydrogen (*30*). The linearity is clearly poorest in nitrogen.

(*b*) *Temperature*

In general, especially with heavy carrier gases, the higher the temperature, whether of the cell or the hot element, the smaller the range of linearity. When nitrogen is used as a carrier gas with vapours of up to about seven carbon atoms, there is often at high temperatures an extreme form of non-linearity in which the response changes sign at low concentrations, but maintains the same sign at large concentrations, so that a single peak appears as a "W." This is shown very well by Keppler, Dijkstra, and Schols (*31*) (Fig. 9.6), who have put side by side a number of chromato-

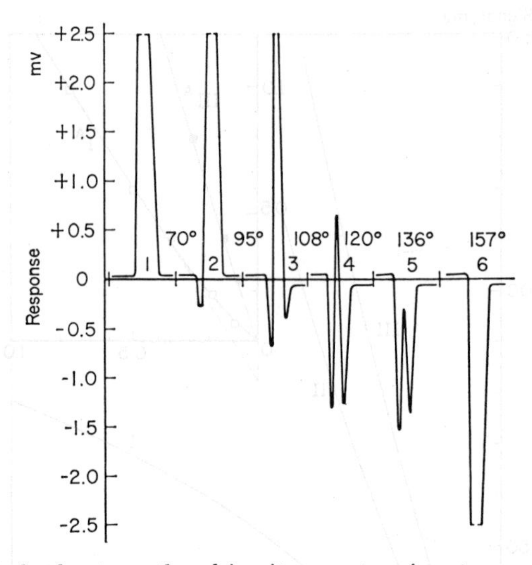

FIG. 9.6. Peaks due to methanol in nitrogen at various temperatures of the hot element. Keppler, Dijkstra, and Schols (*31*).

grams of a similar sample of methanol in nitrogen taken at a succession of hot element temperatures. Schmauch and Dinerstein (*31a*) illustrate the same behaviour by plotting response against concentration of methanol in nitrogen using both T_1 and T_2 as parameters (Fig. 9.7). From this plot it is seen that the response is reasonably linear if both T_1 and T_2 are small, but, as either of these temperatures becomes high, the detector becomes very non-linear, and the peak inversion of Fig. 9.6 is represented as negative response in Fig. 9.7. This result may be interpreted with a plot of λ_{12} for the system against molar composition with temperature as a parameter (Fig. 9.8) (*23*). At low temperatures, the thermal conductivity of the

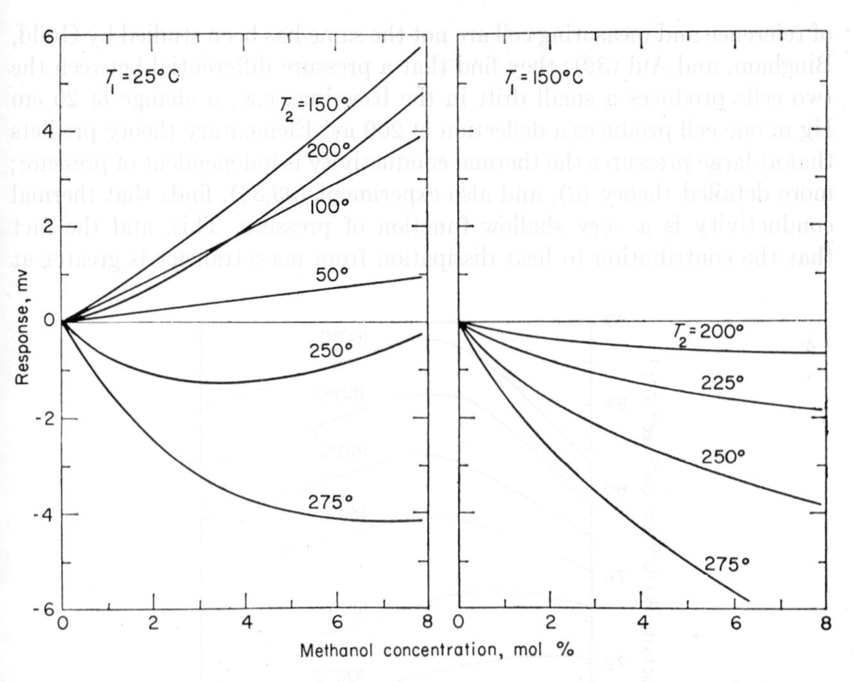

FIG. 9.7. Plots of response against concentration for methanol in nitrogen. Schmauch and Dinerstein (*31a*).

mixture drops monotonically with increase in x_2; at high temperatures, the value of $\partial\lambda_{12}/\partial x_2$ is positive at low concentrations and attains a maximum at a comparatively small value of x_2, after which it changes sign. Thus, at high temperatures the small concentration regions of the peak are inverted.

(c) *Catharometer Design*

Bohemen and Purnell (*18*) find that in heavy carrier gases loss of heat by mass-transfer rather than by conduction [see Sections 9.2(b), and 9.7] may cause non-linearity. In cases where this is true, therefore, a diffusion-fed cell, through which no gas passes, will not suffer from this source of non-linearity.

9.7. INDEPENDENCE OF EXTRANEOUS VARIABLES

The effect of changes in temperature and applied voltage on a catharometer has been considered in Section 9.5.

The effect of pressure on the base line in the case that the pressures of reference and measuring cell are not the same has been studied by Guild, Bingham, and Aul (*32*); they find that a pressure differential between the two cells produces a small drift in the base line, e.g., a change of 20 cm Hg in one cell produces a deflection of 200 μv. Elementary theory predicts that at large pressures the thermal conductivity is independent of pressure; more detailed theory (*6*), and also experiment (*33,34*), finds that thermal conductivity is a very shallow function of pressure. This, and the fact that the contribution to heat dissipation from mass-transfer is greater at

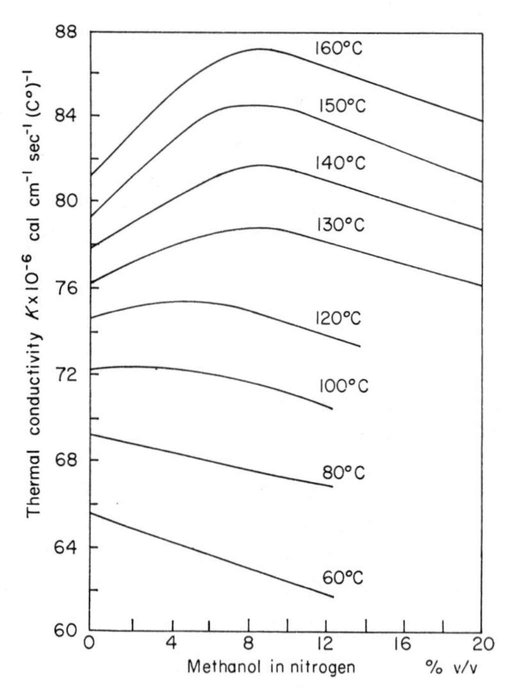

FIG. 9.8. Thermal conductivity of methanol in nitrogen as a function of methanol concentration, with temperature as parameter. Harvey and Morgan (*23*).

the greater pressure, accounts for the small but noticeable dependence of the base line of catharometers on pressure differentials.

In catharometers in which the gas passes over the hot element, a change in the flow rate generally has a large effect on the base line. As discussed in Section 9.10(b), this should ideally be cancelled out by a similar change in flow rate in the adjacent cell if the two cells are connected in series in the gas flow. In practice, however, the matching of the cells is not perfect, and changes in flow rate cause a residual change in the base line.

Bohemen and Purnell (*18*) have studied in detail the effect of flow rate in cells consisting of a heated wire in a glass tube carrying the column effluent. From their equation (9.23) for sensitivity including a mass-transfer term, the greater the flow rate, the greater the loss of heat through mass-transfer. Since the thermal conductivity term is generally of opposite sign to the mass-transfer term, the sensitivity should decline with increasing flow rate, and this is confirmed by results given by the authors.

Bohemen and Purnell also consider that mass-transfer is largely responsible for the increase in non-linearity, with eventual peak inversion, at high temperatures. The quantity $\partial\lambda_{12}/\partial x_2$ generally becomes less negative with increase in temperature, whereas $\partial C_p/\partial x_2$ remains relatively steady. The result is that the contribution of the mass-transfer increases with increase in temperature, until at a particular temperature the two terms are equal, and at small vapour concentrations, the response is zero. At still higher temperatures, the mass-transfer term exceeds the thermal conduction term at small concentrations, but at larger concentration $\partial\lambda_{12}/\partial x_2$ is more negative, as shown in Fig. 9.8, so that the thermal conduction term exceeds the mass-transfer term. This leads to a W-shaped peak. Bohemen and Purnell deduce the importance of the mass-transfer from the fact that W-formation occurs at lower temperatures the greater the flow rate.

Bohemen and Purnell (*35*) also point out that one result of peaks for which there is little or no response at small concentrations is that they appear to be much sharper than they are, so that spuriously large plate-numbers are obtained.

9.8. Calibration of Catharometers

The general rule is that with hydrocarbons or with molecules most of which consist of hydrocarbon chain in a light carrier gas, e.g., helium, the response of a catharometer is proportional to the concentration by weight of vapour. Thus, the weight fraction, w_i, of a component of a mixture is given by:

$$w_i = \frac{A_i}{\sum_j A_j}, \tag{9.39}$$

where A is peak area. The accuracy of this rule has been studied by many authors (*35–38*) in the course of analyses of hydrocarbon mixtures, and the conclusion drawn from the results is that it is accurate to within 1% for unbranched alkanes, and to within about 4% for any non-aromatic hydrocarbon mixtures. It is accurate to within about 1% for mixtures of aromatic hydrocarbons only, but in mixtures containing aromatics and other hydrocarbons there are large errors in the proportions of aromatic and non-aromatic compounds. It is reasonable to suppose that similar errors will arise in analysis of mixtures of hydrocarbons the molecules of which contain aromatic nuclei associated with alkane chains of different lengths.

The above rule may not in general be extended to molecules not containing hydrocarbon chains, and it becomes totally inapplicable in mixtures of components containing elements other than carbon, hydrogen, and oxygen. For example, in mixtures containing halogenated compounds, Eq. (9.39) can lead to errors as great as 40% (*39*).

When nitrogen or other heavy gas is used as carrier gas, Eq. (9.39) may still hold, but in a much restricted set of circumstances. It is probably necessary for the cell temperature to be low, and the rule is probably not even approximately true for molecules lighter than C_6. Hinkle and Johnsen (*40*) have analysed the same mixture in the same conditions using nitrogen, hydrogen, and helium as carrier gases [using Eq. (9.41)], to give the results shown in Table 9.5. It is apparent that with hydrogen or helium, the catharometer gives a correct analysis, but that with nitrogen there are errors of up to 25%. The conclusion is that heavy carrier gases should not be used for quantitative analysis by catharometry unless unavoidable, in which case calibration coefficients (Section 7.2) should be determined.

TABLE 9.5

ANALYSES IN NITROGEN, HYDROGEN, AND HELIUM

Component	Analysis in: N_2	He	H_2	Actual composition
Propane	3.8	5.6	5.4	5.2
i-Butane	19.0	20.1	19.6	19.9
n-Butane	43.0	43.5	44.0	44.0
1-Butene	21.2	20.1	19.8	19.8
2-Butene	5.6	5.0	5.1	5.1
n-Pentane	5.0	3.8	4.1	4.1
1-Pentene	2.4	1.8	2.0	1.9
Mean square error	1.005	0.093	0.020	0

Rosie and Grob (*41*), and Messner, Rosie, and Argabright (*42*) have determined a large number of calibration coefficients for vapours in helium by the analysis of known mixtures, and find that in any homologous series, the molar response is given by the equation:

$$\partial\lambda_{12}/\partial x_2 = A + BM_2, \tag{9.40}$$

where M_2 is the molecular weight of the vapour, and A and B are constants,

TABLE 9.6

CONSTANTS FOR THE GENERAL EQUATION: RELATIVE RESPONSE = $A + BM_2$

Homologous series	Range of experimental points	B (slope)	A (intercept)
n-Paraffins	C_1–C_3	1.015	19.8
	C_3–C_{10}	1.330	7.9
Methyl paraffins	C_4–C_7	1.270	9.3
Dimethyl paraffins	C_5–C_7	1.188	13.5
α-Olefins	C_2–C_4	1.188	13.5
Trimethyl paraffins	C_7–C_8	1.176	12.7
Methyl benzene	C_7–C_9	1.169	8.8
Mono *n*-alkyl benzenes	C_7–C_9	1.070	16.5
Mono *sec*-alkyl benzenes	C_9–C_{10}	1.042	18.7
n-Ketones	C_3–C_8	0.843	37.1
Primary alcohols	C_2–C_7	0.809	35.3
Tertiary alcohols	C_4–C_5	0.809	35.3
Secondary alcohols	C_3–C_5	0.839	35.1
n-Acetates	C_2–C_7	0.831	38.3
n-Ethers	C_4–C_{10}	0.874	44.2

the relative values of which are significant, but the absolute values of which are determined by setting the sensitivity of benzene arbitrarily at 100 units. Values of A and B for various series are given in Table 9.6, and Fig. 9.9 shows the accuracy of such a relation for the *n*-alkanes heavier than propane. Note that the small contribution of A when the carbon number is large is consistent with the approximate truth of the general rule of Eq. (9.39).

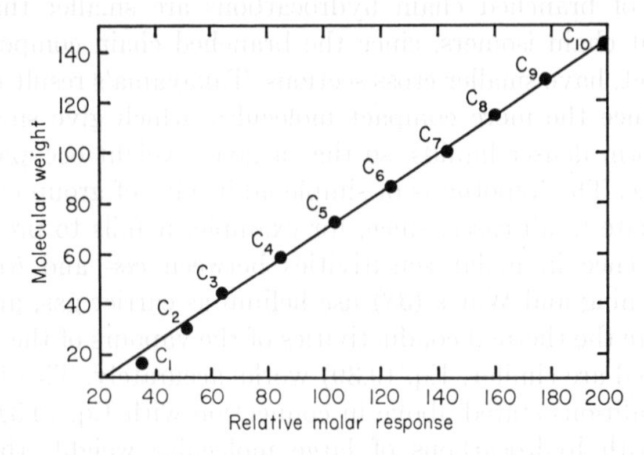

FIG. 9.9. Molar response of *n*-alkanes as a function of molecular weight, relative to benzene = 100. Messner, Rosie, and Argabright (*42*).

There have been at least five other attempts to calculate catharometric responses as far as possible *a priori:*

(1) Hinkle and Johnsen (*40*) find experimentally that for a mixture of gaseous hydrocarbons the response of a catharometer for unit vapour pressure of a component is proportional to the two-thirds power of the vapour density of the component. Thus, a peak area is given by:

$$A_i = Kp_i\rho_i^{2/3}.$$

The authors then assume that the samples behave as perfect gases, so as to give the following equation for the mole fractions of the components:

$$x_i = \frac{A_i\rho_i^{-2/3}}{\sum_j A_j\rho_j^{-2/3}}. \qquad (9.41)$$

Some of the authors' experimental results using this equation are given in Table 9.5, from which it is seen that the equation is accurate when hydrogen or helium are used as the carrier gases.

(2) Takayama (*43*) finds that in the analysis of liquid mixtures, the area of a peak given by a catharometer is proportional to the *liquid* volume of the component, i.e., its weight divided by its liquid density.

(3) Littlewood (*11*), working from Eq. (9.6), assumes that molecular cross sections are the sum of the cross sections of individual groups or atoms in the molecule, so that once the cross sections of the latter have been determined, the molar sensitivities of other compounds may be determined by simple addition. Such a procedure recalls the "Parachor." This procedure is consistent with the straight-line plots such as are shown in Fig. 9.9, for the addition of a methylene group to a compound raises both the molecular weight and the molecular cross section by a constant amount. Littlewood's procedure is also consistent with the observation that the sensitivities of branched chain hydrocarbons are smaller than those of their straight chain isomers, since the branched chain compounds, being more compact, have smaller cross sections. Takayama's result is consistent with this, since the more compact molecules, which give smaller weight responses, form denser liquids, so that a given weight occupies a smaller liquid volume. The hypothesis of simple additivity of group cross sections is not adequate in all cases, since, for example, it fails to predict the observed difference in molar sensitivities between *cis*- and *trans*-isomers.

(4) Browning and Watts (*38*) use helium as carrier gas, and find that in cases where the thermal conductivities of the vapours of the components to be analysed are similar, Eq. (9.39) works accurately. This is consistent with the conditions stated above in connection with Eq. (9.34), for when it is used with hydrocarbons of large molecular weight, their thermal conductivities are all very small, and thus necessarily similar. On account of the complicated relation between $\partial\lambda_{12}/\partial x_2$ and λ_2, however, it is doubtful

whether Browning and Watts' result is valid for components all of relatively small molecular weight which happen to have similar thermal conductivities.

For mixtures where the components do not have similar thermal conductivities, Browning and Watts find that the weight proportions of components are proportional to the peak area divided by the thermal conductivity of the vapour of the component (λ_2). Such a rule works well, for example, for mixtures of carbon tetrachloride and acetone, for which the ratio of the thermal conductivities is 1.93.

(5) Eastman (*44*) finds that the weight fraction of a component is proportional to the peak area multiplied by the square root of the molecular weight of the component [see also Rosie and Grob (*41*)].

We have now given six different approaches to catharometer calibration, all partial, all applying to special cases, and all suffering from a shortage of experimental data. Most of the authors quoted above recognise that heat may also be lost by mass-transfer, thus introducing a possible source of error. Of the six approaches, the first four are all more or less consistent.

9.9. Other Criteria

(*a*) *Speed of Response*

The speed of response is determined by the ratio of detector volume to the flow rate, and by the time constant of the hot element. The detector volume has no upper limit. The minimum volume of many designs appears to be about ¼ cc. This is small enough for use with any kind of packed column, but not small enough to make use of the full separative ability of high-speed capillary columns. Sasaki *et al.* (*45*), however, have described a micro-catharometer suitable for use with capillary columns, and there appears to be no theoretical reason why such catharometers should not be as sensitive as larger ones.

The time constant of the hot element is given by the equation*:

* This equation is derived as follows: At T_2, the rate of loss of heat from the hot element is I^2R/J, so, if free cooling were to take place at temperature T_2, e.g., if the electricity were turned off, the rate of cooling would be I^2R/JC. We assume that C is constant, and that the rate of cooling at temperature T is proportional to $T - T_1$, whence:

$$\frac{dT}{dt} = -\frac{(T - T_1)}{(T_2 - T_1)} \cdot \frac{I^2R}{JC},$$

which gives:

$$T - T_1 = \exp\left\{\frac{-t}{[JC(T_2 - T_1)/I^2R]}\right\} = \exp\left\{\frac{-t}{C/\lambda G}\right\}.$$

The time constant is the denominator of the exponent.

$$k = C/\lambda G, \tag{9.42}$$

where C is the heat capacity of the hot element and G is as defined in Eq. (9.16). For most hot elements, whether wire or thermistor, this is usually small, but not so small that it can be dismissed without consideration. Below are three examples of hot elements together with conditions, and rough calculation of their time constants.

Example 1. Thermistor; $\frac{1}{2}$ mm diameter; weight, 0.2 mg; specific heat assumed to be that of copper oxide, 0.1 cal/(g °C); carrier gas, helium.

$$C = 2 \times 10^{-5} \text{ cal/°C}$$
$$G = 4\pi r_2 = 0.3 \text{ cm}$$
$$\lambda = 34 \times 10^{-5} \text{ cal cm}^{-1} \text{ sec}^{-1} \text{ °C}^{-1},$$

whence

$$k = \frac{2 \times 10^{-5}}{34 \times 10^{-5} \times 0.3} = 0.2 \text{ second.}$$

Example 2. Platinum wire, 44 British standard wire gauge (diameter 0.008 cm), along the axis of a 1-cm tube. Carrier gas, helium; specific heat of platinum, 0.03 cal/(g °C); density 21 g/cc.

$$C = 3.2 \times 10^{-5} \text{ cal/°C per unit length}$$
$$G = 2\pi/(\ln 1/0.004) = 1 \text{ cm per unit length of wire}$$
$$\lambda = 34 \times 10^{-5} \text{ cal cm}^{-1} \text{ sec}^{-1} \text{ °C}^{-1},$$

whence

$$k = \frac{3.2 \times 10^{-5}}{34 \times 10^{-5} \times 1} = 0.1 \text{ second.}$$

Example 3. As Example 2, but nitrogen as carrier gas.

$$\lambda = 5.8 \times 10^{-5} \text{ cal cm}^{-1} \text{ sec}^{-1} \text{ °C}^{-1},$$

whence

$$k = \frac{3.2 \times 10^{-5}}{5.8 \times 10^{-5} \times 1} = 0.6 \text{ second.}$$

Cowan and Stirling (*27*) quote experimental time constants of 6 to 8 seconds in nitrogen and 1 to 2 seconds in hydrogen for thermistors rather larger than those used in the above examples [D = 0.5 mw/°C, see Section 9.10(d)]; Snowden and Eanes (*20*) show curves of response against time for an instantaneous change in vapour composition for wire elements wound on mandrels (Section 9.10) which show time constants in air of between $\frac{1}{2}$ and 1 second.

For packed columns, a time constant of about 1 second is usually adequate, and for capillary columns, 0.1 second. Thus, catharometers as described in the examples are adequate for use with capillary columns if helium or hydrogen is the carrier, but not if the carrier is a heavier gas.

Also, they would become deleteriously sluggish if the hot elements were much bigger.

(*b*) *Chemical Inertness*

A catharometer is normally inert to any vapour passing through, but the hot element may pyrolyse relatively thermo-labile components if it is hot enough. In particular, it should be remembered that metal wire hot elements may act as catalysts.

(*c*) *Range of Application*

When helium is used as the carrier gas, the catharometer will respond adequately to every other gas or vapour. The catharometer is one of the most versatile of detectors, and in this respect is comparable with the ionisation cross-section detector described in Section 8.3.

9.10. Design of Catharometers

A catharometer is the sum of a number of separate components and features of design, and each of these is considered separately.

(*a*) *Position of the Hot Element*

Catharometer cells may have their hot element: (1) in the stream of carrier gas; these may be called directly fed (*18,25,30,45–55*); (2) in a side arm; these may be called diffusion-fed (*20,27,56–60*). These arrangements are illustrated in Fig. 9.10. Each design has one specific drawback.

The drawback of directly fed cells is that heat may be removed by the gas flow as considered in detail by Bohemen and Purnell (*18*). As shown in previous sections, the effect of flow in directly fed cells can be deleterious

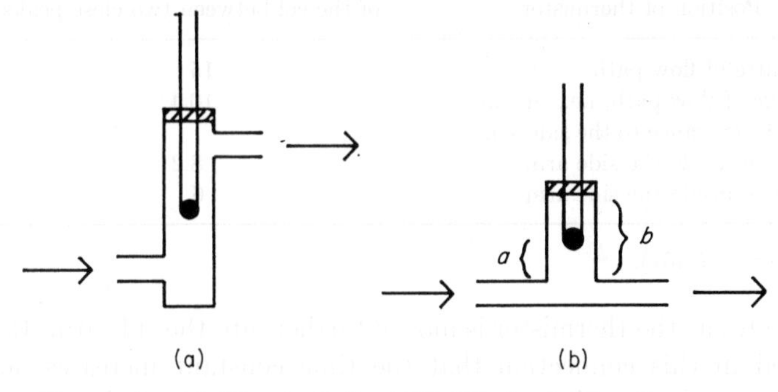

Fig. 9.10. (a) Directly fed and (b) diffusion-fed hot elements.

since it can render the cell sensitive to flow rate, can reduce sensitivity, can cause the calibration to depend on flow rate, and can promote non-linearity. The flow sensitivity can effectively be removed by passing the same flow through opposed cells, as described in Subsection (b) below. The other effects may be minimised by correct selection of the geometry of the hot element. As shown in Section 9.2(b) for axial wires in tubes, the specific heat effect is relatively less the longer the wire and the slower the linear flow rate, and so for a relatively long straight wire in a tube with a small linear flow rate, the specific heat effect is small. When the hot element is short in the direction of the gas flow, e.g., in the case of a coiled wire axially in a tube, or a wire situated in a cavity at right angles to the gas flow, or in the case of a thermistor bead, the specific heat effect is likely to be great; indeed, such an arrangement may be used to measure specific heats. Some such catharometers are described in the literature, but no quantitative data is given from which to judge their performance. It is likely, however, that such designs would not be satisfactory for work in which the specific heat effect would be deleterious.

The drawback of diffusion-fed cells is that they have a longer time constant than directly fed cells, but they do not suffer from the specific heat effect. The effect of the time constant on resolution has been illustrated by Baker *et al.* (*57*), who have used a cell as in Fig. 9.10b, in which thermistor hot element could be moved inside the side arm to any desired position. Table 9.7 shows the way in which the resolution of the two peaks

TABLE 9.7

EFFECT OF THERMISTOR POSITION IN A DIFFUSION-FED CELL ON PEAK RESOLUTION[a]

Position of thermistor	Resolution, expressed as ratio of peak-height to the height of the col between two close peaks
Centre of flow path	15
Edge of flow path, i.e., just at the entrance to the side arm	10.4
$\frac{1}{2}$ inch inside the side arm	8.2
$\frac{1}{4}$ inch inside the side arm	6

[a] Baker *et al.* (*57*).

deteriorates as the thermistor is moved further into the side arm. It should be noted in this connection that the time constant increases not only with increase in the distance a of Fig. 9.10b, but also with increase in b, so that it is important to keep the total depth of the side arm as small as possible.

(*b*) *Methods of Connecting Catharometer Cells in the Gas Flow*

In the normal case that two cells are used, they may be connected in any of the five ways illustrated in Fig. 9.11.

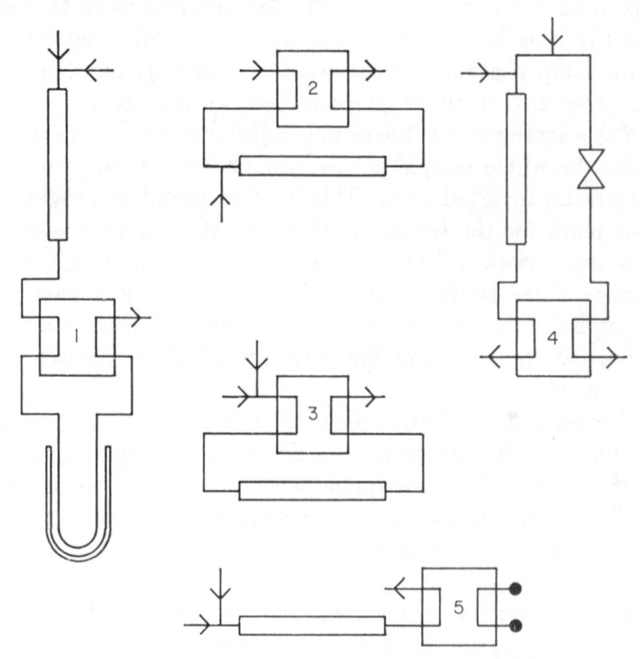

FIG. 9.11. Ways in which catharometer and column may be connected.

(1) In this arrangement, gas first passes from the column through the measuring cell, after which it is stripped out by a cold trap or by an adsorbent or by both, and it then passes through the reference cell. When used with flow-sensitive catharometer cells, this arrangement has the advantage that flow variations are balanced between the cells, and thus do not appear in the output. It has the additional advantage that both cells work at the same pressure and that any changes in the composition of the carrier gas are also cancelled out. A drawback is that, when a large sample is coming through, the flow rate in the reference cell is temporarily reduced while the sample is being condensed. This may produce a spurious response if the cell is excessively flow sensitive. If, in this arrangement, the trap is replaced by a small length of tubing, so that the column effluent is not

condensed, the record given by the detector is the differential with respect to volume of the vapour concentration.

(2) This arrangement is very common in practice. Gas first enters the reference cell, whence it goes to the sample injector and the column, after which it goes through the measuring cell. A minor drawback to this is that the pressure is greater in the reference cell than in the measuring cell, and, as pointed out in Section 9.7, the pressure difference causes a slight change in the base line, which must therefore be adjusted for each flow rate. Flow compensation is poor with this arrangement, and changes in flow produce drift in the response of flow-sensitive cells.

(3) In this arrangement, the sample injector comes before the reference cell, so that the whole sample passes through it on its way to the column and produces an inverted peak. This is often useful in providing an unambiguous mark for the beginning of a run. It should be noted that the area of the input peak will probably not equal the sum of the areas of the output peaks, since at the column inlet the volume flow rate is smaller, $\partial\lambda_{12}/\partial x_2$ may be appreciably different, and the total concentration of vapour may be beyond the region of linearity; indeed if the sample injector is efficient, it should be so.

A further advantage of arrangements (2) and (3) is that if the reference cell is of similar design to the measuring cell, chromatograms may be run with reversed flow. There are applications in which this is useful, e.g., in the analysis for proportions of volatile components of interest in the presence of less volatile components the relative proportions of which are not of interest.

(4) In this arrangement, the reference cell is separately fed.

(5) In this arrangement, there is a reference hot element situated in the same block as the measuring cell, but it is not fed by any gas flow. Such an arrangement has been used occasionally (*60*), and should be satisfactory with a flow-insensitive measuring cell, but it is probably not capable of great sensitivity, and its principal advantage is simplicity.

(*c*) *Design of the Cell Block*

The paramount consideration is that the two opposing cells of the catharometer should be at exactly the same temperature, as is shown in Section 9.4(b). In certain early work (*61*), satisfactory results at small sensitivity were obtained by placing both cells in a common vapour jacket. In current designs, however, the required temperature equality is almost invariably achieved by building the cells into the same metal block, for which purpose copper, brass, stainless steel, monel metal, etc., have all been used. Many individual designs exist, and most of the references given at the beginning of this section include diagrams showing details of construction. A substitute for the metal block is to use glass cells surrounded with a mercury jacket (*19,48,49*). Such cells are cheap and can be made to be sensitive, but they have not been made as free from noise as cells in metal blocks.

Cell blocks are usually contained in a thermostat, and for this purpose vapour baths (*19,49*), circulating air baths (*46,48*), and conventional liquid thermostats have all been frequently used. The normal temperature variation in the cycle of an on-off thermostat is often sufficiently great to cause thermal noise either because of the variation in the temperature of the block as a whole, or because of the establishment of temperature gradients across the block, or both. Variations in the temperature of the block as a whole cause noise or drift only on account of imperfect balancing of the hot elements. Littlewood (*29*) has found that a value of $\partial E_g/\partial T$ of the order of 0.1 mv/°C is typical; with a thermostat cycle spanning 0.01°C (a reasonable value), such noise is therefore of the order of 1 μv, which may normally be neglected. Its effect may further be reduced by using a cell block of large thermal capacity, but this solution is restricted by the inconvenience of a large and heavy block of metal.

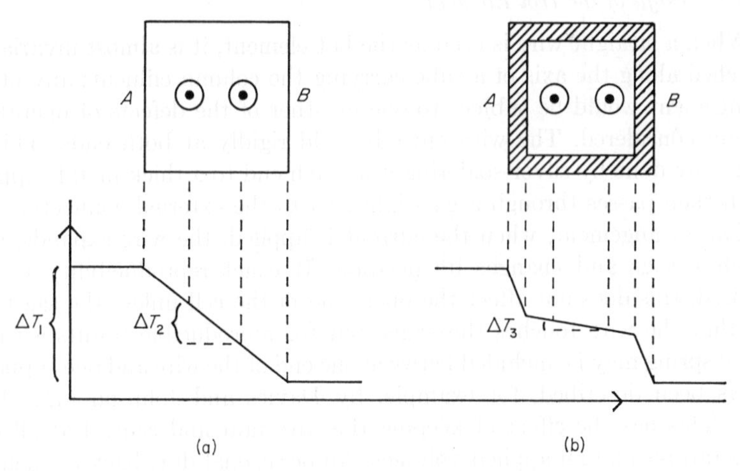

FIG. 9.12. Cross sections of catharometers through their hot elements (a) not thermally insulated, (b) thermally insulated. ΔT_1, temperature drop across the section, ΔT_2, temperature drop across the hot elements, case (a). ΔT_3, temperature drop across the hot elements, case (b).

The writer considers that a far more important source of thermal noise is caused by temperature gradients across the block, which have an effect whether the hot elements are perfectly balanced or not. Let AB (Fig. 9.12a) be a cross section of a typical cell block through both cavities. From the dimensions drawn in the diagram, and the figures given in Section 9.4(b), a noise of 5 μv is produced by a temperature difference between A and B of approximately $3 \times 2.5 \times 10^{-4}\,°C \approx 10^{-3}\,°C$. Such temperature differences can be eliminated only by the most elaborate thermostatting, and with the design shown in Fig. 9.12a, this source of thermal noise cannot be reduced. Such noise can be almost eliminated, however, if the cell is thermally insulated on all surfaces not parallel to a line containing the hot elements, as shown in Fig. 9.12b, which also indicates the distribution of a temperature gradient across the section. With this arrangement, temperature equilibrium of the block as a whole with the thermostat is rapidly reached through the faces of the block parallel to the line of hot elements, and there is no need for the cell block to be massive. The writer finds that thermal noise from any source is invisible with this design.

Other features of the design of cell blocks include details such as the positioning of entry and exit ports, types of union to connecting tubing, etc. The choice is influenced by the temperature at which the cell is to be used, but in general is not critical. Details of cells designed for high-temperature use are given in references *47, 51, 56*.

(*d*) *Design of the Hot Element*

When a straight wire is used as the hot element, it is almost invariably stretched along the axis of a tube carrying the column effluent; any other arrangement would be subject to one or other of the defects of operation already considered. The wire must be held rigidly at both ends. This is commonly done by silver-soldering it at each end to a thick metal support which then passes through a gas-tight seal to the external connection. In such an arrangement, when the current is applied, the wire expands, and therefore sags and changes its position. If exact reproducibility is not required, this does not affect the operation of the cell unless the sag is so bad that the wire touches the walls, but for reproducible results a small helical spring may be included between one end of the wire and one support, as has been described, for example, by Davies and Johnson (*47*) (Fig. 9.13). This has the effect of keeping the wire taut and central at all cell temperatures and all applied voltages. An occasional drawback of such an arrangement is that the taut wire has a natural frequency of vibration which may be actuated by chance, thus producing noise. Apart from this, though stretched or slack wires are somewhat prone to be noisy in the presence of violent vibration, no special precautions are necessary to reduce vibration noise to an adequately small level. Ashbury, Davies, and Drinkwater (*46*) describe a vibration-free support for their catharometer, necessary because of vibration from the circulating fan of their air thermostat.

Wire hot elements may also be wound in helices (*20,48,52*). When a

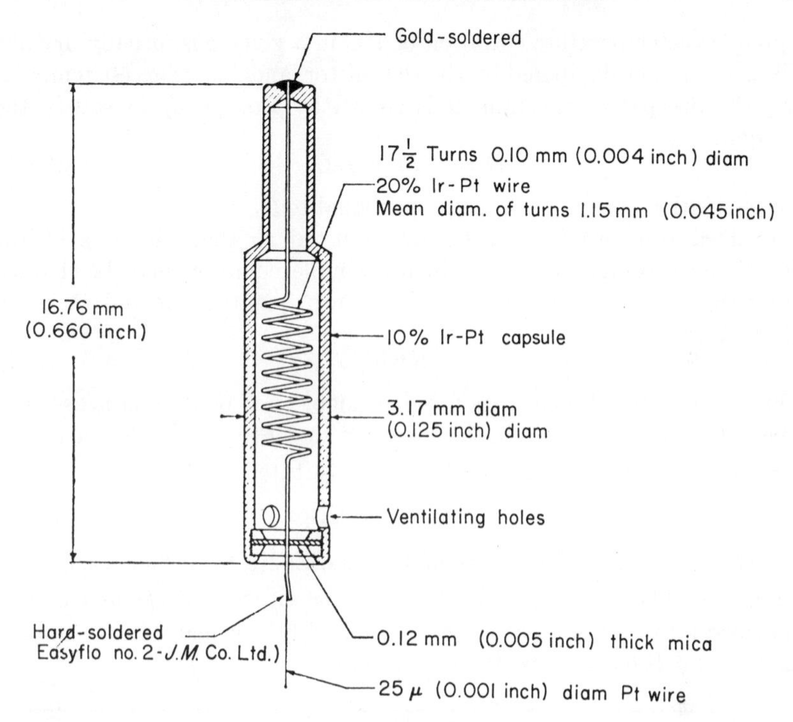

FIG. 9.13. Sprung wire anchorage. According to Davies and Johnson (*47*).

fine wire is wound into an unsupported helix, the resulting hot element is more compact, and can be operated in a smaller cavity, which may be a tube (*48*), or other shape (*52*), or a diffusion side arm (*20*). It is general experience, though, that such hot elements are very sensitive to vibration (*20,52*), and not suitable for normal use (*20*). Helical hot elements from lamp bulbs (*62*) and from "Glow Plugs" designed as firing elements in toy internal combustion engines have, however, been used satisfactorily (*56*.) Snowden and Eanes (*20*) have eliminated the sensitivity to vibration by winding wire helices on mandrels. When the mandrels are solid, the time constant of the hot element becomes larger than can be tolerated in many analytical applications, e.g., of the order of 1 second for mandrels of 0.015 to 0.028 inch diameter operating in nitrogen. Hot elements prepared in this way are extremely rugged, and have been developed for use in process control apparatus.

The selection of thermistors for use in catharometers has been considered in detail by Cowan and Stirling (*27*). A quantitative approach to thermistor sensitivity is assisted by the fact that manufacturers of thermistors generally quote their resistance at a specified temperature and their "Dissipation Constant," defined as the power input in milliwatts required to produce a temperature elevation of 1°C in a given gas, usually dry air. If W is the power dissipated by the thermistor, and θ is its excess temperature, the dissipation constant D is shown by Eq. (9.15) to satisfy the equation:

$$D = W/\theta = J\lambda G. \tag{9.43}$$

The dissipation constant is thus proportional to G.

If fixed resistors R_2 and R_3 are adjusted so that all arms of the Wheatstone's bridge are equal, then a simple equation may be derived giving the sensitivity in terms of the known quantities R and D. From Eq. (9.32),

$$S = KEW/G, \tag{9.44}$$

where K includes all quantities not dependent on E or W, and is assumed to be independent of T. From the condition that $R_1 = R_2 = R_3 = R_4 = R$, $E = 2\sqrt{WR}$. If this and Eq. (9.43) are substituted in Eq. (9.44),

$$S = K'\lambda\theta^{3/2}\sqrt{RD}, \tag{9.45}$$

where $K' = 2KJ$. Note that this equation and Eq. (9.43) include Eqs. (9.34) and (9.35). When θ is constrained to be constant, $S \propto \sqrt{RD}$, as has been confirmed by Cowan and Stirling (*27*) (Fig. 9.14) for many thermistors in which R and D have many different values.

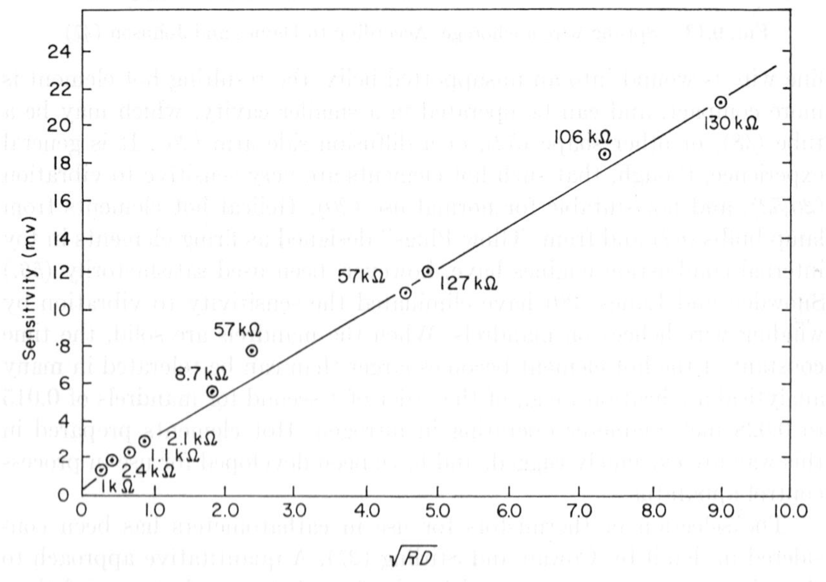

FIG. 9.14. Sensitivity of catharometers using thermistors as a function of $\sqrt{RD}$, for many values of R and D. Values of R are given against each point. Temperature difference, θ = 50°C. Cowan and Stirling (*27*).

From Eq. (9.45), the larger the product RD, the greater the sensitivity, and by design of the shape and size of the thermistor, R and D may be varied more or less independently. The dissipation constant D increases with increase in thermistor size, since the larger the thermistor, the greater the area over which heat may be conducted; the exact relation for wires and for spheres is contained in Eqs. (9.43), (9.17), and (9.18), assuming r_1 to be large in the latter two equations. In practice, the maximum size of a thermistor is limited by its time constant, as described in Section 9.9(a). The value of R may be adjusted by altering the composition of the thermistor; its maximum value is limited in practice by the input impedance of the recorder.

Cowan and Stirling (*27*) have found that thermistors produce considerably more electrical noise than hot wires. This noise is found to vary as I^n, where n lies between 1.2 and 1.8, and increases somewhat with increase in temperature. The noise is generally reduced by ageing the thermistors by heating them either in an oven or electrically.

The mixture of oxides of which thermistors are composed is liable to be reduced by hydrogen at temperatures greater than about 100°C, so that bare thermistors should not be used if hydrogen is the carrier gas unless the temperature is always low. Thermistors manufactured for catharometry are coated with glass; this increases their thermal capacity a little, but overcomes their sensitivity to their medium.

(*e*) *Wheatstone's Bridge Circuit*

The Wheatstone's bridge circuit may be connected in either of the basic ways shown in Fig. 9.15, but, of the two, (a) is universally used, and it will

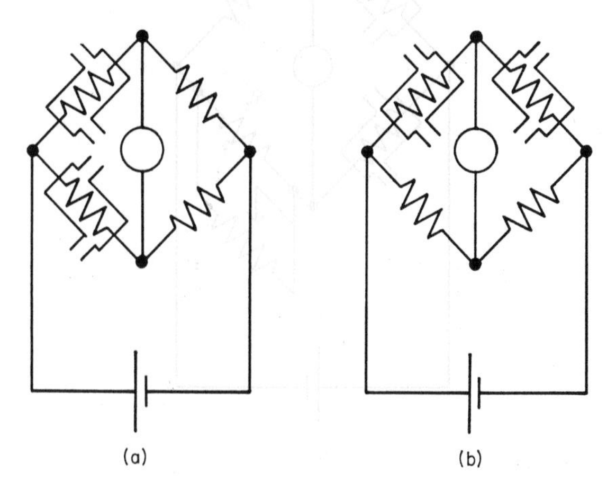

FIG. 9.15. Ways of connecting two catharometer cells in a Wheatstone's bridge.

be noted that this is implicit in all previous discussion of Wheatstone's bridges. Drawbacks to (b) are that the current in the measuring cell is subject to any fluctuations in the reference cell, that the current through the cells may not be controlled in any way other than by altering E, and that the appearance of a peak in the measuring cell alters the current in the reference cell in such a manner as to increase the non-linearity. In the case that thermistors are used, a special drawback of circuit (b) is that an

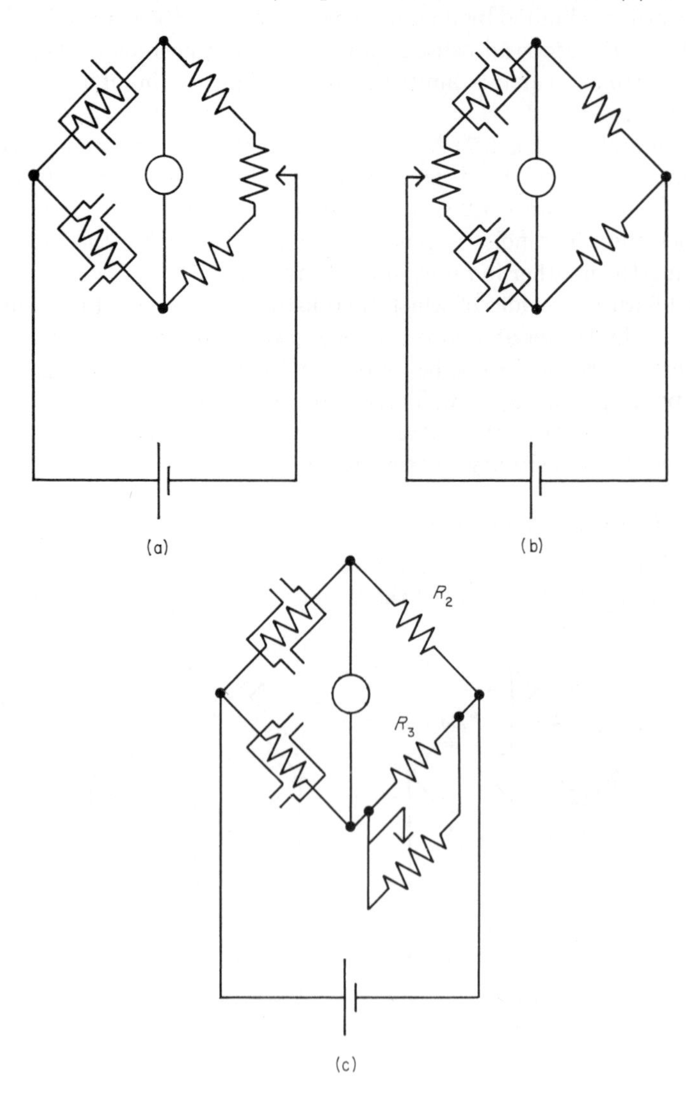

FIG. 9.16. Ways of adding a balance control to the circuit in Fig. 9.15a.

accidental increase in E, or use of a carrier gas with small thermal conductivity, or even the presence of a large concentration of a vapour, may promote the infinite catastrophe in which an increase in temperature reduces the resistance of without reducing the voltage across the thermistor, so that the power dissipation increases, causing a further rise in temperature, *ad inf.*, until the thermistor burns out.

Several methods have been used for adding a balance control to the basic circuit of Fig. 9.15a; the basic arrangements are shown in Fig. 9.16, but several variants are available by combining them. Arrangement (b) is not recommended, for adjustment of the balancing resistance affects the sensitivity of the cell and its liability to temperature and voltage drift. Arrangement (a) is satisfactory, and is frequently used; it has the minor drawback that any imperfection on the slide-connection of the resistance (or at the contacts, if a switched resistor is used) causes much noise. Arrangement (c) does not suffer from the above drawback, but it is impossible to tell initially whether the resistance should go with R_2 or R_3; with exceptionally well balanced hot elements, it may even be necessary for it to change position if the conditions in the cells are altered. A solution to this problem is to make $R_2 \neq R_3$.

In most normal practice, it is necessary to have both fine and coarse balancing controls. When arrangement (a) is used, an additional fine control may be incorporated in the manner of arrangement (c). When arrangement (c) is used, a fine control (R_f) may be incorporated in parallel with the coarse control (R_c), with $R_f \gg R_c \gg R_{2,3}$.

As described in Section 9.2(d), the sensitivity for a given bridge resistance is greatest when $R_1 = R_2$. It has been pointed out (*24*), however, that though such an arrangement is very commonly employed, it is subject to drawbacks. The principal drawback lies in the fact that the smaller the ratio R_2/R_1, the greater the dependence of I_1 upon R_1, thus producing non-linearity as mentioned in the restrictions on the application of Eq. (9.32) [Section 9.2(e)]. For hot elements of given resistance and for a given power dissipation, therefore, the non-linearity due to this can be reduced in comparison with the equal arm circuit by making $R_{2,3} \gg R_{1,4}$, and increasing E to compensate. Manipulation of the equations of Section 9.2(d) will show that this procedure also produces a small increase in sensitivity.

References

1. Shakespear, G. A., *Proc. Phys. Soc.* (*London*) **33,** 163 (1921).
2. Claesson, S., *Arkiv Kemi, Mineral Geol.* **23A** (1), 1 (1946).
3. Daynes, H. A., "Gas Analysis by Measurement of Thermal Conductivity." Cambridge Univ. Press, London and New York, 1933.
4. Weaver, E. R., *in* "Physical Methods in Chemical Analysis" (W. G. Berl, ed.), Vol. 2, Academic Press, New York, 1951.

5. Chapman, S., and Cowling, T. G., "The Mathematical Theory of Non-Uniform Gases," 2nd ed. Cambridge Univ. Press, London and New York, 1952.
6. Hirschfelder, G. O., Curtiss, C. F., and Bird, R. B., "Molecular Theory of Gases and Liquids." Wiley, New York, 1954.
7. Kennard, A. E., "Kinetic Theory of Gases." McGraw-Hill, New York, 1938.
8. Wassiljewa, A., *Physik. Z.* **5,** 737 (1904).
9. Lindsay, A. L., and Bromley, L. A., *Ind. Eng. Chem.* **42,** 1508 (1950).
10. Van der Craats, F., quoted in Keulemans, A.I.M., Kwantes, A., and Rijnders, G.W.A., *Anal. Chim. Acta* **16,** 29 (1957).
11. Littlewood, A. B., *Nature* **184,** 1631 (1959).
12. Sneddon, I., "Elements of Partial Differential Equations." McGraw-Hill, New York, 1957.
13. Ray, N. H., *Nature* **182,** 1663 (1958).
14. Schmauch, L. J., and Dinerstein, R. A., and Ray, N. H., *Nature* **183,** 673 (1959).
15. Eden, M., Karmen, A., and Stephenson, J. L., *Nature* **183,** 1322 (1959).
16. Scott, B. A., and Williamson, A. G., *Nature* **183,** 1322 (1959).
17. Fredericks, E. M., Dimbat, M., and Stross, F. H., *Nature* **184** *BA* 54 (1959).
18. Bohemen, J., and Purnell, J. H., *J. Appl. Chem.* (*London*) **8,** 433 (1958).
19. Wiseman, W. A., *Ann. N.Y. Acad. Sci.* **72,** 685 (1959).
20. Snowden, F. C., and Eanes, R. D., *Ann. N.Y. Acad. Sci.* **72,** 764 (1959).
21. For example, "Handbook of Chemistry and Physics." Chemical Rubber Publishing Co., Cleveland, Ohio, published annually.
22. Dimbat, M., Porter, P. E., and Stross, F. H., *Anal. Chem.* **28,** 290 (1956).
23. Harvey, D., and Morgan, G. O., *in* "Vapour Phase Chromatography," Proceedings of the First Symposium, London, May, 1956 (D. H. Desty, ed.) p. 74. Academic Press, New York, 1957.
24. Wiseman, W. A., *Chem. & Ind.* (*London*) p. 1356 (1957).
25. Burg, S. P., and Stolwijk, J. A. J., *J. Biochem. Microbiol. Technol. Eng.* **1,** 245 (1959).
26. Mellor, N., *in* "Vapour Phase Chromatography," Proceedings of the First Symposium, London, May, 1956 (D. H. Desty, ed.), p. 63. Academic Press, New York, 1957.
27. Cowan, C. B., and Stirling, P. H., *in* "Gas Chromatography," I.S.A. Symposium, August, 1957 (V. J. Coates, H. J. Noebels, and I. S. Fagerson, eds.), p. 165. Academic Press, New York, 1958.
28. Ray, N. H., *I.S.A. Proc. Anal. Instr. Div. 2nd Intern. Gas Chromatography Symposium, June 1959,* Preprints, p. 66.
29. Littlewood, A. B., *J. Sci. Instr.* **37,** 185 (1960).
30. van der Craats, F., *in* "Gas Chromatography 1958," Proceedings of the Second Symposium, Amsterdam, May, 1958 (D. H. Desty, ed.), p. 248. Academic Press, New York, 1958.
31. Keppler, J. G., Dijkstra, G., and Schols, J. A., *in* "Vapour Phase Chromatography," Proceedings of the First Symposium, London, May, 1956 (D. H. Desty, ed.), p. 222. Academic Press, New York, 1957.
31a. Schmauch, L. J., and Dinerstein, R. A., *Anal. Chem.* **32,** 343 (1960).
32. Guild, L. V., Bingham, S., and Aul, F., *in* "Gas Chromatography 1958," Proceedings of the Second Symposium, Amsterdam, May, 1958 (D. H. Desty, ed.), p. 226. Academic Press, New York, 1958.
33. Kannaluick, W. G., and Martin, L. H., *Proc. Roy. Soc.* **A144,** 496 (1934).
34. Lambert, J. D., Staines, E. N., and Woods, S. D., *Proc. Roy. Soc.* **A200,** 262 (1950).
35. Bohemen, J., and Purnell, J. H., *Chem. & Ind.* (*London*) 815 (1957).

36. Fredericks, E. M., and Brooks, F. R., *Anal. Chem.* **28**, 297 (1956).
37. Nunez, L. J., Armstrong, W. H., and Cogswell, H. W., *Anal. Chem.* **29**, 1164 (1957).
38. Browning, L. C., and Watts, J. O., *Anal. Chem.* **29**, 24 (1957).
39. Schomburg, G., *Z. anal. Chem.* **164**, 147 (1958).
40. Hinkle, E. A., and Johnsen, S. E. J., *in* "Gas Chromatography," I.S.A. Symposium, August, 1957 (V. J. Coates, H. J. Noebels, and I. S. Fagerson, eds.), p. 165. Academic Press, New York, 1958.
41. Rosie, D. M., and Grob, R. L., *Anal. Chem.* **29**, 1263 (1957).
42. Messner, A. E., Rosie, D. M., and Argabright, P. A., *Anal. Chem.* **31**, 230 (1959).
43. Takayama, Y., *J. Chem. Soc. Japan, Ind. Chem. Sect.* **61**, 685 (1958).
44. Eastman, R. H., *J. Am. Chem. Soc.* **79**, 4243 (1957).
45. Sasaki, N., Tominaga, K., and Aoyagi, M., *Nature* **186**, 309 (1960).
46. Ashbury, G. K., Davies, A. J., and Drinkwater, J. W., *Anal. Chem.* **29**, 918 (1957).
47. Davies, A. J., and Johnson, J. K., *in* "Vapour Phase Chromatography," Proceedings of the First Symposium, London, May, 1956 (D. H. Desty, ed.), p. 185. Academic Press, New York, 1957.
48. Littlewood, A. B., *in* "Gas Chromatography 1958," Proceedings of the Second Symposium, Amsterdam, May, 1958 (D. H. Desty, ed.), p. 23. Academic Press, New York, 1958.
49. Littlewood, A. B., Phillips, C. S. G., and Price, D. T., *J. Chem. Soc.* p. 1480 (1955).
50. dal Nogare, S., and Safranski, L. W., *Anal. Chem.* **30**, 894 (1958).
51. Ogilvie, J. L., Simmons, M. C., and Hinds, G. P., *Anal. Chem.* **30**, 25 (1958).
52. Ryce, S. A., Kebarle, P., and Bryce, W. A., *Anal. Chem.* **29**, 1386 (1957).
53. Bennett, C. E., dal Nogare, S., Safranski, L. W., and Lewis, C. D., *131st Am. Chem. Soc. Meeting, Miami, April, 1957.*
54. Davis, A. D., and Howard, G. A., *J. Appl. Chem.* (*London*) **8**, 183 (1958).
55. Bayer, E., *in* "Gas Chromatography 1958," Proceedings of the Second Symposium, Amsterdam, May, 1958 (D. H. Desty, ed.), p. 333. Academic Press, New York, 1958.
56. Felton, H. R., and Buehler, A. A., *Anal. Chem.* **30**, 1163 (1958).
57. Baker, W. J., Norlin, H. L., Zinn, T. L., and Wall, R. F., *Am. Chem. Soc. Symposium, New York, Sept. 1957*, p. 43 (1957).
58. Ambrose, D., and Collerson, R. R., *J. Sci. Instr.* **32**, 323 (1955).
59. Walker, R. E., and Westenberg, A. A., *Rev. Sci. Instr.* **32**, 323 (1955).
60. Musgrave, W. K. R., *Chem. & Ind.* (*London*) p. 46 (1959).
61. Ray, N. H., *J. Appl. Chem.* (*London*) **4**, 21 (1954).
62. Stuve, W., *in* "Gas Chromatography, 1958," Proceedings of the Second Symposium, Amsterdam, May, 1958 (D. H. Desty, ed.), p. 178. Academic Press, New York, 1958.

Chapter 10

Other Detectors—Ancillary Apparatus

The majority of gas chromatographs use one or other of the detectors described in the preceding two chapters, but there are many other devices which have been used for the detection of vapours in the carrier gas stream. The use of some of these has been reported only once or twice. The use of others is more familiar, and some such devices, briefly described below, have great advantages for specialised applications. In addition to the column and the detector, a complete gas chromatographic apparatus requires a flow control, sample injector, and possibly a flowmeter and devices for collection of samples. There may also be other items such as thermostats, apparatuses for providing constant electrical supply, integrators, etc. Most of this ancillary apparatus is common scientific hardware and for its description the reader is referred to standard texts on scientific apparatus (*1*). The design of the sample injector, however, is unique to gas chromatography, and is considered in a section of this chapter.

10.1. Measurement of Gas Volume or Pressure

(*a*) *Principle*

Gaseous solutes emerging from the column may be detected by the volume they occupy or by the pressure they exert. A method of detection in which the gas volume is measured was introduced by Janak (*2*), and has found considerable application since. The technique and apparatuses using it often carry Janak's name.

The basic apparatus is shown in Fig. 10.1. The carrier gas is pure carbon dioxide. Gas emerging from the column merely passes to a gas buret tube (nitrometer, azotometer) filled with potassium hydroxide solution. When pure carrier gas is coming through, it is completely adsorbed, and no gas enters the buret. When a gaseous vapour emerges, however, it is not adsorbed and it enters the buret. When it is completely emerged, its volume may be read. Successive components add to the gas in the buret, and their volumes may be read by difference. The result is that a plot of volume of gas in the buret against time is a series of steps, each step representing the appearance of each component. This constitutes an integral chromatogram

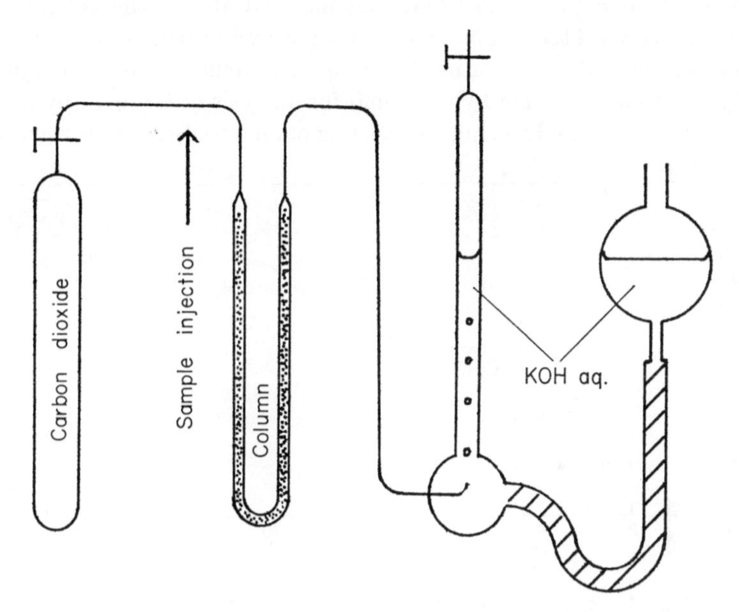

FIG. 10.1. Basic apparatus for Janak's technique.

as defined in Section 1.3. An example of such a chromatogram for a mixture consisting of light hydrocarbons is reproduced in Fig. 10.2.

(*b*) *Details of Apparatus*

It is apparent that if the carbon dioxide is impure, the impurities will fail to be adsorbed by the potassium hydroxide and there will be a slow continuous bleed of gas into the buret, so that the steps of Fig. 10.2 are not flat. All authors emphasise the importance of using pure carrier gas, and general experience is that the gas obtained from commercial cylinders is insufficiently pure. Dry ice is generally purer, especially if this is crushed before use (*3*), and a convenient source of the gas consists of a bottle filled with crushed dry ice with one outlet to the apparatus and another outlet to a blow-off, e.g., through a column of mercury, so that the pressure of carbon dioxide may be controlled (*3*,*4*). If required, the last traces of air may be removed from solid carbon dioxide by distillation *in vacuo* (*3*), but this is not generally necessary.

Since this technique is normally used only for volatile substances, e.g., permanent gases and hydrocarbons up to C_4, adsorption columns are frequently used, and were used exclusively by Janak in his pioneer work. With the samples commonly used this results in unsymmetrical differential peaks, which show on the integral chromatogram as "worn" steps. It is, however, perfectly feasible to use partition columns, and any of the columns described in Section 11.2 for analysis of the light hydrocarbons can be used in connection with the apparatus. For example, Rouit (*3*) uses columns of dioctyl phthalate or dimethylformamid for analysis of C_1 to C_4 hydrocarbons. Ray (*4*) has used a column consisting of an initial section carbon with

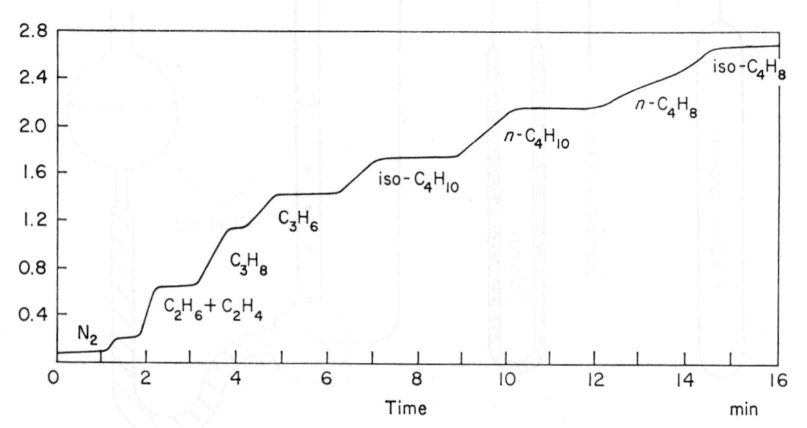

FIG. 10.2. Janak chromatogram of light hydrocarbons. Mixture of 22% dibutyl phthalate on zeolite and 6% free sodium zeolite. Janak (*2a*).

adsorbed bromine, followed by a second section of pure carbon for the analysis of trace non-olefinic impurities in ethylene. The ethylene is removed by the initial section, and unadsorbed trace impurities are chromatographed in the second section.

The operation of the buret is usually straightforward. It is necessary to level the reservoir with the surface of the liquid in the buret in the usual way, and it is necessary to take the usual precautions of gas analysis, e.g., capillarity corrections, etc. Correction for vapour pressure of water above the potassium hydroxide solution should be made; tables of vapour pressure are published, for example, in reference *5*. It should be recalled that the adsorption of carbon dioxide causes the potassium hydroxide solution to become warmer, and this may cause errors through increasing the vapour pressure of the solution and changing the density of the liquid in the buret tube.

A drawback to the use of the Janak apparatus for higher gaseous olefins, e.g., butenes, is that they are appreciably soluble in water. This drawback is overcome in the modification of the apparatus described by van der

Craats (*6*). The effluent from the column is fed via a special design of adsorber using a relatively small volume of potassium hydroxide solution into an evacuated chamber. Unadsorbed vapours in the gas stream show as a step-by-step rise in pressure in the chamber, and the pressure is continuously measured by a recording manometer. In the conditions used by van der Craats, solution of the olefins in the hydroxide solution is negligible.

Several methods have been described for providing automatic recording for the Janak apparatus (*7–11*). These employ various designs of servo-systems. Thus, Leibnitz, Hrapia, and Konnecke (*7*) describe a system in which a drop in the level of liquid in the buret causes a contact to break; this operates a servo-motor which operates a piston so as to increase the volume above the liquid in the buret, thus restoring the level of the liquid, and simultaneously operates a recorder pen.

(c) *Performance of the Janak System*

The prime virtue of the Janak apparatus is its simplicity and its independence of ordinary laboratory services. It is therefore suitable for field use, and for incorporation into a portable apparatus; such apparatuses have been manufactured commercially. Its principal restriction is that it can only handle solutes which are gaseous at room temperature. Its range can be increased, e.g., by heating the buret, and it is made more convenient by addition of automatic recording, but in this way it loses its simplicity, and must be used in a laboratory, where its general performance compares unfavourably with standard laboratory chromatographs.

10.2. Gas Density Meter

(a) *Principles*

Martin and James (*12*) have developed an instrument providing a continuous measure of the density of effluent gas, so that vapours with densities different from that of the carrier are recorded. This instrument has often been called the "Gas Density Balance"; this name should be avoided, since it is usually applied to the buoyancy balance frequently used for accurate determination of vapour densities, see, e.g., reference *13*.

The instrument designed by Martin and James is a series of chokes and cavities consisting of wide vertical tubes arranged in a manner originally inspired by the Wheatstone's bridge circuit, though the electrical analog of the gas density meter is considerably more complicated than a simple Wheatstone's bridge (*14*). It is illustrated in Fig. 10.3. Gas from the column enters at A, and reference gas enters at F. Both gases emerge at E. N, N', P, and P' are wires movable in and out of narrow tubes D, D', G, and G', and thus constitute variable valves by which the hydrodynamic resistance to flow through these tubes can be adjusted. The instrument operates on the pressure difference between points L' and L, by means of a device M which measures the slight breeze caused by the pressure difference. Initially, N and N' are adjusted so that change in the flow through A causes no response, and then P and P' are adjusted so that change of flow through F also produces no response. In this condition, the pressure drop across

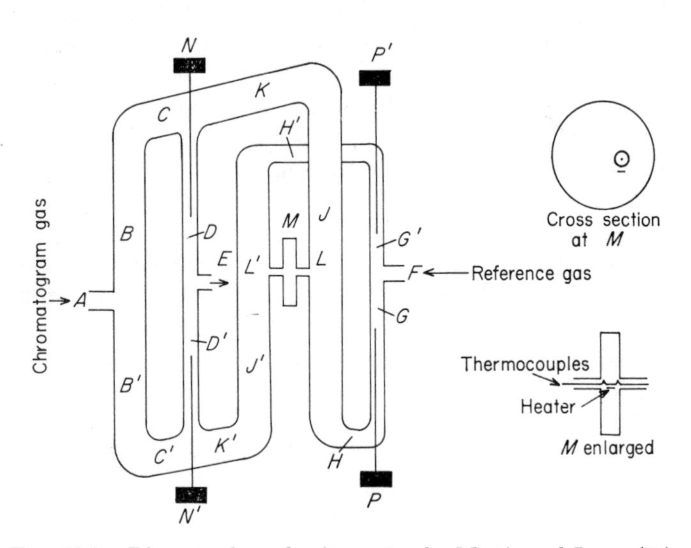

FIG. 10.3. Diagram of gas-density meter, by Martin and James (*12*).

$L'L$ is either zero or constant. As soon as gas entering A becomes denser than the reference gas, the column of relatively dense gas in BB' tends to set up a circulation. Actual circulation does not occur, since gas is continuously entering and leaving in a steady stream, but the effects of the tendency remain, and the result is that the pressure at L' becomes greater than the pressure at L, as would be the case for a circulation actuated from $B'B$ around the circuit $B'C'K'J'L'H'G'GHLKJCB$.

The slight pressure differences between L and L' are measured by an anemometer illustrated in the right-hand side of Fig. 10.3. It consists of two fine thermocouples in series opposition arranged symmetrically above a small electric heater. In the absence of a breeze, both thermocouples are heated equally, and there is no output. A breeze causes the convection current produced by the heater to be blown further towards one or the other of the thermocouples, and there is a net output. The output is amplified by a DC amplifier and recorded.

(*b*) *Details of the Apparatus*

Since very small changes in density can also be caused by a temperature difference between the vertical cavities, it is important to keep all parts of the instrument at a constant temperature. Martin and James (*12*) achieved this by constructing the unit by drilling holes in a massive block of copper, which was then operated in a vapour bath. The arrangement of a complete apparatus using the density meter is shown in Fig. 10.4 In this, the density meter is mounted near the bottom of the vapour jacket,

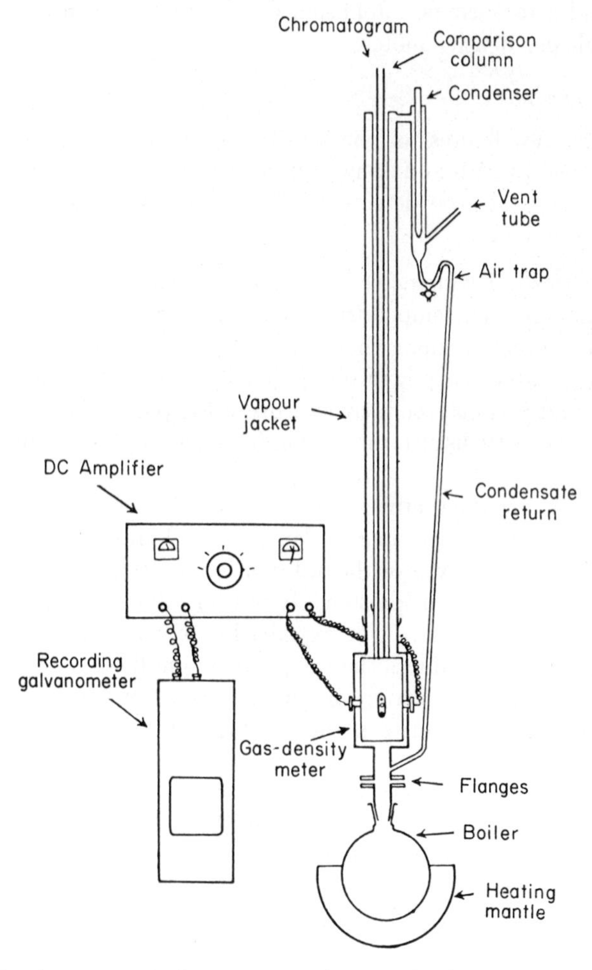

FIG. 10.4. Arrangement of apparatus using gas-density meter, by Martin and James (*12*).

with a chromatographic column above it, and also a reference column supplying the reference gas. Other authors using gas density meters (*14–19*) have generally used the same kind of apparatus, but methods of construction of the density meter have varied, mainly with a view to reducing the labour required for its construction. Thus, Munday and Primavesi (*14*) have constructed a unit out of tubing, and find that its performance is not noticeably worse than the solid block design. Ellis *et al.* (*18*) have constructed a unit out of monel tubing, subsequently cast into a block of copper. In this way, the instrument can be used for corrosive fluorinated substances which would attack copper. Johnson, Childs, and Beaven (*19*) describe a demountable gas density meter.

(*c*) *Performance*

There are few figures for the sensitivity or for the noise level of gas density meters. Martin and James quote that 1 part of pentanol in 10^4 of nitrogen may readily be detected. The sensitivity is subject to various features in the design.

(1) The sensitivity increases the thinner the wires of the thermocouples, since the difference in temperature between these is liable to be lessened by thermal conduction along them.

(2) The greater the power dissipated by the heater, the greater the sensitivity, and this may be increased up to the point where the heat generated is sufficient to disturb the temperature identity of the different parts of the unit.

(3) The smaller the thermal conductivity of the carrier gas, the greater the sensitivity. Thus, according to Martin and James (*12*), and also Ellis *et al.* (*18*), the sensitivity is of the order of ten times greater for vapours in nitrogen than in hydrogen (presumably not for vapours of density comparable with that of nitrogen). The explanation of this is probably that large thermal conductivity reduces the temperature gradient across the convection current from the heater of the anemometer, thus reducing the temperature difference between the thermocouples when the convection current is deflected.

(4) The sensitivity is also increased by increasing the diameter of the cavities, for the wider these are, the more breeze is available for a given difference in density. The greater the diameter of BB', however, the greater the effective volume of the detector, and therefore the greater the time constant due to this. Thus a compromise must be made between sensitivity and resolution.

The principal advantage of this detector is that, within its range of linearity, its response is proportional to the change in density caused in the carrier gas by the presence of vapour. The molar sensitivity therefore is proportional to the difference between the molecular weight of the vapour and the molecular weight of the carrier gas. Hence, if the weight sensitivity as defined in Section 7.1 is S,

$$S \propto \frac{M - m}{M}, \tag{10.1}$$

where M is the molecular weight of the vapour and m is that of the carrier gas. The relation between the weight of vapour w and the area of a peak A is given by:

$$A = w \cdot \frac{(M - m)k}{M}, \tag{10.2}$$

where k is a constant. This equation can thus be used for *a priori* determination of sensitivities in terms of molecular weight.

The accuracy and utility of Eqs. (10.1) and (10.2) is shown best by an adaptation in which they are used to determine molecular weights using samples of known size. Phillips and Timms (*20*) have reported a technique in which they measure the pressure P and volume V of a sample of a pure vapour, which is then passed in a stream of carrier gas through a gas density meter. Since at a given temperature $PV \propto w/M$ for any vapour, Eq. (10.2) transforms to:

$$PV = \frac{K \cdot A}{M - m}, \tag{10.3}$$

where K is a constant. The authors have checked the constancy of K, using several vapours of known molecular weight, and have then used the method for determining the molecular weights of unknown substances. The results indicate that molecular weights can be measured to better than 1%.

As Phillips and Timms point out, a drawback to the above method for determining molecular weights is that it is necessary for the vapour for which P and V are measured to be pure. This drawback is eliminated in a technique for determining molecular weights of vapours described by Liberti, Conti, and Crescenzi (*16*). A sample of the unknown vapour is mixed in any proportion with a standard, the molecular weight of which is known, M_k, and the mixture is chromatographed in each of two carrier gases whose molecular weights are m_1 and m_2. If the areas of the peaks due to the unknown and standard, respectively, in each carrier gas are A_{x1}, A_{k1}, A_{x2}, and A_{k2}, then a simple calculation based on the calibration property given in the preceding paragraph yields:

$$\frac{A_{x1}(M_k - m_1)}{A_{k1}(M_x - m_1)} = \frac{A_{x2}(M_k - m_2)}{A_{k2}(M_x - m_2)}. \tag{10.4}$$

From this, the molecular weight of the unknown, M_x, may be calculated. According to the above authors, the method gives an accuracy of about 4%.

An important advantage of the gas density meter is that the sensing elements never come in contact with vapours from the column, and therefore this detector may be used with corrosive vapours. This advantage has been used by Ellis *et al.* (*18*) for analysis of vapours such as chlorine trifluoride and bromine pentafluoride, as described in Section 11.13.

10.3. Surface Potential Detector

(*a*) *Principle*

In this device (Fig. 10.5) (*21–23*), there are two close parallel metal plates and the effluent from the column passes through the space between them. One of the plates is arranged to vibrate at an audio frequency, most conveniently by fixing it with a light mounting to an earphone or the coil of a loudspeaker actuated by an audio oscillator.

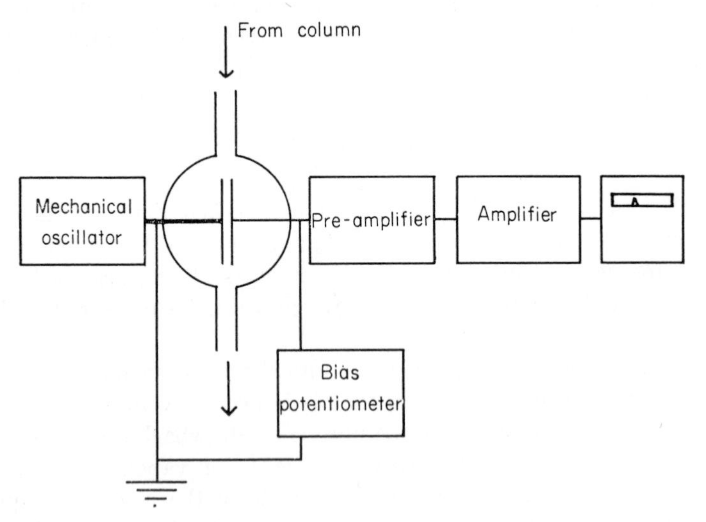

Fig. 10.5. Schematic diagram of surface potential detector. After Griffiths and Phillips (*21*).

If the plates are identical, the potential at the surface of each plate is the same, so that the moving plate is moving in zero electric field and no potential is induced in it. If, however, the plates are dissimilar, the potentials at the surfaces of each plate are different, and a potential is induced in the moving plate. In this detector, similar metals are used for both plates, but one plate is covered with a monomolecular layer of a substance which will adsorb vapours appearing in the column effluent. When no vapour is coming through, the monomolecular layer causes an alteration in the surface potential of one plate, so that there is a constant alternating EMF, the frequency of which is the frequency of oscillation of the plate between the two plates. When a vapour passes through, it equilibrates with the monomolecular layer, and that portion of the vapour which is condensed into the monomolecular layer causes an alteration of its surface potential. This change registers as a change in the EMF between the plates, and this is the signal of the detector. The EMF's involved are of the order of tens or hundreds of millivolts.

In practice, it is convenient to earth the moving plate, and measure the potential relative to earth of the fixed plate; this is heavily insulated, and connected straight to a pre-amplifier housed in the detector. The constant response obtained when no vapour is coming through is backed off by applying across the plates a constant potential so as to neutralise the field caused by the monomolecular layer. This potential is conveniently obtained from a potentiometer operated by a battery.

(*b*) *Performance*

The respect in which this detector differs from nearly every other is that the vapour is detected while it is in the condensed phase, and not while it is in the vapour phase. This difference has several consequences.

The sensitivity of the detector is comparatively large. Griffiths and Phillips quote a noise level corresponding to about 1 part of ethyl oxalate in 10^6 parts of nitrogen, and suggest that this sensitivity can be improved with improved electronics. A more significant feature is that the weight sensitivity depends markedly on the volatility of the vapour, increasing as the vapour becomes less volatile. Presumably, this is because the less volatile the solute, the greater its partition coefficient in the monomolecular layer, and hence the greater its concentration in this layer for a given vapour concentration. In chromatography, this is of particular significance, for in isothermal operation, successively less volatile vapours usually emerge at successively smaller concentrations. On a surface potential detector, the peaks, instead of getting shallower and shallower, remain at approximately the same height.

The detector responds very differently to different vapours. Within any one molecular type, e.g., a homologous series, the weight sensitivity increases with molecular weight as described above in such a way that the response of vapour in equilibrium with the liquid of the vapour at a given temperature is very approximately constant whatever the homolog. Thus, the response of saturated ethyl acetate vapour at 0°C is similar to that of saturated pentyl butyrate vapour at 0°C. Different chemical classes, however, give widely different responses. Halogenated compounds give responses in the reverse direction from compounds containing carbon, hydrogen, and oxygen; thus the detector has limited use in qualitative diagnosis. A large drawback to its general use is that there are several large classes of compounds, apparently including all paraffins and most other hydrocarbons, which give no response at all. It appears as if it is necessary for the molecules of the vapour to have a dipole moment in order for it to have a response, but there are not enough results for this to be certain.

The adsorption of the vapour in the monomolecular layer follows a Langmuir isotherm, and since the response depends on the adsorbed phase, the response is non-linear. Griffiths and Phillips have confirmed in several cases that the relation between response and the vapour concentration can be fitted to a Langmuir isotherm equation. If ΔE is the change in surface potential produced by a concentration of vapour c, they find that:

$$\Delta E = \frac{ac}{b + c} \tag{10.5}$$

where a and b are constants. Apparently, adsorption and desorption are rather slow, and the time constant of the detector is rather long, sometimes prohibitively so. For example, the time constant of ethyl oxalate at room temperature is 5 minutes.

10.4. Heat of Combustion—Hydrogen Flame Detector

(a) *Principle*

Scott (*24–26*) has described a very simple detector in which hydrogen is used as carrier gas, and the column effluent is burned at a jet just beyond the far end of the column. A thermocouple is placed above the flame, the output of which is recorded. When no vapour is present, the output of the thermocouple is constant, and leads to a steady base line. When an organic vapour enters the flame, the flame temperature increases, and the flame as a whole becomes larger. These effects cause the thermocouple to become hotter, and the increased thermoelectric EMF is recorded.

(b) *Details of Construction*

The basic apparatus is shown in Fig. 10.6. The effluent gas passes to a capillary jet, the material of which does not appear to be critical. Thus glass (*25*), or metal (*26,27*), has been used with success. The geometry of the jet does not appear to be critical; thus cylindrical (*25,26*) or divergent conical (*27*) jets have been used successfully. Various thermocouples have been used, e.g., Pt/Pt – Rh (*25,28*), Au/Pt, Fe/constantan (*25*); again the choice is not critical, so long as they can stand a temperature of up to about 700°C. It is recommended that the thermocouples be welded rather than hard-soldered, since the melting of hard solder can cause irregular results (*27*). The thermocouple should normally be held in a rigid support at a distance above the jet such that the visible portion of the flame while carrying no vapour does not quite reach it. When a vapour comes through,

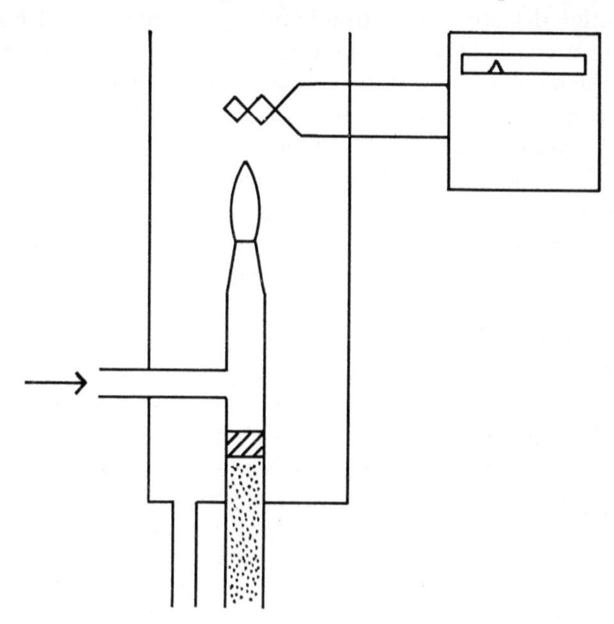

FIG. 10.6. Schematic diagram of hydrogen flame detector.

the flame engulfs the thermocouple. The effect of the position of the thermocouple with respect to sensitivity, linearity, and calibration has been studied in detail by Primavesi, Oldham, and Thompson (*29*) [see discussion in Subsection (c)]. The detector is very sensitive to draughts, and the flame must be carefully shielded, though at the same time sufficient air must be allowed inside the shield to support the combustion of the flame. Different authors describe various systems of shields and baffles for this purpose.

As described originally by Scott, a drawback of the detectors was that hydrogen must be used as the carrier gas. Wirth (*27*) modified this by using nitrogen as the carrier gas, and introducing sufficient hydrogen to make a flame between the end of the column and the jet, i.e., at the tube marked with the arrow in Fig. 10.6. If the ratio of hydrogen to nitrogen is greater than about 2:1, there is a satisfactory flame which is not easily extinguished. Baddiel and Cullis (*30*) have used carbon monoxide as carrier gas. This has the advantage that the combustion of halogenated compounds does not lead to corrosive products, e.g., hydrogen halides, and, with the use of a wide jet, halogenates do not extinguish the flame [see Subsection (c) below].

(*c*) *Performance*

There are few explicit figures for the sensitivity of the detector. It appears that in general it is sensitive when compared with detectors other than ionisation detectors. As with other detectors giving an electrical output, the sensitivity is in practice determined by the noise level. Scott (*25*) finds that the minimum detectable concentration for benzene is about 0.05 μg/ml of carrier gas, giving 1 part by weight in 2000 of hydrogen, or one molecule of benzene in about 10^5 of carrier.

Since the response of the detector depends on the heat of combustion of the vapours, the temperature of the thermocouple depends on the rate of burning of vapour. If the rate of burning is increased, either by increasing the flow rate, or by increasing the vapour concentration in the gas stream, the response increases. Thus, the sensitivity is best expressed quantitatively in terms of the temperature rise of the thermocouple for unit rate of burning. Suitable units are °C per (mg/minute), i.e., °C minute mg^{-1}. The noise is best specified by the magnitude in degrees of the random fluctuations in temperature of the thermocouple. Published figures suggest that sensitivities are of the order of 10°C minute mg^{-1}. Thus measurement of results given by Primavesi *et al.* (*29*) gives a figure of 30°C minute mg^{-1}, and Henderson and Knox (*28*) give a figure of 21.8°C minute mg^{-1}. A noise level of about 0.25°C is reported by Primavesi *et al.* (*29*). With hydrogen flow rates of the order of 10 to 100 ml $minute^{-1}$, these figures give a concentration equivalent to the noise of 0.1 to 1 μg/ml, which is consistent with the figures of Scott (*25*) quoted above. Henderson and Knox emphasise that the detector is very sensitive to the hydrogen flow rate, which must be controlled to 1 part in 10^5 in order to give noise levels as small as those quoted above.

Primavesi *et al.* (*29*) have studied the sensitivity as a function of the height of the thermocouple above the jet, and find that at distances greater than 1 cm, the sensitivity declines slowly with increase in distance up to at least 6 cm. The effect is not large, and the sensitivity of the instrument with the jet at 6 cm is only about half that with the jet at 1 cm.

The linearity of the detector has been studied by Scott and by Primavesi *et al.* In particular, the latter authors find that the instrument gives a linear response with ordinary vapours up to concentrations which are adequate for ordinary applications. It is necessary, however, that the thermocouple is sufficiently far from the jet, for when it is very close, the range of linearity becomes very restricted. The authors conclude that in choosing the position of the thermocouple, the deleterious effect of closeness on the linearity outweighs the slight increase in sensitivity, so that the thermocouple should be situated well above the flame.

An important advantage of this detector is that it may be calibrated in terms of a well-known molecular property, the heat of combustion. It appears that the response of the detector is proportional to extra rate of production of heat in the flame on account of the vapour; this was originally suggested by Scott (*25*), and has been confirmed experimentally by Henderson and Knox (*28*). Hence, molar calibration coefficients are proportional to the molar heats of combustion. The accuracy of this relation is indicated in Fig. 10.7, from Henderson and Knox (*28*), which shows molar

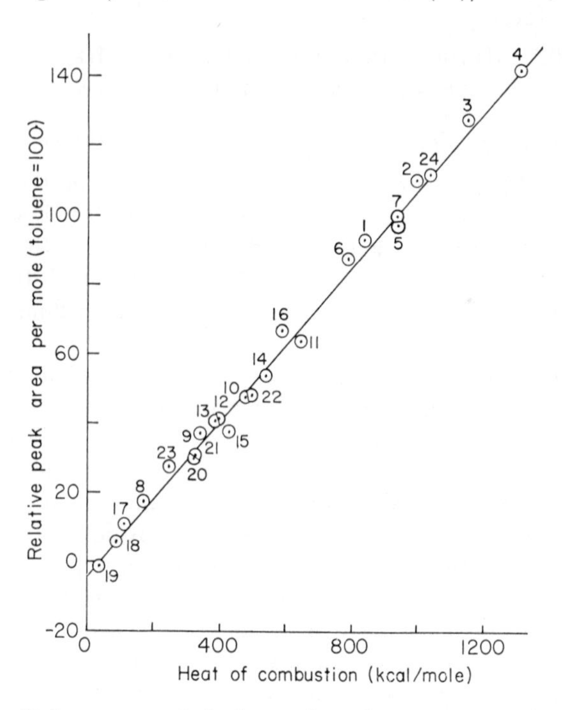

FIG. 10.7. Molar response of a hydrogen flame detector as a function of molar heat of combustion of the vapours. Henderson and Knox (*28*). 1–4, *n*-pentane-*n*-octane; 5, cyclohexane; 6, benzene; 7, toluene; 8–11, methyl-*n*-butyl alcohols; 12, ethyl formate; 13, methyl acetate; 14, ethyl acetate; 15, acetone; 16, methyl ethyl ketone; 17, methylene chloride; 18, chloroform; 19, carbon tetrachloride; 20, ethyl chloride; 21, ethyl bromide; 22, isopropyl bromide; 23, carbon disulphide; 24, triethylamine.

sensitivity as a function of molar heat of combustion. It is seen that the points for a wide range of substances of widely differing chemical classes all lie on a single straight line.

Non-combustible or materials combustible only with difficulty give irregular or small responses in the hydrogen flame detector. Thus, water gives a slight indefinite response (*27*), permanent gases and carbon dioxide give negative responses. Large concentrations of halogenated compounds frequently extinguish the flame. Their action in this respect is the same as their function in fire extinguishers.

Of all reasonably sensitive detectors, the hydrogen flame detector is probably the cheapest, and the easiest to construct and operate. A design of instrument suitable for use in teaching establishments has been described by Cowan and Sugihara (*31*).

10.5. Methods Involving a Chemical Reaction of Vapours before Detection

(*a*) *Conversion of Vapours to Carbon Dioxide and Water*

In this technique, organic vapours emerging from the column are oxidised to carbon dioxide and water, following which the carbon dioxide and possibly the water are detected and measured rather than the vapour itself. In most practice, this is achieved by placing a small tube of copper oxide heated to about 700°C between the end of the column and the detector (*32–46*).

If nitrogen is used as carrier gas in this technique, the response in a catharometer is poor, since neither CO_2 nor water vapour have large enough molecules to give linear responses. Many of the earlier English users of this technique were restricted to using nitrogen as carrier gas, since in England helium is expensive, and the other common light gas, hydrogen, is obviously inapplicable. Hence, the carbon dioxide was commonly detected by a non-dispersive infrared analyser set to register adsorption at the frequency of a strong adsorption band of carbon dioxide (*32,33,36*). The possibility of incomplete reaction is avoided by Heaton and Wentworth (*41*) in a modification in which they use oxygen as the carrier gas and oxidise the vapours by passing the column effluent into a catalyst heated to about 900°C. The carbon dioxide formed in the reaction can conveniently be detected by other methods, e.g., colorimetry (*34,42*), or coulometry (*35*). Mellor (*37*) has succeeded in getting adequate results using either air or oxygen as carrier gas and a catharometer as detector, especially if the water is removed by including a drying trap immediately beyond the furnace in which oxidation occurs. If this is not done the negative peak given by water subtracts from the positive peak from carbon dioxide. Satisfactory results using nitrogen as carrier gas and catharometer detection have been obtained by Stuve (*39*). Though not apparent from the particular results given by the above authors, it is unlikely that the range of linearity of catharometers for carbon dioxide or carbon dioxide-water mixtures would be very great if nitrogen or oxygen were used as carrier. Norem (*38*), however, has used helium as carrier gas in conjunction with this technique. If helium is used, the theoretical objection to catharometry raised above is removed, but the results indicate that the linearity is still suspect.

(*b*) *Conversion of Vapours to Hydrogen*

A modification of the above technique has been described by Green (*47*). After the organic vapour has been converted to carbon dioxide and water, the effluent passes to a further reactor filled with heated iron powder, in which the water is reduced to hydrogen. Following this, the carbon dioxide is removed by a trap containing soda-lime, following which the effluent is detected by a catharometer. In this way, everything in the organic vapour emerging from the column is removed apart from the hydrogen, which remains. If nitrogen is used as carrier gas, the hydrogen gives a very large response in a catharometer.

(*c*) *Conversion of Vapours to Methane*

Zlatkis and Ridgeway (*48*) describe a technique in which hydrogen is used as the carrier gas, and a short reactor filled with hydroforming catalyst at the end of the column converts any hydrocarbon into methane, and converts any organic compound containing carbon, hydrogen, and oxygen into methane and water.

(*d*) *General Discussion*

Detectors relying on chemical conversion of the column effluent were introduced initially to try to increase the sensitivity of the detector. Thus, by burning organic vapours to carbon dioxide and water, every 12 parts of carbon gives 44 of carbon dioxide, and every 2 parts of hydrogen gives 18 of water, and in detectors which respond mainly to mass, the response for a given mass of vapour is thereby increased. The effect of this increase in sensitivity has been indicated by several authors, though Norem (*38*) has pointed out that the actual gain in sensitivity may in practice be less than that calculated from the accretion of mass to the vapour. Green (*47*) has shown that, using nitrogen as carrier gas, the use of the hydrogen conversion technique causes a sensitivity increase of about eightfold.

Recently, however, the increase in sensitivity given by the use of reactors has become of less importance; their principal virtue arises from the fact that the detector operates upon one compound, e.g., CO_2, H_2, or CH_4, whatever the compound forming the original vapour. Thus, when a detector is used in conjunction with a reactor, the molar calibration coefficients are proportional to the number of atoms producing the species actually detected, e.g., the number of carbon atoms in the case of CO_2 and CH_4 reactors, and the number of hydrogen atoms in the case of the hydrogen conversion reactor. Reference to Chapters 8 and 9 shows that the calibration of current sensitive detectors is one of their weaker features, and their poor performance in this respect may be cured by using a reactor. Further advantages of the use of reactors are that in the analysis of relatively involatile substances at an elevated temperature, the detector does not need to be at or near the column temperature in order to avoid condensation, and gives linear responses with vapours that if detected unchanged would give non-linear responses, e.g., alcohols, acids. A drawback to the use of reactors is that they inevitably increase the volume between the column and the detector in which diffusion and anastomosis can occur, with the result that resolution suffers. The literature contains evidence that this drawback is often serious.

10.6. Sample Injectors

Since most analyses by gas chromatography aim to determine not absolute weights but relative weight proportions of the components of a sample of interest, most sample injectors aim to inject a representative sample of a mixture of interest and not an accurately known weight. In practice, many sample injectors inject an approximately known weight, and there are some systems by which accurately known weights or whole samples may be injected. The sample injector remains one of the least satisfactory items of gas chromatographic equipment; possibly for this reason, many designs for it have been produced.

Sample injectors must satisfy the general conditions that their volume should be small (Section 5.7) and that the temperature of devices designed to handle liquids or solids should be sufficiently high (Section 5.15). Many of the devices described below are fitted with facilities for heating separate from those provided for the column, so that the sample injector may be hotter than the column. Such heaters are referred to as "Flash Heaters."

(a) *Designs Involving Use of Hypodermic Syringes and Their Modifications*

The commonest kind of sample injector consists of a rubber cap attached to a very short side arm in the gas flow immediately before the column. The sample is contained in a hypodermic syringe, and is injected through the cap into the gas stream immediately above the column. In many early apparatuses [e.g., Ray (*49*)], the cap is a "serum cap" of the kind used to seal bottles of serum, etc., used for medical injections. In most later designs, the cap is a compressed rubber of silicone rubber disc. Such a device is currently used on many commercial apparatuses, as it is inexpensive and moderately satisfactory for most applications.

The quantities of liquid required for injection into gas chromatographic apparatus are usually smaller than those used in medicine, and the normal range of hypodermic syringes is unsatisfactory. Calibrated syringes of very small volume in which the plunger consists of a stainless steel wire rather than a glass barrel are available and may be used satisfactorily. The accuracy with which a given volume may be injected is increased by attaching a micrometer screw head to the syringe; the two may be combined by using a syringe with screwed barrel and plunger (*50*). A drawback of the use of micrometer screws for the delivery of samples is that the time taken to turn the screw and complete the injection may be several seconds, which may be sufficient to contribute to peak broadening. Sweeting, therefore, has modified a commercial micro-syringe with micrometer screw head so that an accurately measured sample can be delivered rapidly without the need to turn the screw (*51*).

A common drawback of the use of syringes with most gas chromatographic apparatuses is that, as pressure inside the sample injector is greater than atmospheric, the sample must be injected against a positive pressure. With syringes of ordinary design, this causes the sample to be forced between barrel and plunger, and the quantity of sample actually injected is less than the amount registered on the micrometer. If the syringe is well made, if the injection is done expertly and rapidly, and if the amount injected is relatively large, the error may be small, but, in other circumstances, the error may be and frequently is large. Syringes have been manufactured using Teflon plungers or gaskets (*50,52*) which are said not to leak at the pressures normally encountered in gas chromatography. The problem may also be overcome by interrupting the carrier gas flow, and relieving the pressure in the sample injector during injection (*50*). This, however, leads to errors in the measurement of retention volumes, since the flow rate does not attain a constant value instantaneously after the flow is resumed. Samsel and Aldrich (*53*) overcome the problem of back-pressure by a design of sample injector in which the compressed rubber disc closes not a T-junction in the gas stream, but a separate cavity which may be connected to or disconnected from the gas stream by an external control. The sample is injected into the cavity while this is shut off from the gas stream, after which the hypodermic needle is withdrawn, and the control operated so as to connect the cavity with the gas stream. The device is constructed from machined stainless steel and other materials.

Samples for analysis frequently contain components that are either completely non-volatile or are virtually non-volatile at the temperature of operation, and about which no information is required. In this case, the sample injector should be arranged so that the non-volatiles are not carried on to the column, where they may contaminate it. This may be achieved, by a small auxiliary cavity or tube in the gas stream between sample injector and column filled with glass wool or other inert material (*54–56*).

(*b*) *Methods Involving Pipets*

Tenney and Harris (*57*) have described a form of sample injector in which the sample is introduced in a pipet and this has had considerable success. The apparatus is shown diagrammatically in Fig. 10.8. Carrier

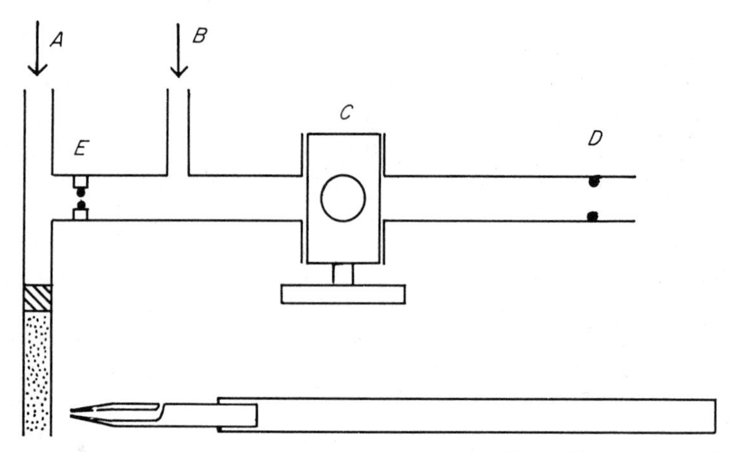

FIG. 10.8. Sample injector according to Tenney and Harris. Redrawn from Tenney and Harris (*57*).

gas flows from the supply to the column through *A*. A supply of carrier gas at slightly higher pressure is available at *B*. In steady operation, the wide-bore stopcock *C* is closed. The pipet consists of a small glass cylinder tapering more or less conically at one end; it contains a cavity which is open at the apex of the cone and at a point in the side of the cylinder. The pipet is held in a long cylindrical holder of slightly larger diameter. The pipet is filled by capillarity when the end is dipped in the liquid to be analysed. To introduce this sample, the pipet is inserted through *D*, which contains a rubber O-ring, the internal diameter of which is larger than that of the pipet but slightly smaller than that of its handle, so that the handle slides through the O-ring making a gas-tight seal with it. Stopcock *C* is opened, and the pipet is pushed through it till the conical end penetrates and beds down on a second O-ring *E*. The auxiliary gas flow *B* forces the sample into *A*, after which the pipet may be withdrawn through *D* until it is outside *C*; *C* may then be closed, and finally the pipet may be withdrawn.

Another simpler device related to the above and designed for use when the inlet pressure to the column is less than atmospheric has been described by Stanford (*58*). Scott (*59*) describes a device by which a small pipet containing the sample may be introduced into a very high pressure in a manner resembling the techniques used for sealed ampoules described in Subsection (c).

(c) *Methods Involving Sealed Ampoules*

Several designs of sample injector have been described in which the sample is sealed into some kind of frangible ampoule which is then inserted into the carrier gas stream, preferably without disturbing the gas flow, after which it is broken by some external control (*60–65*). As an example, Fig. 10.9 shows the device of Bowman and Karmen (*65*). The piston slides in

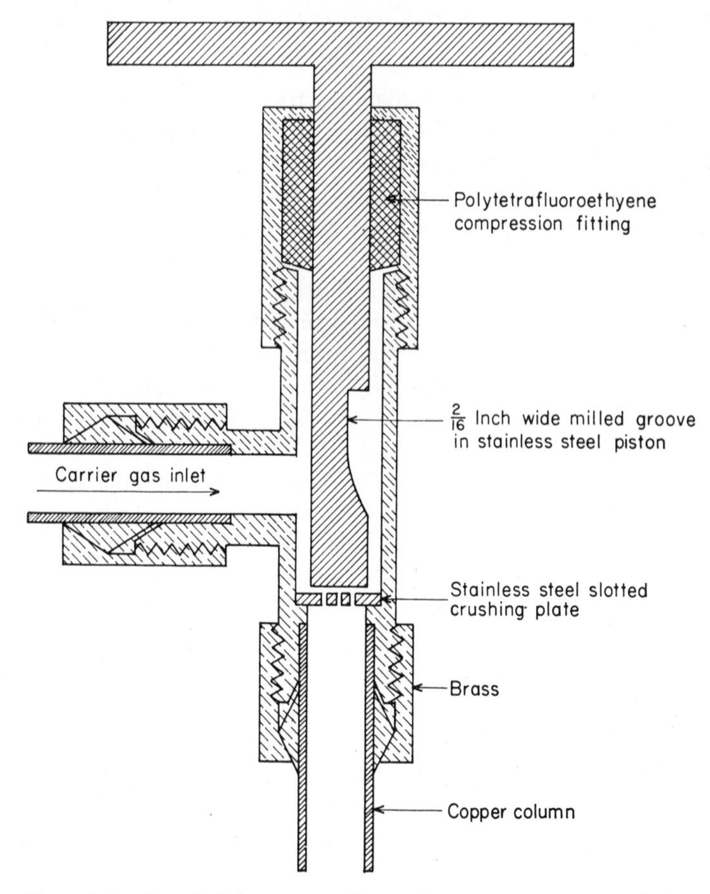

FIG. 10.9. Sample injector according to Bowman and Karmen (*65*).

the pressure-tight seal. With the piston pulled up, a sealed glass capillary containing the sample is placed in the slot. The piston is then pushed down, taking the capillary through the seal. Since the diameter of the tube inside the seal is relatively large, the capillary falls out on to the metal grid. The piston is then lifted up, and pushed down on to the capillary, which is thereby crushed.

An adaptation of the above technique used by Dubsky and Janak (*66*) for introducing solid samples at a high temperature is to seal the sample in capillary of Wood's metal, and by means of an ingenious device to introduce the capillary into a small heated saddle in the carrier gas stream. The metal melts, and the sample volatilises. The saddle is made sufficiently large to contain the metal from several capillaries, and thus the device need not be cleaned after every use.

(*d*) *Sample Injection into Capillary Columns*

The methods hitherto described fail or are very inaccurate for very small samples, and none can handle quantities small enough for a capillary column. Sample injectors for capillary columns, therefore, consist of one or other of the devices described above, followed by a "stream splitter," in which the great majority of the sample is vented and goes to waste, and a small proportion goes to the capillary column (*67–69*). The stream splitter consists essentially of a T-piece. One arm carries incoming carrier gas plus the vapourised sample. The other two arms lead to the atmosphere, one through the capillary column, and the other through an adjustable choke. The choke and the capillary column form two resistances to flow of gas, which is distributed between them. By adjusting the choke, the distribution of flow can be adjusted. In normal practice, the adjustment is such that 99–99.9% of the gas is vented, and 1–0.1% passes through the column.

It has been recognised that it is very easy to get poor quantitative analyses using capillary columns even with a detector of proven linearity and reliable calibration, and it is probable that the most difficult item in the apparatus is the sample injector (*70*). Halasz (*71*), however, has demonstrated that accurate quantitative analysis is possible with apparatuses using capillary columns. It is possible that the geometry of the stream splitter is relevant, and that some geometries may lead to some kind of fractionation in the portion of the sample passing into the column.

(*e*) *Gas Sampling Valves*

The basis for most schemes for the injection of gases or samples of gases into chromatographic apparatuses is the circuit shown in Fig. 10.10. A sample cavity may be filled from the gas to be analysed, after which it may be isolated, and then swept into the column. Many apparatuses have been described in which this scheme or some obvious variant is used. Glass or metal stopcocks may be used, or the system of stopcocks may be made up into a "flat face valve," i.e., a valve in which flat discs of either metal or plastic carrying holes and cavities and sprung together are caused to rotate axially relative to one another. The tubes and cavities are arranged to

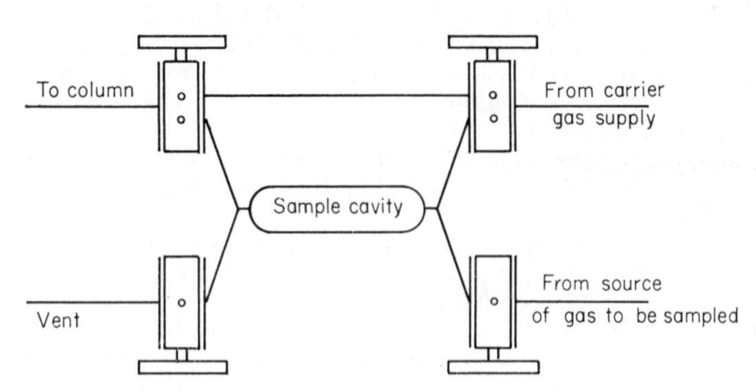

FIG. 10.10. Basic circuit for gas-sampling valves for gas chromatographic apparatuses.

provide sample cavities of suitable volume and the correct switching of gas streams when the discs are turned (*72,73*). Pratt and Purnell (*74*) describe a system in which there are two concentric cylinders, the outside diameter of the inner one being smaller than the inside diameter of the larger. The smaller cylinder is fitted with suitably arranged O-rings which divide the annular space between the cylinders into cavities; the cavities are fed by suitably bored holes in the cylinders.

REFERENCES

1. Weissberger, A., ed., "Technique of Organic Chemistry," Vol. 1 of "Physical Methods of Organic Chemistry," 2nd ed., Sections in Part 1. Interscience, 1949; Reilly, J., and Rae, W. N., "Physico-Chemical Methods." Methuen, London, 1943, 1948.
2. Janak, J., *Chem. Listy* **47**, 464, 817, 828, 837, 1184, 1348 (1953); *Collection Czech. Chem. Communs.* **18**, 798 (1953), **19**, 684, 917 (1954).
2a. Janak, J., *in* "Vapor Phase Chromatography," Proceedings of the First Symposium, London, May, 1956 (D. H. Desty, ed.), p. 235. Academic Press, New York, 1957.
3. Rouit, C., *in* "Vapour Phase Chromatography," Proceedings of the First Symposium, London, May, 1956 (D. H. Desty, ed.), p. 291. Academic Press, New York, 1957.
4. Ray, N. H., *Analyst* **80**, 853 (1955).
5. "Handbook of Chemistry and Physics," Chemical Rubber Publ. Co., Cleveland, Ohio, published annually.
6. van der Craats, F., *Anal. Chim. Acta* **14**, 136 (1956).
7. Leibnitz, E., Hrapia, H., and Konnecke, H. G., *Brennstoff-Chem.* **38**, 14 (1957).

8. Janak, J., and Tesarik, K., *Chem. Listy* **51,** 2048 (1957); *Z. anal. Chem.* **164,** 62 (1958).
9. Sevenster, P. G., *S. African Ind. Chemist* **12,** 75 (1958).
10. Janak, J., and Tesarik, K., *Collection Czech. Chem. Communs.* **24,** 536 (1959).
11. Velut, M., and Jourda, J., *Rev. inst. franç. pétrole et Ann. combustibles liquides* **13,** 1635 (1958).
12. Martin, A. J. P., and James, A. T., *Biochem. J.* **63,** 138 (1956).
13. Whytlaw-Gray, R., *Quart. Revs.* (*London*) **4,** 153 (1950).
14. Munday, C. W., and Primavesi, G. R., *in* "Vapour Phase Chromatography," Proceedings of the First Symposium, London, May, 1956 (D. H. Desty, ed.), p. 146. Academic Press, New York, 1957.
15. Hawkes, J. C., *in* "Vapour Phase Chromatography," Proceedings of the First Symposium, London, May, 1956 (D. H. Desty, ed.), p. 266. Academic Press, New York, 1957.
16. Liberti, A., Conti, L., and Crescenzi, V., *Nature* **178,** 1067 (1956).
17. Liberti, A., Conti, L., and Crescenzi, V., *Atti. accad. natl. Lincei. Rend., Classe sci. fis. mat. e nat.* **20,** 623 (1956).
18. Ellis, J. F., Forrest, C. W., and Allen, P. L., *Anal. Chim. Acta* **22,** 27 (1960).
19. Johnson, E. A., Childs, D. G., and Beaven, C. H., *J. Chromatog.* **4,** 429 (1960).
20. Phillips, C. S. G., and Timms, P. L., *J. Chromatog.* **5,** 131 (1961).
21. Griffiths, J. H., and Phillips, C. S. G., *J. Chem. Soc.* p. 3446 (1954).
22. Griffiths, J. H., James, D. J., and Phillips, C. S. G., *Analyst* **77,** 897 (1952).
23. Phillips, G., *J. Sci. Inst.* **28,** 342 (1951).
24. Scott, R. P. W., *Nature* **176,** 793 (1955).
25. Scott, R. P. W., *in* "Vapour Phase Chromatography," Proceedings of the First Symposium, London, May, 1956 (D. H. Desty, ed.), p. 131. Academic Press, New York, 1957.
26. Scott, R. P. W., Benzol Producers Ltd., Watford, England, Research Paper 4–1957.
27. Wirth, M. M., *in* "Vapour Phase Chromatography," Proceedings of the First Symposium, London, May, 1956 (D. H. Desty, ed.), p. 154. Academic Press, New York, 1957.
28. Henderson, J. I., and Knox, J. H., *J. Chem. Soc.* p. 2299 (1956).
29. Primavesi, G. R., Oldham, G. F., and Thompson, R. J., *in* "Gas Chromatography 1958," Proceedings of the Second Symposium, Amsterdam, May, 1958 (D. H. Desty, ed.), p. 156. Academic Press, New York, 1958.
30. Baddiel, C. B., and Cullis, C. F., *Chem. & Ind.* (*London*) p. 1154 (1960).
31. Cowan, P. J., and Sugihara, J. M., *J. Chem. Educ.* **36,** 246 (1959).
32. Martin, A. E., British patent 790, 217 (1958).
33. Martin, A. E., and Smart, J., *Nature* **175,** 422 (1955).
34. Juranek, J., *Chem. Listy* **51,** 2280 (1957).
35. Liberti, A., *Anal. Chim. Acta* **17,** 247 (1957); Liberti, A., and Cartoni, G. P., *Atti. accad. Lincei. Rend., Classe sci. fis. mat. e nat.* **20,** 787 (1956); *in* "Gas Chromatography 1958," Proceedings of the Second Symposium, Amsterdam, May, 1958 (D. H. Desty, ed.), p. 321. Academic Press, New York, 1958; Liberti, A., Cartoni, G. P., and Pallotta, U., *Latte* **30,** 581 (1956); Liberti, A., and Cartoni, G. P., *Chim. e ind.* (*Milan*) **39,** 821 (1957).
36. Liberti, A., Costa, G., and Pauluzzi, E., *Chim. e ind.* (*Milan*) **38,** 674 (1955).
37. Mellor, N., *in* "Vapour Phase Chromatography," Proceedings of the First Symposium, London, May, 1956 (D. H. Desty, ed.), p. 63. Academic Press, New York, 1957.

38. Norem, S. D., *in* "Gas Chromatography," I.S.A. Symposium, 1957 (V. J. Coates, H. J. Noebels, and I. S. Fagerson, eds.), p. 191. Academic Press, New York, 1958.
39. Stuve, W., *in* "Gas Chromatography 1958," Proceedings of the Second Symposium, Amsterdam, May, 1958 (D. H. Desty, ed.), p. 178. Academic Press, New York, 1958.
40. Franc, J., and Wurst, M., presented at the 3*rd Conf. on Anal. Chem., Prague, Sept. 1959.*
41. Heaton, W. B., and Wentworth, J. T., *Anal. Chem.* **31,** 349 (1959).
42. Juranek, J., *Collection Czech. Chem. Communs.* **24,** 135 (1959).
43. Nel, W., Mortimer, J., and Pretorius, V., *S. African Ind. Chemist* **13,** 68 (1959).
44. Franc, J., and Wurst, M., *Collection Czech. Chem. Communs.* **25,** 701 (1960).
45. Simmons, M. C., Taylor, L. M., and Nager, M., *Anal. Chem.* **32,** 731 (1960).
46. Hunter, I. R., Ortegren, V. H., and Pence, J. W., *Anal. Chem.* **32,** 682 (1960).
47. Green, G. E., *Nature* **180,** 295 (1957).
48. Zlatkis, A., and Ridgeway, J. A., *Nature* **182,** 130 (1958).
49. Ray, N. H., *J. Appl. Chem.* **4,** 82 (1954).
50. Langer, S. H., and Pantages, P., *Anal. Chem.* **30,** 1889 (1958).
51. Sweeting, J. W., *Chem. & Ind.* (*London*) p. 1150 (1959).
52. Anonymous, *Anal. Chem.* **31** (12), 105A (1959).
53. Samsel, E. P., and Aldrich, J. C., *Anal. Chem.* **31,** 1288 (1959).
54. Brealey, L., Elvidge, D. A., and Proctor, K. A., *Analyst* **84,** 221 (1959).
55. Porter, R. S., and Johnson, J. F., *Anal. Chem.* **31,** 866 (1959).
56. Ciepelinski, E. W., and Ettre, L. S., *J. Chromatog.* **4,** 169 (1960).
57. Tenney, H. M., and Harris, R. J., *Anal. Chem.* **29,** 317 (1957).
58. Stanford, F. G., *Analyst* **84,** 321 (1959).
59. Scott, R. P. W., *in* "Gas Chromatography 1958," Proceedings of the Second Symposium, Amsterdam (D. H. Desty, ed.), p. 189. Academic Press, New York, 1958.
60. McReadie, S. W. S., and Williams, A. F., *J. Appl. Chem.* **7,** 47 (1957).
61. Sorensen, I., and Soltoft, P., *Acta Chem. Scand.* **12,** 814 (1958).
62. Franc, J., and Jokl, J., *Collection Czech. Chem. Communs.* **24,** 144 (1959).
63. Joklik, J., and Bazant, V., *Chem. Listy* **53,** 277 (1959).
64. Singliar, M., and Brida, J., *Chem. průmysl* **8,** 588 (1958).
65. Bowman, R. L., and Karmen, A., *Nature* **182,** 1233 (1958).
66. Dubsky, H. E., and Janak, J., *J. Chromatog.* **4,** 1 (1960).
67. Lipsky, S. R., Landowne, R. A., and Lovelock, J. E., *Anal. Chem.* **31,** 852 (1959).
68. Desty, D. H., Goldup, A., and Whyman, B. H. F., *J. Inst. Petrol.* **45,** 287 (1959).
69. Condon, R. D., *Anal. Chem.* **31,** 1717 (1959).
70. Discussion, Informal Symposium of the Gas Chromatography Discussion Group, London, April, 1960.
71. Halasz, I., Informal Symposium of the Gas Chromatography Discussion Group, London, April, 1960.
72. Hausdorff, H. H., *in* "Vapour Phase Chromatography," Proceedings of the First Symposium, London, May, 1956 (D. H. Desty, ed.), p. 377. Academic Press, New York, 1957.
73. Hill, D. W., and Hook, J. R., *J. Sci. Instr.* **37,** 253 (1960).
74. Pratt, G. L., and Purnell, J. H., *Anal. Chem.* **32,** 1213 (1960).

Chapter 11

Applications of Gas Chromatography

11.1. Permanent Gases and Methane

Permanent gases are almost invariably analysed on adsorbents, of which charcoal, molecular sieves, silica gel, and alumina are the commonest, given in order of importance and application. It is possible to use partition columns at low temperatures, and occasionally this may be desirable with some inorganic gases, see Section 11.12, but published data generally refers to the adsorbents mentioned.

It should be emphasised that the retaining power of adsorbents is not reproducible in ordinary practice, and depends sharply on pre-treatment and on the amount of material such as water already adsorbed; it is not uncommon for retention volumes to increase by a factor of 10 or more on removal of water from charcoal or silica gel, and thus it is impossible to quote reproducible retention data. Greene and Roy (*1*)* have pointed out that adsorbed carrier gas can also affect retention volumes (Section 3.11), so that in the survey given below, note should be taken of the carrier gas used, lest changing the carrier gas changes relative retention volumes.

(*a*) *Inert Gases*

Mixtures of all the inert gases have been separated by Janak (*2*) and by Greene (*3*). Janak has listed the relative retention volumes given in Table 11.1, column (a), for the gases on charcoal at 20°C, from which it is apparent that helium and neon do not separate, but the other gases separate easily, though the retention of xenon is likely to be long. Oxygen and nitrogen do not separate from argon. Greene has analysed the rare gases in mixtures also containing oxygen, nitrogen, and methane on three columns as specified in Table 11.1, columns (b), (c), and (d). The retention volumes show that helium and neon, which are not resolved on charcoal at 20°C,

* *Note:* References are numbered beginning with (*1*) in each section, and are grouped together according to sections at the end of the chapter.

are easily resolved at 77°K (−196°C, i.e., liquid nitrogen bath). Argon, krypton, and xenon are easily resolved at room temperature on silica gel, but if methane is present, it interferes with the krypton. In the latter case, the separation of argon, krypton, methane, and xenon may be achieved on a molecular sieve column (*4*) at room temperature. With this, the xenon is retained excessively long, so, after the other three gases are eluted, it may be removed by heating the column to 100°C. Krypton, nitrogen, and

TABLE 11.1

SEPARATION OF INERT GASES[a]

Gas	Retention volumes			
	(a)[b]	(b)[c]	(c)[d]	(d)[e]
Helium	1	180		
Neon	1	360		
Argon	2.1		150	160
Krypton	6.4		240	540
Methane			240	660
Xenon	38		840	960[f]

[a] See references *2* and *3*.
[b] (a) Charcoal at 20°C, hydrogen carrier; relative to helium and neon.
[c] (b) Charcoal at −196°C, hydrogen carrier. *Note.* For columns (b), (c), and (d), 10-foot × ¾-inch columns of 20 to 40 mesh material, flow rate 60 ml/minute.
[d] (c) Silica gel at 23°C, oxygen carrier.
[e] (d) Molecular sieve at 23°C, oxygen carrier.
[f] Accelerated by heating to 100 after CH_4.

methane may be separated at room temperature with a mixture of one part of charcoal and 10 parts of molecular sieve 5A (*5*). It is apparent that relative retentions are greater on molecular sieve than on charcoal or silica gel.

Hydrogen cannot be separated from helium and neon on charcoal at room temperature (*2*), but it may be with molecular sieve 5A (*5*). Using molecular sieve, helium and neon may be separated at −78°C (*5*).

The separation of krypton and xenon has been studied separately by Gluekauf and Kitt (*6*) and by Koch and Grandy (*7,8*), in each case using convenient radioactive isotopes of the gases for following the separation. Gluekauf has studied in detail the case of the separation of krypton and xenon which are sufficiently radioactive to heat the column in the course of their elution (*9,10*).

(b) *Atmospheric Gases* O, N, *and* Ar

Oxygen and nitrogen are most easily separated on molecular sieve 5A (*3,4,11–14*), on which oxygen comes through with about half the retention volume of nitrogen. The separation can be conveniently done in a few minutes using hydrogen or helium as carrier gas at a column temperature of about 100°C (*12,13*) with columns of about 1 metre or longer. With less active adsorbent, it can also be done at room temperature. These gases can also be separated on other adsorbents, but the retention ratio is smaller; thus on charcoal at 20°C the retention ratio is 1.18 (*15*), so that a longer column is required. Alumina and silica gel can also be used for the O/N separation, but their retention of permanent gases is rather small, so that the value of k is small and separations are poor on that account; they are not recommended unless there is some other good reason for using them.

In all cases that oxygen and nitrogen are appreciably retained, e.g., on molecular sieves up to about 100°C or on charcoal, hydrogen is easily separated, for it is scarcely retained by any adsorbent.

Hydrogen, oxygen, and nitrogen are all easily separated from the common air contaminants, carbon monoxide, carbon dioxide, and methane, all of which come through considerably later [see Subsection (c)]. Greene and Pust (*14*) have separated hydrogen, air, carbon monoxide, methane, carbon dioxide, etc., on silica gel and alumina; Patton, Lewis, and Kaye

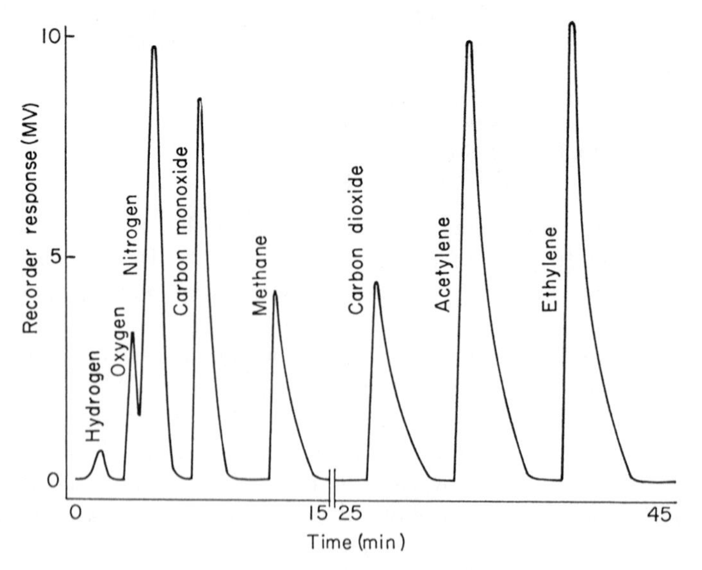

Fig. 11.1. Separation of gases on a 9-foot charcoal column programmed from room temperature to 170°C. Greene, Moberg, and Wilson (*17*).

(*16*) have done the same separation on a charcoal column which also resolves the oxygen and nitrogen of the air. Greene, Moberg, and Wilson (*17*) have separated H_2, O_2, N_2, CO, CH_4, and CO_2, in that order, on continuously heated charcoal as shown in Fig. 11.1.

Argon has a similar retention to oxygen on all adsorbents, and its separation from oxygen is relatively difficult. Many authors studying the separation of air gases report argon and oxygen as coming through together. Greene (*11*) has analysed argon in a mixture of argon, nitrogen, and oxygen only by difference. Szonntag and Stewart (*18*) analyse Ar and O_2 in two runs, using argon as carrier in one run, and oxygen as carrier in the other. Argon and oxygen can, however, be separated. Vizard and Wynne (*19*) have used a 10-metre column of molecular sieve 5A pre-heated in an oven at 400°C, with hydrogen as a carrier gas at room temperature. The chromatogram is shown in Fig. 11.2. Lord and Horn (*20*) have performed

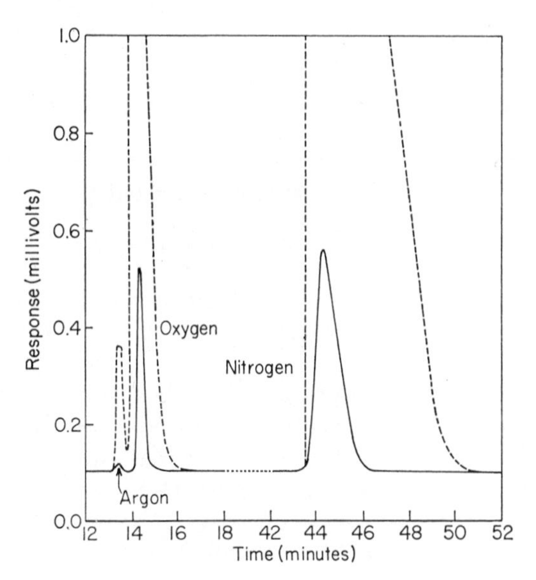

FIG. 11.2. Separation of argon, oxygen, and nitrogen on a 10-metre column of molecular sieve 5A operated at room temperature. Vizard and Wynne (*19*); (a) 9.831 ml of sample (—), (b) 0.768 ml of sample (- - -).

the same analysis on a 6-foot column of the same material used in two runs; a run at room temperature serves to separate O_2 and Ar from N_2, after which a run −72°C serves to separate O_2 from Ar, the nitrogen not being eluted. This procedure is quicker. A U.S. patent (*21*) describes the use of molecular sieve 4A for the separation of argon and oxygen in commercial quantities.

(c) Carbon Monoxide and Carbon Dioxide from Other Gases

Carbon monoxide is separable from oxygen, nitrogen, and methane with ease either on a molecular sieve 5A (*13,22*) at about 100°C or on charcoal at room temperature (*15,16,23–27*). In either case, a length of about 1 metre is adequate. Carbon monoxide and methane may be separated easily from the air gases on silica gel or alumina (*14*), but, as described above, the air gases themselves do not separate easily (*22*). Approximate relative retention data for the four gases are given in Table 11.2; note the

TABLE 11.2

SEPARATION OF CARBON MONOXIDE AND METHANE FROM AIR GASES

Substance	Relative retention times		
	(a)[a]	(b)[b]	(c)[c]
Oxygen	0.85	3.5	0.4
Nitrogen	1.0	4.8	1.0
Carbon monoxide	1.6	13.2	3.4
Methane	5	—	1.8

[a] (a) 25-foot charcoal column at room temperature (*15*).
[b] (b) 6-foot silica gel column at −78°C (*28*).
[c] (c) 16-foot molecular sieve 5A column at 100°C (*13*).

remarkable inversion of elution order on molecular sieve 5A for carbon monoxide and methane. Alumina gives the same elution order as charcoal and silica gel (*14*).

Analyses of mixtures containing carbon dioxide are restricted by the fact that carbon dioxide is almost irreversibly adsorbed on molecular sieve 5A and on alumina. Graven (*26*), however, has succeeded in analysing a mixture of O_2, N_2, CO, C_2H_6, N_2O, and CO_2 in the order given with a 10-foot column of 40–60 mesh molecular sieve 5A temperature-programmed from room temperature to 400°C in 25 minutes. If the air gases need not be resolved, mixtures containing these together with CO, CH_4, CO_2, and hydrocarbons may be analysed on silica gel (*14*). If, in addition, the air gases are to be resolved, a charcoal column of at least 2 metres may be used, but the elution time of carbon dioxide is long. Greene, Moberg and Wilson (*17*) use a 9-foot charcoal column for the separation of H_2, O_2, N_2, CO, CH_4, and CO_2, and accelerate the analysis by temperature programming. The details of the analysis and chromatogram are shown in Fig. 11.1. Brenner and Ciepelinski (*29*) analyse mixtures containing O_2, N_2, and CO_2 by putting a column of molecular sieve 5A and a column of silica gel in parallel. The molecular sieve 5A separates the oxygen and nitrogen satisfactorily, but irreversibly retains the carbon dioxide; the silica gel passes the oxygen and nitrogen without retention or separation, but separates the carbon dioxide so as to give a peak. The result is that the detector, recording both streams of gas, first records unseparated oxygen and nitrogen, followed by separate oxygen and nitrogen peaks from one column, and the carbon dioxide peak from the other. By making independent adjustments of the relative permeabilities and masses of the columns, the relative heights and relative positions of the carbon dioxide and the other two peaks may be altered at will. A sample chromatogram made in this manner of expired air is shown in Fig. 11.3.

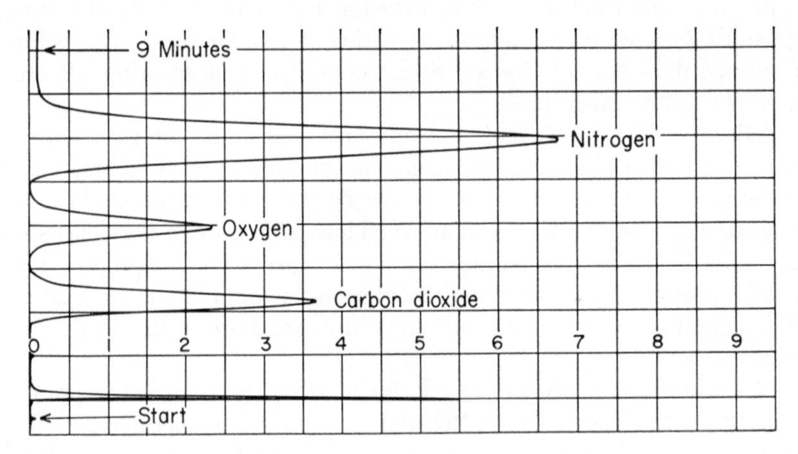

Fig. 11.3. Chromatogram of expired air made on parallel columns of molecular sieve 5A and silica gel, using Perkin-Elmer 154C vapour fractometer. Brenner and Ciepelinski (*29*).

(*d*) *Oxides of Nitrogen*

Szulczewski and Higuchi (*28*) have separated N_2, O_2, NO, CO, N_2O, and CO_2 on 40–60 mesh silica gel. At room temperature, the first four gases appear together, followed by N_2O and CO_2, which are well separated on a 6-foot column. At −78°C, the first four gases are resolved in the order given, but the last two are retained unduly long. All six gases may be satisfactorily resolved by running the chromatogram at −78°C until CO is through, and by warming the column to room temperature for the last two, which separate in the order given above. Similar results are obtained by Marvillet and Tranchant (*30*), who show that if resolution of NO and CO is not required the whole analysis may be run at an intermediate temperature, e.g., −20°C, or 0°C. In addition, the separation of N_2O and CO_2 on molecular sieve 5A at or near 300°C has been reported by Graven (*26*).

Smith, Swinehart, and Lesnini (*31*) describe a technique using a 10-foot silica gel column containing an 8-inch section of powdered iodine pentoxide followed by a $\frac{1}{2}$-inch section of silver powder in the middle. When a mixture containing CO or NO is passed through the column at room temperature, the gases are scarcely retained. They reach the central section at the same time as the air gases, but, unlike the air gases, they react, CO forming CO_2, and NO forming NO_2, which is removed by the silver. Thus, CO is converted to CO_2, which is eluted slowly in the second half of the column and comes through as a separate peak, and NO may be determined by difference.

Schwenk and Hachenberg (*32*) make use of the complex formed between NO and $FeSO_4$ aq. for the specific retention of NO. On a 10-metre column of saturated $FeSO_4$ solution on Sterchamol, NO appears after all other gases as a symmetrical peak.

Adlard and Hill (*33*) find that mixtures containing air gases, nitrous oxide, and carbon dioxide, such as are encountered in respired anaesthetic mixtures, can be analysed more rapidly on polar partition columns than on adsorbents such as described above. Thus, a mixture of these gases can be resolved (without resolution of the air gases) on a 24-foot column of 28% propylene carbonate on firebrick in $2\frac{1}{2}$ minutes, or on a 20-foot 20% dimethyl sulfoxide column in 1 minute, both columns at room temperature.

NO_2 cannot be analysed as such, for it is too reactive; in the presence of moisture it reacts to give NO and nitric acid; furthermore, if nitric oxide is present, it reacts reversibly to form N_2O_3 which causes very broad peaks (*34*). It may be analysed satisfactorily by the method of Greene and Pust (*35*), in which it is caused to react to completion with water by the reaction:

$$6NO_2 + 3H_2O \rightarrow 4HNO_3 + 2NO + H_2O,$$

after which the nitric oxide is passed through a molecular sieve 5A column. The technique of Greene and Pust is obviously inapplicable if oxygen is also present. In such a case, Smith, Nakayama, and Clarke (*36*) remove NO_2 in a cold trap, and analyse the uncondensed fraction which contains the oxygen. The NO_2 is then separately determined by chromatographing it by Greene and Pust's technique in an inert carrier gas.

(e) *Isotopes and Isomers of Hydrogen*

Molecular hydrogen can occur as H_2, D_2, T_2, HD, HT, DT, o-H_2, p-H_2, o-D_2, or p-D_2, where D stands for ^2H and T stands for ^3H. The separation of hydrogen isotopes is generally easy, for their physical properties differ considerably.

H_2, HD, and D_2 can be easily separated at $-196°C$ on either molecular sieve 5A (*37–39*), or chromia-alumina catalyst material (*40*). Ohkoshi *et al.* (*37–39*) use an 80-cm column of molecular sieve 5A with hydrogen as carrier gas, so that hydrogen is not detected, but peaks are produced for the other two isotopes, the chromatogram taking about 8 minutes. Smith and Hunt (*40*) use a 12-foot column of chromia-alumina, with neon as carrier gas, so that three peaks are obtained. With freshly activated column material, the separations are good, but the chromatogram is slow. It may be accelerated by treating the column with water. In all the cases the order of elution is the order of volatility, with H_2 first and D_2 last.

Gant and Yang (*41*) have analysed mixtures of H_2, HT, and T_2 on a 6.1-metre molecular sieve column operating at $-160°C$, using helium as carrier gas.

In analyses for hydrogen isotopes, particularly for analysis of traces of D and T in H, or H and T in D, it is convenient to use the major component as carrier gas, so that peaks are obtained only from minor components. In such a case, accurate quantitative analyses require the introduction of reproducible samples, but with permanent gases this is relatively easy. Riedel and Uhlmann (*42*), and Arnett (*43*) describe a special case of this technique; the deuterium content of a substance (not necessarily volatile) is converted to HD, e.g., by means of calcium hydride, and the HD is estimated in a gas-chromatography apparatus, using hydrogen as carrier gas. In this case, the column is not really necessary, for HD is the only species measured. A column, however, serves to retain any other impurities which may be present in the gas.

When ordinary adsorbents are used for hydrogen isotope analyses, no equilibration occurs between mixed and simple molecular species, e.g., between H_2, HD, and D_2. On any substrate which adsorbs atoms rather than molecules, however, this equilibration occurs, and the result is that, if such a substrate is used as a column, HD is changed to H_2 and D_2 in the course of the analysis. Gluekauf and Kitt (*44*) and Thomas and Smith (*45*) have used this fact for the preparation of pure deuterium. The column material is palladium, which adsorbs hydrogen readily, and deuterium rather less readily. Since the adsorption occurs as atoms, the Law of Mass Action implies that the adsorption isotherm has the form:

$$q \propto \sqrt{c},$$

so that the chromatography is not linear; thus frontal and displacement techniques were used. With a column of 44×0.8 cm of a mixture of Pd black and purified asbestos operating at temperatures between 0° and 100°C, with the column initially filled with helium, using a sample of mixed H_2-HD-D_2, and with pure hydrogen as the displacer, Gluekauf and Kitt produced a zone of pure deuterium. Similar experiments have been made by Thomas and Smith (*45*), using a 43-foot column containing 7 g of palladium suspended on quartz. Thomas and Smith also partially separated D_2 and H_2 by elution on this column using helium as carrier gas. Unlike the separation on adsorbents, the deuterium appears first. For practical analysis, palladium is inferior to adsorbents.

Ortho- and para-hydrogen may easily be separated on columns of activated alumina at −196°C pre-treated in nitrogen at 200°C (*46,47*), or molecular sieve at −160°C (*41*), or carbon (*48*). In all cases, the *p*-form appears before the *o*-form. Ortho- and para-deuterium are not so easily separated. Moore and Ward (*46*) obtain a partial separation, with *o*-appearing first, but van Hook and Emmett (*47*) fail to get any separation. On alumina, HD has a very similar retention to *o*-H_2 (*46*), and in mixtures the two may not be separable (*47*). A complete analysis of a mixture containing *p*-H_2, *o*-H_2, HD, and D_2 on alumina can be obtained in spite of overlap of HD/*o*-H_2 if the *o*-/*p*-ratio is known independently. Furuyama and Kwan (*49*) obtain a complete analysis of the four gases by using two columns in series, the first of pure alumina, and the second of alumina mixed with ferric oxide. The alumina separates the mixture into three zones, one of *p*-H_2, one of mixed *o*-H_2 and HD, and one of D_2. When the *o*-H_2 enters the second column, the ferric oxide catalyses its equilibration, so that *p*-H_2 is formed, which at once moves faster through the column, and the peak due to the original *o*-H_2, now converted to *p*-H_2, is eluted before the HD. It is noteworthy that no sign of *o*-/*p*- separation either of H_2 or D_2 was reported on molecular sieve (*38*), so it may be presumed that a complete analysis of *o*-H_2, *p*-H_2, HD, *o*-D_2, and *p*-D_2 may also be obtained by combining results from chromatograms taken on alumina and on molecular sieve 5A. Approximate relative retention data on alumina are given in Table 11.3. On alumina or molecular sieve at low temperatures,

TABLE 11.3

RELATIVE RETENTION TIMES OF SOME HYDROGEN ISOTOPES ON ALUMINA[a]

Substance	Relative retention
p-Hydrogen	1.0
o-Hydrogen	1.2
o-Deuterium	1.7
p-Deuterium	1.8

[a] See reference *46*.

there is no evidence of equilibration of *o*-/*p*- forms, but Erb (*48*) finds that this may be a source of error when using charcoal columns.

(f) Summary

Part of the rather detailed information given in this section is summarised in Table 11.4.

TABLE 11.4

A ROUGH GUIDE TO THE SEPARATION OF COMMON GASES[a]

				Ne	He	H_2	
O_2	M 20° D M -72° F			M 20° E	M 20° E C 20° F S,A 20° F/D S,A <0° E/F	M 20° E C 20° F S,A 20° F/D S,A <0° E/F	Ar, etc.
N_2	M 20° E C 20° F S,A 20° D S,A -78° F	M 20° E C 20° F S,A 20° D S,A -78° F			M -78° F C -196° F	M 20° F M -20° E	Ne
CO	M 100° E C 20° F S,A 20° F/D S -20° E	M 100° E C 20° F S,A 20° F/D S -20° E	M 100° E C 20° F S,A 20° F/D S -20 E			M 20° F M -20° E	He
CH_4	M 100° E/F C 20° E S,A 20° F/D	M 100° E/F C 20° E S,A 20° E/F	M 100° E C 20° E S,A 20° E/F	M 100° E C 20° E S 20° F S -78° E			
CO_2 (C and S only except >300°)	C,S 20–100 E	C,S 20–100 E	C,S 20–100 E	C,S 20–100 E	C,S 20–100 E		
N_2O	M,C,S,A 20–100 E	M,C,S,A 20–100 E	M,C,S,A 20–100 E	M,C,S,A 20–100 E	C,S,M,A 20–100 E	C 20° E S 20° F S -20° E (M 300° F)	
NO (S only)	S <0° E	S <0° E	S <0° E	S -20 F	(S -20 F)	S 20 E	S 20 E
	Ar	O_2	N_2	CO	CH_4	CO_2	N_2O

[a] M, molecular sieve 5A. C, charcoal. S, silica gel. A, alumina. E, easy separation. Two completely separate peaks should be obtainable in a few minutes on a column not more than 1 metre long. F, fair separation. More or less complete separation in a fairly short time on a column of about 2 metres. D, difficult separation. Complete separation will require a long, carefully packed column operated so as to obtain good column efficiency.

11.2. Light Hydrocarbons, C_1–C_5

All the light hydrocarbons may be separated from each other on various kinds of column, and the problem has been studied widely. A column designed to separate every member from every other is necessarily long, since a large number of components must be included in the chromatogram; such an analysis takes a long time. If few members of the group are to be separated, shorter and simpler columns may be used, thus speeding the analysis. The compounds normally encountered in light hydrocarbon analysis are listed in Table 11.5. Other compounds in the group are not normally

TABLE 11.5

Light Hydrocarbons and Their Boiling Points

Hydrocarbon	b.p. (°C)	Hydrocarbon	b.p. (°C)
Methane	−161.5	1-Butyne	8.7
Ethylene	−103.7	Neopentane	9.5
Ethane	−88.6	1,2-Butadiene	10.85
Acetylene	−84.0	3-Methyl-1-butene	20.1
Propene	−47.7	1,4-Pentadiene	26.1
Propane	−42.1	Isopentane	27.8
Propadiene	−35.0	1-Pentene	30.1
Cyclopropane	−33.5	2-Methyl-1-Butene	31.1
Propyne	−23.3	Isoprene	32.6
Isobutane	−11.7	*n*-Pentane	36.1
Isobutene	−6.9	*trans*-2-Pentene	36.4
1-Butene	−6.3	*cis*-2-Pentene	37.4
1,3-Butadiene	−4.5	2-Methyl-2-butene	38.5
n-Butane	−0.5	Cyclopentadiene	41.0
trans-2-Butene	0.9	1-*trans*-3-Pentadiene	42.1
Cyclobutene	2.4	1-*cis*-3-Pentadiene	44.1
cis-2-Butene	3.7	Cyclopentene	44.2
Methylcyclopropane	4.5	Cyclopentane	49.3
Butenyne	5.3		

found in conditions where they need be separated from many other light hydrocarbons. Every separation of any member from every other member of the group, except the separation of hydrogen and permanent gases from methane, may be achieved on a partition column. The partition coefficients at room temperature of the C_1 to C_4 hydrocarbons are rather small, so that they are only slightly retained, and, even though their relative retentions are great, the ratio of their retention volumes is small (Section 4.8). This means that rather long columns are necessary, and packed columns with a large proportion of stationary phase should be used. The retention times, however, are short. The small retention of the C_1 to C_4's may be overcome by using reduced temperatures, but this is usually more of an inconvenience than the use of long columns. Capillary columns are not really suitable for light hydrocarbon analysis, and, even though they may be used at room temperature for the purpose (*1,2*), their large separating potentialities are wasted on account of their small retentions.

Adsorbents may be used for light hydrocarbon separations, and their performance is comparable with that of partition columns; in certain cases, they have advantages. They have been extensively used in Russia (*3*).

(*a*) *Methane,* C_2, *and* C_3 *from Each Other, from Higher Hydrocarbons, and from Permanent Gases*

Complete separations of mixtures of permanent gases and hydrocarbons to C_3 may be achieved on adsorbents. On charcoal, the separation follows the order of boiling points (*4*), so that the order of elution of gases and C_1 and C_2 is (*4,5,6*):

$$H_2, O_2, N_2, CO, CH_4, CO_2, C_2H_2, C_2H_4, C_2H_6.$$

These may be separated on a charcoal column at room temperature, though the analysis is rather long if the charcoal is too active.

A similar separation may be achieved on silica gel or alumina so long as the air gases do not need to be resolved, but in this case alkenes and alkynes are selectively retained relative to alkanes. The orders of elution on silica gel and alumina are (*7,8,9*):

Silica gel H_2, air, CO, CH_4, C_2H_6, CO_2, C_2H_4, C_3H_8, C_2H_2
Alumina H_2, air, CO, CH_4, C_2H_6, C_2H_4, C_3H_8, C_3H_6, C_2H_2.

The analysis from hydrogen to acetylene may be accommodated on an isothermal chromatogram run at or slightly above room temperature, depending on the activity of the alumina. An analysis time of 10 to 15 minutes would be reasonable, and, for this range of compounds, temperature programming is unnecessary.

If the resolution of methane and the permanent gases is not required, partition columns run at room temperature may be used. On paraffinic or only weakly polar stationary phases, separation is in order of boiling point, with the result that ethylene and ethane fail to separate. Polar stationary phases provide a specific retention of alkenes, and a very large specific retention of alkynes, and for separations up to C_3 the choice of such stationary phase is immaterial. Adjusted retention volumes relative to ethylene are given in Table 11.6.

The alkenes may be separated from the alkanes by a column containing a saturated solution of silver nitrate in glycol or benzyl cyanide as a sta-

TABLE 11.6

RETENTIONS RELATIVE TO ETHENE OF C_1–C_3 HYDROCARBONS

	Stationary phase							
	Paraffin oil	Tri-isobutylene	Dionyl phthalate or didecyl phthalate	Alumina modified with silicone	Acetonylacetone	Dimethylformamide	Dimethylsulfolane	Ethylene glycol/$AgNO_3$
Temperature (°C):	40	20	0	70	20	0	0	20
Reference:	*9*	*12*	*10,11*	*9*	*12*	*9,10*	*11*	*12*
Methane	0	0	0	0.2	0	0	0	0
Ethene	*1.0*	*1.0*	*1.0*	*1.0*	*1.0*	*1.0*	*1.0*	*1*
Ethane	1.0	2.0	1.0	0.7	1.0	0.6	0.75	0
Ethyne		0.75			10.3	23	10.5	
Propene	3.3	8.0	4.0	3.8	5.0	4.2	4.2	1
Propane	3.3	9.5	4.0	2.4	2.7	2.2	2.2	0
Propyne		10.2	34		36	56		

tionary phase. This does not retain the alkanes at all, but provides good retention for the alkenes, as is shown in the last column of Table 11.6. (The fact that the retentions of ethene and propene are given as the same is deceptive; the results derive from inaccurate measurements of rapid peaks, and the first place of decimals is not significant.)

In the separation of ethane, ethene, propane, and propene, Table 11.6 shows that the best separation of alkane from alkane is given by $AgNO_3$/glycol, that good separation of C_2 from C_3 is given by any other column, but that no column provides more than adequate separation of all four components. At best, tri-isobutylene produces ethane and ethene in one pair of peaks, with propene and propane in another pair. Primavesi (*13*) describes the use of columns of mixed tri-isobutylene and $AgNO_3$/glycol or series columns of these stationary phases to secure a more even spread of the four components; the technique is described in Section 6.4. Barnard and Hughes (*14*), using the same two stationary phases, prefer mixed packing rather than series columns, but Primavesi finds that either is satisfactory. Note that the stationary phases are immiscible, so the mixing is purely mechanical.

On some polar stationary phases, e.g., acetonylacetone at 20°C (*12*) (but not at 0°C) (*15*), dimethylformamide, or dimethylsulfolane (*16*), isobutane may overlap with propene, the relative retention being about 1.1. A better separation of these two substances is secured with hexamethyl phosphoramide or with any non-polar stationary phase.

(*b*) C_4 *Hydrocarbons*

The saturated alkanes may be easily separated in almost any reasonable conditions, i.e., any column providing adequate retention for chromatography to occur.

The separation of the C_4 alkanes and alkenes present in a single mixture normally involves the two butanes, the four butenes, and 1,3-butadiene. The separation of these has been extensively studied. Adjusted retention volumes relative to *n*-butane are given in Table 11.7.

TABLE 11.7

RETENTIONS RELATIVE TO *n*-BUTANE OF C_4 HYDROCARBONS

	Stationary phase											
	Mineral oil	Tri-isobutylene	Di-isodecyl phthalate	Dinonyl phthalate	Acetonylacetone	Acetonylacetone	Dimethylformamide	Dimethylformamide	Dimethylsulfolane	Dimethylsulfolane	Carbitol	Ethylene glycol/$AgNO_3$
Temperature (°C):	25	20	35	40	20	0	0	0	0	25	0	20
Reference:	*19*	*12*	*11*	*10*	*12*	*15*	*10*	*9*	*11,18*	*19*	*17,18*	*12*
Isobutane	0.63	0.72	0.66	0.68	0.65	0.64	0.65	0.62	0.61	0.61	0.64	0
Isobutene	0.80	0.88	1.0	1.0	1.74	1.90	2.14	2.09	1.84	1.71	1.32	2.5
1-Butene	0.81	0.88	1.0	1.0	1.74	1.72	1.89	1.87	1.68	1.61	1.32	5.5
1,3-Butadiene	0.83	0.88		1.53	4.05	4.21	5.55		4.1	3.58		9.25
n-Butane	*1.0*	*1.0*	*1.0*	*1.0*	*1.0*	*1.0*	*1.0*	*1.0*	*1.0*	*1.0*	*1.0*	0
trans-2-Butene	1.08	1.08	1.8	1.53	2.2	2.28	2.57	2.52	2.29	2.08	1.74	1.0
cis-2-Butene	1.25	1.21	1.8	1.74	2.65	2.73	3.06	3.00	2.74	2.44	2.10	4.7

On non-polar stationary phases, separation is in order of boiling points, which results in the overlaps: *n*-butane – *trans*-2-butene; isobutene – 1-butene – 1,3-butadiene; so that such stationary phases are unsuitable for this separation (*20*).

On weakly polar stationary phases, e.g., phthalate esters, olefins are somewhat retained; with dinonyl phthalate and didecyl phthalate, this selective retention is just sufficient to make the 1-butene and isobutene overlap with the *n*-butane, but with the slightly more polar dibutyl phthalate these two olefins appear on the slow side of *n*-butane, though they are not themselves resolved. With any of the phthalate esters, the *cis*- and *trans*-2-butenes are resolved (*20*), though poorly with didecyl phthalate (*11*).

With moderately polar phases, e.g., dimethylformamide, dimethylsulfolane, acetonylacetone, etc., all the seven compounds are resolved, but the relative retention of isobutene and 1-butene is always small. McKenna and Idleman (*21*) have studied a large number of moderately polar nonvolatile liquids for their ability at this separation. Among the liquids tested, the order of value for those more familiar as stationary phases is: acetonylacetone, β,β'-oxydipropionitrile, dimethylsulfolane, γ-butyrolactone, propylene carbonate, the last giving the best separation. Propylene carbonate secures good separation of the other butenes, but belongs to those referred to in the preceding subsection which cause overlap between isobutane and propene. A mixture of glutaronitrile and propylene carbonate, however, produces as good a separation of the C_4's, with propene appearing between isobutane and *n*-butane. The separation of the C_4's on this mixture is shown in Fig. 11.4.

A saturated solution of silver nitrate in glycol gives zero retention for the alkanes, but retains the alkenes as shown in Table 11.7. The retention order bears no relation to volatility, since it is determined by the stability of the silver nitrate complex and not by vapour pressure.

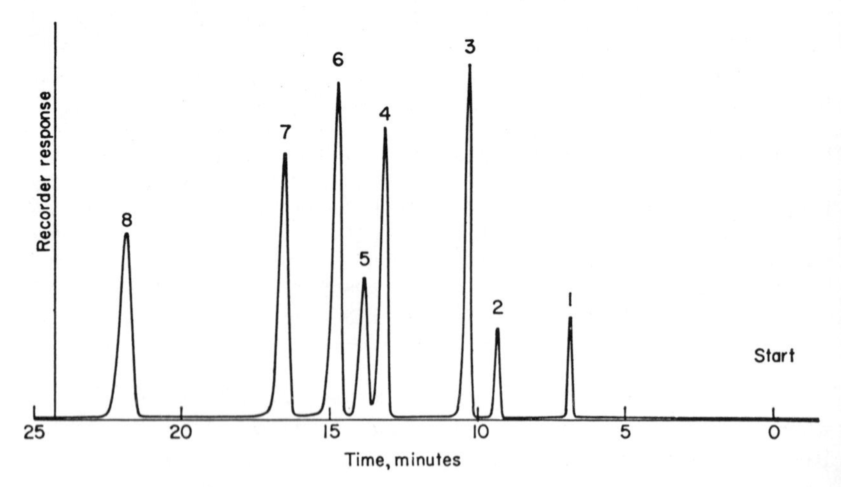

FIG. 11.4. Chromatogram of C_4 hydrocarbons on mixed glutaronitrile and proplyene carbonate. McKenna and Idleman (*21*). 1, Air; 2, isobutane; 3, *n*-butane; 4, 1-butene; 5, isobutene; 6, *trans*-2-butene; 7, *cis*-2-butene; 8, 1,3-butadiene.

With non-polar phases or weakly polar phases such as phthalic esters, no overlap occurs between C_4's and C_5's, except that the comparatively rarely encountered 1,2-butadiene is retained into the C_5's on dinonyl phthalate (*10*). On the more polar phases used for complete separation of the C_4's, however, *cis*- and *trans*-2-butenes may overlap with iso- and *n*-pentane. On acetonylacetone and dimethylsulfolane, *trans*-2-butene overlaps with isopentane, with *n*-pentane coming through after *cis*-2-butene. On dimethylformamide, isopentane comes through with isobutene, with *n*-pentane between the two 2-butenes (*10*). Fredericks and Brooks (*11*) have eliminated this overlap with series columns of 6 feet of didecyl phthalate and 16 feet of dimethylsulfolane, but in this case 1-butene and isobutene fail to resolve.

All the C_4's may be separated on polar adsorbents, especially silica gel and alumina. Molecular sieves may also be used, but it is reported that a certain amount of almost irreversible adsorption also occurs (*22*), causing a slow continuous elution of hydrocarbons after a period of use. The use

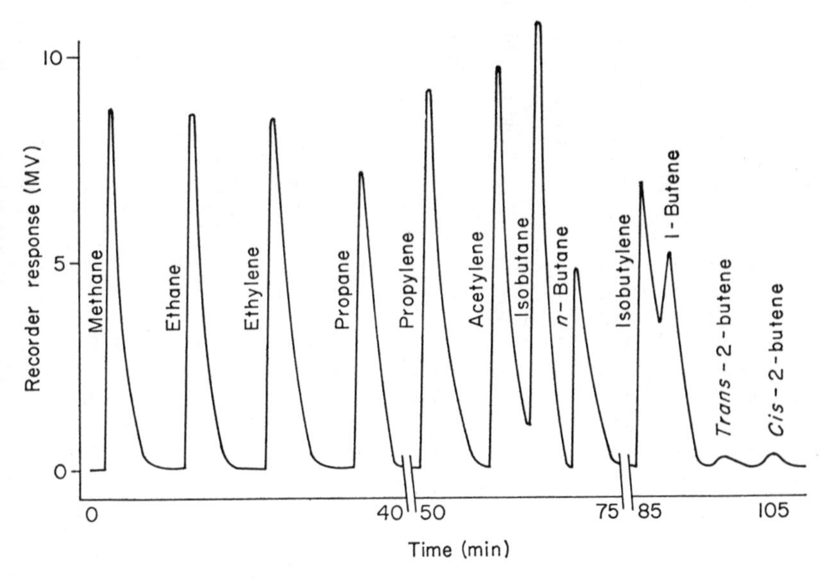

FIG. 11.5. Separation of light hydrocarbons on alumina programmed between 20° and 140°C. Greene, Moberg, and Wilson (*7*).

of silica gel has been extensively reported by Russian workers (*3*). Scott (*23*) has shown that alumina acts as a polar stationary phase, with all the alkenes appearing after the alkanes. Of the alkenes, isobutene is separate from 1-butene, but overlaps with *trans*-2-butene. Greene, Moberg, and Wilson (*7*) have used alumina programmed between 20° and 140°C, and obtain good separation of all C_4's from each other and from C_3's except for a partial separation of 1-butene and isobutene (Fig. 11.5).

The separation and analysis of the C_4 hydrocarbons is described in simple detail in reference *18*.

(*c*) C_5 *Hydrocarbons*

Relative retention data is tabulated in Table 11.8.

TABLE 11.8

RETENTIONS RELATIVE TO *n*-PENTANE OF C_5 HYDROCARBONS

	Stationary phase											
	Mineral oil	Dinonyl phthalate	Didecyl phthalate	Dimethylformamide	Dimethylformamide	Tricresyl phosphate	Carbitol	Hexamethylphosphoramide	Acetonylacetone	Dimethylsulfolane	Dimethylsulfolane	β,β'-Oxydipropionitrile
Temperature (°C):	25	40	25	0	0	25	0	30	0	0	25	25
Reference:	*19*	*10*	*19*	*10*	*17*	*19*	*17*	*24*	*15*	*11*	*19*	*19*
Neopentane	0.35		0.35			0.34			0.35		0.36	0.41
3-Methyl-1-butene	0.56	0.71	0.66	1.17	1.15	0.78	0.81	0.83	1.08	1.05	1.03	1.35
1,4-Pentadiene	0.65		0.95			1.42						3.76
Isopentane	0.74	0.76	0.74	0.75	0.66	0.72	0.74	0.75	0.71	0.73	0.74	0.72
1-Pentene	0.81	1.0	0.98	1.79	1.78	1.20	1.28	1.29	1.67	1.60	1.54	1.90
2-Methyl-1-butene	0.89		1.07	2.18	2.19	1.35	1.46	1.39	2.03	1.95	1.81	
Isoprene	0.99	1.48	1.54		5.55	2.32	2.65	2.75	4.85	4.06	3.93	6.2
n-Pentane	*1.00*	*1.00*	*1.00*	*1.00*	*1.00*	*1.00*	*1.00*	*1.00*	*1.00*	*1.00*	*1.00*	*1.00*
trans-2-Pentene	1.04	1.30	1.22	2.26	2.19	1.56	1.61	1.53	2.13	2.06	1.90	2.24
cis-2-Pentene	1.08	1.30	1.30	2.49	2.42	1.66	1.76	1.63	2.31	2.28	2.08	2.70
2-Methyl-2-butene	1.21	1.48	1.48	3.02	2.88	1.86	1.93	1.75	2.70	2.76	2.41	3.10
Cyclopentadiene	1.30		2.30		11.52	4.34	4.66				7.7	
trans-Piperylene	1.24		2.04		7.69	3.22	3.51	3.34	6.60		5.3	8.1
cis-Piperylene	1.38		2.22		8.73	3.70	4.02	3.71	7.47		5.9	9.8
Cyclopentane	2.12	2.19	2.28		3.16	2.88	2.65	2.31	3.19		2.88	3.42
Cyclopentene	1.80	2.19	2.30		5.02	3.44	3.11				4.18	6.4

The three C_5 alkanes may be separated by any column capable of providing adequate retention; this includes any column containing at least some alkyl groups operated at temperatures not higher than approximately

100°C. The relative retention of neopentane and isopentane is large; the relative retention of isopentane and *n*-pentane is between 1.2 and 1.3, so for complete separation of these two a column of not less than approximately 1000 plates is required.

On all columns, cyclopentane appears after and is well separated from *n*-pentane.

Mixtures containing all or some of the six C_5 monoalkenes appear to be separated easily on diethylene glycol monomethyl ether (carbitol, *17*), though this material has not been extensively used for this separation; it differs from more commonly reported stationary phases in that *n*-pentane appears after the most volatile olefin. The six monoalkenes alone may be easily separated on dimethylsulfolane at 0°C (*11*), and less completely at 25°C (*25*), but with this the separation factor of 3-methyl-1-butene and *n*-pentane is 1.05, so that complete separation requires an efficient column. Acetonylacetone behaves similarly to dimethylsulfolane (*15*), but the relative retention of the above pair is improved to 1.08. With dimethylformamide, the separation of 3-methyl-1-butene and *n*-pentane is adequate (relative retention 1.15), but the relative retention of 2-methyl-1-butene and *trans*-2-pentene is only 1.035, which produces overlap on all but the most efficient columns.

The separation of the C_5 hydrocarbons, C_5H_8, which comprise five pentadienes, two methylbutadienes, and cyclopentene, has been studied by Knight (*25*). All these compounds have approximately unit activity coefficients in nonpolar stationary phases, but have small activity coefficients in polar stationary phases. On moderately polar phases, such as dimethylformamide, dimethylsulfolane, β,β'-oxydipropionitrile, etc., the dienes are all well separated from the monoenes, probably including the most volatile diene, 1,4-pentadiene, though no sample of this has been tested. Knight does not give any stationary phase which will separate all the above eight compounds; his results show, however, that the important members isoprene and cyclopentene are separated on dimethylsulfolane, reference to Table 11.8 shows that these may also be separated on dimethylformamide and dinonyl phthalate. A complete separation would require either a capillary column of very great efficiency, or two stages, e.g., use of dinonyl phthalate to separate the cyclopentene, followed by a more polar stationary phase.

Cyclopentadiene, C_5H_6, is very strongly retained on a polar stationary phase, and its separation from any other C_5 hydrocarbon presents no difficulty. It is retained so long on polar phases that it is probably better in practice to use a weakly polar stationary phase, e.g., carbitol.

When C_5 hydrocarbons are separated as a class from a more complex mixture by means of a carbon-number selective stationary phase, the most volatile of the hexenes, 3,3-dimethyl-1-butene, may be associated with the pentenes. On dimethylsulfolane, this is adequately separated, appearing between 1-pentene and 2-methyl-1-butene (*25*), but on either more or on less polar stationary phases, there is possibility of overlap.

(*d*) *Mixtures of* C_1 *to* C_5 *Hydrocarbons*

It is apparent from the preceding subsections that overlaps between members of the C_1 to C_5 range can all be avoided, particularly among the commoner members usually found in natural gas or light petroleum fractions. Thus, it is possible to analyse the whole range in a single isothermal run. Several examples of such runs have been published. Figure 11.6 shows

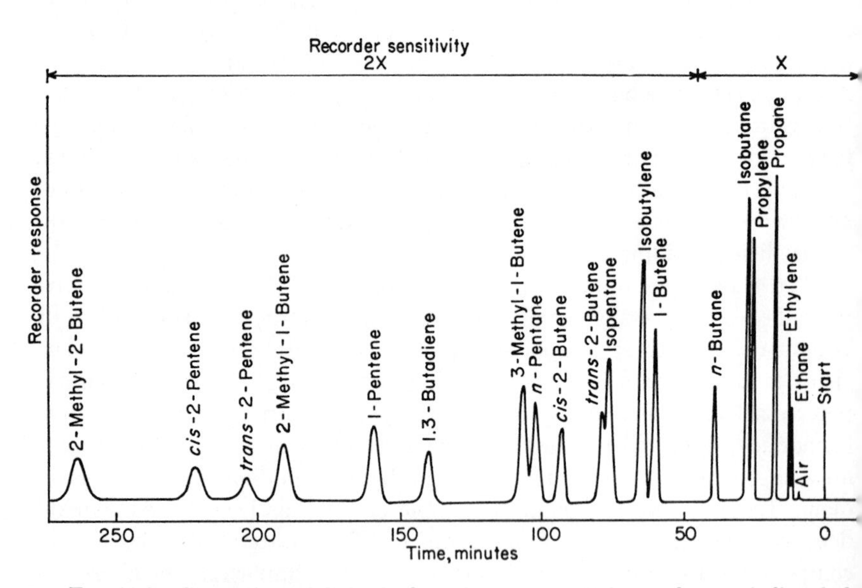

FIG. 11.6. Separation of light hydrocarbons on a 50-foot column of dimethylsulfolane. Fredericks and Brooks (*11*).

the chromatogram of a C_1 to C_5 mixture on dimethylsulfolane (*11*). If the conditions are such that there is appreciable resolution of methane, ethane, and ethene, a complete run to the end of the pentenes on a packed column occupies 2–3 hours, and this time can be considerably reduced by using two columns, e.g., a silica gel adsorption column at room temperature for C_1 to C_2 or C_1 to C_3, together with a partition column for the rest (*26*). If the number of components is relatively few, e.g., in the analysis of saturates only, the parallel column technique of Brenner and Ciepelinski (*27*)

(Section 11.1) may be used. These authors illustrate the use of parallel columns of 1 metre molecular sieve 5A and 4 metres sebacic ester for analysis of C_1 to C_4 saturates together with permanent gases.

The analysis of the full range of hydrocarbons from C_1 to C_5 saturates, but not including the C_5 alkenes, has been studied by Scott (*23*), who has made use of the fact (Section 3.11) that relative retentions on adsorbents of successive carbon numbers decline with decline in the activity of the adsorbent. Using alumina which is intentionally de-activated with water until the specific retention volume of ethane has been reduced to the prescribed value of 0.5 cc/g, permanent gases and the C_1–C_5 hydrocarbons are resolved as indicated in the first column of Table 11.9. Scott has also

TABLE 11.9

RETENTIONS RELATIVE TO *n*-BUTANE OF C_1 TO C_5 HYDROCARBONS ON TREATED ALUMINA[a]

	Column (at 20°C)	
	Alumina + water	Alumina + silicone
Hydrogen	0.00	0.00
Methane	0.03	0.03
Ethane	0.12	0.12
Ethene	0.15	0.15
Propane	0.35	0.35
Acetylene	0.45	0.40
Propene	0.58	0.55
i-Butane	0.87	0.87
n-Butane	*1.00*	*1.00*
1-Butene	1.60	1.50
i-Butene	1.80	1.70
trans-2-Butene	1.80	1.70
cis-2-Butene	2.00	1.90
1,3-Butadiene	2.40	2.05
i-Pentane	2.40	2.35
n-Pentane	2.80	2.75

[a] See reference *23*.

used alumina de-activated with silicone oil, which gives the relative retention times of the second column of Table 11.9. It is seen that the relative retention times are altered only slightly, and that the column acts more as a deadened adsorbent than as a partition column, though the silicone has the effect of slightly accelerating the acetylene and the 1,3-butadiene.

11.3. Petroleum Alkanes, Alkenes, and Naphthenes

This section deals with a very large range of compounds, the chromatography of relatively few of which has been considered in the literature in detail. It includes specific details of published work and also general relations derived both from the literature and from the discussion of Chapter 3.

(a) *Alkanes in General*

The chromatography of alkanes on paraffinic stationary phases has been studied by several authors (*1–6,13*). Details of the activity coefficients in these cases have been given by Kwantes and Rijnders (*4*), who find that the activity coefficients for *n*-alkanes on other *n*-alkanes are nearly equal to or just less than unity, and that the values are almost completely explained by the difference in molecular size between solute and solvent (Section 3.5). Activity coefficients for adjacent alkanes are virtually identical on a given paraffinic stationary phase. The results of Kwantes and Rijnders are confirmed from relative retention volumes given by several workers using different stationary phases of either pure or mixed paraffins.

TABLE 11.10

Absolute Activity Coefficients of Alkanes on Intermediate and Polar Stationary Phases[a]

Solute	Stationary phase					
	Didecyl phthalate (95°C)	Dinonyl phthalate (77°C)	Dibutyl phthalate (80°C)	Tricresyl phosphate (77°C)	Dimethyl-sulfolane (35°C)	Poly-ethylene glycol 400 (100°C)
Isobutane				2.77 (30°C)		
Isopentane					6.5	
n-Pentane					6.7	3.69
2,2-Dimethylbutane					8.3	
2-Methylpentane			2.14	3.00		
n-Hexane	0.92	1.03	2.16		8.6	5.37
n-Heptane	0.97	1.12	2.45	3.10	10.9	7.14
Isooctane		1.22				
n-Octane	0.99	1.23	2.59	3.49		9.52
n-Nonane	1.10					
n-Decane						16.64

[a] Data from references *7–10*.

Activity coefficients of branched alkanes also appear to be close to unity, with the result that the retention volumes of alkanes on paraffinic stationary phases are generally in order of boiling points. There are, however, small differences in activity coefficients between different isomers which may be used for securing unexpected separations on an efficient column, as described in Section 3.9(c).

On stationary phases other than paraffins, alkanes have activity coefficients greater than unity which tend to increase with increase in molecular weight of the alkane, as illustrated in Fig. 3.5. With stationary phases of the intermediate class [Section 3.9(b)], exemplified by esters such as dibutyl phthalate and tricresyl phosphate, absolute activity coefficients are in the region of 2 or 3 (*7*), so that such stationary phases are satisfactory for the general analysis of alkanes. Table 11.10 shows activity coefficients of alkanes on three stationary phases of this class. On intermediate stationary phases there appears to be a slight tendency for activity coefficients to show greater scatter among different isomers than on paraffinic stationary phases. This is illustrated, for example, by the data of Table 11.11, which gives relative activity coefficients of a series of isomers both on hexatriacontane (results copied from Table 3.15) and on benzyldiphenyl. It is seen that there is more scatter for the relative activities on benzyldiphenyl. The fact that there is a significant difference between the two phases is seen from the last column, in which the relative retentions of the isomers on each phase are divided one by the other. Such small apparently random but experimentally significant differences between not very dissimilar stationary phases are useful in hydrocarbon analysis [e.g., see Knight (*10a*), also Subsection (e)], but as yet have not been classified.

On polar stationary phases, alkanes have large activity coefficients increasing with carbon number. This has the result that, firstly, the relative retentions of successive homologs are smaller than normal so that a chromatogram spanning several carbon numbers is compressed, and that, secondly, specific retention volumes are small, so that the column must be designed to accommodate them by using a large proportion of stationary liquid and a low temperature. Absolute values for activity coefficients for some alkanes in polar stationary phases are also given in Table 11.10. Activity coefficients of the order of 10 are not unreasonably large, and such polar stationary phases are frequently used with alkanes. Examples of this are given in the previous section in connection with light hydrocarbons. With stationary liquids containing even less methylene component, e.g., hydrogen bonding liquids such as glycerol, activity coefficients are of the order of 100. Such liquids are generally unsuitable for use with alkanes except in the case that the liquid is used to separate alkanes as a group from other more soluble solutes.

TABLE 11.11

RELATIVE ACTIVITY COEFFICIENTS OF ALKANES ON A PARAFFINIC AND AN INTERMEDIATE STATIONARY PHASE COMPARED[a]

	Stationary phase		
Solute	Hexatriacontane	Benzyldiphenyl	Ratio of relative retention volumes
n-Pentane	*1.00*	*1.00*	*1.00*
2,2-Dimethylbutane	1.03		1.06
2,3-Dimethylbutane	1.03		1.05
2-Methylpentane	1.11		1.02
3-Methylpentane	1.03		1.03
n-Hexane	1.09	1.15	1.05
2,2-Dimethylpentane	1.18	1.38	1.17
2,4-Dimethylpentane	1.20	1.40	1.17
2,2,3-Trimethylbutane	1.06	1.26	1.19
3,3-Dimethylpentane	1.08	1.15	1.08
2,3-Dimethylpentane	1.15	1.27	1.13
2-Methylhexane	1.20	1.37	1.14
3-Methylhexane	1.17	1.32	1.13
3-Ethylpentane	1.08	1.20	1.12
n-Heptane	1.13	1.23	1.09
2,2,4-Trimethylpentane	1.24	1.70	1.24

[a] See reference *1*.

(*b*) *Hexanes*

Relative retention data for the five hexanes, together with *n*-pentane, cyclopentane, and cyclohexane for cross-reference, are given in Table 11.12.

Of the five hexanes, any non-polar or intermediate stationary phase produces adequate separation of all pairs other than the pair 2,3-dimethylbutane–2-methylpentane, which have a relative retention of less than 1.03. The separation of all five using a non-polar stationary phase may be achieved with a capillary column (*14*), but not otherwise. The above pair is resolved on polar stationary phases, e.g., polyethylene glycol or β,β'-oxydipropionitrile, in which case the 2-methylpentane appears before the 2,3-dimethylbutane (*6,13*). In this case, however, the relative retention of 3-methylpentane and *n*-hexane is small, and a long column is necessary because of this and also because the activity coefficients are of the order of 10.

Zlatkis (*15*) has found that a mixture containing only the five hexanes may easily be resolved on a column of isoquinoline; a $2\frac{1}{2}$-metre column used at room temperature performs the separation in about 20 minutes.

TABLE 11.12

RETENTIONS OF HEXANES RELATIVE TO *n*-PENTANE

		Stationary phase												
	Boiling point	Mineral oil	Apiezon A oil	Paraffin wax	Squalane	Squalane	Didecyl phthalate	Dinonyl phthalate	Tetrahydrofurfuryl phthalate	Benzyldiphenyl	2,5-Hexanedione	Dimethylsulfolane	2,2′-Oxydipropionitrile	Polyethylene glycol
Temperature (°C):	—	45	65	78.6	80	105	20	118	20	78.6	0	25	25	78
Reference:	—	*13*	*3*	*5*	*4*	*4*	*11*	*3*	*11*	*1*	*12*	*13*	*13*	*3*
n-Pentane	36.1	*1.00*	*1.00*	*1.00*	*1.00*	*1.0*	*1.00*	*1.00*	*1.00*	*1.00*	*1.00*	*1.00*	*1.00*	*1.00*
2,2-Dimethylbutane	49.7	1.40	1.42	1.34	1.44	1.4	1.45	1.25	1.15	1.26	1.51	1.32	1.28	1.00
2,3-Dimethylbutane	58.0	1.93	1.91	1.90			2.10	1.65	1.65	1.74	2.10	1.88	1.73	1.72
2-Methylpentane	60.3	1.98	1.95	1.87		1.8	2.15	1.59	1.65	1.79		1.90	1.55	1.39
3-Methylpentane	63.3	2.27	2.22	2.17			2.60	1.78	2.30	2.05		2.26	1.97	1.62
n-Hexane	68.7	2.72	2.58	2.46	2.42	2.3	3.10	1.92	2.20	2.31	2.59	2.62	2.00	2.28
Cyclohexane	80.2	5		4.46	4.38	4.0		3.42		5.54		6.65	6.8	6.2
Cyclopentane	49.3	1.92	1.94		1.86	1.8		1.77		2.54		2.89	3.42	2.82

The drawback to this is that cyclopentane has the same retention as *n*-hexane; this can be overcome by including in series a short column of some less polar stationary phase on which the naphthenes are not so selectively retained, e.g., squalane. Figure 11.7 shows the chromatogram of the hexanes and cyclopentane on squalane and isoquinoline columns in series.

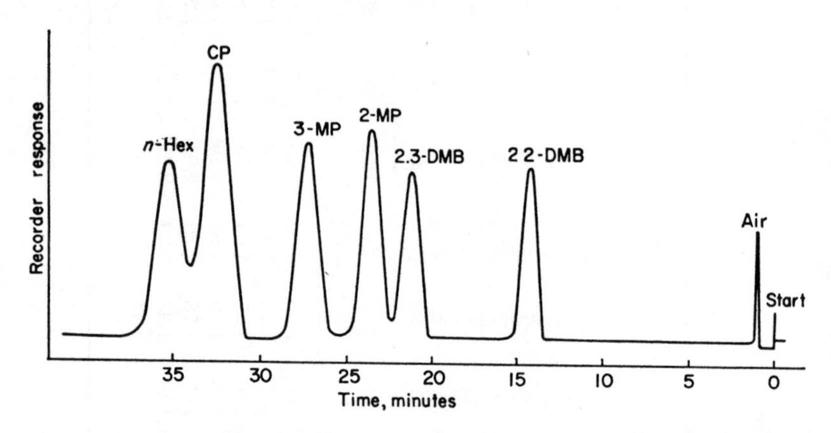

FIG. 11.7. Separation of the hexanes and cyclopentane on series columns of squalane and isoquinoline. Zlatkis (*15*).

The hexanes also separate on active charcoal modified with 1.5% by weight of squalane (*16*), though relative retentions are not large and a long column is required. There is no interference from C_5's or C_7's, for the principal characteristic of this column is that it separates compounds into their carbon numbers [see Subsection (d) and Section 3.11].

(*c*) *Heptanes*

Table 11.13 shows the retention volumes of the nine heptane alkanes on various stationary phases relative to *n*-heptane. Three sets of data are given for retentions on paraffinic stationary phases. The first column of the table has data obtained on columns packed with a relatively large proportion of stationary liquid on celite (*1*), and is supported by data from another source which is identical within experimental error (*5*). The second and third columns contain data measured from chromatograms published as diagrams (*6,17*). The data is not entirely consistent, the inconsistencies being greater than would be expected from the differences in temperature of the columns, and this is probably an illustration of the doubtful reproducibility of retention data when the proportion of stationary phase is small (Section 6.3). On paraffinic stationary phases, there are several overlaps, e.g., 2,2-dimethylpentane–2,4-dimethylpentane and others about

TABLE 11.13

RETENTION OF HEPTANE ALKANES RELATIVE TO *n*-HEPTANE

	Stationary phase					
	Hexatriacontane	Squalane (capillary column)	Squalane (3% on packed column)	Benzyldiphenyl	Polyethylene glycol	β,β'-Oxydipropionitrile
Temperature (°C):	78	100	25	78	78	25
Reference:	*1,5*	*17*	*6*	*1*	*3*	*6*
2,2-Dimethylpentane	0.523	0.49	0.42	0.49		0.55
2,4-Dimethylpentane	0.538		0.46	0.500	0.49	0.55
2,2,3-Trimethylbutane	0.610		0.49	0.560		0.69
3,3-Dimethylpentane	0.720		0.61	0.730		0.84
2,3-Dimethylpentane	0.795	0.78	0.70	0.765		0.90
2-Methylhexane	0.745	0.71	0.70	0.710		0.75
3-Methylhexane	0.815	0.87	0.77	0.789	0.745	0.85
3-Ethylpentane	0.905	0.88	0.84	0.880		1.00
n-Heptane	*1.00*	*1.00*	*1.00*	*1.00*	*1.00*	*1.00*

which the different results are not consistent. On benzyldiphenyl, there is a significantly greater spread in the relative retentions, which are different, though there are still overlaps. On a column of 40% β,β'-oxydipropionitrile, both the bad overlaps produced on a column of 3% squalane on firebrick are resolved, so a complete resolution of the heptanes is possible using these two columns consecutively (*6*). In the work referred to, 50 foot columns were used, each chromatogram requiring about 2 hours. Activity coefficients of the heptanes on β,β'-oxydipropionitrile are of the order of 10, so that specific retentions per gram of packing on 40% β,β'-oxydipropionitrile are of the same order as those on 3% squalane columns.

Desty, Goldup, and Whyman (*14*) have shown that the heptanes can be resolved using the paraffinic stationary phase squalane on a capillary column with not less than 100,000 theoretical plates. Their chromatogram is reproduced in Fig. 11.8.

(*d*) *Naphthenes*

On paraffinic columns, naphthenes have significantly smaller activity coefficients than the corresponding alkanes, so that they are retained

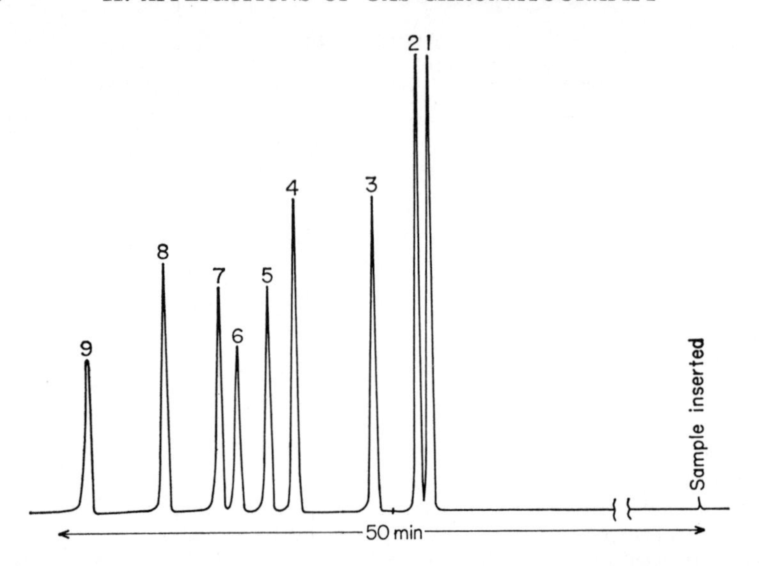

FIG. 11.8. Separation of the heptanes on a capillary column coated with squalane. Desty, Goldup, and Whyman (*14*). 1, 2,2-Dimethylpentane; 2, 2,4-dimethylpentane; 3, 2,2,3-trimethylbutane; 4, 3,3-dimethylpentane; 5, 2-methylhexane; 6, 2,3-dimethylpentane; 7, 3-methylhexane; 8, 3-ethylpentane; 9, *n*-heptane.

for longer. This is illustrated in Table 11.14, which shows absolute activity coefficients of some naphthenes obtained by Kwantes and Rijnders (*4*) and also activity coefficients relative to *n*-pentane determined from retention data for a number of naphthenes. On benzyldiphenyl and probably on other intermediate stationary phases, the effect is intensified, so that the relative retention of the naphthene and its corresponding alkane is greater. On polar stationary phases such as polyethylene glycol (*3*) or β,β'-oxydipropionitrile (*6*), the relative effect is further magnified, though absolute activity coefficients are considerably increased. Remarkable exceptions are glycerol and diglycerol (*18*) which show the same alkane/naphthene relative retention as a paraffinic stationary phase. On these, however, absolute retentions are very small.

Within any one carbon number, the naphthenes are less volatile than the alkanes, and the effect of their small activity coefficients is to augment the difference in vapour pressures, so that naphthenes are retained longer than the corresponding alkanes on both counts. Thus, the relative retentions of cyclopentane and *n*-pentane, cyclohexane and *n*-hexane, cycloheptane and *n*-heptane, are all large (e.g., 2 to 3), and these separations are very easy. Branched naphthenes also have small activity coefficients, as is apparent from the entries on Table 11.14. The branching, however, produces the usual increase in vapour pressure, and thus, as is general,

TABLE 11.14

ABSOLUTE AND RELATIVE ACTIVITY COEFFICIENTS FOR ALKANES AND NAPHTHENES IN DIFFERENT STATIONARY PHASES COMPARED

	Stationary phase				
	Squalane	1,2,4-Trichloro-benzene	Hexatriacontane	Benzyldiphenyl	Polyethylene glycol 1000
Coefficient:	γ_{abs}	γ_{abs}	γ_{rel}	γ_{rel}	γ_{rel}
Temperature (°C):	80	30	78	78	78
Reference:	*4*	*4*	*1*	*1*	*3*
n-Pentane	0.67	2.97	1.00	1.00	1.00
Cyclopentane	0.52	2.11			
n-Hexane	0.66	2.93	1.09	1.15	1.52
Cyclohexane	0.52	2.32	0.83	0.675	0.60
Methylcyclopentane	0.55	2.37	0.89	0.77	0.64
n-Heptane	0.68		1.13	1.23	1.31
Methylcyclohexane	0.54		0.89	0.81	0.76

retentions of branched members are smaller than those of the unbranched naphthenes of the same carbon number. Whether or not branched naphthenes of a particular carbon number overlap into the corresponding alkanes of the same carbon number appears to depend on the amount of branching, on the carbon number, and on the stationary phase. With C_5 hydrocarbons, the most volatile dimethylcyclopropane, 1,*trans*-2-dimethylcyclopropane, appears in front of *n*-pentane on a paraffinic stationary phase and on di-*n*-decyl phthalate, but *n*-pentane appears first on tricresyl phosphate and more polar stationary phases (*13*). On polar stationary phases, therefore, there is complete separation of C_5 alkanes and naphthenes. With C_6 hydrocarbons, methylcyclopentane is eluted after *n*-hexane whatever the stationary phase. With C_7 hydrocarbons, the most volatile of the common naphthenes, 1,1-dimethylcyclopentane, is sufficiently branched to appear well before *n*-heptane on a paraffinic stationary phase (*1*) and just before *n*-heptane on an intermediate stationary phase (benzyldiphenyl) (*1*). It is probable that on a more polar stationary phase, complete separation of C_7 alkanes and naphthenes into two groups would occur.

Another result of the small activity coefficients of naphthenes is that the unbranched naphthene of one carbon number overlaps into the branched alkanes of the next carbon number, thus spoiling a group separation according to carbon number. In order to overcome this, Eggertsen, Knight, and Groennings (*16*) make use of the observation that adsorbents such as charcoal adsorb naphthenes less readily than alkanes (Section 3.11). On pure charcoal, peaks are too asymmetrical with solutes so involatile as petroleum fractions, and furthermore, the relative acceleration of naphthenes is too great. Both these drawbacks are overcome by modifying the adsorbent by mixing it with a small (1.5% w/w) proportion of a paraffinic stationary liquid, squalane. This has the effect of saturating all the more active sites in the charcoal, thus reducing peak asymmetry, and also superimposing a certain amount of the character of a paraffinic stationary phase, so that cyclohexane is retained longer than *n*-hexane, but not so long as the first of the heptanes, 2,2-dimethylpentane. This stationary phase acts as a group separator for carbon numbers in mixtures containing alkanes and naphthenes which is effective at least up to C_8. Tenney (*19*) has reported that perfluorobutylamine is a stationary phase which acts in the same way, but this suffers from being rather volatile and also being a poor solvent for hydrocarbons, so that activity coefficients are very large.

(*e*) *Olefins*

In paraffinic stationary phases olefins all have almost unit activity coefficients, so that, like alkanes, they usually separate in order of boiling point. In many cases, however, small deviations in activity coefficient may be sufficient to cause overlap in pairs of solutes of slightly different boiling

TABLE 11.15

ACTIVITY COEFFICIENTS RELATIVE TO *n*-PENTANE OF SOME ALKENES IN MINERAL OIL

Substance	Retention volume at 45°C relative to *n*-pentane[a]	b.p. (°C)	Vapour pressure at 45°C (mm/Hg)	Relative activity coefficient
3-Methyl-1-butene	0.56	20.06	1850	1.02
1-Pentene	0.81	29.97	1250	1.01
trans-2-Pentene	1.02	36.35	1015	0.985
cis-2-Pentene	1.07	36.94	990	0.965
2-Methyl-2-butene	1.15	38.57	950	0.925
1-Hexene	2.30	63.49	410	1.08
trans-Piperylene	1.19	42.03	840	1.02
cis-Piperylene	1.29	44.07	785	1.01
n-Pentane	*1.00*	36.07	1020	*1.00*

[a] See reference *13*.

point or to cause resolution of pairs of solutes of very similar boiling point. This is illustrated in Table 11.15, where retention volumes and activity coefficients of alkanes in a paraffinic stationary liquid relative to *n*-pentane are given. In intermediate stationary phases there is no definite data about absolute values of activity coefficients, but activity coefficients relative to alkanes are somewhat less than unity, so that in contrast to paraffinic stationary phases, intermediate stationary phases retain olefins relative to alkanes. The effect is not very large, and is not enough to be able to separate completely the alkanes and alkenes of a particular carbon number into two discrete groups of peaks, but it is sufficient to be useful in individual separations. Thus, hexene-1, which is eluted just in front of *n*-hexane on a paraffinic column, is unresolved from *n*-hexane on di-isodecyl phthalate (*11*) and is eluted just after *n*-hexane on benzyldiphenyl (*1*). Again, on intermediate stationary phases, olefins separate among themselves roughly in order of boiling point, as may be seen from the results of Sullivan *et al.* (*11*). On polar stationary phases, olefins are also retained relative to alkanes, but the effect is still not large, so that, for example, on β,β'-oxydipropionitrile, hexene-1 appears on the middle of the heptanes (*10a*). As with alkanes (Section 3.9), the spread of activity coefficients within a carbon number on a polar stationary phase may not be much larger than on a paraffinic stationary phase, but at least it is different, so there is a good chance that what is not separated on the one may be separated on the other.

For olefins, there is a useful specific stationary phase made by dissolving silver nitrate in some non-volatile polar substrate, of which ethylene glycol, propylene glycol, and benzyl cyanide are most common (*9,20,21*). The silver nitrate forms complexes with the olefins, with the effect that they are selectively retained. Non-olefinic compounds behave as if the silver nitrate were not there. Thus, when glycerol or ethylene glycol are used as solvents for the silver nitrate, the retention of alkanes is virtually nil, and such a stationary phase serves to separate olefins and acetylenes as a group from alkanes over several carbon numbers. If less silver nitrate is used, or if the solvent is not so polar (generally the one accompanies the other, since the more polar the solvent, the more soluble the silver nitrate), the properties of the solvent become more significant. If benzyl cyanide is used as solvent, the alkanes are considerably retained, and simple mixture of alkanes and alkenes can be analysed in a single run, as is shown by the retention data of Table 11.16 (*9*). All solutions of silver nitrate are unstable when heated above about 50°C and should not be allowed to exceed this temperature. 1-Alkynes react with silver nitrate, and spoil columns containing it.

TABLE 11.16

RETENTION DATA RELATIVE TO ISOPRENE OF HYDROCARBONS AT 30°C ON BENZYL CYANIDE-SILVER NITRATE[a]

Substance	Relative retention
n-Butane	0.041
Ethylene	0.042
Propylene	0.100
n-Pentane	0.111
Propadiene	0.115
trans-2-Butene	0.154
Isobutylene	0.195
n-Hexane	0.268
1-Butene	0.287
cis-2-Butene	0.345
Cyclopentane	0.367
1,3-Butadiene	0.366
trans-2-Pentene	0.371
2-Methyl-2-butene	0.393
3-Methyl-1-butene	0.452
2-Methyl-1-butene	0.598
1-Pentene	0.597
n-Heptane	0.649
Cyclohexane	0.811
cis-2-Pentene	0.810
Isoprene	*1.00*
2-Methyl-1-pentene	1.122
trans-1,3-Pentadiene	1.377
2-Butyne	1.619
1,4-Pentadiene	1.571
cis-1,3-Pentadiene	1.825
Cyclopentadiene	2.464
Cyclopentene	2.461
2-Pentyne	3.236

[a] Reference *9*.

(*f*) *Ancillary Techniques*

The analysis of complex hydrocarbon mixtures with the aid of gas chromatography is frequently assisted when other techniques are also used in conjunction. Some such cases are given below.

(*1*) *Group separations by liquid chromatography.* Though there are gas chromatographic stationary phases which separate hydrocarbon mixtures into aromatics, alkenes, and alkanes, a standard technique using liquid chromatography on silica gel does this efficiently (*22,23*).

(*2*) *Use of subtractors.* In a complex mixture containing peaks caused by substances of unknown chemical type, the chromatogram of the mixture can be compared with a chromatogram obtained by removing a specific chemical type with a selective reagent. Thus, olefins may be removed with a pre-column containing sulphuric acid (*24*). See also references *25–27*. A useful substractor for alkane analysis is molecular sieve 5A, which retains straight chain hydrocarbons almost irreversibly, but allows free passage to any hydrocarbon containing a branch (*28*).

(*3*) *Use of reactors.* Hydrocarbon analysis may be aided by carrying out preliminary chemical operations on the mixture; these operations may be separate from the gas chromatography or may take place in a column placed in the gas stream between the introducer and the analysing column. For example, the analysis of complicated mixtures of olefins is eased, though made less precise, by saturating them to the corresponding alkanes before analysis, so that the olefins are separated according to their skeletal structure but not according to the positions of their double bonds (*29,30*). In a similar manner oxidative degradation, followed by gas chromatographic analysis of fragments, can be used for determining the positions of branches in alkane chains (*31,32*).

(*4*) *Use of other physical analytical techniques.* Unknown hydrocarbons separated by gas chromatography have frequently been identified by other physical methods of analysis, e.g., mass spectrometry (*33–36*) or infrared spectrophotometry (*37,38*).

11.4. Aromatic Hydrocarbons

(*a*) *Common* C_6–C_9 *Hydrocarbons*

The common C_6–C_9 aromatic hydrocarbons are listed in order of boiling point in Table 11.17. Many workers have determined relative retention volumes on many different stationary phases; Table 11.17 contains a selection of the results. Aromatic hydrocarbons are retained on all stationary phases except those containing a very large proportion of hydroxyl groups, e.g., glycerol. On polyethylene glycols, activity coefficients are rather large, and, though relative retentions are large, values of k are small, with the consequent drawbacks described in Chapters 3, 4, and 5.

A considerable amount of specific retention data is available, especially for the first members of the series. This is given in Table 11.18. The specific retention volume of benzene in dinonyl phthalate has been determined with accuracy at many temperatures by Adlard, Khan, and Whitham (*7*), who find the following Antoine equation (Section 3.7):

TABLE 11.17

RETENTIONS OF AROMATIC HYDROCARBONS RELATIVE TO BENZENE

	Boiling point	Apiezon A oil	Liquid paraffin	Apiezon L grease	Benzyldiphenyl	Benzyldiphenyl	Dinonyl phthalate	Tricresyl phosphate	Trixylenyl phosphate	Dimethylsulfolane	1-Chloronaphthalene	Polyethylene glycol 1000	Polyethylene glycol 400
Temperature (°C):	—	101	120	147	78.5	100	118	78.5	120	50	50	78	100
Reference:	—	*1*	*2*	*3*	*4*	*5*	*1*	*4*	*2*	*5*	*5*	*1*	*6*
Benzene	80.1	*1.00*	*1.00*	*1.00*	*1.00*	*1.00*	*1.00*	*1.00*	*1.00*	*1.00*	*1.00*	*1.00*	*1.00*
Toluene	110.6	2.30	2.06	1.54	2.34	2.05	2.05	2.30	1.87	2.35	3.30	1.89	1.72
Ethylbenzene	136.2	4.58	3.84	2.46	4.92	3.93	3.75	4.65	3.29	5.00	8.96	3.27	
p-Xylene	138.4	5.10	4.37	2.25	5.24	4.14	4.07	4.93	3.43	5.45	10.30	3.42	
m-Xylene	139.1	5.15	4.51	2.25	5.48	4.27	4.17	5.06	3.64	5.75	10.92	3.59	2.93
o-Xylene	144.4	6.09	4.93	2.82	6.86	5.25	4.95	6.49	4.31	7.73	14.39	4.71	3.77
Cumene	152.4	7.12	5.63	3.00			5.47		4.53			4.39	
n-Propylbenzene	159.2	8.74	7.55	3.50			6.61		5.77			5.46	
Mesitylene	164.6	11.21	8.73	4.18			8.27		6.48			6.65	4.97
Pseudocumene	169.2	13.0	11.20				9.61		7.84				
sec-Butylbenzene	171.0		11.31						7.89				
p-Cymene	175.0		13.45				10.7		8.44				
tert-Amylbenzene	191.0		20.60						13.18				
Hydrindene	178.0		12.60				12.1		10.78				
Styrene	145.2	5.86	4.98				5.33		4.89			7.06	
α-Methylstyrene	161.5		9.18				8.94		8.11			11.0	
Indene	182.0		14.65				14.9		15.25				

$$\log_{10} V_g = \frac{1.196472 \times 10^3}{220.95 + t} - 1.96252.$$

At 77°C, this gives V_g = 113.6, agreeing closely with Table 11.18. In several other cases, results given in Table 11.18 check with other sources, but the results quoted have not been critically evaluated. Aromatic hydrocarbons can often conveniently be used as internal standards, and the specific retention data given above can enable data relative to them to be specified.

TABLE 11.18

SPECIFIC RETENTION VOLUMES OF AROMATIC HYDROCARBONS

	Stationary phase										
	Squalane	Silicone fluid DC 702	Silicone fluid DC 702	Benzyldiphenyl	Dinonyl phthalate	Dibutyl phthalate	Tricresyl phosphate	Tricresyl phosphate	7,8-Benzoquinoline	Dipropyl tetrachloro-phthalate	Methyl propyl tetrachlorophthalate
Temperature (°C):	78.5	77.0	111	78.5	77	80.7	78.5	132	78.5	110	110
Reference:	*4*	*8*	*8*	*4*	*8*	*8*	*4*	*8*	*4*	*9*	*9*
Benzene	95	98	40	91	115		86	20.4	78	71	65
Toluene	238	225	81	213	279	262	197	37.1	193	155	142
Ethylbenzene	506			448			400		412	270	241
p-Xylene	567	505	158	476		576	424	70.8	440	330	301
m-Xylene	581			499			435		475	316	289
o-Xylene	694		196	624		733	558	77.6	610	417	385
Cumene			235					85.1			

On paraffinic stationary phases, there are overlaps between *m*- and *p*-xylenes, pseudocumene and *sec*-butylbenzene, styrene and *o*-xylene. The last overlap is easily remedied by use of any other type of stationary phase, e.g., dinonyl phthalate; the other two overlaps persist in other stationary phases. The overlap of *m*- and *p*-xylene, in particular, has been extensively studied.

The di-isopropyl benzenes have been studied by Paterson (*10*), who finds that they may be separated relatively easily on dicarbitol phthalate, though probably any fairly polar column would serve adequately.

(*b*) *Separation of the* C_8 *Hydrocarbons*

Of the four compounds ethylbenzene and the three xylenes, *o*-xylene is easily separated from the others on any stationary phase. Ethylbenzene is adequately separated from the other two xylenes on paraffinic stationary phases, but the relative retention becomes rather small on more polar phases. The separation of *m*- and *p*- xylenes on common stationary phases is relatively difficult, for the relative retention is less than about 1.04. However, such a separation can easily be achieved in a capillary column, as is shown in Fig. 11.9.

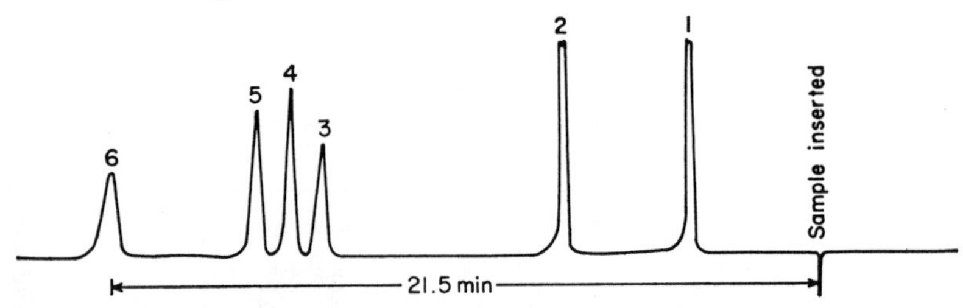

FIG. 11.9. Separation of aromatic hydrocarbons up to C_8 on a capillary column coated with 7,8-benzoquinoline. Desty, Goldup, and Whyman (*11*). 1, Benzene; 2, toluene; 3, ethylbenzene; 4, *p*-xylene; 5, *m*-xylene; 6, *o*-xylene.

Several authors (*4,5,9*) have sought specific stationary phases for the separation of *m*- and *p*-xylenes, the analysis of mixtures of which is a common problem. Table 11.19 summarises the results by giving the relative retentions of *m*-xylene/*p*-xylene and of *p*-xylene/ethylbenzene for various stationary phases that have been investigated. It is seen that, in general, the relative retention is greater the lower the temperature, as usual. In addition to this 1-chloronaphthalene and 7,8-benzoquinoline are effective in considerably increasing the natural separation due to the slight difference in volatility, and chlorophthalic esters have a specific effect which reverses the effect of the natural volatility sufficiently to produce an adequate separation in the reverse order. In the case of 7,8-benzoquinoline, the relative retention of *p*-xylene/ethylbenzene is no greater than that of *m*-xylene/*p*-xylene, so that the three peaks are about equally spaced.

An even more specific stationary phase for this separation is alkylammonium montmorillonite used by Hughes, White, and Roberts (*12*). On dimethyldioctadecylammonium montmorillonite, the approximate relative retention volumes of the xylenes are: *p*-xylene, *1.00*; *o*-xylene, 1.28; *m*-xylene, 1.51. The order of elution is different from that on any other phase. In the results presented by the authors, the column constructed from the above material appears inefficient, and the separations are not

TABLE 11.19

RELATIVE RETENTIONS OF C_8 AROMATIC HYDROCARBONS ON VARIOUS STATIONARY PHASES ARRANGED IN APPROXIMATE ORDER OF SPECIFICITY

Stationary phase	Temp. (°C)	Relative retentions of: *m*-Xylene / *p*-Xylene	Relative retentions of: *p*-Xylene / Ethylbenzene	Ref.
Squalane	78.5	1.025	1.120	*4*
Tricresyl phosphate	78.5	1.026	1.060	*4*
Benzyldiphenyl	78.5	1.046	1.064	*4*
Benzyldiphenyl	100	1.031		*5*
Benzyldiphenyl	110.8	1.040	1.061	*4*
Dimethylsulfolane	50	1.055		*5*
Phenanthrene	110.8	1.053	1.101	*4*
1-Chloronaphthalene	50	1.060		*5*
7,8-Benzoquinoline	78.5	1.080	1.068	*4*
7,8-Benzoquinoline	110.8	1.053	1.088	*4*
Methyl propyl tetrachlorophthalate	110	0.959		*9*
Di-*n*-propyl tetrachlorophthalate	110	0.959		*9*
Di-*n*-propyl tetrabromophthalate	110	0.969		*9*

obviously superior to those produced with conventional partition columns, in spite of the large relative retentions.

It should be noted that the analysis of *m*- and *p*-xylenes has long been satisfactorily performed other than by gas chromatography, e.g., by ultraviolet or infrared spectrophotometry. Franc and Jokl (*13*) combine ultraviolet spectrophotometry and gas chromatography by analysing mixtures containing *m*- and *p*-xylenes on a relatively inefficient column, collecting the combined *m*- and *p*-xylene band and taking its ultraviolet spectrum.

(c) *Polynuclear Hydrocarbons*

Naphthalene and its hydrogenation products have been studied by Hendriks, Soemantri, and Waterman (*14*), Soemantri and Waterman (*15*), Soemantri (*16*), and Castiglioni (*17*). Naphthalene, tetralin, and decalin all boil near 200°C, but they are easily separated on any non-paraffinic stationary phase, since any slight polarity is sufficient to retain the molecules containing aromatic nuclei. Thus, the order of elution on dioctyl phthalate, together with approximate retention volumes is as given in Table 11.20 (*15*). It is observed that the separation of naphthalene and

TABLE 11.20

RETENTION VOLUMES OF NAPHTHALENE AND ITS HYDROGENATION PRODUCTS RELATIVE TO *trans*-DECALIN[a]

Substance	Relative retention at 170°C on:	
	Dioctyl phthalate	Silicone DC 702
trans-Decalin	*1.00*	*1.00*
cis-Decalin	1.24	1.29
Tetralin	2.13	1.86
Naphthalene	3.27	2.24

[a] See reference *15*.

tetralin is slightly better on dioctyl phthalate than on silicone. At a column temperature of 170°C, there is no dehydrogenation of the tetralin or decalin.

Hendriks, Soemantri, and Waterman (*14*), and Gordon, Dyken, and Doumani (*18*) have separated mixtures of dicyclohexyl, phenylcyclohexane, and diphenyl on an ester stationary phase, with a clear separation occurring in the order given at temperatures at or near 170°C.

The chromatography of substituted diphenyls has been studied in detail by Beaven, James, and Johnson (*19*), and by Johnson (*20*), using a column of Apiezon M grease at 197°C. Retention data relative to diphenyl are given in Table 11.21. A notable feature of these data is that all compounds which have ortho-substituents have abnormally small retention volumes; for example, the retention volume of 2,2′-diphenyl is scarcely greater than that of diphenyl, which has two fewer carbon atoms, yet the retention volume of 3,3′-diphenyl is 2.4 times that of diphenyl. There is also a significantly greater retention for *p*-substituted compounds than for *m*-substituted compounds. The authors interpret these observations in terms of the steric hindrance caused by the ortho-methyl groups.

Baxter and Keen (*21*) have analysed a few very high boiling polyphenyls and their derivatives at temperatures up to 450°C on a polyphenyl tar as stationary phase.

(*d*) *Aromatic Compounds in Quantitative Analysis*

With common detectors including catharometers, argon ionisation detectors, and flame ionisation detectors, the area of a peak is very roughly proportional to the weight per cent of a component consisting of a non-aromatic hydrocarbon (Sections 8.4, 8.6, and 9.8). This rule, which is usually accurate within a few per cent for such compounds, cannot be applied to aromatic hydrocarbons, for which the sensitivities of detectors

TABLE 11.21

RETENTION VOLUMES RELATIVE TO DIPHENYL ON APIEZON M GREASE AT 197°C OF SUBSTITUTED DIPHENYLS[a]

Substance	Relative retention
Diphenyl	*1.000*
2-Methyl diphenyl	0.96
3-Methyl diphenyl	1.55
4-Methyl diphenyl	1.65
2,2′-Dimethyl diphenyl	1.005
3,3′-Dimethyl diphenyl	2.40
4,4′-Dimethyl diphenyl	2.69
2,3′-Dimethyl diphenyl	1.43
2,4′-Dimethyl diphenyl	1.55
3,4′-Dimethyl diphenyl	2.54
2,3′-Dimethyl diphenyl	1.67
2,4-Dimethyl diphenyl	1.55
2,5-Dimethyl diphenyl	1.49
2,6-Dimethyl diphenyl	1.09
3,4-Dimethyl diphenyl	2.86
3,5-Dimethyl diphenyl	2.36
2-Ethyl diphenyl	1.22
3-Ethyl diphenyl	2.19
4-Ethyl diphenyl	2.45
2,6,2′-Trimethyl diphenyl	1.17
2-*n*-Propyl diphenyl	1.56
2-*i*-Propyl diphenyl	1.30
2,4,2′,4′-Tetramethyl diphenyl	2.50
3,4,3′,4′-Tetramethyl diphenyl	8.10
2,6,2′,6′-Tetramethyl diphenyl	1.33
2,2′-Diethyl diphenyl	1.72
3,3′-Diethyl diphenyl	4.55
4,4′-Diethyl diphenyl	5.95
2-*i*-Propyl-5-methyl diphenyl	1.91
2-*n*-Butyl diphenyl	2.24
2,4,6,2′,4′,6′-Hexamethyl diphenyl	2.90
2,2′-Di-isopropyl diphenyl	2.20
2,2′-Di-tert-butyl diphenyl	5.05

[a] See references *19* and *20*.

(Section 7.1) are up to about 50% different. This may be illustrated for argon detectors by the points for aromatic compounds on Fig. 8.12, which are very far astray from the others. For catharometers, the relative weight sensitivities of a number of compounds [calculated from Rosie and Grob (*22*)] is presented in Table 11.22(a), illustrating the difference produced

TABLE 11.22

WEIGHT SENSITIVITIES OF VAPOURS IN A CATHAROMETER

Compound	Relative weight sensitivity
(a) Vapours in helium relative to n-hexane	
n-Pentane	1.02
n-Hexane	*1.00*
n-Heptane	0.98
n-Decane	0.97
2,2-Dimethylbutane	0.94
2-Methylpentane	0.97
2-Methylhexane	0.95
Benzene	0.89
Toluene	0.88
Ethylbenzene	0.85
o-Xylene	0.86
sec-Butylbenzene	0.83
(b) Vapours in nitrogen relative to diphenyl	
Diphenyl	*1.00*
Cyclohexylbenzene	1.20
Dicyclohexyl	1.35
Naphthalene	1.60
Tetralin	2.10
Decalin	2.20

by the presence of an aromatic nucleus. An extreme example of this appears from the results of Hendriks, Soemantri, and Waterman (*14*), who find the weight sensitivities given in Table 11.22(b) for naphthalene, diphenyl, and their hydrogenation products, using nitrogen as carrier gas in a catharometer.

11.5. SUMMARY OF GROUP SEPARATIONS OF HYDROCARBONS

The four principal groups of hydrocarbons, i.e., alkanes, alkenes, naphthenes, and aromatics, can frequently be separated one from another by group separations (Section 3.9). The group separation of alkanes from naphthenes is discussed in Section 11.3(d), and that of alkanes from alkenes in Section 11.3(e). Other group separations involving hydrocarbons are discussed below.

Information on the possibility of group separations in general is easily obtained from graphs of the kind given in either Fig. 3.11 or Fig. 3.12. If, on a particular stationary phase, two lines are spaced by a sufficient boiling point difference (Fig. 3.12) or a sufficient number of carbon atoms (Fig. 3.11), then a group separation covering that range is feasible.

(*a*) *Alkane—Aromatic*

On paraffinic stationary phases, activity coefficients of aromatics are similar to those of alkanes, and they are not selectively retained. Thus, it is seen from Table 11.23 that on Apiezon A oil, benzene appears between

TABLE 11.23

RETENTIONS RELATIVE TO BENZENE OF *n*-ALKANES ON VARIOUS STATIONARY PHASES ARRANGED IN ORDER OF SELECTIVE RETENTION OF BENZENE

		Stationary phase					
	Boiling point	Apiezon A oil	Apiezon A oil	Dinonyl phthalate	Polyethylene glycol 1000	Polyethylene glycol 400	Dimethylsulfolane
Temperature (°C):	—	65	101	118	78	100	31
Reference:	—	*1*	*1*	*1*	*1*	*2*	*3*
n-Hexane	69.0	0.627	0.63	0.48	0.089	0.117	0.058
n-Heptane	98.4	1.58	1.37	0.80	0.192	0.205	0.145
n-Octane	125.8			1.54	0.391	0.343	
n-Nonane	150.8			2.98	0.799		
n-Decane	174				1.2	0.97	
Benzene	80.1	*1.00*	*1.00*	*1.00*	*1.00*	*1.00*	*1.00*

n-hexane and *n*-heptane, as does its boiling point. As the polarity of the stationary phase increases, however, the activity coefficients of the alkanes increase rapidly but those of the aromatics do not, with the result that the aromatics are retained relative to the alkanes. On stationary phases classed as "polar" in Section 3.9, the extra retention of aromatics relative to alkanes is sufficient for these phases to secure complete separation of alkanes from aromatics so long as the least volatile alkane does not boil higher than approximately 150°–170°C. Thus, on polyethylene glycol 400 (*4*) (Table 11.23) or on oxydipropionitrile (*5*), *n*-decane (b.p. 174°C) is eluted before benzene (b.p. 80.1°C). Polar stationary phases are thus perfect group separators for alkanes and aromatics for all alkanes up to *n*-decane, and, if a mixture contains alkanes less volatile than decane, the crudest distillation is adequate to separate them. Figure 11.10 shows a chromatogram on polyethylene glycol 2000 illustrating the separation of alkanes and aromatics.

On less polar and on intermediate stationary phases, the behaviour is also intermediate. Table 11.23 gives relative retentions of benzene and various *n*-alkanes on various stationary phases, with the stationary phases in order of ability to retain benzene relative to alkanes. It will be observed that this order is also an approximate order of polarity.

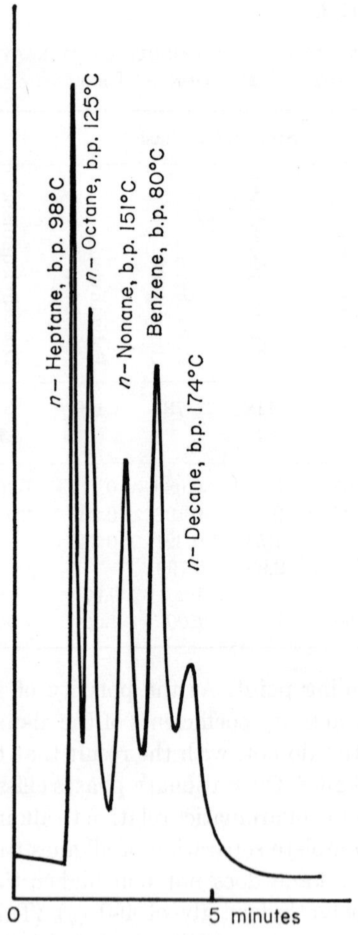

Fig. 11.10. Chromatogram illustrating the retention of benzene relative to alkanes on a polar column (polyethylene glycol 2000).

Alkylammonium montmorillonite also provides specific retention of aromatics relative to alkanes (*6,7*). The relative retentions of some alkanes and aromatics are given in Table 3.18, from which it is seen that the relative retentions are probably about the same as those on polar stationary liquids.

(*b*) *Alkene—Naphthene*

The general features of the separation of alkenes from naphthenes is deducible from comparison of Sections 11.3(d) and 11.3(e). On paraffinic stationary phases, alkenes behave like alkanes, but naphthenes are retained both because of higher boiling point and because of smaller activity coefficients; the result is that naphthenes separate easily from alkenes of the same empirical formula, but that there is no marked separation into groups over more than one carbon number. The magnitude of the activity effects can be shown by the relative retention of methylcyclohexane (b.p. 100.9°C) and 2,4,4-trimethylpentene-1 (b.p. 101.4°C), which is 1.28, or of cycloheptane (b.p. 118.9°C) and octene-1 (b.p. 121.3°C) which is 1.20, with the octene being eluted first.

On intermediate and polar stationary phases, both alkenes and naphthenes are retarded somewhat relative to alkanes, so their relations to one another are little changed. A survey of published data (*1,3,8,9*) does not reveal any simple stationary phase on which there is any effective group separation of the two classes.

Silver nitrate does not complex with naphthenes, and thus stationary phases containing silver nitrate retain alkenes relative to naphthenes. The effect of the silver nitrate is more than sufficient to overcome the naturally small activity coefficients of the naphthenes, with the result that the activity coefficients of alkenes in silver nitrate columns are about half those of naphthenes. This again is insufficient to form the basis of a useful group separation covering more than one carbon number, and the use of silver nitrate columns in this connection is further restricted by their low maximum temperature. Tenney (*5*) suggests the use of diphenylformamide for this separation, but this material has no obvious advantages.

(*c*) *Aromatic—Alkene*

Since polar stationary phases secure a large retention of aromatics relative to alkanes, and a very moderate retention of alkenes relative to alkanes, then they secure a moderate retention of aromatics relative to alkenes. Survey of published data shows that polar stationary phases secure a useful group separation of monoalkenes from aromatics. Thus, on polyethylene glycol 1000, olefins more volatile than nonene-1 (b.p. 146°C) are eluted before benzene (*1*), and Fig. 3.12 shows that on β,β'-oxydipropionitrile, olefins boiling below approximately 160°C are eluted before benzene (*5*). The use of silver nitrate columns makes the separation of alkenes and aromatics worse, since it retards the faster moving alkenes so that they are eluted closer to the aromatics.

(*d*) *Aromatic—Naphthene*

On paraffinic stationary phases, naphthenes have slightly smaller activity coefficients than aromatics. Thus, benzene and cyclohexane, both of which boil at 80°C, separate in the order given with a relative retention of approximately 1.1 on a paraffinic stationary phase. On polar stationary phases, the aromatics are retarded relative to the naphthenes in much the same way as with alkenes, and thus such stationary phases provide a useful group separation. For example, Fig. 3.12 shows that on β,β'-oxydipropionitrile, any naphthene boiling below approximately 180°C (e.g., *n*-butylcyclohexane) is eluted in front of benzene. On intermediate stationary phases, the retention of aromatics is less marked.

11.6. Fatty Acids and Esters

There is much literature on the gas chromatography of fatty acids and esters, the analysis of which is required in many branches of technology, e.g., plastics, oil, etc. Most of the work, however, is on the analysis of the higher fatty acids found in animals and plants. The lower acids may be conveniently analysed as acids or as esters. Acids above about C_6 cause undesirable tailing which is reduced only with difficulty, so that they are usually esterified, usually to the methyl ester, before analysis.

(*a*) *Chromatography of the Lower Fatty Acids*

Acids up to dodecanoic (C_{12}) were analysed by James and Martin in their original work on gas-liquid chromatography (*1*). On silicone oil on diatomaceous earth, bad tailing was found, but this was considerably reduced by the incorporation of 10% by weight of stearic acid (C_{18}) with the silicone. One possible reason for the advantageous effect of stearic acid is the reduction of adsorption in the support discussed in Section 6.3. Another possibility considered by Beerthuis *et al.* (*2*) is that there is a certain amount of specific chemical combination between the solute acids and the stearic acid similar in kind to the familiar dimers formed by acetic acid and other lower fatty acids. Retention volumes of acids on silicone-stearic acid relative to *n*-butyric are given in Table 11.24.

Acids up to behenitic (C_{22}) have been chromatographed by Beerthuis, Dijkstra, Keppler, and Recourt (*2*). Up to C_{12}, a fraction molecularly distilled from silicone oil DC 550 was found to be a satisfactory stationary phase, but, for acids heavier than C_{12}, the temperature of analysis was so high that the silicone was appreciably volatile. For acids from C_{12} to C_{22}, Apiezon L grease on diatomaceous earth was found to be satisfactory at an operating temperature of approximately 300°C. The peaks were, however,

TABLE 11.24

RETENTION VOLUMES RELATIVE TO *n*-BUTYRIC ACID OF LOWER FATTY ACIDS ON SILICONE-STEARIC ACID[a]

Acid	Relative retention at:	
	100°C	137°C
Formic	0.076	—
Acetic	0.20	0.26
Propionic	0.47	0.54
Isobutyric	0.77	0.81
n-Butyric	*1.00*	*1.00*
Isodimethylpropionic	1.15	—
Isovaleric	1.51	1.48
α-Methylbutyric	1.70	—
n-Valeric	2.17	1.91
α-Methylvaleric		2.94
Hexanoic		3.58
Heptanoic		6.55
Octanoic		12.0
Nonaoic		22.0
Decanoic		40.5
Undecanoic		72.8
Dodecanoic		138.5

[a] See reference *1*.

broad, and the method is not suitable for resolution of any acids other than the normal saturated series.

(*b*) *Analysis of Esters of Lower Fatty Acids*

The methyl esters of the common fatty acids have been analysed on a variety of stationary phases by James and Martin (*3*) at either 78.5° or 100°C. Retention data relative to methyl *n*-butyrate is given in Table 11.25.

A number of vinyl esters of saturated fatty acids, and esters of unsaturated acids with saturated fatty alcohols, e.g., ethyl, butyl, etc., have been chromatographed on many stationary phases by Jones (*4*). Retention data relative to ethyl caprylate (C_8) are given in the paper. Most of the solutes chosen are monomers used in the preparation of "vinyl" type polymers. Other data on lower fatty acid esters are given in Section 11.7.

(*c*) *Preparation of Methyl Esters of Higher Fatty Acids*

In most applications, biological material containing fatty acids must be broken down, e.g., from a glyceride to the free acids, which must then be converted to the methyl ester. There are several methods.

TABLE 11.25

RETENTION VOLUMES OF LOWER FATTY ACID METHYL ESTERS RELATIVE TO METHYL *n*-BUTYRATE ON VARIOUS STATIONARY PHASES[a]

Methyl ester	Stationary phase				
	Liquid paraffin	Dioctyl phthalate	Paraffin wax	Benzyl-diphenyl	Dioctyl phthalate
Temperature (°C):	78.5	78.5	100	100	100
Formate	0.071	0.098	0.09	0.117	0.124
Acetate	0.177	0.216	0.228	0.261	0.256
Propionate	0.445	0.485	0.495	0.53	0.51
Isobutyrate	0.724	0.71	0.75	0.67	0.706
n-Butyrate	*1.000*	*1.000*	*1.000*	*1.000*	*1.000*
αα-Dimethylpropionate	1.04	0.87	1.0		0.875
α-Methylbutyrate	1.67	1.51	1.52		1.45
Isovalerate	1.63	1.56	1.53	1.34	1.45
n-Valerate	2.42	2.31	2.15	2.13	2.12
3-Methylvalerate	4.25	3.66	3.53		
Isohexanoate	4.5	3.96	3.60	3.03	3.24
n-Hexanoate	5.86	5.16	4.70	4.37	4.36

[a] See reference *3*.

A convenient method of methylating free acids is for them to be dissolved in a mixture of methanol and ether, and the solution to be treated with sufficient of a methanolic solution of diazomethane. After reaction, excess diazomethane may be stripped, leaving a solution of the esters (*5*).

The diazomethane technique has been criticised by Stoffel, Chu, and Ahrens (*6*), since the diazomethane may add to double bonds forming pyrazolines, and also structural changes may occur during the saponification of the original organic material [see Subsection (f)]. These authors suggest an interesterification technique employed on the original material. The following recipe is taken from the above authors' paper.

The esters or acids to be methylated (1 to 10 mg) are dissolved in 4 ml of 5% hydrochloric acid in superdry methanol and 0.5 ml of dry benzene in a 15 ml microsublimation tube to which a condenser with a calcium chloride moisture trap is connected. The mixture is refluxed in a silicone bath at 80°C to 100°C for two hours, with frequent shaking at the start to dissolve the mixture. After cooling to room temperature, two volumes of water are added, and the methyl esters are extracted three times with 3 ml of petroleum ether. The pooled extracts are simultaneously neutralised and dried over sodium sulphate-sodium bicarbonate mixture for 1 hour. The esters are then quantitatively transferred with petroleum ether to a second microsublimation tube and the solvent is evaporated to dryness at reduced pressure in a 40°C water bath.

In the technique of Luddy, Barford, and Riemenschneider (*7*), the transesterification is performed by potassium methylate in methanol, and the resulting fatty acid esters are removed from unsaponifiable material by silicic acid chromatography.

Craig *et al.* (*8*) have found that, with the more volatile fatty acids, it is convenient to prepare esters less volatile than methyl. In their procedure, the acids are converted to their sodium salts, which are reacted with α-bromacetophenone to yield phenacyl esters, which may then be chromatographed at 200°C.

It is possible to chromatograph glyceryl esters at very high temperatures. Huebner (*9*) has partially hydrolysed glycerides derived from coconuts, acetylated the product, and chromatographed the resulting partially acetylated fat at temperatures from 240° to 360°C.

(*d*) *Methyl Esters on Non-Polar Stationary Phases*

The chromatography of the methyl esters of the higher fatty acids was first reported by Cropper and Heywood (*10–12*), who used silicone grease as the stationary phase, and found that sodium chloride crystals were most satisfactory as a support, since these had a small resistance to flow at the high temperatures used. Most other workers, however, have used diatomaceous earth as support. Many authors give details of separations performed on silicone grease (*2,13–16*), Apiezon L (*2,15,17*), or Apiezon M (*3,16,18*) grease. Using one or other of these, fatty acid esters up to at least C_{34} (*13*) may be analysed. For this, a temperature of 295°C was used, but for most biochemical applications, which do not involve many acids above about C_{22}, a temperature of approximately 200°C is suitable, and has been used by the majority of workers.

Many authors have given relative retention data for common fatty acid esters on the above stationary phases; a selection of this is included in Table 11.26.

As is general (Section 3.9), retention times of successive normal saturated esters differ by a constant factor, so that a plot of the logarithm of the retention time against carbon number is an accurate straight line. At temperatures of approximately 200°C, the factor is approximately 1.5, as may be seen from Table 11.26.

The retention volumes of unsaturated fatty acid esters are slightly smaller than those of their saturated analogs, and to a rough approximation,

TABLE 11.26

RETENTIONS RELATIVE TO METHYL STEARATE OF METHYL ESTERS OF HIGHER FATTY ACIDS[a]

		Stationary phase									
		Apiezon M	Apiezon M	Apiezon M	Silicone grease	Apiezon L	Reoplex 400	Reoplex 400	Poly(diethylene glycol succinate)	Poly(diethylene glycol succinate)	Poly(vinyl acetate)
Temperature (°C):		197	197	200	200	240	197	240	200	203	210
Reference:		*3*	*18*	*16*	*16*	*21*	*18*	*19*	*16*	*22*	*20*
Caprylate	(C_8)	0.013		0.012	0.026			0.07	0.055		
Nonanoate	(C_9)	0.02		0.018	0.038				0.078		
Caprate	(C_{10})	0.03	0.029	0.031	0.057	0.047	0.10	0.123	0.108		
Undecanoate	(C_{11})		0.047	0.049	0.078	0.07	0.13		0.136		
Laurate	(C_{12})	0.076	0.075	0.077	0.116	0.099	0.16	0.21	0.185	0.22	
Tridecanoate	(C_{13})		0.112	0.117	0.166	0.145	0.22		0.236		
Myristate	(C_{14})	0.179	0.174	0.182	0.237	0.22	0.31	0.355	0.324	0.36	
Myristolenate	($C_{14}^{1:}$)		0.159				0.36				
Pentadecanoate	(C_{15})		0.270	0.279	0.342	0.32	0.41		0.424		
Palmitate	(C_{16})	0.43	0.414	0.435	0.488	0.47	0.56	0.61	0.573	0.60	0.58
Palmitolenate	($C_{16}^{1:}$)	3.73	0.366					0.67		0.70	
Palmitolenate(*trs*)	($C_{16}^{1:}$)	0.386									
Heptadecanoate	(C_{17})		0.649	0.632	0.690		0.74		0.742		
Stearate	(C_{18})	*1.00*	*1.00*	*1.00*	*1.00*	*1.00*	*1.00*	*1.00*	*1.00*	*1.00*	*1.00*
Eleiadate	($C_{18}^{1:}$)	0.88	0.896			0.90	1.12		1.15		
Oleate	($C_{18}^{1:}$)	0.85	0.860	0.880		0.89	1.12	1.09	1.12	1.16	1.13
Linoleate	($C_{18}^{2:}$)	0.81	0.801	0.857			1.33	1.26	1.41	1.44	1.26
Linolenate	($C_{18}^{3:}$)		0.801	0.805		0.85	1.68	1.52	1.81	1.68	1.48
Arachidate	(C_{20})		2,38		2.01	2.13	1.77	1.70	1.78	1.84	
	($C_{20}^{1:}$)		1.99				1.98				
Arachidonate	($C_{20}^{4:}$)		1.46			1.47	2.96		3.11		2.81

[a] *Note:* The superscript to the symbol for the fatty acid groups stands for the number of ethylenic bonds.

the relative retention of an unsaturated ester and its saturated analog is multiplied by a constant factor for every additional unsaturated group, though deviations from this rule can lead to accidental overlaps. This is illustrated from the figures of Table 11.26, but is seen to best advantage in Fig. 11.11, which shows the chromatogram of a mixture of fatty acid esters taken on a 200-foot capillary column (*23*), and shows the way in which unsaturated esters precede the saturated esters in order of unsaturation. The difference in retention between saturated and unsaturated

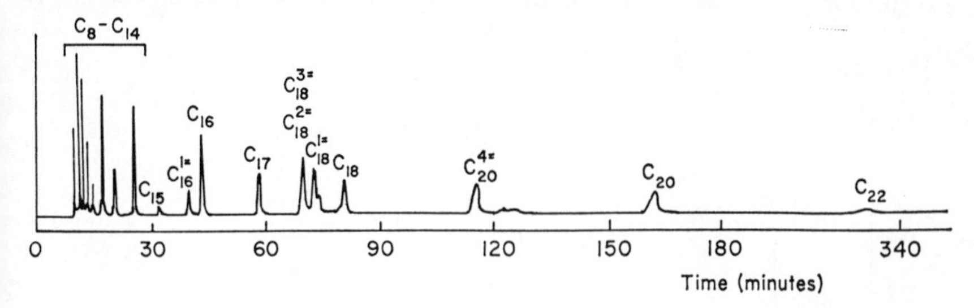

FIG. 11.11. Separation of fatty acid esters at 240°C on a 200-foot capillary column coated with Apiezon L grease. Lipsky, Landowne, and Lovelock (*23*).

esters of the same carbon number is small, and columns of considerable efficiency are required to secure good resolution. In particular, columns of non-polar stationary phases cannot separate the important pair linoleic-linolenic acids, which occur in many fats and oils.

(e) *Methyl Esters on Polar Stationary Phases*

The overlaps involving unsaturated esters on non-polar stationary phases have led many workers to use polar stationary phases; many of the common polar stationary phases, however, may not be used on account of the high temperatures necessary for the analysis. Orr and Callen (*19,24*) have used Reoplex 400, which is a commercial polyester material used as a plasticiser. Other workers have used this and a number of other polyesters, which are materials made by the esterification of dibasic acids with alcohols containing more than one hydroxyl group. In particular, the polyester of succinic acid and diethylene glycol has been extensively used (*22,25*).

The principal characteristic of the polar stationary phases is that, in contrast to the paraffinic stationary phases, olefinic esters are selectively retained so that they are eluted after the corresponding saturated esters. This is illustrated in Fig. 11.12 from Orr and Callen (*24*), which compares chromatograms of a mixture of saturated and unsaturated esters from C_{16} to C_{20} on a polar and on a non-polar stationary phase. Relative retention data for common fatty acid esters on a variety of polar stationary phases is included in Table 11.26.

The relative positions of a saturated ester and its corresponding unsaturated analogs depend on the exact nature of the stationary phase, and, by making polyesters from different acids and alcohols, the relative retentions can be varied almost at will. This is illustrated in Table 11.27 (after the similar table given by Orr and Callen (*24*), with additions), which shows the relative retention of methyl stearate/methyl linoleate on a number of different polyester stationary phases. According to the principles given in Section 3.9 and the details of the chromatography of alkenes in

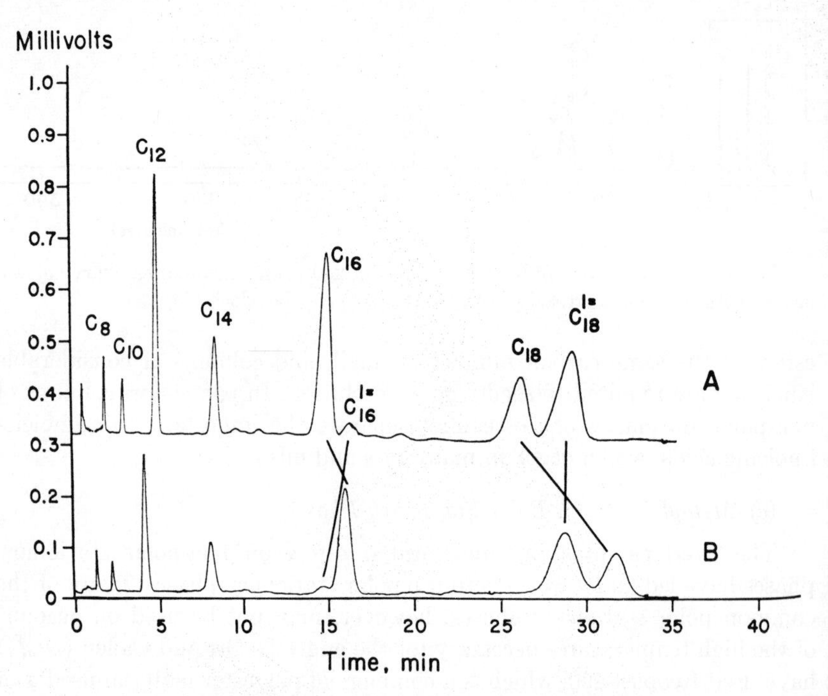

FIG. 11.12. Chromatograms of fatty acid esters on Reoplex 400 polyester and on Apiezon L grease Compared. Orr and Callen (*24*).

	A	B
Column packing:	20.0 g 40% Reoplex 400 on 60–80 mesh Celite	23.8 g 20% Apiezon L on 60–80 mesh Celite
Column:	275 × 0.5 cm	275 × 0.5 cm
Flow rate:	117 ml/minute at STP	139 ml/minute at STP
Temperature:	244°C	240°C
Sample volume:	5 μl	4 μl

comparison with alkanes given in Section 11.3(e), it is to be expected that the smaller the proportion of methylene or methyl groups in the stationary phase, the larger the relative retention, and study of the table appears to confirm this. Thus, the relative retention on polyethylene sebacate is greater than that on polypropylene sebacate; similarly for polydiethylene glycol succinate in comparison with polydiethylene glycol adipate.

TABLE 11.27

RELATIVE RETENTION OF METHYL STEARATE/METHYL LINOLEATE ON VARIOUS POLYESTER STATIONARY PHASES

Stationary phase	Relative retention	Temp. (°C)	Ref.
Non-polar	≈0.85	200	
Polypropylene sebacate/laurate	1.00	240	*24*
Butyl glyceryl sebacate	1.05	240	*24*
Polypropylene sebacate/phthalate	1.06	240	*24*
Polypropylene sebacate	1.06	240	*24*
Polydiethylene glycol adipate	1.10	240	*24*
Polyvinyl acetate	1.26	210	*24*
Polyethylene sebacate	1.28	240	*24*
Polyoxyalkylene adipate (Reoplex 400)	1.29	240	*24*
Polyoxyalkylene adipate (Reoplex 400)	1.33	197	*18*
Polydiethylene glycol/pentaerithritol adipate	1.32	240	*24*
Polydiethylene glycol succinate	1.41	200	*16*
Polydiethylene glycol succinate	1.44	203	*22*

On nearly all the polyester stationary phases, the polyunsaturated esters are retained longer than the saturated ester with one more carbon atom. Since, however, in very many natural mixtures, the acids with odd number of carbon atoms are virtually absent, this causes no overlaps. With some of the more polar polyester stationary phases, the polyunsaturated esters are retained beyond the saturated ester with two more carbon atoms, and this may well cause undesirable overlaps. With Reoplex 400 at least, which is a moderately polar stationary phase, monounsaturated esters appear before the saturated ester with one more carbon atom, so that mixtures containing acids with even and odd carbon numbers may be satisfactorily analysed on this so long as polyunsaturated esters are not present which might cause overlaps.

There are two drawbacks to the use of polyesters as stationary phases. The preparation of the materials leads to a product which contains material spanning a large range of molecular weight, and some of it is appreciably volatile. This leads to a slow volatilisation of the column material, causing noise in the detector and eventual deterioration in the efficiency of the column. This effect can be reduced to some extent by pre-treatment of the column at the temperature to be used for the analysis (*24*). The other drawback is the possibility of a transesterification reaction in the column not unlike the reaction described in Subsection (c) above for the preparation of methyl esters. This leads to an exchange between the volatile methyl esters and the non-volatile polyesters the extent of which is proportional to the residence time of the volatile ester in the column, with the result that, in quantitative analyses, esters eluted quickly appear in too large a proportion, and esters eluted slowly appear in too small a proportion. Orr and Callen have found that this effect is serious at 240°C, and may lead to as much as 30% error in analysis, but it can be considerably reduced by reducing the temperature of the column. Thus, at 200°C, the error is no greater than 8%. Such an error is still large, however, and further reduction in temperature lengthens analysis times unduly.

It has been suggested that both the above effects may be caused by the acidic activity of the support.

Hornstein, Elliott, and Crowe (*20*) have suggested the use of commercial polyvinyl acetates in place of the polyesters described above. These decompose slowly at about 220°C, but the only product is acetic acid, which does not interfere with the operation of the detector. Such a stationary phase secures a good separation of the C_{18} esters, as may be seen from the appropriate column of Table 11.26.

(*f*) *Effect of Ester Structure on Retention*

On all kinds of stationary phase, the linear relation between carbon number and the logarithm of the retention volume holds with great accuracy for the higher fatty acid esters, as is seen from Fig. 11.13 (*16*) and similar figures given by many authors.

The effect of unsaturated links in a linear methylene chain on the retention has been discussed in the previous two sections, most of the results being for the C_{18} acids. In general, it is found, in accord with the principles of Chapter 3, that substitution of a double bond for a single bond in a particular position multiplies the retention by a constant factor whatever the carbon number of the acid, with the result that, on plots of log V_R' or log r against carbon number, monounsaturated, diunsaturated, etc., acids give lines parallel to the line for saturated esters, and, to a first approximation, successive lines for successively more unsaturated esters are equally spaced. This is shown in Fig. 11.14 for esters chromatographed on a polyester stationary phase (*26*), and also in Fig. 11.13. Similar plots may be obtained for any stationary phase. In non-polar stationary phases the lines are less well spaced and lie in the reverse order, but are slightly steeper (*26*) [see Section 3.9(c)].

Though the retention of an unsaturated ester of a given carbon number is governed largely by the number of double bonds, there is ample evidence that it is also governed to a lesser extent by the positions of the double bonds. Thus, Janak, Dobiasova, and Vereš (*27*) have shown that isomers such as 3-hexene-1-carboxylic ester and 2-hexene-1-carboxylic ester may be resolved on polyester stationary phases. Daniels and Richmond (*28*) have shown that polyunsaturated fatty acid esters containing conjugated double bonds have considerably greater retentions on polar stationary phases than their unconjugated isomers such as are found in fats. Since double bond migration with the formation of conjugated chains occurs if fatty acids are treated with strong alkali, care should be taken to avoid

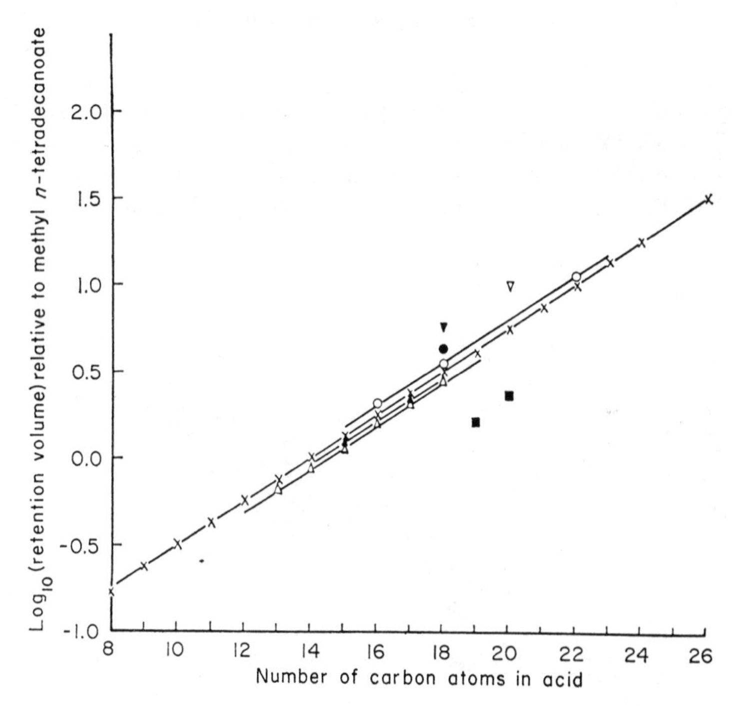

FIG. 11.13. Plot of the logarithms of the relative retentions of fatty acid esters against carbon number. Hawke, Hansen, and Shorland (*16*). ×, straight chain acids; △, iso-acids; ▲, + -anteiso-acids, □, multibranched acids; ○, monounsaturated acids; ●, diunsaturated acid; ▼, triunsaturated acid; ▽, tetraunsaturated acid.

strong alkali in the preparation of samples for fatty acid analysis. It is apparent also that geometrical isomers have different retentions, for oleic and eliadic acids may be resolved.

The effect of chain branching on the retentions of fatty acid esters is very much as would be anticipated by analogy with alkanes. On both polar and non-polar stationary phases, shifting a carbon atom from the chain into a branch causes a reduction in the retention. This has been studied for acids of the type:

$$\begin{matrix} CH_3 \\ \quad\diagdown \\ \quad\quad CH—(CH_2)_{n-4}—COOH \\ \quad\diagup \\ CH_3 \end{matrix} \quad \text{(iso-acids)}$$

and of the type:

$$\begin{matrix} CH_3 \\ \quad\diagdown \\ \quad\quad CH—(CH_2)_{n-5}—COOH \\ \quad\diagup \\ CH_3—CH_2 \end{matrix} \quad \text{(anteiso-acids)}$$

the retention of which may be compared with that for the straight chain acid $C_nH_{2n}O_2$. At or near 200°C on either polar or non-polar stationary phases, the relative retention of an iso-acid or an anteiso-acid and its *n*-acid of the same carbon number is approximately 1.20, and a short

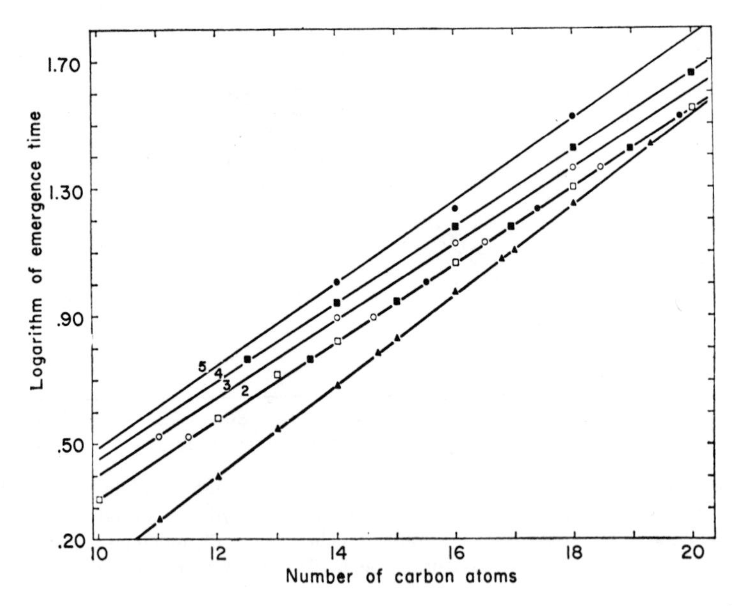

FIG. 11.14. Plot of the logarithms of relative retentions on a polyester stationary phase of variously unsaturated fatty acid esters against carbon number; also, a similar plot for saturated esters on silicone oil. Craig and Murty (*26*). 1, Saturated esters on silicone oil; 2, saturated esters; 3, monoethenoid; 4, diethenoid; 5, triethenoid esters on plasticiser.

column cannot resolve an iso- and an anteiso-acid of the same carbon number (*3*). On a polar stationary phase, however, Hawke, Hansen, and Shorland (*16*) give results which show that the relative retention of iso- and *n*-acids is slightly greater than that of anteiso- and *n*-acids. The magnitude of the effect is shown in Fig. 11.13, which shows plots of log *r* against carbon number for all three series of saturated acids.

(*g*) *Methods of Qualitative Identification*

Many fats and natural products give a large number of peaks the qualitative identification of which may be difficult. In many applications, there are only two unknown parameters for each component of the mixture, carbon number and degree of unsaturation, and, for determining these, the techniques in which the retention is determined on each of two different stationary phases are particularly useful (*17*). Details of the graphical ways of using retention data on two stationary phases are described in Section 3.10.

Miwa *et al.* (*29,30*) and Woodford and van Gent (*31*) have introduced a modification of the idea of relative retention for the description of the retention of fatty acid esters. In this, the line for saturated normal esters on a plot of log *r* against carbon number is taken as the reference line, and the retention of a substance of relative retention *r* is described by the abscissa of the point on the line for saturated normal esters the ordinate of which is log *r*. The retention is thus described by its "Equivalent Carbon Number," i.e., what the carbon number would be of a saturated normal ester having a relative retention *r*. Equivalent carbon numbers of saturated normal esters are integers equal to their actual carbon number. Equivalent carbon numbers of unsaturated or branched esters are generally non-integral. On polar stationary phases, equivalent carbon numbers of unsaturated esters are greater than their actual carbon number; on non-polar

TABLE 11.28

EQUIVALENT CARBON NUMBERS OF METHYL ESTERS OF HIGHER FATTY ACIDS[a]

Acid	Equivalent carbon number	
	Apiezon L	Diethylene glycol/ Pentaerithritol adipate
Stearic	18.0	18.0
Palmitoleic (*cis*-Δ^9-C_{16})	15.7	16.4
Oleic (*cis*-Δ^9-C_{18})	17.7	18.4
Petroselenic (*cis*-Δ^6-C_{18})	17.7	18.4
Erucic (*cis*-Δ^{13}-C_{22})	21.7	22.4
Linoleic	17.6	19.0
Linolenic	17.6	19.8
Arachidonic	19.2	21.6

[a] See reference *30*.

stationary phases, they are less. The advantage of this scheme is that the equivalent carbon number of an ester is independent of most column conditions, and only very slightly dependent on temperature. For practical purposes, equivalent carbon number is a function of the stationary phase only. Table 11.28 exemplifies equivalent carbon numbers of some fatty acid esters on a polar and on a non-polar stationary phase. Unknown esters can be identified from their equivalent carbon numbers on each of two stationary phases in the same way that they can be identified from their position on graphs of the kind described in Section 3.10.

Landowne and Lipsky (*32*) have tried the technique of brominating a mixture containing saturated and unsaturated esters, thus turning the unsaturated esters into brominated derivatives of much lower volatility. The chromatogram of brominated oleic acid shows a variety of peaks, none of which are widely separated from the peaks of substances likely to accompany oleic acid in real mixtures.

(*h*) *Use of Capillary Columns*

Lipsky, Landowne, and Lovelock (*21,23*) have used capillary columns for the analysis of fatty acid esters. Using a 200-foot stainless steel capillary of 0.01 inch diameter coated with Apiezon L grease, an extremely efficient column capable of up to 200,000 plates is obtained. This efficiency is such as to overcome the drawback provided by the small relative retentions between saturates and ethylenics provided by Apiezon L, except in the case of linoleic and linolenic acids, which separate poorly. A chromatogram is shown in Fig. 11.11.

The above authors have also used a 100-foot capillary column packed with the polar stationary phase diethylene glycol glutarate polyester, but the maximum plate number is only 2800, which is less than that of most packed columns. It is common experience that capillary columns are poor when coated with polar materials.

(*i*) *Quantitative Analysis*

The simple lower fatty acids give anomalous responses in catharometers, since the hot element supplies heat in partly dissociating the dimerised molecules. With acetic acid, this may result in the hot element becoming cooler rather than warmer, thus producing a reversed peak.

The simple lower fatty acids can also give anomalous responses in ionisation detectors (*33*); no simple reason can be given.

The methyl esters of the higher fatty acids consist principally of a hydrocarbon chain, with the result that weight sensitivities are virtually constant, and that weights are proportional to peak areas independently of the compound. This has been assumed by many workers, including many of those quoted above, and both in catharometers and in ionisation detectors has been found to lead to accurate quantitative analyses. It has been specifically checked by Killheffer and Jungermann (*34*). In calculating percentages of various fatty acids in a natural product, care must be taken to allow for the weight of the esterifying group, which is included in the gas chromatographic analysis but which must be subtracted cut before giving the proportions of fatty acids. With methyl esters of higher fatty acids, the correction is small, but if, for example, phenacyl esters are used, it may be large.

(*j*) *Reviews*

Reviews of the applications of gas chromatography to biochemistry, including large sections on fatty acids, have been written by Lipsky and Landowne (*35*) and by James (*36*). Also see the book by Burchfield and Storrs (*37*).

11.7. Oxygenated Compounds

Oxygenated aliphatic compounds are polar, and many of them tend to associate into weakly bound dimers. This has two consequences when they are chromatographed on non-polar stationary phases:

(1) They are not very soluble in the non-polar stationary phase, and their activity coefficients (Section 3.5) change rapidly with concentration; the normal effect of this is to produce a diffuse front profile to the peak, which is thus broadened, and to retain the peak maximum so that retention volumes appear too great.

(2) Polar compounds, especially those with OH groups, are easily adsorbed by the support, and, since the solution in the stationary phase is small, the effect of the support is comparatively important; the normal effect of this is to produce a diffuse rear profile to the peak, which is thus broadened. This is further discussed in Section 6.3.

Knight (*1*) has discussed both of these phenomena in connection with hydroxylated compounds, and concludes that non-polar stationary phases should not generally be used for these; he finds that di-isodecyl phthalate, tricresyl phosphate, polyethylene glycols, silicone DC 550, and β,β'-oxydipropionitrile are all suitable stationary phases for use with alcohols. By use of such phases, the leading effect due to poor solubility is overcome; the tailing due to adsorption may be overcome by any of the means given in Section 6.3. Though there is little doubt that the conditions for analysis of oxygenated compounds are less restrictive on polar stationary phases, there are many workers who have achieved satisfactory separations on non-polar phases, especially for the higher members of homologous series at elevated temperatures.

(*a*) *Alcohols*

The lower alkanols up to and including 4-methylbutanol-1 (isoamyl alcohol) and *n*-pentanol-1, but not including the other six less common pentanols, may all be easily separated on any of several stationary phases, subject to the restrictions given above. Table 11.29 gives specific and relative retention data for these compounds.

TABLE 11.29

SPECIFIC AND RELATIVE RETENTION VOLUMES OF LOWER ALKANOLS

	Stationary phase												
	Silicone fluid DC 702	Silicone fluid DC 702	Tricresyl phosphate	Tricresyl phosphate	Polyethylene glycol 400	Silicone oil	Dioctyl sebacate	Dioctyl sebacate	Didecyl phthalate	Didecyl phthalate	Hexamethylene glycol dimethyl ether	Polyethylene glycol	β,β′-Oxydipropionitrile
Specific or Relative:	S	S	S	S	S	R	R	R	R	R	R	R	R
Temperature (°C):	56.2	97.0	56	97	100	100	50	100	50	100	70	100	70
Reference:	*2*	*2*	*2*	*2*	*3*	*4*	*4*	*4*	*4*	*4*	*5*	*4*	*5*
Methanol	18.8	63.1	16.6		38.5	0.34	1.26	0.71	1.19	0.94	0.53	23.4	0.91
Ethanol	35	14.5	102	24.0	46.1	0.69	2.47	1.49	2.22	1.68	0.73	31.5	1.1
Isopropanol	50	17.9	112	27.5		1.03	3.46	2.13	2.96	2.16	0.78	28.8	1.0
n-Propanol	88	27.8	229	52	80.0	1.51	5.38	3.75	6.79	3.91	1.6	59.3	1.2
tert-Butanol													0.9
sec-Butanol											1.7		1.8
Isobutanol	155	43		77.6							2.4		2.6
n-Butanol	224.5	57.7			146	3.57		8.72	20.0	9.11	3.6	111	3.5
Isopentanol		94											
n-Pentanol		118			239								
n-Pentane						*1.00*	*1.00*	*1.00*	*1.00*	*1.00*		*1.00*	
Benzene											*1.00*		*1.00*

The two optically active *sec*-butanols have been partially resolved on a column of an optically active stationary phase, e.g., ethyl *d*-tartarate, by Karagounis and Lippold (*6*).

The eight pentanols have been studied by Kuffner and Kallina (*7*) on two stationary phases; the relative retention data is given in Table 11.30.

TABLE 11.30

RELATIVE RETENTION VOLUMES OF PENTANOLS AT 100°C[a]

Substance	b.p. (°C)	Class	Relative retention volume: Carbowax 300 (polyethylene glycol)	Relative retention volume: Ricinusol
1,1-Dimethylpropanol	102	Tertiary	5.2	3.6
2,2-Dimethylpropanol	113	Primary	8	4.4
3-Methylbutanol-2	113	Secondary	8.8	5
Pentanol-3	115	Secondary	9.6	7.6
Pentanol-2	118	Secondary	10.8	6.4
2-Methylbutanol-1	128	Secondary	15.2	9.2
3-Methylbutanol-1	132	Primary	16.0	9.4
Pentanol-1	138	Primary	19.2	13.1

[a] See reference *7*.

It is seen that on polyethylene glycol, the smallest relative retention is 1.05 between 2-methylbutanol and 3-methylbutanol, and any column capable of resolving such a relative retention will resolve all eight isomers. The overlap of 2-methylbutanol and 3-methylbutanol is also reported by Warren *et al.* (*8*).

There has been no systematic study of the higher alcohols other than the normal alkanol-1's; Kallina and Kuffner (*9*), however, give retention data for 15 out of the 89 possible octanols. This is given in Table 11.31.

A plot of the logarithm of the retention volumes of the *n*-alkanol-1's against carbon number gives a good straight line with all members of the series other than methanol, both on dinonyl phthalate (*10*) and on polyethylene glycol (*3*). As is usual, branching produces a reduction in retention volume, and, to a good approximation, the same kind of branching produces the same change in log V_R'. Thus, the line for "iso"-alcohols lies parallel to and below the plot of *n*-alcohols. There are not sufficient results to enable one to deduce general relations between retention and structure in more complicated branched structures. A tentative observation derived from Table 11.31 is that activity coefficients in polyethylene glycol decline from tertiary through primary alcohols, thus the primary 2-methylheptanol-1 is retained beyond the secondary octanol-4, even though the former is branched, and has the lower boiling point.

TABLE 11.31

RELATIVE RETENTION VOLUMES OF OCTANOLS[a]

Substance	b.p. (°C)	Class	Relative retention volume: Polyethylene glycol	Relative retention volume: Ricinusol
2,2,4-Trimethylpentanol-4	146	Tertiary	3.6	5
2,2,4-Trimethylpentanol-3	153	Secondary	4	5.5
4-Methylheptanol-3	155	Secondary	7.5	6.8
2,3,4-Trimethylpentanol-3	156	Tertiary	7.2	7
3-Methylheptanol-3	161	Tertiary	4.8	6
3-Ethylhexanol-4	163	Secondary	6.7	7
4-Ethylhexanol-2	165	Secondary	8.2	7.2
2-Methylheptanol-5	166	Secondary	7.5	7
Octanol-3	173	Secondary	8.7	7.3
2-Methylheptanol-1	175	Primary	12.5	9.5
Octanol-4	176	Secondary	9.3	8
2-*n*-Propylpentanol-1	180	Primary	14	11.5
Octanol-2	180	Secondary	10.5	9
2-Ethylhexanol-1	183	Primary	14	11.6
Octanol-1	195	Primary	19	14

[a] See reference *9*.

The gas chromatography of tertiary alcohols is often accompanied by dehydration, leading to smeared peaks and poor quantitative analysis, possibly because of the catalytic effect of the support (Section 6.3).

The chromatography of the higher alcohols resembles closely the chromatography of the fatty acid esters described in Section 11.5. Thus, Broughton and Wheatley (*11*) have analysed wax alcohols obtained from human skin-fat on a column of Apiezon M grease at 197°C, and have obtained chromatograms in which iso- and unsaturated alcohols come through before the corresponding *n*-alcohol, but after the *n*-alcohol with one carbon atom fewer, just as was described for methyl esters of fatty acids on Apiezon L. In the conditions described, the relative retention of iso-alcohols and monounsaturated alcohols is small, so that they overlap on ordinary packed columns. Higher fatty alcohols have also been studied by Link *et al.* (*12,13*) and by Cropper and Heywood (*14*).

The lower glycols and polyglycols may be analysed by gas chromatography. Ginsberg (*15*) describes the separation of mono-, di-, and triethylene glycols on Apiezon L grease in a standard commercial apparatus at 200°C, and Nogare and Safranski (*16*) describe a similar separation, also including tetraethylene glycol, on silicone grease at 206°C. Ring (*17*) performs this separation on polyethylene glycol 1000 at 150°C.

An important application of gas chromatography is the analysis of sterols. Beerthuis and Recourt (*18*) find that many common sterols are easily separated on a column of molecularly distilled silicone oil on kieselguhr treated with dimethyldichlorosilane operated at 287°C. Vandenheuvel, Sweeley, and Horning (*19,20*) have used columns of methyl silicone oil (G.E., SE30) on kieselguhr. At a column temperature of 260°C, with 7% by weight of silicone in the column packing, some peaks, especially those of steryl esters, were broadened due to decomposition, but if the proportion of silicone is reduced to 2 or 3% and the operating temperature is reduced to 220°C, satisfactory analyses are obtained without any trace of decomposition. Figure 11.15 [Vandenheuvel *et al.* (*20*)] shows a chromatogram

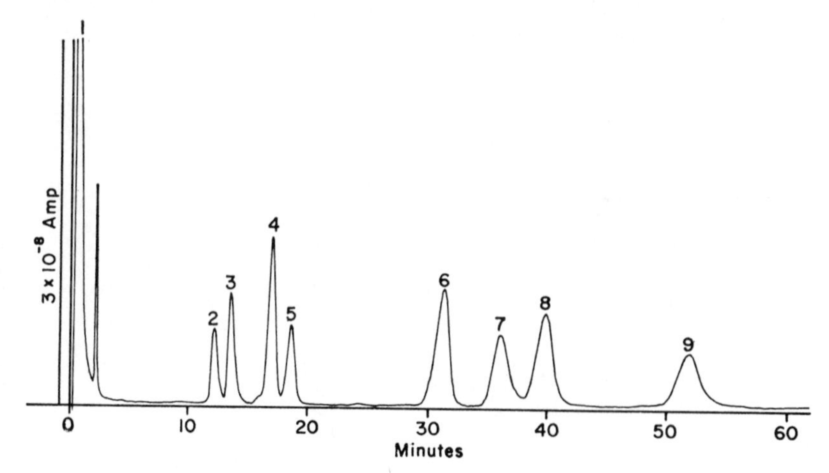

FIG. 11.15. Separation of some sterols, etc., on a column packed with 3% w/w silicone oil on kieselguhr at 222°C. Vandenheuvel, Sweeley, and Horning (*20*). 1, Androstane; 2, pregnane-3,20-dione; 3, allopregnane-3,20-dione; 4, coprostane; 5, cholestane; 6, stigmastane; 7, cholesterol; 8, cholestan-3-one; 9, stigmasterol.

of a mixture of sterols. Retention data for sterols on silicone is given in Table 11.32. Sweeley and Horning (*21*) have analysed sterols on the polyester poly(ethylene glycol isophthalate) satisfactorily, giving a chromatogram with relative retentions significantly different from those on silicone.

(*b*) *Esters*

Esters as usually encountered in biological applications are discussed in Section 11.6. This section deals with other esters, e.g., as found in commercial solvents, etc.

TABLE 11.32

RETENTION OF STEROLS RELATIVE TO CHOLESTEROL ON SILICONE OIL

Substance	Relative retention at:	
	220°C[a]	287°C[b]
Androstane	0.055	
Androstan-17-one	0.11	
Androstan-3,17-dione	0.24	
4-Androsten-3,17-dione	0.29	
Pregnan-3,20-dione	0.34	
Allopregnan-3,20-dione	0.37	
Allopregnan-3,20-diol	0.35	
Coprostane	0.45	
Allopregnan-3,11,20-trione	0.50	
Cholestane	0.505	
Cholesteryl methyl ether	0.87	
Stigmastane	0.83	
Cholestanyl methyl ether	0.90	
Coprostanol		0.90
Cholesterol	*1.00*	*1.00*
Cholestanol	1.01	1.00
Cholestan-3-one	1.08	
7-Cholestenol		1.14
7-Dehydrocholesterol		1.14
Methostenol		1.28
Ergosterol		1.30
Stigmasterol	1.47	1.36
4-Cholesten-3-one	1.37	
Cholesteryl acetate	1.42	1.42
(Tetratriacontane)		1.45
Cholestanyl acetate	1.47	
Cholesteryl propionate		1.83
Cholesteryl isobutyrate		2.0
Cholesteryl butyrate		2.32
Cholesteryl isovalerate		2.64
Cholesteryl valerate		3.02
(Octatriacontane)		3.96

[a] See reference *20*.
[b] See reference *18*.

Table 11.33 contains retention data for a number of common solvent esters arranged in order of boiling point, including relative retention data and sufficient specific retention volumes to be able in principle to specify all the other data. On all the stationary phases listed in the table, calcula-

TABLE 11.33

SPECIFIC AND RELATIVE RETENTION VOLUMES OF LOWER ESTERS

		Stationary phase										
	Boiling point	Silicone	Silicone fluid DC 702	Didecyl phthalate	Didecyl phthalate	Dinonyl phthalate	Hexamethylene glycol dimethyl ether	Tricresyl phosphate	Polyethylene glycol	Polyethylene glycol	Polyethylene glycol 400	β,β′-Oxydipropionitrile
Specific or relative:	—	R	S	R	R	S	R	S	R	R	S	R
Temperature (°C):	—	100	97	50	100	97.5	70	97	50	100	100	70
Reference:	—	*4*	*22*	*4*	*4*	*22*	*5*	*22*	*4*	*4*	*3*	*5*
Methyl formate	31.5	0.53		0.85	0.91		0.24		15.2	6.95		0.50
Ethyl formate	54.1	1.23	20	2.16	1.91		0.43		23.6	11.7		0.75
(Acetone)	56.5	0.96		2.14	1.92		0.41		24.2	13.7		1.1
Methyl acetate	57.1	1.26	21	2.38	2.12		0.43	19.0	23.6	14.1		0.82
Vinyl acetate	72.5						0.73					0.97
Ethyl acetate	77.1	2.36	38.2	5.33	3.70	42.5	0.73	33.1	38.4	19.3	28.1	1.1
Methyl propionate	79.7	2.40	43.1	6.27	4.32		0.82		44.9	22.6		1.24
Methyl acrylate	80.5						0.96					1.41
Isopropyl acetate	89.0	3.04		7.44	4.95		0.88	41.7	42.5	20.9		1.0
Methyl isobutyrate	92.3	3.73		8.90	6.16		1.0		53.3	26.3		
Ethyl propionate	99.1	4.60		11.8	7.43				69.2	31.7		
n-Propyl acetate	101.6	4.63	77	12.8	7.81	88.7	1.5	66.0	71.8	34.9	46.5	1.8
Methyl *n*-butyrate	102.3	5.20		13.5	8.63		1.5		84.7	39.4		
Ethyl isobutyrate	110.1	6.89			10.0				71.8	32.7		
Isobutyl acetate	116.5	7.09			13.2			91.2	105	48.6		
Ethyl *n*-butyrate	120.0	8.60			14.5		2.5			48.5		2.3
n-Butyl acetate	126.5	8.89			16.8	188	3.1			63.9	79.4	3.0
n-Pentane		*1.00*		*1.00*	*1.00*				*1.00*	*1.00*		
Benzene							*1.00*					*1.00*

tion shows that the activity coefficients of the lower esters are all of the order of unity, and, though there are significant small differences between the activity coefficients of isomers, there is not sufficient reliable data to classify them or to relate them to the structure of the esters. In particular it should be noticed that mixtures of isomers such as ethyl acetate, methyl propionate, and *n*-propyl formate can be satisfactorily resolved even though their boiling points are comparatively close.

Less volatile esters, esters of dibasic acids, etc., can be chromatographed by the same techniques as are described for esters of biochemical interest in the previous section, as has been illustrated for various sebacates, adipates, etc., by Bartsch *et al.* (*23*).

(*c*) *Ethers*

There is very little data on the lower aliphatic ethers. A few relative retentions given by Raupp (*4*) and by Kelker (*5*) suggest that their chromatography presents no novelties. The chromatography of diethyl ether has been carried out many times, and diethyl ether is frequently used as a solvent for less volatile samples of interest; the ether gives a large peak before any of the peaks caused by the mixture. Diethyl ether is commonly contaminated with ethanol; on any but a paraffinic stationary phase, the activity coefficients of both ether and alcohol are of the order of unity, and the two separate widely. On a paraffinic stationary phase, however, the activity coefficient of the alcohol is large, and diethyl ether and ethanol may overlap.

Mixtures for anaesthesia containing ether, ethanol, and other substances have been considered by Adlard and Hill (*24*) and by Hill (*25*); see also Section 11.9(a).

Many sugars and sugar derivatives which are themselves non-volatile have been analysed by gas chromatography by converting them to methyl ethers, which are sufficiently volatile. McInnes *et al.* (*26*), Bishop and Cooper (*27*), and Kircher (*28*) describe the analysis of methylated sugars. Apiezon M at 170°C (*26*), Apiezon M grease at 150°C, poly(butanediol succinate) at 150°C (*27*), and methylated hydroxyethylcellulose at approximately 200°C (*28*) have been used as stationary phases. The combination of one polar and one non-polar column enables a large range of such sugar derivatives to be analysed.

Gas chromatography has been used in connection with the Zeisel method for the determination of alkoxy groups, e.g., by Vertalier and Martin (*29,30*), Kratzl and Gruber (*31*), and Haslam, Hamilton, and Jeffs (*32*). The alkyl iodides corresponding to the alkyl groups from the alkoxy compounds are analysed and identified chromatographically, e.g., on dinonyl sebacate at 75°C (*32*).

(*d*) *Aldehydes*

The chromatography of the lower aliphatic aldehydes other than formaldehyde is straightforward. Though there are no extensive tables of retention data, results given by Kovats (*33*) indicate an accurate linear relation between carbon number and the logarithm of the retention. Raupp (*4*) gives the relative retentions listed in Table 11.34, and it may

TABLE 11.34

RELATIVE RETENTIONS OF LOWER ALDEHYDES AND KETONES

		Stationary phase					
	Boiling point	Silicone	Dioctyl sebacate	Didecyl phthalate	Hexamethylene glycol dimethyl ether	Polyethylene glycol	β,β'-Oxydipropionitrile
Temperature (°C):	—	100	100	100	70	100	70
Reference:	—	*4*	*4*	*4*	*5*	*4*	*5*
Acetaldehyde	21				0.16		0.43
Propionaldehyde	48.8	0.80	1.36	1.70	0.34	10.5	0.72
Acraldehyde	52.2	0.74	1.49	1.96	0.46	13.9	0.96
Isobutyraldehyde	61.5	1.48	2.26	2.82	0.46	12.2	0.78
n-Butyraldehyde	75.7	1.97	3.12	4.06	0.69	19.3	1.2
Crotonaldehyde	104.0	3.22	6.00	8.43	1.9	58.4	4.0
Paraldehyde	124.4	12.8	26.8	13.2		61.7	
Acetone	56.5	0.96	1.34	1.92	0.41	13.7	1.1
Methyl ethyl ketone	79.6	2.07	3.21	4.44	0.79	22.7	1.7
Diethyl ketone	102.7	4.29	6.68	9.01	1.5	37.9	2.4
Acetylacetone	139.0	8.10	17.5	22.9		159	
Ethanol	78.3	0.69	1.49	1.68	0.73	31.5	1.1
n-Pentane		*1.00*	*1.00*	*1.00*		*1.00*	
Benzene					*1.00*		*1.00*

be presumed that the relative retentions of other aldehydes may be obtained by extrapolation of a plot of carbon number and the logarithms of these relative retentions. The C_8 aldehydes have been specifically studied by Matthews, Burow, and Snyder (*34*).

On many stationary phases, formaldehyde is polymerised before being eluted; this is common experience, and is reported specifically for ethylene carbonate and propylene carbonate by Zlatkis and Oro (*35*). It is, however, possible to get peaks for formaldehyde (*36–38*). Schepartz and McDowell (*36*) have used a column of polyethylene glycol 20,000 at 90°C, Kelker (*37*) has used Citroflex A, which is *O*-acetyl triethylhexyl citric ester, at 120°C, and Sandler and Strom (*38*) have used the surfacant agent extracted from commercial detergent at 145°C. In all cases, other conditions are such that formaldehyde is eluted in 1 or 2 minutes. Kelker describes the quantitative estimation of formaldehyde by gas chromatography.

Aldehydes have also been analysed by gas chromatography as their oximes (*39*) and as their dimethyl acetals (*40*). Gray (*40*) uses acetals for the gas chromatography of long chain fatty aldehydes, using techniques similar to those for long chain fatty acid esters, and finds that their chromatography resembles that of the fatty acid esters. Retention data for some acetals of lower aldehydes is given by Kelker (*5*).

Aldehydes, and also several other classes of carbonyl compound, can be analysed by "Flash Exchange Gas Chromatography," described by Ralls (*41*). In this, the aldehydes, etc., are concentrated from their medium by a chemical agent, e.g., 2,4-dinitrophenylhydrazine, and the 2,4-dinitrophenylhydrazones are isolated. These are then mixed with a reagent which will displace the original aldehydes when heated, e.g., α-ketoglutaric acid. The mixture is placed in the sample injector of the chromatograph. The chromatogram is then started by heating the mixture of reagents rapidly, so that the reaction occurs rapidly, and the aldehydes are released on to the column. In the microtechnique for aldehydes described by Stephens and Teszler (*42*), the tube in which the reaction is to occur also contains a mixture of α-ketoglutaric acid and formaldehyde dinitrophenyl-hydrazone, the formaldehyde thus acting as a chaser for the aldehydes of interest when the flash reaction occurs.

Aldehydes are gas-chromatographed in the course of the determination of aminoacids by the ninhydrin method [see Section 11.8(e)].

(*e*) *Ketones*

The lower aliphatic ketones have not been much studied. Raupp (*4*) and Kelker (*5*) give some relative retention data of which a selection is given in Table 11.34. As with aldehydes, it may be presumed that other data may be obtained by suitable extrapolation. Young (*43*) also gives constants for a two-parameter equation [Eq. (3.59)] for specific retention data for a number of alkyl ketones.

(*f*) *Phenols*

The gas chromatography of phenols has been studied by Irvine and Mitchell (*44,45*), Janak and Komers (*46–49*), Bergmann and Jentzsch

TABLE 11.35

RETENTION DATA FOR PHENOLS

	Boiling point	Stationary phase												
		Silicone (Dimethyl polysiloxane)	Apiezon L grease	Apiezon M grease	Apiezon L grease	Apiezon L grease	Silicone grease	Didecyl phthalate	Dinonyl phthalate	Benzyl arabinoside	Galactonic acid γ-lactone	Glycerol	Dulcitol	Erithritol
Temperature (°C):	—	170	170	170	155	165	165	150	170	176	150	160	170	150
Reference:	—	*47*	*47*	*47*	*44*	*53*	*53*	*50*	*47*	*47*	*47*	*47*	*47*	*47*
Phenol	182	*1.00*	*1.00*	*1.00*	*1.00*	*1.00*	*1.00*	*1.00*	*1.00*	*1.00*	*1.00*	*1.00*	*1.00*	*1.00*
o-Cresol	191	1.93	1.65	1.67	1.52	1.68	1.46	1.39	1.38	1.03	0.61	0.60	0.50	0.52
m-Cresol	202	2.15	1.79	1.80	1.83	1.77	1.57	1.77	1.73	1.39	0.98	0.97	0.84	0.94
p-Cresol	201	2.15	1.75	1.79	1.83	1.77	1.57	1.77	1.71	1.36	0.97	0.97	0.83	0.88
o-Ethylphenol	207	2.52	2.54			2.77	2.14	2.15		1.25		0.50		0.40
m-Ethylphenol	217	2.75	2.88		3.14	3.12	2.44	2.89		1.99		0.90		0.83
p-Ethylphenol	218	2.75	2.83				2.44	2.89		1.97		0.92		0.84
2,3-Dimethylphenol	218	3.07	3.44	3.38	3.24	3.38	2.62	2.66	2.69	1.72	0.75	0.76	0.54	0.67
2,4-Dimethylphenol	211	2.70	2.90	2.93	2.76	2.93	2.28	2.55	2.21	1.34	0.56	0.62	0.46	0.47
2,5-Dimethylphenol	211	2.72	2.90	2.92	2.79	2.93	2.28	2.24	2.27	1.37	0.50	0.53	0.38	0.45
2,6-Dimethylphenol	212	2.63	2.75		2.38	2.77	2.01	1.52		0.78	0.35	0.33	0.30	0.23
3,4-Dimethylphenol	226	3.34	3.64	3.50	3.69	3.56	2.77	3.26	3.19	2.32	1.28	1.26	0.89	1.17
3,5-Dimethylphenol	220	3.27	3.16	2.97	3.24	3.12	2.44	2.94	2.90	1.92	0.94	0.96	0.81	0.86
m-*n*-Propylphenol	231		4.45		4.76									0.66
2-Methyl-4-ethylphenol			4.42		4.72									0.40
3-Methyl-5-ethylphenol	235		4.90		5.07									0.82
4-Methyl-2-ethylphenol			4.10											0.33
3-*n*-Butylphenol			7.7											0.64
V_g for phenol		18.8	32.6	35.2	29					294	59.6		16.9	132

(*50*), Karr *et al.* (*51*), Brooks (*52*), Kreyenbuhl and Weiss (*53*), and others. A selection of retention data published by these authors is given in Table 11.35.

On non-polar stationary phases, lower phenols separate in almost perfect order of boiling points, and there is little or no selection according to chemical type. Since there are no cases in which a phenol boils at a lower temperature than a phenol with one carbon atom fewer, phenols on non-polar stationary phases are collected into groups according to carbon number. This may be seen from Fig. 11.16a, or from the observation from

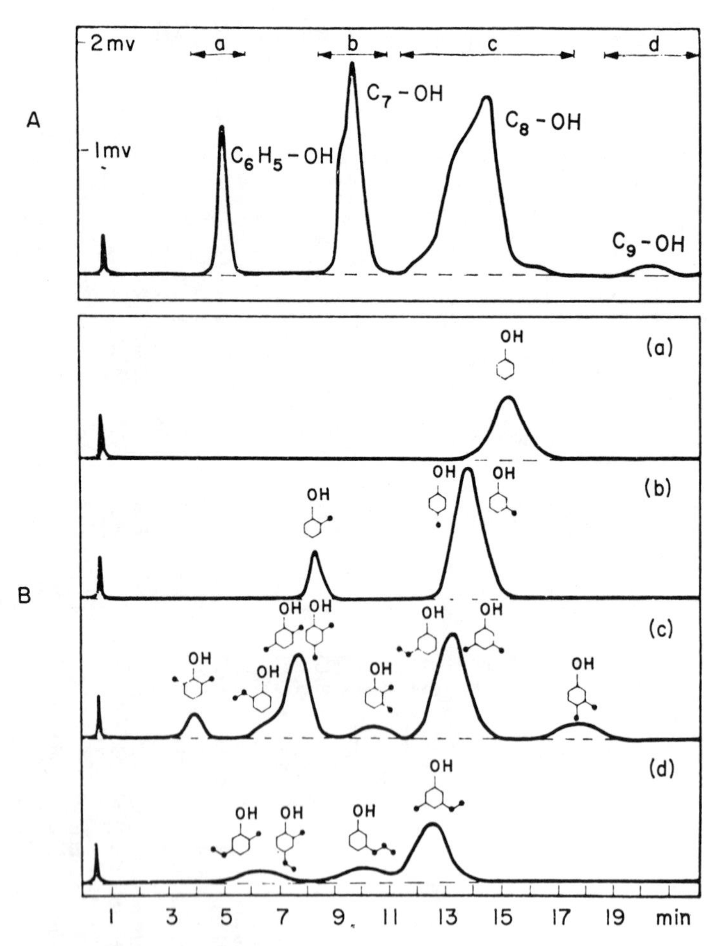

FIG. 11.16. Analysis of a mixture of phenols according to Janak and Komers (*47*). A, Separation by carbon number on silicone oil; B, separations of the contents of each of the peaks labelled (a) to (d) in A on a column of erithritol.

Table 11.35 that the relative retentions of phenol, the cresols, and the xylenols at temperatures at or near 175°C are very roughly 1:2:3. In contrast, Janak and Komers show that on hydroxylic stationary phases the molecules of which contain at least three —OH groups there is considerable specificity among different isomers, but very much less separation according to carbon number. Since there is no single stationary phase which will separate all the C_6–C_8 phenols, Janak and Komers recommend the use of a silicone column to provide an initial separation into carbon numbers, followed by individual analyses of separate carbon number fractions on a hydroxylic column, e.g., erithritol. Chromatograms obtained in this manner are shown in Fig. 11.16.

The most notable feature of the specificity shown on hydroxylic stationary phases is the specific acceleration of *o*-substituted phenols relative to others. Thus, on silicone or Apiezon grease, *o*-cresol appears only just before *m*- and *p*-cresols, but on erithritol its retention volume is only just over half that of the other two. The same applies with *o*-ethylphenol, and with all the 2-substituted dimethylphenols. In particular, the diortho compound 2,6-dimethylphenol is enormously accelerated in hydroxylic stationary phases. The other notable feature is that in the hydroxylic stationary phases the methyl groups tend to accelerate rather than retard. Thus, in erithritol, all the cresols and all the dimethylphenols except one appear before phenol. It was pointed out in Section 3.9 that polar phases tended to crowd successive homologs. The phenols (and also the pyridines, see Section 11.8) demonstrate this particularly well, since they are soluble in very polar hydroxylated stationary phases. Most other series of compounds with which the effect might be demonstrated in such stationary phases are virtually insoluble, so that all retentions are virtually nil, and no such demonstration is possible. Stationary phases of the ester type give intermediate behaviour in which there is a moderate separation according to carbon number and a moderate specificity for isomers. Thus, with dinonyl or didecyl phthalate, 2,6-dimethylphenol appears in the middle of the cresols (*51*).

It will be observed from Table 11.35 that no stationary phase, polar, hydroxylic, or non-polar, can separate certain pairs, e.g., *m*- and *p*-cresols, *m*- and *p*-ethylphenols, and in no case is there any large relative retention of 2,4- and 2,5-dimethylphenols. Brooks (*52*) has sought stationary phases to resolve such pairs, and has tried a number of phosphate esters of various phenols. He finds that tri(2,4-xylenyl) phosphate gave the best separation of *m*- and *p*-cresols and 2,4- and 2,5-xylenols, but that it also causes overlaps not found on many other stationary phases, e.g., *p*-ethylphenol and 3,5-xylenol. The conclusion is that there is not yet a single stationary phase which can produce an easy separation of all thirteen C_6–C_8 phenols.

Some such overlaps may be cured by chromatographing phenyl ethers as described below rather than the phenols themselves.

(*g*) *Phenyl Ethers*

The methyl ethers of phenols have been chromatographed in Apiezon M grease by Carruthers *et al.* (*54*) and on didecyl phthalate and on silicone oil by Bergmann and Jentzsch (*50*). Relative retention data is given in Table 11.36. It is seen that the order of elution on non-polar stationary phases re-

TABLE 11.36

RELATIVE RETENTIONS OF PHENYL ETHERS

Aryl part	Stationary phase				
	Apiezon M grease	Didecyl phthalate	Didecyl phthalate	Silicone	Di-*n*-butyl tetrachloro-phthalate
Temperature (°C):	145	150	150	125	125
Reference:	*54*	*50*	*50*	*55*	*55*
Other part:	Methyl	Methyl	Ethyl	Tri-methylsilyl	Tri-methylsilyl
Phenyl	*1.00*	*1.00*	*1.00*	*1.00*	*1.00*
o-Cresyl	1.56	1.54	1.47	1.59	1.68
m-Cresyl	1.67	1.73	1.72	1.71	1.75
p-Cresyl	1.67	1.73	1.75	1.84	1.89
o-Ethylphenyl		2.26	1.60	2.36	2.34
m-Ethylphenyl		2.80	2.80	2.80	2.81
p-Ethylphenyl		2.89	2.90	3.05	3.10
2,3-Xylenyl	2.96	3.03	3.13	3.3	3.75
2,4-Xylenyl	2.42			2.77	3.01
2,5-Xylenyl	2.50	2.57	2.43	2.48	2.69
2,6-Xylenyl	2.05	2.00	1.54	3.06	3.55
3,4-Xylenyl	3.16	3.42	3.82	3.61	3.89
3,5-Xylenyl	2.50	3.03	3.11	2.86	2.85
o-Methoxyphenyl	2.51			3.23	3.48
m-Methoxyphenyl	3.11				
2,4,6-Trimethylphenyl				5.33	6.07
V_g for phenyl				330	477

sembles that for the parent phenols, and that there are overlaps between the ethers of *m*- and *p*-cresols, etc., as with the parent phenols. On didecyl phthalate, the results of Bergmann and Jentzsch show that there is a slight relative acceleration of *o*-substituted ethers, especially noticeable in the case of 2,6-dimethylphenyl ethers.

Langer, Pantages, and Wender (*55*) have studied the chromatography of phenols by first converting them to their trimethylsilyl ethers by reaction with either trimethylchlorosilane, or preferably with hexamethylsilazane (see Section 6.3). Retention volumes of the trimethylsilyl ethers relative to the phenyl ether on silicone and on di-*n*-butyl tetrachlorophthalate are given in Table 11.36. It is seen that on either stationary phase all three cresols are easily resolved, and that all the xylenols may be separated, though there are overlaps between xylenols and ethylphenols. The trimethylsilyl ethers do not show the specificity characteristic of *o*-phenols, even on the polar stationary phase; neither is the relative retention of the *m*- and *p*-cresyl ethers changed by use of a tetrachlorophthalate ester as stationary phase as was reported by Langer *et al.* in connection with the separation of *m*- and *p*-xylenes (Section 11.4).

(*h*) *Aromatic Oxygenated Compounds*

Several other aromatic oxygenated compounds have been chromatographed incidentally, but apart from phenols and phenyl ethers there appear to be no systematic studies. Komers and Bazant (*56*) report the separation of the dimethyl esters of terephthalic, isophthalic, and phthalic acid in the order given on a column of erithritol. Brown *et al.* (*57*) describe the resolution of *o*-, *m*-, and *p*-methylacetophenones on various stationary phases.

11.8. Nitrogen Compounds

(*a*) *Ammonia and Methylamines*

The separation of these was one of the first applications of partition chromatography by James, Martin, and Smith (*1*), and is also described by James and Martin (*2,3*).

Relative retention data for ammonia and the methylamines are given in Table 11.37 (*1*). On stationary phases of polarity comparable with that of the amines, separation is in order of boiling points; this is the case on hendecanol. On non-polar stationary phases, dimethylamine, which would otherwise be selectively retained because of hydrogen bonding, is not so retained, and appears together with the trimethylamine; this is the case on liquid paraffin. James *et al.* also tried several mixtures of hendecanol and paraffin, from which they found that the greatest relative retention of di- and trimethylamine was given on a mixture containing 15% paraffin. On very hydroxylated stationary phases, the retention is largely determined by hydrogen bonding. Ammonia, monomethylamine, and dimethylamine are all retained longer than trimethylamine which

TABLE 11.37

Retention Data for the Methylamines Relative to Ammonia at 20°C[a]

	Boiling point (°C)	Stationary phase						
		Hendecanol	Hendecanol + 15% paraffin	Hendecanol + 50% paraffin	Paraffin + 33% hendecanol	Paraffin	Glycerol	Silicone DC 550 + 10% hendecanol
Ammonia	−33.4	*1.00*	*1.00*	*1.00*	*1.00*	*1.00*	*1.00*	*1.00*
Methylamine	−6.5	3.4	3.6	4.2	3.8	1.65	2.5	1.33
Dimethylamine	7.4	5.2	5.8	7.5	6.8	2.7	1	0.78
Trimethylamine	3.5	4.2	4.6	7.5	6.8	2.7	0.47	0.36

[a] See reference *1*.

possesses no labile hydrogens. On these stationary phases, activity coefficients increase in the same order as boiling points, and this has the result that, on glycerol at least, ammonia and dimethylamine are eluted together. The conclusions are that if all four compounds are present, hendecanol is a suitable stationary phase, and, if only the methylamines are present, glycerol is suitable. There is little doubt that hendecanol may be replaced by any of many stationary liquids of similar polarity.

(*b*) *Higher Aliphatic Amines*

James (*4*) gives the relative retention data for aliphatic amines from methyl to butyl including benzyl on silicone oil DC 550, liquid paraffin oil, and Lubrol MO, which is a polyethylene oxide oil of moderate polarity (Table 11.38). Figure 11.17 shows log v as a function of carbon number for amines on paraffin oil. The relative retention of successive homologs at 100°C is 2.1; the relative retention of an n-alkylamine and its isomeric isoalkylamine is 1.3–1.4.

The chromatography of higher fatty amines has been described by Link *et al.* (*5*) and by Nelson and Milun (*6*). The chromatography of these compounds resembles that of the higher fatty acids and higher fatty alcohols described in previous sections.

(*c*) *Aromatic Amines*

James (*7*) has given retentions relative to aniline of a large number of N- and C-substituted anilines. A small selection of the data is given

TABLE 11.38

RETENTION DATA FOR ALIPHATIC AMINES RELATIVE TO ETHYLAMINE AT 100°C[a]

Amine	b.p. (°C)	Stationary liquid	
		Paraffin	Lubrol MO
Methyl	−6.5	0.61	0.68
Dimethyl	7.4	0.93	0.81
Ethyl	16.6	*1.00*	*1.00*
Trimethyl	3.5	1.17	0.67
i-Propyl	34	1.49	1.42
n-Propyl	48.7	2.20	2.10
Diethyl	55.5	3.25	2.10
sec-Butyl	63	3.57	2.8
i-Butyl	68	3.70	3.1
Ethylenediamine	118	4.65	15.5
n-Butyl	77.8	4.7	4.4
Ethanolamine	172.2	5.25	25.8
Di-*i*-propyl	83	6.8	3.00
Triethyl	89.5	8.6	3.1
i-Pentyl	95	8.8	7.3
n-Pentyl	104	10.5	9.7
Di-*n*-propyl	110.7	13.2	7.2
4-Methylpentyl-1-	123.9	17.8	13.8
n-hexyl	132.7	22.6	19.6
Di-*sec*-butyl	132.0	27.6	9.74
Cyclohexyl	134	28.4	25.9
Di-*i*-butyl	139	30.4	10.9
n-Heptyl	158.3	49.5	40.05
Tri-*n*-propyl	156	49.6	15.1
Di-*n*-butyl	159	62.1	27.6
Tri-*n*-butyl	214		85.5
Benzyl	185	81.0	91.5

[a] See reference *4*.

in Table 11.39. Many separations involving specific activity effects are possible on both polar and non-polar stationary phases. In general, polar stationary phases accelerate *N*-substituted amines relative to those possessing free N—H bonds; non-polar stationary phases accelerate amines possessing free N—H bonds relative to *N*-substituted amines. This may be seen from the figures given in Table 11.39 for methylaniline and dimethylaniline, which boil within one degree. On paraffin wax, dimethylaniline is eluted first, but on the polar stationary phase Lubrol MO methylaniline is eluted first. In either case, the pair is well resolved.

Jones, Ritchie, and Heine (*8*) have chromatographed a number of

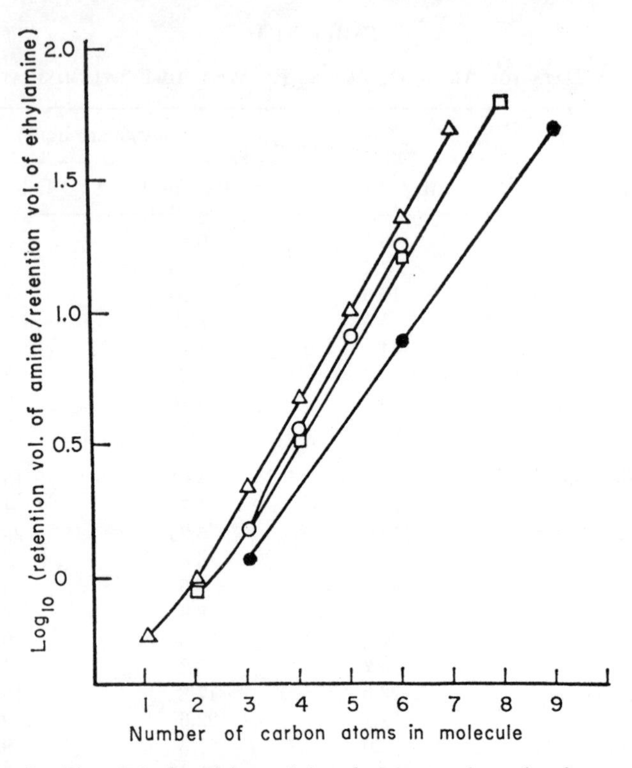

Fig. 11.17. Plot of the logarithms of the relative retentions of amines as a function of carbon number on a column of paraffin oil. James (*4*). △, Primary *n*-alkylamines; ○, primary isoalkylamines; □, secondary straight chain amines; ●, tertiary straight chain amines.

TABLE 11.39

Retentions at 137°C Relative to Aniline of Some Aromatic Amines[a]

	Paraffin wax	Lubrol MO (polyethylene oxide condensate)	Benzyldiphenyl
Aniline	*1.00*	*1.00*	*1.00*
p-Toluidine	1.95	1.63	1.75
m-Toluidine	2.0	1.56	1.86
o-Toluidine	2.05	1.53	1.8
N-Methylaniline	2.05	1.28	1.73
N-Dimethylaniline	2.60	1.05	1.68
N-Ethylaniline	3.18	1.66	2.33

[a] See reference 7.

alkylaminobenzenes from toluidine onwards on silicone fluid at 200°C. They point out that the relative positions and the number of alkyl groups on the benzene nucleus appear to be more significant in determining the retention than the position of the amino group. Thus, two aminoethyl benzenes are eluted together, as are the three possible amino-*m*-xylenes and the two amino-*o*-xylenes. Furthermore, the relative retentions of these three groups of peaks are close to those of ethylbenzene, *o*-xylene, and *p*-xylene. The authors show that this behaviour applies with all alkyl-aminobenzenes up to at least four alkyl carbon atoms. The retention data of James, however, shows that isomers differing only in the position of the amino group may be resolved with a sufficiently efficient column.

(*d*) *Pyridine and Its Homologs*

Table 11.40 gives relative retention data on various stationary phases

TABLE 11.40

RETENTIONS OF PYRIDINE HOMOLOGS RELATIVE TO PYRIDINE

		Stationary phase						
	Boiling point	Liquid paraffin	Squalane	Silicone oil M430	Trixylenyl phosphate	Tricresyl phosphate	Polyethylene glycol 1000	Glycerol
Temperature (°C):	—	120	130	140	120	130	120	90
Reference:	—	*9*	*10*	*9*	*9*	*10*	*9*	*9*
Pyridine	115.3	*1.00*	*1.00*	*1.00*	*1.00*	*1.00*	*1.00*	*1.00*
2-Picoline	129.4	1.80	1.53	1.60	1.72	1.33	1.22	0.82
3-Picoline	144.1	2.55	2.13	2.10	3.12	2.02	1.98	1.54
4-Picoline	145.4	2.55	2.13	2.10	3.12	2.08	2.07	1.86
2,6-Lutidine	144.0	2.90	2.43	2.31	2.64	1.70	1.43	0.53
2,5-Lutidine	157.0	4.34	3.34	3.06	4.40	2.50	2.25	1.22
2,4-Lutidine	157.9	4.42	3.34	3.06	4.47	2.68	2.43	1.55
2,3-Lutidine	160.8	4.95	3.64	3.45	4.85	3.02	2.79	1.51
3,5-Lutidine	172.2	6.10		4.07	6.85		3.68	2.30
2-Ethylpyridine	148.7	3.25	2.70	2.72	3.24	1.95	1.74	0.62
3-Ethylpyridine	165.0	5.25		3.44	5.73		2.99	1.65
4-Ethylpyridine	167.7	5.20	3.97	3.84	6.25	3.58	3.60	2.11
2,4,6-Collidine	170.3	6.95	5.00	4.27	6.20	3.55	2.83	1.00
2,3,5-Collidine	186.8	11.17		6.29	11.08		4.74	2.46
2,3,4-Collidine	192.7	13.75		7.33	13.15		6.80	4.03
2-Methyl-6-ethyl-pyridine	160.1	5.00		3.84	4.40		1.83	0.30

for pyridine, the picolines (methylpyridines), the lutidines (dimethylpyridines), and the collidines (trimethylpyridines), selected from tables of Brooks and Collins (*9*), and Decora and Dineen (*10*). Data on other stationary phases are also given by Brooks and Collins and Decora and Dineen; where comparable, James (*4*) gives results which agree well with those of Brooks and Collins. The results of Brooks and Collins on glycerol are confirmed by Murray and Williams (*11*). The apparently large discrepancy between the columns of results on paraffin oil and on squalane is in fact caused solely by a discrepancy in the retentions of pyridine.

The chromatography of the pyridines is very similar to that of the phenols. It is seen from Table 11.40 that liquid paraffin or silicone oil are effective in separating the compounds listed into groups according to carbon at least up to $C_8H_{11}N$. On paraffinic stationary phases, isomers other than those with substituents in the ortho position are not well separated. Thus, 3- and 4-picolines fail to separate, as do 2,4- and 2,5-lutidines. On ester type phases, e.g., trixylenyl phosphate, the separation according to carbon number still predominates, but there is a slightly greater spread, so that 2,6-lutidine spreads out into the picolines, and 2,4,6-collidine into the lutidines. On glycerol, the separation according to carbon number is completely absent, and a good separation is obtained within each carbon number, with 3- and 4-picolines clearly resolved. The separation of 2,4- and 2,5-lutidines is satisfactory, but there is a new overlap of 2,4- and 2,3-lutidines. Polyethylene glycol 1000, which is not so polar as glycerol, provides a compromise by which it is possible to resolve all the picolines and lutidines on a single column, so long as the efficiency is great enough to resolve the 3- and 4-picolines the relative retention of which is approximately 1.15. It is apparent, however, that the easiest route to complete separation of all components involves the consecutive use of a non-polar and a polar column.

The pyridine homologs provide a very clear example of the operation of the effect in which ortho-substituted components are accelerated on polar columns. Thus, on glycerol, 2,4,6-collidine overlaps with pyridine boiling 55°C lower, and the 2-methyl-*o*-ethylpyridine gives the first peak to appear.

The chromatography of quinolines, isoquinolines, and indoles is described by Janak and Hrivnac (*12,13*), who give extensive relative retention data for several common stationary phases.

(*e*) *Amino Acids*

Amino acids themselves are involatile; they must therefore be converted to characteristic volatile derivatives before they can be analysed by gas chromatography. The two principal derivatives are (1) aldehydes formed by reaction with ninhydrin and (2) esters. Several authors writing on the gas chromatographic determination of amino acids comment that the method is more rapid and more sensitive than standard methods using ion exchange or liquid-liquid partition chromatography.

(*1*) *Aldehyde method.* In this, the mixture of amino acids is converted to aldehydes by the quantitative reaction:

$$C_6H_4(CO)_2C(OH)_2 + R\text{—}\underset{NH_2}{\underset{|}{CH}}\text{—}COOH \rightarrow C_6H_4(CO)_2CHOH + RCHO + NH_3 + CO_2.$$

The aldehydes may then be chromatographed (*14–18*). Table 11.41 shows

TABLE 11.41

ALDEHYDES OBTAINED BY NINHYDRIN OXIDATION OF AMINO ACIDS[a]

Acid	Aldehyde	Aldehyde b.p. (°C)
Glycine	Formaldehyde	−21
Alanine	Acetaldehyde	21
2-Aminobutyric acid	Propionaldehyde	48
Valine	2-Methylpropanal-1	63
Leucine	3-Methylbutanal-1	92.5
Isoleucine	2-Methylbutanal-1	93
Norleucine	Pentanal-1	103
Methionine	Methylmercaptopropanal	60/12 mm
Phenylalanine	Phenylacetaldehyde	194

[a] See reference *16*.

the aldehydes obtained from some of the common amino acids. The pair 3-methylbutanal and 2-methylbutanal arising from leucine and isoleucine are rather hard to separate (*19*), but Hunter *et al.* (*14*) show that they may be resolved on a column of silicone oils with a retention of approximately 1.1. Apart from the problem of resolving leucine and isoleucine, the stationary phase used for this analysis is probably not very critical; silicone oil (*14*), dimethylsulfoxide (*16*), and a mixture of ethylene and propylene carbonates (*17*) have all been used satisfactorily. In the technique of Zlatkis *et al.*, 1 part of 0.28 *M* amino acid solution is mixed with 1 part of saturated aqueous ninhydrin solution, and the mixture is introduced into a gas-chromatographic apparatus containing a preliminary reaction tube filled with 30% ninhydrin supported on firebrick held at 140°C. After separation in the column, the aldehydes are converted to methane by the device of Zlatkis and Ridgeway described in Section 10.5(c). A chromatogram obtained from a mixture of amino acids in this way is shown in Fig. 11.18. Zlatkis *et al.* find that their technique gives an average deviation of approximately 5% in quantitative analysis.

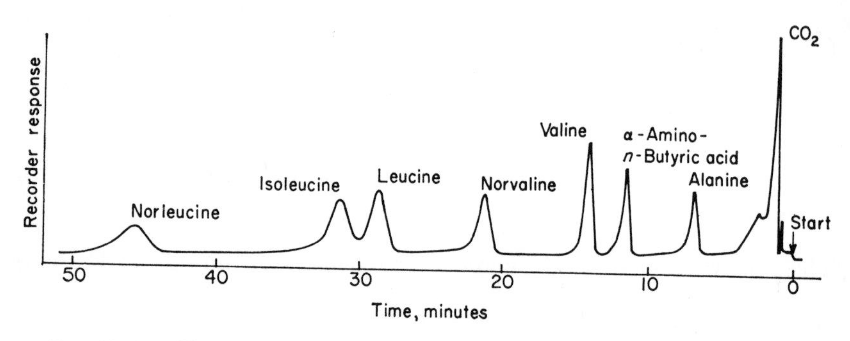

FIG. 11.18. Chromatogram of aldehydes derived from the amino acids indicated. Zlatkis, Oro, and Kimball (*17*).

Amino acids may also be converted into aldehydes by reaction with alkaline hypochlorite. This reaction has been used by Bayer (*20*) prior to chromatography of the aldehydes, but the method is restricted by the fact that different amino acids may give the same products, and that amino acids containing sulphur or acid groups give complex products.

(*2*) *Esterification method.* Though amino acids themselves are involatile, their esters are volatile and may be chromatographed. Both the COOH group and the NH_2 group of the amino acid may be esterified, and the principal difference between the techniques of different workers is the choice of esterifying groups. Table 11.42 summarises the work by giving the esterifying groups, columns, and conditions described in the papers specified. Melamed and Renard react the amino acids with a mixture of hydrochloric and nitric acids, thus converting the NH_2 group to a Cl atom, and they chromatograph the ester of the corresponding chloro acid. The last three authors listed in Table 11.42 give relative retention data for the amino acid derivatives. The esters of most common amino acids may be resolved with a sufficiently efficient column.

(*f*) *Other Nitrogen Compounds*

Many alkaloids are sufficiently volatile to be chromatographed at temperatures near 200°C in much the same conditions as are used for fatty acid esters, etc. Thus, Quin (*26,27*) describes the chromatography of

TABLE 11.42

SUMMARY OF WORK ON THE DETERMINATION OF AMINO ACIDS BY GAS CHROMATOGRAPHY OF VOLATILE ESTERS

Authors	Ref.	Group esterifying the NH_2—	Group esterifying the —COOH	Column material	Column temp. (°C)
Bayer	*20,21*	None Perfluoroacetyl	Methyl Methyl	Silicone grease + sodium caproate	140–190
Youngs	*22*	Acetyl	*n*-Butyl	Hydrogenated vegetable oil	220
Saroff and Karmen	*23*	Perfluoroacetyl	Methyl	Polyethylene glycol adipate	162
Johnson *et al.*	*24*	Acetyl	*i*-Butyl *n*-Butyl *i*-Pentyl *n*-Pentyl	Polyethylene glycol	150
Melamed and Renard	*25*	NH_2/Cl (see text)	Methyl	Polyethylene glycol + silicone/stearic acid	130

tobacco alkaloids on polyethylene glycol, polypropylene glycol, and polybutylene glycol. There are significant differences in the relative retentions of alkaloids on each of these stationary phases, and, by consecutive analyses on more than one, complicated mixtures of natural alkaloids may be characterised. Lloyd *et al.* (*28*) describe the chromatography of a number of alkaloids on a non-polar stationary phase, silicone oil SE 30. Both Lloyd *et al.* and Quin (*27*) give tables of relative retention data.

In addition to the classes of nitrogen compounds described above in detail, many authors have described the chromatography of others, usually in connection with some specific chemical problem. Examples are pyrazines (*29*), alkyl isothiocyanates (*30*), tetraalkyltetrazines (*31*), oximes (*32*), etc.

(*g*) *Use of Transition Metal Salt Columns*

Barber, Phillips, Tusa, and Verdin (*33*) have shown that partition columns may be made using melted transition metal stearates and oleates as the stationary liquid. The transition metal ions present in these form complexes of varying stability with many compounds, including amines, and thus provide great specificity for such compounds. Table 11.43 gives the activity coefficients of various compounds in cobalt stearate at 156°C. It is seen that the solution of hydrocarbons is more or less normal, but alcohols are selectively retained, and the amines are retained to a very

TABLE 11.43

ACTIVITY COEFFICIENTS OF SUBSTANCES ON COBALT STEARATE AT 156°C[a]

Substance	Activity coefficient
Heptane	0.88
Octane	0.80
m-Xylene	0.59
Mesitylene	0.55
Butanol-1	0.33
Pentanol-1	0.41
Diethylamine	0.011
Triethylamine	0.15

[a] See reference *33*.

great degree. Also notable is the great difference between the secondary and the tertiary amine. The above authors also show that manganese stearate gives a relative retention of 1.3 for 3- and 4-picolines.

11.9. HALOGENATED COMPOUNDS

(a) *Halogenated Methanes*

Retention data for the chlorinated methanes have been studied by many authors, and a selection of the results is given in Table 11.44. Pollard and Hardy (*1,2*) have studied many halogenated methanes including the chlorinated methanes. Their data are most conveniently presented as plots of log V_g against inverse temperature, which are reproduced in Figs. 11.19–11.21 (*1*). The chlorinated methanes provided one of the earliest illustrations of a change in the order of elution being produced by a change in stationary phase. On non-polar stationary phases, the compounds are eluted in order of boiling point, which is also the order of increasing chlorination. On intermediate stationary phases, carbon tetrachloride, which alone of the four compounds is non-polar, is accelerated relative to the others so that it is eluted before chloroform. On polar stationary phases, carbon tetrachloride is further accelerated so that it appears before methylene dichloride. The columns of Table 11.44 are arranged in approximate order of polarity of the stationary phase, so that the progress of carbon tetrachloride from the end of the chromatogram to close to the beginning as the polarity of the stationary phase increases may be clearly seen.

TABLE 11.44

SPECIFIC AND RELATIVE RETENTION VOLUMES OF CHLORINATED METHANES

	Boiling point	Stationary phase													
		Liquid paraffin	Silicone oil DC 702	Silicone oil DC 702	Silicone oil MS 710	Dinonyl phthalate	Dinonyl phthalate	Dibutyl phthalate	Tricresyl phosphate	Hexamethylene glycol dimethyl ether	β-β'-Oxydipropionitrile	Glycerol	Silicone oil DC 702	Dinonyl phthalate	Glycerol
Specific, relative, or activity coefficient:	—	R	S	S	R	S	R	S	R	R	R	S	γ	γ	γ
Temperature (°C):	—	35	20.2	56.7	35	57.2	35	57.0	35	70	70	24.4	77.0	76.8	40.1
Reference:	—	*3*	*2*	*2*	*3*	*2*	*3*	*2*	*3*	*4*	*4*	*2*	*5*	*5*	*5*
Methyl chloride	−23.7		25.1	10.0						0.06	0.08	2.16	0.37	0.45	14.8
Methyl dichloride	40.1	196	232	60.5	332	82.8	595	108	530	0.76	0.64	12.9	0.44	0.46	25.7
Chloroform	61	580	595	136	775	210	1620	254	1520	1.6	0.91	16.75	0.40	0.38	39.2
Carbon tetrachloride	76.5	960	746	180	940	173	1180	182	980	0.70	0.36	3.85	0.50	0.71	226

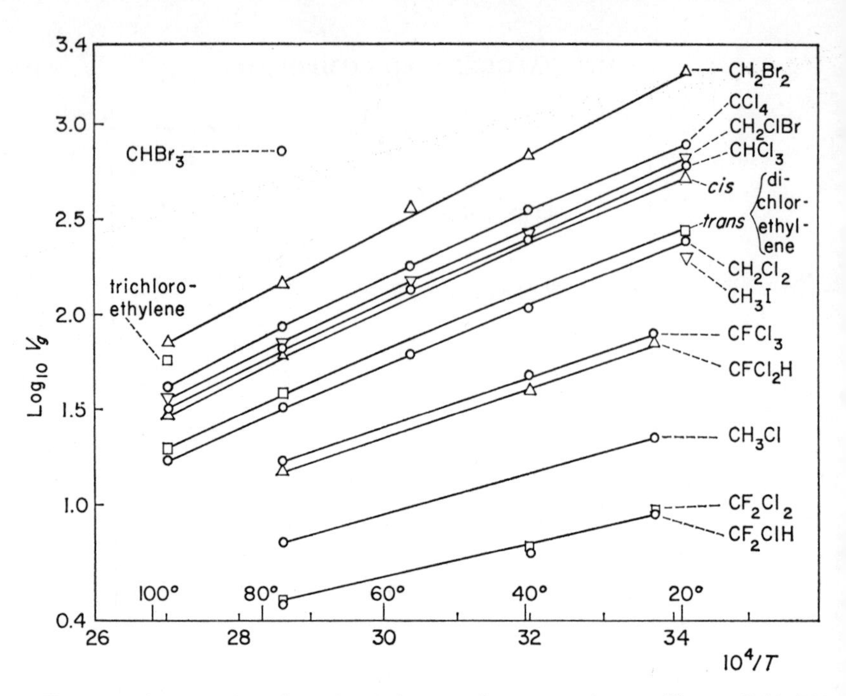

Fig. 11.19. Retention data for halogenated compounds on silicone fluid 702. Pollard and Hardy (*1*).

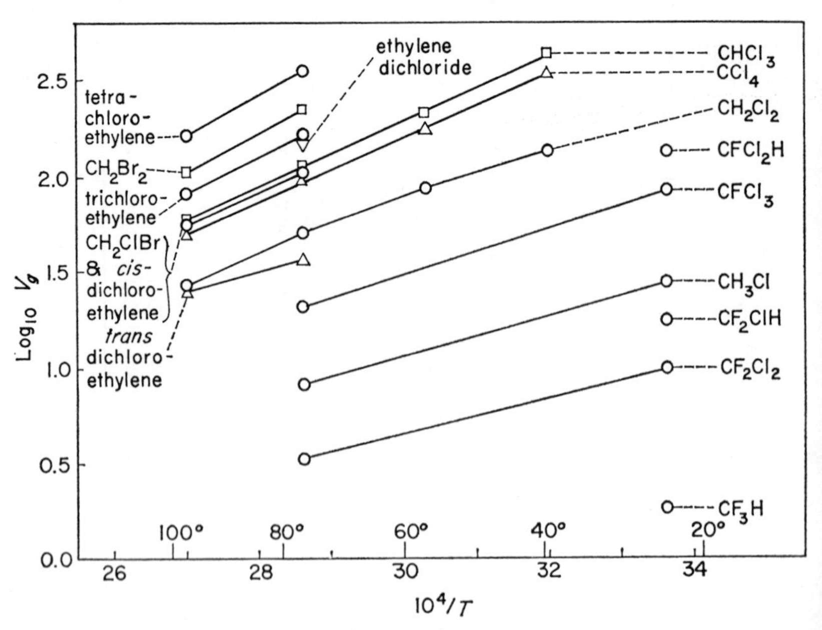

Fig. 11.20. Retention data for halogenated compounds on dinonyl phthalate. Pollard and Hardy (*1*).

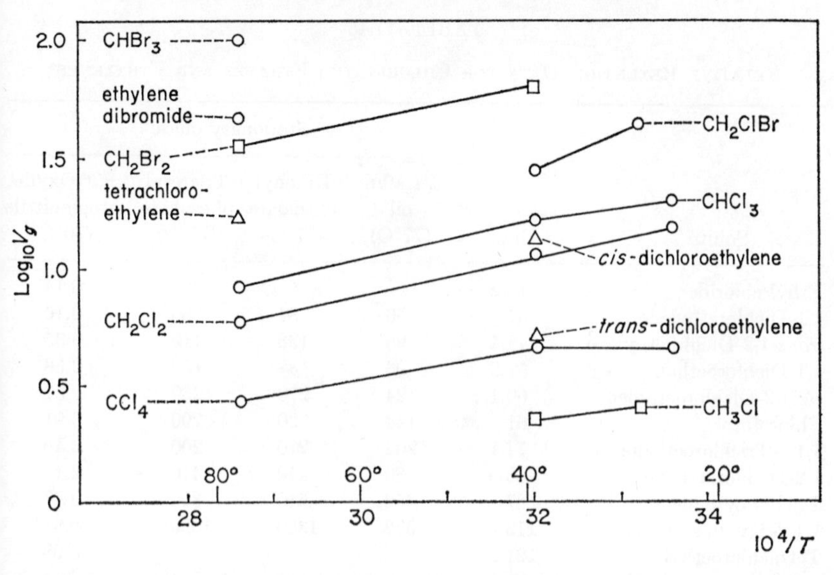

FIG. 11.21. Retention data for halogenated compounds on glycerol. Pollard and Hardy (*1*).

The activity coefficients of the chlorinated methanes on various stationary phases have been calculated by Hardy (*5*) from the results of Pollard and Hardy (*1,2*); these are contained in the last three columns of Table 11.44. It is apparent that on the non-polar or the intermediate stationary phases, activity coefficients are small, but on the polar stationary phase, they are of the order of 10, and of the order of 100 for carbon tetrachloride, with the consequent tendency to cause peak broadening, as described in Chapters 3 and 5.

The chromatography of the chlorinated methanes on pure kieselguhr and wet kieselguhr, etc., has been studied by Purnell and Spencer (*6*) in the course of a study of the properties of kieselguhr.

A variety of chlorinated ethanes and ethylenes commonly used as solvents has been chromatographed by Harrison (*3*) and by Kelker (*4*). A selection of their retention data is given in Table 11.45. Harrison *et al.* (*7*) describe the chromatography of compounds such as these by programmed temperature chromatography.

The chromatography of methanes, etc., halogenated with bromine or iodine appears to be similar to that of the chlorinated compounds; thus, Hardy (*5*) shows that activity coefficients of bromomethanes and bromochloromethanes in silicone or dinonyl phthalate are of the order of unity, whereas activity coefficients in glycerol are of the order of 10. The special features of fluorinated compounds are discussed in Subsection (d).

TABLE 11.45

RELATIVE RETENTION DATA FOR CHLORINATED ETHANES AND ETHYLENES[a]

Solute	b.p.	Stationary phase			
		Paraffin oil (77°C)	Dinonyl phthalate (77°C)	Tricresyl phosphate (77°C)	β,β′-Oxydi-propionitrile (70°C)
Ethyl chloride	12.2				0.14
1,1-Dichlorethylene	37	56	84	60	0.16
trans-1,2-Dichlorethylene	48.4	96	136	110	0.35
1,1-Dichloroethane	57.3	96	188	150	0.58
cis-1,2-Dichloroethylene	60.1	124	270	250	0.87
Chloroform	61	144	320	290	0.91
1,1,1-Trichloroethane	74.1	204	270	200	0.49
1,2-Dichloroethane	83.5	180	410	410	2.1
Trichloroethane	87	352	510	390	0.77
1,1,2-Trichloroethane	113.5	372	1350	1350	5.8
Tetrachloroethylene	121.2				0.98

[a] See references *3* and *4*.

The mixture of chloroform, ether, and ethyl chloride, "Schleich's Mixture," which is used for anaesthesia, has been studied by several authors (*8–10*). The separation is easily carried out on columns of any of several stationary phases, e.g., silicone (*9*) at 35°C, on which the components appear in order of boiling point. On silicone or other non-polar stationary phase, ethanol, if present, may overlap with ether. In this case, an intermediate stationary phase should be satisfactory.

(*b*) *Higher Alkyl Halides*

The chromatography of the homologous series of alkyl chlorides has no special features of interest. James and Martin (*11*) have shown that the *n*-alkyl chlorides give a linear plot of log V_R' versus carbon number; the same conclusion is derived from results given by Kovats (*12*) and by Harrison (*3*).

A number of alkyl bromides has been studied by McFadden (*13*), using temperature programmed columns of mixed silicone and Tween 60. No difficulties are encountered in the separation of monobromoalkanes, but a number of dibromoalkanes overlap on either pure stationary phase. Dibromo-substituted alkanes have smaller activity coefficients on the more polar Tween 60, and by correct choice of proportions in a mixture of both stationary liquids good separation may be obtained. In another paper, Harris and McFadden (*14*) find that the secondary halide 2-bromobutane overlaps with primary halide 1-bromo-2-methylpropane on all stationary phases. The authors make use of the fact that silver nitrate will react completely with secondary or tertiary bromides, but not with primary. Two runs are performed on the mixture, one with a silver nitrate pre-column, and one without, so that the proportion of 2-bromobutane may be determined by difference. The secondary butyl nitrate formed in the reaction may be removed by acidifying the silver nitrate with sulfuric acid. This method can be used for distinguishing other secondary and tertiary bromides from primary.

Other bromides which have been chromatographed are alkyl bromides (*15*), *d*- and *l*-2-bromobutanes (*16*) [see Section 11.6(a)], and 1,2-dibromo-1-propenes (*17*).

Alkyl iodides have been chromatographed in connection with alkoxy-determinations [see Section 11.7(c)]. Moussebois and Duyckaerts (*18*) have chromatographed *n*-alkyl and isoalkyl iodides on dinonyl phthalate at 100°C, obtaining satisfactory separations of all species up to C_5, with a good linear relation between log V_R' and carbon number for both *n*- and isoiodides.

(*c*) *Aromatic Halides*

Chlorobenzene, *o*- and *p*-chlorotoluenes, and *o*- and *p*-dichlorobenzenes may be separated easily on columns of silicone DC 702 (*19*) or dinonyl phthalate (*20*) at temperatures in the region of 150°C. Freeman (*21*) describes the separation of various monochloro- and dichlorotoluenes.

(*d*) *Fluorocarbons*

Methanes and ethanes variously substituted with fluorine and chlorine are used extensively, e.g., as refrigerants and as components of aerosol products. Specific retention volumes (*2*) and activity coefficients (*5*) for some of these compounds are listed in Table 11.46. It is seen that on silicone oil or charcoal, the substances separate in order of boiling point, and that activity coefficients, though by no means constant, are of the order of unity and exhibit no large irregularities. Separations of incompletely fluorinated methanes and chlorofluoromethanes in order of boiling point on non-polar stationary phases are also shown by Root (*22*). On intermediate stationary phases, the order of elution is not necessarily that of boiling point, as the results of Table 11.46 show, but Green shows that the series of CCl_nF_{4-n} separate on dibutyl phthalate in serial order of *n* which is also the order of boiling point (*23*).

The chromatography of perfluorinated compounds appears to be distinct from that of compounds also containing any kind of bond other than C—C and C—F. Reed (*24*) has studied the chromatography of perfluoro-

TABLE 11.46

SPECIFIC RETENTION VOLUMES AND ACTIVITY COEFFICIENTS OF SOME FLUOROMETHANES[a]

		Stationary phase					
	Boiling point	Silicone DC 702 fluid	Dinonyl phthalate	Dibutyl phthalate	Charcoal	Silicone	Dinonyl phthalate
Temperature (°C):	—	40.1	24.5	20	137	40	24.5
Coefficient:	—	V_g	V_g	V_g	V_g	γ	γ
CF_3H	−82.2	0.45	1.8	2.5	7.6	1.61	0.82
CF_3Cl	−80	0.54	0.6	0.6	17.3	1.80	3.4
CF_2ClH	−40.8	5.57	17.3	21.6	53.0		0.57
CF_2Cl_2	−28	6.10	9.5	8.3	152	0.76	0.91
$CFCl_2H$	8.9	41.0	131.5	88.0	453	0.37	0.29
$CFCl_3$	24.1	47.0	80.5	171	1160	0.53	0.80
CH_3Cl	−23.7	22.0	27.3		57.5		

[a] See references *2* and *5*.

alkanes, C_5F_{12}, C_6F_{14}, and C_7F_{16} (*n*-compounds, together with unidentified isomers), on a range of stationary phases. On stationary phases that are themselves perfluorinated, e.g., perfluorokerosine, or perfluorotributylamine, activity coefficients are of the order of unity, and the chromatography is normal. Such stationary phases are suitable for the chromatography. On ordinary paraffinic stationary phases, however, activity coefficients of perfluoroalkanes are very large indeed; Reed quotes activity coefficients of 16.6, 53, and 75 for C_5F_{12}, C_6F_{14}, and C_7F_{16} on *n*-hexadecane at 30°C. The result is that the perfluoroalkanes are scarcely retained at all. If, however, the compound possesses at least one hydrogen atom or atom of another halogen, the chromatography on paraffinic stationary phases is normal, with activity coefficients of the order of unity; this is shown by the figures of Table 11.46. Perfluoronaphthenes on paraffinic stationary phases appear to resemble perfluoroalkanes in that they are scarcely retained at all, but the substitution of one of the fluorines by any other atom produces a significant retention, as is shown by the figures of Table 11.47 (*19*). Serpinet (*25*) describes the chromatography of a number of fluoro- and fluorochlorocarbons on dibutyl phthalate at 20°C. As in other cases, perfluorinated compounds are eluted almost at once, followed by compounds containing at least one other atom, which are retained and resolved. Among the compounds retained are perfluoro-

TABLE 11.47

RELATIVE RETENTIONS OF SOME PERFLUOROALKYLCYCLOHEXANES AND THEIR DERIVATIVES ON SILICONE DC 702 FLUID AT 35°C[a]

Substance	Relative retention
$C_6F_{10}Cl_2$	553
$C_6F_{10}HCl$	404
$C_6F_{11}Cl$	58
$C_8F_{15}H$ (21°C)	200
C_7F_{14}	≈0
C_8F_{16}	≈0

[a] See reference *19*.

alkenes; thus, perfluorocyclobutane is eluted immediately, but perfluorocyclobutene is retained.

Evans, Tatlow *et al.* (*26–30*) have used gas chromatography extensively for the analysis and preparative separation of a number of perfluorinated and almost perfluorinated cyclohexanes, cyclohexenes, and benzenes.

11.10. SULPHUR COMPOUNDS

The lower thiols have been chromatographed by Spencer, Baumann, and Johnson (*1*), Amberg (*2*), Ryce and Bryce (*3*), Sunner *et al.* (*4*), Karchmer (*5*), and others. Temperature-programmed analyses of thiols are described by Sullivan *et al.* (*6*). Carson *et al.* (*7*) describe a flash-exchange technique [Section 11.7(d)] suitable for use with thiols. Relative and specific retention data for these compounds is given in Table 11.48. Thiols are compounds with a slightly polar group, and they may be chromatographed satisfactorily in either polar or non-polar stationary phases. The data of Table 11.48 indicate that the activity coefficients of thiols are of the order of unity whatever the stationary phase.

The lower sulphides have been chromatographed by Spencer *et al.* (*1*), Amberg (*2*), Karchmer (*5*), Desty and Whyman (*8*), and Petranek (*9*). Retention data for sulphides are given in Table 11.49. The characteristics of the chromatography are similar to those for thiols. On non-polar stationary phases, separations are in order of boiling point. On polar stationary phases, there is no gross difference in retention, but there are significant differences which enable close boiling isomers to be resolved. Retention data for disulphides and trisulphides is given by Carson and Wong (*10*).

The separation of benzene (boiling point, 80.2) and thiophene (boiling

TABLE 11.48

RETENTION DATA FOR THIOLS

	Boiling point	Stationary phase: Mineral oil	Dinonyl phthalate	Tricresyl phosphate	β,β'-Iminodipropionitrile
Relative or specific:	—	R	S	R	R
Temperature (°C):	—	84	50	85	84
Reference:	—	*5*	*1*	*2*	*5*
Methanethiol	6.0		19.6		
Ethanethiol	35.0		53.3		
2-Propanethiol	53.6	0.45	82.1	0.36	0.29
2-Methyl-2-propanethiol	64.2		109	0.41	
1-Propanethiol	67.6	0.67	143	0.58	0.50
2-Butanethiol	85.0		238		
2-Methyl-1-propanethiol	88.7	1.19	271	0.92	0.66
1-Butanethiol	98.5	1.59	389		0.88
1-Pentanethiol	126.6	3.74	1070		1.50
Benzene		*1.00*		*1.00*	*1.00*

point, 84.1), which commonly occur together and which are not easily separated by distillation, is easily performed by gas chromatography on any but paraffinic stationary phases. Table 11.50 gives the relative retentions of the two compounds on a variety of stationary phases.

Gas chromatography enables many sulphur compounds which have not hitherto been characterised chemically to be isolated and identified. Thompson *et al.* (*12*), therefore, desulphurise complex mixtures of sulphur compounds catalytically, and obtain partial knowledge of the mixture by identifying the hydrocarbon so produced. This procedure is comparable with that in which the skeletal structure of olefins is determined by hydrogenation followed by identification of the alkanes described in Section 11.3(f).

11.11. POLYMERS AND OTHER NON-VOLATILES

Polymers and other non-volatile organic compounds can frequently be identified and analysed by a technique in which the polymer, etc., is pyrolysed, and the volatile products of pyrolysis are gas chromatographed. The pyrolysis may be performed in a separate apparatus, the pyrolysis products being condensed and subsequently transferred to gas

TABLE 11.49

RETENTION DATA FOR SULPHIDES

Alkyl groups of sulphides	Boiling point	Stationary phase: Silicone oil	Dinonyl phthalate	Tricresyl phosphate	7,8-Benzo-quinoline
Relative or specific:	—	R	S	R	R
Temperature (°C):	—	100	50	85	100
Reference:	—	*9*	*1*	*2*	*9*
Dimethyl	38	0.34	63.2	0.137	
Methyl ethyl	67	0.66	122	0.272	
Diethyl	92	1.17	311	0.49	
Ethyl isopropyl	107	1.62	494		1.74
Methyl isobutyl	113	1.96			2.05
Methyl *sec*butyl	113	1.96			2.19
Ethyl *n*-propyl	118		772		
Di-isopropyl	120	1.96			2.19
n-Propyl isopropyl	132	3.08			3.12
Ethyl isobutyl	133	3.08	1260		3.45
Ethyl *sec*butyl	133	3.08			3.45
Di-*n*-propyl	143	4.35			4.98
Ethyl *n*-butyl	143	4.35	2000		4.98
*iso*Propyl isobutyl	143	4.35			4.01
*iso*Butyl *sec*butyl	166	8.25			7.75
n-Propyl *n*-butyl	167	8.25			9.19
Di-*n*-butyl	182	15.2			
Benzene	80	*1.00*			*1.00*
Thiophene	84			*1.00*	
V_g for benzene		37			46

TABLE 11.50

RELATIVE RETENTION OF BENZENE AND THIOPHENE (THIOPHENE/BENZENE) ON VARIOUS STATIONARY PHASES

Stationary phase	Temp. (°C)	Relative retention	Ref.
Hexatriacontane	78.5	1.09	*8*
Paraffin oil	84	1.11	*5*
Tricresyl phosphate	65	1.38	*2*
Benzyldiphenyl	78.5	1.40	*8*
Polypropylene glycol adipate	85	1.62	*11*
β,β'-Iminodipropionitrile	84	1.63	*5*

chromatography apparatus; or, as in the more recent papers, the pyrolysis may be conducted on a micro-scale in the introducer of a gas chromatography apparatus. The method has so far been applied principally to acrylate and methacrylate polymers, polyvinyl chloride and acetate, polystyrene, and hydrocarbon elastomers. It is most obviously useful for linear polymers which can be caused to pyrolyse principally to monomer, though its applications are almost certainly wider than this.

(*a*) *Apparatus and Technique*

When the pyrolysis is performed separately from the chromatography (static technique), a sample of the polymer is placed in a small glass pyrolysis vessel and heated. A small condenser is attached, and volatile products are condensed. Different authors use slightly different pyrolysis temperatures and different conditions. Davison, Slaney, and Wragg (*1*) pyrolyse rubber, artificial rubbers, and acrylate polymers at 650°C in a stream of nitrogen, following which they chromatogram that part of the pyrolysate boiling below 100°C. Strassburger *et al.* (*2*) pyrolyse methacrylate polymers and copolymers at 350°C in a glass tube enclosed in a furnace, and condense all but the gaseous part of the pyrolysate. Radell and Strultz (*3*) attach to the gas-handling section of a commercial gas chromatograph a small metal pyrolysis tube in which methacrylate polymers are pyrolysed by surrounding the tube with a bath of Wood's metal at 500°C.

When the pyrolysis is performed in the introducer of the gas chromatograph (micro-technique), most authors use a technique in which a small sample of polymer is placed on a helix or other such shape of wire, which may then be heated electrically to the required pyrolysis temperature; the general features of the apparatus are shown in Fig. 11.22. In the technique, the coil is generally of nichrome or other such heat resistant wire of large specific electrical resistance; the polymer is dissolved in or made into a fine suspension in a suitable solvent; a sample of the solution or suspension is painted or otherwise deposited on the wire, after which the solvent dries off. The wire is then inserted in the introducer and carrier gas is set flowing. The chromatogram is then started by passing a predetermined current through the wire. The heat capacity of the wire is small, so that it may be heated very rapidly to the required pyrolysis temperature, and the quantity of polymer is sufficiently small that the pyrolysis is complete within seconds. Thus the introduction of the pyrolysate to the column is sufficiently fast that band spreading at introduction is negligible.

In the above technique, different authors differ in detail. Roland-Jones (*4*) recommends using gold-plated pyrolysis wire to reduce secondary reactions. Miller, Samsel, and Cobler (*5*) use a wire basket containing a miniature Vycor crucible which contains the polymer. Barlow, Lehrle, and Robb (*6*) use a helical wire slightly spiralled outwards towards each end from the middle, thus giving a shape like an upholstery spring; such a shape can be made so as to have small temperature differential along its length. Roland-Jones (*4*) has applied insoluble samples to the wire by suspending them in gum tragacanth solution, and applying the slurry so formed. Apparently, the pyrolysis of the gum does not interfere.

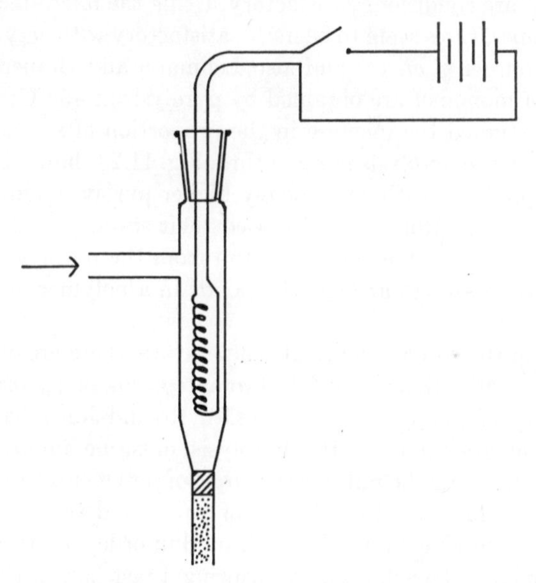

Fig. 11.22. Schematic diagram of apparatus for pyrolysis at the column inlet.

Lehrle and Robb (*7*) have described a related technique in which a polymer is formed into a dielectric in the introducer of a gas chromatograph, and the dielectric is broken down by applying a powerful spark discharge. They found that the degradation produced by this was very profound. The principal products are very simple molecules, e.g., acetylene, ethylene, and these have insufficient structure characteristic of the original polymer to be used for identification.

(*b*) *Products and Conditions*

In the pyrolytic identification of linear polymers, the ideal sole product is monomer, or, in the case of copolymers, a mixture of monomers. In practice, there is very often a large proportion of monomer and conditions can be adjusted to maximise this, but there are also secondary products. This is firstly because the bond linking the monomer units in a polymer may not be the weakest bond, and therefore pyrolysis does not necessarily yield monomer alone, and secondly, because primary products of pyrolysis may undergo further reaction before they leave the hot region of the pyrolyser.

In general, low pyrolysis temperatures favour monomer formation. Thus, in their static technique described above, Radell and Strultz (*3*) find that above 500°C, the pyrolysis yields secondary products and analyses are irreproducible, that below 500°C, the pyrolysis is incomplete, and that only at 500°C are conditions satisfactory. Using the micro-technique, lower pyrolysis temperatures seem to be more satisfactory with acrylate polymers. Thus, Strassburger *et al.* (*2*) and also Lehmann and Brauer (*8*) find that pure yields of monomer are obtained by pyrolysis at 450°C; Lehmann and Brauer have studied the increase in the proportion of secondary products with increasei n the pyrolysis temperature; Fig. 11.23 shows chromatograms of pyrolysis products with successively higher pyrolysis temperatures (*8*). Barlow, Lehrle, and Robb (*6*) have used their spiral helical pyrolyser coil at successively greater temperatures, and from the pyrolysis products obtained have been able to arrange the bonds in a polymer in order of their stability to heat.

Apart from the correct choice of temperature, there are other necessary conditions for formation of useful chromatograms of pyrolysis products. In a summary of pyrolysis analysis (*4,9*), Roland-Jones has pointed out that in the micro-technique the pyrolysis must be rapid; this may be achieved by spreading the minimum sample of polymer over a large heating area, and this is facilitated by the use of sensitive detectors. Gas diffusion of the pyrolysis products must be minimised in order to prevent secondary reactions; this may be achieved by ensuring a fast flow of carrier gas over the pyrolyser. Also, risk of condensation of the pyrolysate should be avoided by containing the pyrolysis unit in a region at the column temperature. With conditions such as these, pyrolysis analyses are reproducible, but it is apparent by comparing papers in which the same polymers are pyrolysed by different techniques, that it is very easy to get irreproducible, or at least non-transferable, results.

(c) *Analysis of Copolymers and Mixed Polymers*

Copolymers and mixed polymers pyrolyse in suitable conditions to give mixtures of the monomers from which they are composed. Ideally, a copolymer or mixed polymer should pyrolyse to give a mixture of monomers in the same proportions as present in the polymer; this would provide a very simple means of determining the constitution of the polymer. Most authors, however, find that the composition of the mixture of monomers is significantly different from the composition of the polymer (*2,11*). However,

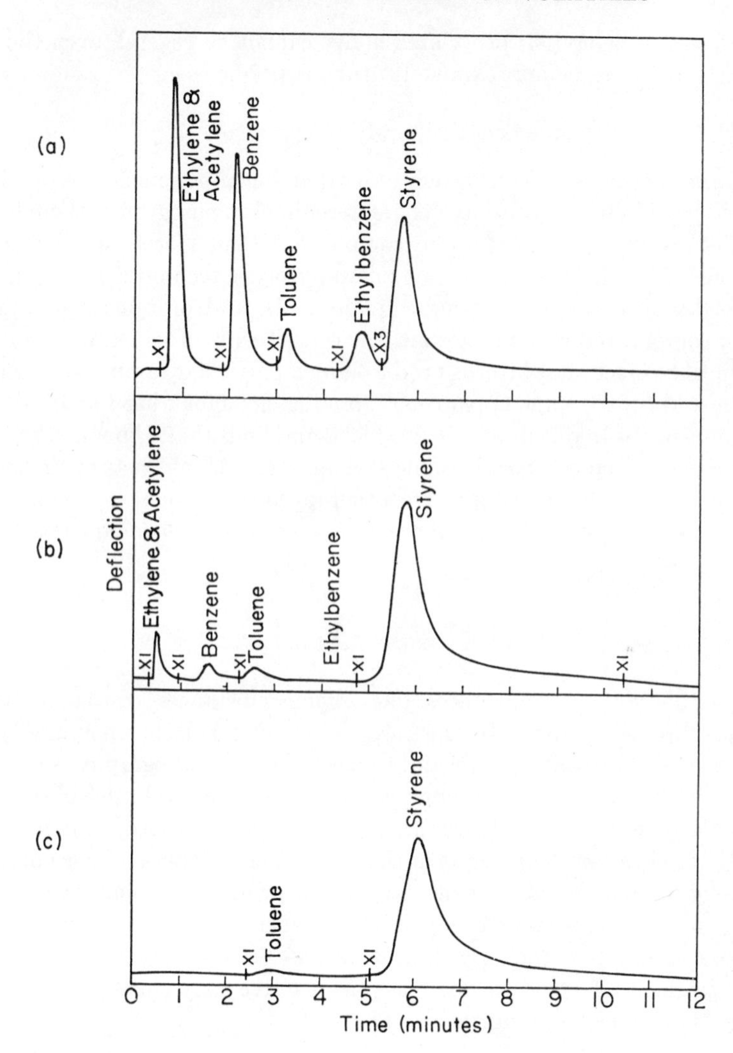

FIG. 11.23. Chromatograms of pyrolysis products from polystyrene. Lehmann and Brauer (*8*). Pyrolysis at (a) 1025°C, (b) 825°C, (c) 425°C.

there appears to be a reproducible relation between monomer composition and pyrolysate composition, so that if one is plotted against the other, a smooth curve is obtained which serves as a calibration for the analysis of unknown mixtures (*2,10*). Strassburger *et al.* (*2*) have shown that the chromatogram of the products of pyrolysis of a mixture of two polymers differs from that of a copolymer of the two in the same proportions (using methyl methacrylate and ethylene dimethacrylate); from this it is apparent that the ideal behaviour postulated above cannot be general, even though it may sometimes be approximately true in specific cases.

(*d*) *Other Applications of the Pyrolysis Technique*

Classes of involatile compounds other than linear polymers also pyrolyse to give pyrolysates which have characteristic chromatograms, though the pyrolysates are necessarily more complicated than merely a mixture of monomers. Janak (*11–13*) uses the micro-pyrolysis technique for the analysis of barbiturates, other drugs, amino acids, and proteins. These give rather complicated chromatograms, the constituents of which need not all be identified since the patterns produced by a particular sample are characteristic and (in the same apparatus) reproducible. Janak has in fact identified some of the major pyrolysis products, and finds that, though in several cases their molecules have the same skeletal structure as parts of the molecule of the pyrolysand, there are other pyrolysis products which have different skeletal structures, and are clearly formed in secondary reactions.

11.12. Inorganic Substances

Volatile inorganic substances, like organic substances, can be analysed by gas chromatography. In the case of covalent volatile inorganic substances which are stable to air and to heat, the chromatography is usually normal both in theory and in practice. Many inorganic volatile substances, particularly many of fairly recent discovery, are reactive, and may be sensitive to heat or components of the atmosphere. The use of gas chromatography for analysis of such substances is growing. It is apparent that the theory of their chromatography is the same as that of more amenable substances, and that the only difficulties arise from their reactivity. Most of the workers referred to below who use reactive substances also describe the technology of handling them.

(*a*) *Separation of Metals*

Nearly all metals form some kind of volatile compound, and these may be chromatographed, thus enabling mixtures of metals to be separated. The technology of the preparation, manipulation, and gas chromatography of such metal compounds is rather more difficult than that of most organic compounds, but recently several workers have reported successful gas chromatographic separations of metals. Notable classes of volatile metal compounds are:

(*1*) *Halides.* All but the most electropositive metals form appreciably volatile halides. Table 11.51 gives the boiling points of some of the more familiar metal halides.

TABLE 11.51

BOILING POINTS OF VOLATILE METAL HALIDES[a]

	Boiling point (°C)		
	Chloride	Bromide	Iodide
Boron	13	91	210
Silicon	58	153	290
Germanium	86	186	375
Tin (IV)	114	202	340
Arsenic (III)	130	221	403
Titanium (IV)	136	230	360
Vanadium (IV)	149		
Antimony (V)	172		400
Aluminium	178	268	382
Gallium	215		
Antimony (III)	220	280	401
Niobium (V)	240.5	270	
Tantalum (V)	242	320	
Gold (III)	265		
Molybdenum (V)	268		
Tungsten (V)	275	333	
Mercury (II)	304	322	354
Hafnium (IV)	317		
Iron (III)	319		
Zirconium (IV)	331		
Tungsten (VI)	337		

[a] See reference *1*.

(*2*) *Chelate complexes.* Nearly all metals form complexes with chelating ligands; by choice of ligand and the conditions, neutral (i.e., non-ionic) complexes may be prepared, and these are appreciably volatile.

(*3*) *Metal-organic compounds.* Most metals form covalent compounds with organic groups, e.g., alkyl groups or alkoxy groups. Many such compounds, especially the metal alkyls, are volatile.

(*4*) *Elements.* Some elementary metals are sufficiently volatile for gas chromatography at high temperatures.

The gas chromatography of metal halides has been studied by Wachi (*2*), Juvet and Wachi (*3*), Keller (*4*), Freiser (*5*), and Keller and Freiser (*1*).

Metal halides may be chromatographed on packed columns of ordinary design using various hydrocarbons as stationary phases. Keller (*4*), however, finds that not all paraffinic stationary phases are satisfactory. Of octadecane, squalane, Apiezon L grease, silicone oil, and paraffin wax, the first two were satisfactory, but the others were less satisfactory, and with silicone grease and Apiezon L grease, peaks sometimes failed to be eluted. Similar results were obtained by Wachi (*2*). It is clear from these results, and also from the fact that pure substances sometimes produce spurious peaks, that the halides react with certain paraffinic stationary phases, though the nature of the reactions is as yet uncertain. On octadecane and squalane, the chromatography of metal halides is normal. Keller (*4*) and Keller and Freiser (*1*) list specific retention volumes of the halides $SnCl_4$, $TiCl_4$, $NbCl_5$, and $TaCl_5$, which are eluted in the order given. Keller (*4*) has determined specific retention volumes at different temperatures, and finds that plots of log V_g against $1/T$ are reasonably linear, and that the heats of solution obtained from them are not very different from differential heats of volatilisation obtained from vapour pressure data. The specific retention volume of $SnCl_4$ at 100°C on squalane is 134 ml/g; and though the author has not calculated the activity coefficient, it is apparent that it is not far removed from unity.

The halides $NbCl_5$ and $TaCl_5$ separate with a relative retention of approximately 2. Gas chromatography is thus shown to secure an easy separation of two elements the separation of which by chemical methods is rather difficult.

Wachi (*2*), and Juvet and Wachi (*3*) have argued that organic stationary phases are not satisfactory for halides in general because they are not sufficiently involatile. They have therefore used inorganic stationary phases consisting of eutectic mixtures of ionic halides. Juvet and Wachi (*3*) show a chromatogram of $SnCl_4$ and $TiCl_4$ which are well separated on a stationary phase consisting of the eutectic mixture of $BiCl_3$ and $PbCl_2$ (m.p. 217°C) operated at 240°C. Other suitable eutectic mixtures are KCl-$CdCl_2$, m.p. 383°C, and $AlCl_3$-$NaCl$, m.p. 183°C. The use of the latter, however, is restricted, since the $AlCl_3$ is itself volatile.

The gas chromatography of metal halides is complicated in practice by the fact that the halides react with water. Care must be taken not to allow either the samples or the column to come into contact with moist air.

The gas chromatography of chelate complexes has been studied by Duswalt (*6*) and by Bierman and Gesser (*7*). Both authors have used acetylacetone as the complexing agent. The latter authors have chromatographed the complexes of beryllium, aluminium, and chromium on columns of Apiezon L. With conventionally packed columns with 20 to 30% by weight of stationary phase on firebrick, the residence time of the complexes on the column is sufficient for some decomposition to take place. The authors therefore used columns with glass beads as a support, and a very small proportion of stationary liquid.

The gas chromatography of metal alkyls has been briefly reported by Abel, Nickless, and Pollard (*8*), who find that the tetramethyls of silicon, germanium, tin, and lead separate easily on Apiezon L at 80°C. The chromatography is normal.

The possibility of chromatographing metals has been demonstrated by DeBoer (*9*), who used a column consisting of lithium chloride (20%) on sea sand (80%) heated above the melting point of the salt. Using a sample consisting of an alloy of zinc and cadmium, he showed that the vapour appearing at the end of the column consisted of pure cadmium with less than 0.5% zinc, and, by omitting the column, showed that the process was one of chromatography and not of simple distillation.

(b) *Boron Derivatives*

The gas chromatography of the more volatile boron hydrides has been studied by Kaufman, Todd, and Koski (*10*), and Borer, Littlewood, and Phillips (*11*). The most familiar hydrides are the compounds B_2H_6, B_4H_{10}, B_5H_9, B_5H_{11}, and $B_{10}H_{14}$. Of these, the first is a gas, the following three are volatile liquids, and the last is a relatively involatile solid. The first four hydrides are easily separated by gas chromatography on either silicone oil (*11*) at 35°C, or on paraffin oil at room temperature (27°C). The specific retention volumes of the four compounds are 12, 65, 254, and 355 ml/g (*11*); these figures indicate activity coefficients not far removed from unity.

For practical purposes, B_2H_6, B_4H_{10}, and B_5H_9 are completely stable during gas chromatography, but B_5H_{11}, which is the most thermally labile of the common hydrides, is liable to decomposition. Borer *et al.* find that this compound decomposes about 10% during a retention time of about 5 minutes; Kaufman *et al.* find more serious decomposition during a retention time of about 25 minutes. The authors differ as to the products of decomposition of B_5H_{11}; Kaufman *et al.* find B_2H_6 and B_4H_{10} while Borer *et al.* find B_4H_{10} and B_5H_9. Since the decomposition of B_5H_{11} is sensitive to catalysts, especially bases (*12*), the different results are not irreconcilable. The conclusion is that B_5H_{11} may be satisfactorily analysed if its retention time is less than approximately 5 minutes.

Since a common simple preparation of diborane involves the use of $BF_3 \cdot Et_2O$, ether and ethane are common contaminants of diborane. Kaufman *et al.* (*10*) find that B_2H_6, C_2H_6, and Et_2O are separated in the order given on columns of dioctyl sebacate at 60°C. This stationary liquid is not so suitable for analysis of other boron hydrides.

Alkylated boranes have been chromatographed by Schomburg, Koster, and Henneberg (*13*), Koster and Bruno (*14*), Seely, Oliver, and Ritter (*15*), and Blay, Dunstan, Williams, and Williams (*16,17*). Most of such compounds are relatively stable, and their chromatography on paraffinic stationary phases presents no problems. Schomburg *et al.* (*13*) and Koster and Bruno (*14*) describe the chromatography of compounds of the kind BR_3, BR_2R', and $BRR'R''$, where R is an alkyl group from methyl to *n*-butyl. They give relative retentions for most of the compounds in this group. Seely *et al.* describe the chromatography of mixtures of methyldiboranes, B_2H_5Me, BMe_3, 1,1-$B_2H_4Me_2$, 1,2-$B_2H_4Me_2$, $B_2H_3Me_3$, and $B_2H_2Me_4$, which six compounds are eluted in the order given from a mineral oil column operated at 0°C. Blay *et al.* (*16*) describe the chromatography of the ethylated pentaboranes and decaboranes obtained from the reaction of ethylene and diborane. They give relative retention data for compounds of the kind $B_5H_{9-n}Et_n$ ($n = 2$ to 5), $B_{10}H_{14-n}Et_n$ ($n = 2$ to 4) chromatographed on Apiezon L grease.

The usual general relations between composition and retention appear to hold for substituted boranes as for hydrocarbons and other compounds containing alkyl groups. Thus, Blay *et al.* demonstrate the linear relation between log V_g and the number of ethyl groups substituted, and Seely *et al.* demonstrate a linear relation between log V_g and inverse temperature. In the case of the substituted monoboranes studied by Schomburg *et al.*, it is apparent that there is a linear relation between log V_g and carbon number for change in any one of R, R′, or R″ in BRR′R″.

(*c*) *Silicon, Germanium, and Tin Derivatives*

The gas chromatography of the silanes, Si_nH_{2n+2}, has been studied by Borer and Phillips (*18*), who obtained a chromatogram containing 21 peaks from a sample of mixed silanes prepared by the action of phosphoric acid on magnesium silicide. The authors have assumed that, as with alkanes, log V_g is a linear function of number of silicon atoms, and in this way they have classified the 21 peaks into a monosilane, a disilane, a trisilane, two tetrasilanes, three pentasilanes, five hexasilanes, five heptasilanes, and three octasilanes. The silanes forming the earlier peaks have been collected and identified, thus providing some confirmation of the gas-chromatographic classification. In the same way, a similar mixture of germanes yielded seven peaks, of which the first five were allocated to germanes through Ge_4H_{10}.

Several authors have studied the chromatography of substituted silanes, particularly methylchlorosilanes, which are used in the manufacture of silicones. Different authors give relative retention data for different selections of compounds. They are summarised in Table 11.52.

Franc, Wirst, and Moudry (*22*) have chromatographed a large number

TABLE 11.52

RELATIVE RETENTIONS OF CHLOROSILANES, METHYLSILANES, AND METHYLCHLOROSILANES

	Boiling point	Stationary phase		
		Tri-isobutylene	Silicone/diethyl phthalate	Nitrobenzene
Temperature (°C):	—	30	30	25
Reference:	—	*19*	*20*	*21*
SiH_4		0.27		
$SiClH_3$	−30.5		0.24	
SiH_3Me		0.36		
SiH_2Me_2	−20	0.59	0.32	
$SiHMe_3$		*1.0*		
$SiCl_2H_2$	8		0.95	
$SiMe_4$	27	1.63	*1.00*	
$SiCl_3H$	32		2.68	0.76
$SiCl_2HMe$	41			1.43
$SiCl_4$	58		3.78	*1.00*
$SiClMe_3$	58		6.35	1.79
$SiCl_3Me$	66		11.10	2.84
$SiCl_2Me_2$	70		13.95	3.82

of volatile organic tin derivatives, and have listed relative retention data for these relative to *n*-tetrapropyltin on silicone oil and phthalic esters, etc. They find linear plots of the logarithms of their retention volumes against carbon number, one line for each class of compound.

(*d*) *Phosphorus Derivatives*

The mixture of phosphorus trichloride and phosphorus oxychloride has been analysed by gas chromatography by Stanford (*23*) and by Shiptofsky and Moser (*24*). Stanford obtained a satisfactory analysis using a column of 23% of silicone fluid E301 on celite 545 at 63°C, using nitrogen dried by anhydrone as carrier gas. The response of each component in a catharometer was linear; the relative retention was approximately 2. Shiptofsky and Moser used a polytrifluoromonochloroethylene as stationary liquid, and powdered polytetrafluoroethylene as support; at temperatures of approximately 70°C, a good separation was obtained, and the apparatus gave reproducible and accurate quantitative analyses. Mixtures of phosphorus trichloride and $PSCl_3$ may be separated in the same way.

Phosphonitrilic chloride polymers and their derivatives have been gas chromatographed by Gimblett (*25*), using silicone oil at 200°C as stationary liquid. In this way, polymers from $(PNCl_2)_3$ to $(PNCl_2)_6$ are clearly separated and give good peaks, but higher polymers give diffuse peaks and are poorly separated from one another. Gimblett finds that derivatives, e.g., $[PN(OH)_2]_4$, $(PN \cdot NHC_6H_5)_3$, $P_3N_3Cl_4(C_6H_5)_2$, etc., give poor peaks.

Dimethyl and diethyl phosphites are shown to separate easily on di-*n*-butyl phthalate (*24*).

(*e*) *Halogens and their Inorganic Derivatives*

The halogens and interhalogen compounds have been chromatographed by Ellis and Iveson (*26*), Ellis, Forrest and Allen (*27*), and apparatuses for the analysis of such mixtures in a manufacturing plant are described by Iveson and Hamlin (*28*). Chlorine and some interhalogen compounds have been chromatographed on capillary columns by Phillips and Owens (*29*); the impurities in chlorine from chlorine cells have been studied by Neely (*30*). The three halogens Cl_2, Br_2, and I_2 have been chromatographed on silica gel by Janak, Nedrost, and Bubenikova (*31*).

The halogens and interhalogen compounds are covalent volatile substances, and, in principle, their chromatography is regular. In practice, however, the corrosive and reactive nature of the substances causes difficulties. Ellis, Iveson *et al.* (*26–28*) consider that the only materials that may be allowed to come into contact with the substances are nickel, monel metal, polytetrafluoroethylene, or polytrifluoromonochloroethylene. They describe apparatuses containing valves and tubing made out of either of the above two metals. A column packing suitable for the analysis of the substances is made using polytetrafluoroethylene as support, and polytrifluoromonochloroethylene oil (Kel-F oil) as stationary liquid. In this way, satisfactory analyses of the compounds given in Table 11.53 are obtained, with the relative retention data given. The efficiency of the columns is poor, but no better support can be found that does not react

TABLE 11.53

RETENTIONS OF HALOGENS AND INTERHALOGEN COMPOUNDS RELATIVE TO CHLORINE ON POLYTRIFLUOROMONOCHLOROETHYLENE OIL

Substance	b.p. (°C)	Relative retention
Chlorine monofluoride	−100.8	0.25
Hydrogen fluoride	19.4	0.6
Chlorine	−34.6	*1.0*
Chlorine trifluoride	11.3	2.0
Bromine	58.8	4.2
Bromine pentafluoride	40.5	6.1
Uranium hexafluoride	56	11.6

with the fluorinated compounds, particularly with the highly reactive fluorinating agent, chlorine trifluoride. In particular, polythene is unsuitable, for polythene exchanges hydrogen for fluorine with ClF_3. A similar column material is used by Neely for the analysis of chlorine cell gas, which contains small quantities of hydrogen, oxygen, nitrogen, carbon monoxide, and carbon dioxide. The permanent gases, carbon dioxide, and chlorine (in that order) are thus separated, and the permanent gases are routed to another column whereon they are separated (Section 11.1).

Phillips and Owens (*29*) have experimented with the use of capillaries of either copper or tetrafluoroethylene coated with polytrifluoromonochloroethylene oil for the analysis of chlorine, hydrogen fluoride, and chlorine trifluoride. Peaks were obtained with all three substances, but, as other workers have also found, efficiencies were poor, and the capillary columns do not show any advantage as yet.

The corrosive nature of fluorinated compounds puts some restriction on the choice and design of detectors. Ellis, Iveson *et al.* (*26–28*) have used a catharometer in which the hot element is a nickel wire, and in which all insulation in contact with the column effluent is of polytetrafluoroethylene. These authors have also used a gas density meter constructed from nickel tubes subsequently cast into copper; they have thus made use of the property of this detector that its sensing element never comes into contact with the gases sensed. Neely has used an ordinary general purpose catharometer in his chlorine analyses, but this would almost certainly fail for fluorinated gases. Phillips and Owens use a hydrogen flame detector, but find that it is necessary to have a separate hydrogen flame into which the column effluent is injected, instead of either using hydrogen as carrier gas, or pre-mixing the column effluent with hydrogen. The authors use a jet consisting of the ends of two concentric tubes, the inner tube carrying hydrogen which burns, and the outer one carrying the column effluent.

References.*

Section 11.1.

1. Greene, S. A., and Roy, H. E., *Anal. Chem.* **29,** 569 (1957).
2. Janák, J., *Collection Czechoslov. Chem. Communs.,* **19,** 917 (1954).
3. Greene, S. A., *Anal. Chem.* **31,** 480 (1959).
4. Gnauk, G., and Frenzel, J., presented at the Symposium on Gas Chromatography, Leipzig, October, 1958.
5. Krejci, M., Tesarik, K., and Janak, J., *in* "Gas Chromatography," I.S.A. Symposium, June, 1959 (H. J. Noebels, R. F. Wall, and N. Brenner, eds.), p. 255. Academic Press, New York, 1961.
6. Gluekauf, E., and Kitt, G. P., *Proc. Roy. Soc.* **A234,** 557 (1956).
7. Koch, R. C., and Grandy, G. L., Presented at the Pittsburgh Conference on Analytical Chemistry, March 1960.
8. Koch, R. C. and Grandy, G. L., *Anal. Chem.* **33,** 43 (1961).
9. Gluekauf, E., *in* "Gas Chromatography 1958," Proceedings of the Second Symposium, Amsterdam, May, 1958 (D. H. Desty, ed.), p. 69. Academic Press, New York, 1958.
10. Gluekauf, E., *Ann. N.Y. Acad. Sci.* **72,** 562 (1959).
11. Greene, S. A., Advances in Gas Chromatography, *Am. Chem. Soc. Symposium, New York, Sept. 1957,* p. D 105.
12. Bethune, J. L., and Rigby, F. L., *J. Inst. Brewing* **64,** 170 (1958).
13. Kyryacos, G., and Boord, C. E., *Anal. Chem.* **29,** 787 (1957).
14. Greene, S. A., and Pust, H., *Anal. Chem.* **29,** 1055 (1957).
15. Madison, J. J., *Anal. Chem.* **30,** 1859 (1958).
16. Patton, H. W., Lewis, J. S., and Kaye, W. I., *Anal. Chem.* **27,** 170 (1955).
17. Greene, S. A., Moberg, M. L., and Wilson, E. M., *Anal. Chem.* **28,** 1369 (1956).
18. Szonntag, E. L., and Stewart, J. R., Symposium on Gas Chromatography, Third Delaware Regional Meeting, Am. Chem. Soc., Feb., 1960.
19. Vizard, G. S., and Wynne, A., *Chem. & Ind. (London)* p. 196 (1959).
20. Lord, E. W., and Horn, R. C., *Anal. Chem.* **32,** 878 (1960).
21. Anonymous, *Chem. Age (London)* **82,** 771 (1959).
22. Pietsch, H., *Erdöl. u. Kohle* **11,** 157 (1958).
23. Fukuda, T., Omori, H., and Kusama, T., *Bunseki Kagaku* **6,** 647 (1957).
24. Wencke, K., *Chem. Tech. (Berlin)* **8,** 728 (1956).
25. Wencke, K., *Chem. Tech. (Berlin)* **9,** 404 (1957).
26. Graven, W. M., *Anal. Chem.* **31,** 1197 (1959).
27. Falconer, J. W., and Knox, J. H., *Proc. Roy. Soc.* **A250,** 493 (1959).
28. Szulczewski, D. H., and Higuchi, T., *Anal. Chem.* **29,** 1541 (1957).
29. Brenner, N., and Ciepelinski, E., *Ann. N.Y. Acad. Sci.* **72,** 705 (1959).
30. Marvillet, L., and Tranchant, J., Third Symposium on Gas Chromatography, Edinburgh, June, 1960, Paper No. 22 (Preprint).
31. Smith, R. N., Swinehart, J., and Lesnini, G. D., *Anal. Chem.* **30,** 1217 (1958).
32. Schwenck, U., and Hachenberg, H., *Brennstoff-Chem.* **41,** 183 (1960).
33. Adlard, E. R., and Hill, D. W., *Nature* **186,** 1045 (1960).
34. Horton, A. D., from Office of Technical Services, Dept. of Commerce, Washington D.C., ORNL-2866, U.C.-4 Chemistry-General, TID 4500 (15th ed.).

* *Note*: References are numbered beginning with (*1*) in each section, and are here grouped together according to section.

35. Greene, S. A. and Pust, H., Advances in Gas Chromatography, *Am. Chem. Soc. Symposium, New York, Sept. 1957*, p. D 107; *Anal. Chem.* **30,** 1039 (1958).
36. Smith, D. H., Nakayama, F. S., and Clark, F. E., *Soil Sci. Am. Proc.* **24,** 145 (1960).
37. Ohkoshi, S., Fujita, Y. and Kwan, T., *Bull. Chem. Soc. Japan* **31,** 770 (1958).
38. Ohkoshi, S., Tenma, S., Fujita, Y., and Kwan, T., *Bull. Chem. Soc. Japan* **31,** 772 (1958).
39. Ohkoshi, S., Tenma, S., Fujita, Y., and Kwan, T., *Bull. Chem. Soc. Japan* **31,** 773 (1958).
40. Smith, H. A., and Hunt, P. P., *J. Phys. Chem.* **64,** 383 (1960).
41. Gant, P. L., and Yang, K., *Science* **129,** 1548 (1959).
42. Riedel, O., and Uhlmann, E., *Z. anal. Chem.* **166,** 433 (1959).
43. Arnett, E. M., Presented at the Pittsburgh Conference on Analytical Chemistry, March, 1960.
44. Gluekauf, E., and Kitt, G. P., *in* "Vapour Phase Chromatography," Proceedings of the First Symposium, London, June, 1956 (D. H. Desty, ed.), p. 422. Academic Press, New York, 1957.
45. Thomas, C. O., and Smith, H. A., *J. Phys. Chem.* **63,** 427 (1959).
46. Moore, W. R., and Ward, H. R., *J. Am. Chem. Soc.* **80,** 2909 (1958).
47. van Hook, W. A., and Emmett, P. H., *J. Phys. Chem.* **64,** 673 (1960).
48. Erb, E., *in* "Gas Chromatography," I.S.A. Symposium, June, 1959 (H. J. Noebels, R. F. Wall, and N. Brenner, eds.), p. 357. Academic Press, New York, 1961.
49. Furuyama, S., and Kwan, T., *J. Phys. Chem.* **65,** 190 (1961).

Section 11.2.

1. Condon, R. D., *Anal. Chem.* **31,** 1717 (1959).
2. Desty, D. H., Goldup, A., and Whyman, B. H. F., *J. Inst. Petrol.* **45,** 287 (1959).
3. Turkeltaub, N. M., *Zhur. Anal. Khim.* **5,** 200 (1950); *Chem. Abstr.* **50,** 7663 (1956); Turkeltaub, N. M., and Zhukhovitskii, A. A., *Zavodskaya Lab.* **22,** 1032 (1956) (review); Turkeltaub, N. M., Kolyubyakina, A. I., and Selenkina, N. S., *Zhur. Anal. Khim.* **12,** 302 (1957); Turkeltaub, N. M., Porshneva, N. V., and Kancheeva, O. A., *Zavodskaya Lab.* **22,** 735 (1956); Vyakhirev, D. A., and Bruk, A. I., *Zhur. Fiz. Khim.* **31,** 1713 (1957); Vyakhirev, D. A., Bruk, A. I., and Guglina, S. A., *Doklady Akad. Nauk S.S.S.R.* **90,** 577 (1953); Zhukhovitskii, A. A., Kasansky, B. A., Sterligov, O. D., and Turkeltaub, N. M., *ibid.* **94,** 77 (1954).
4. Patton, H. W., Lewis, J. S., and Kaye, W. I., *Anal. Chem.* **27,** 170 (1955).
5. Ohkoshi, S., Fujita, Y., and Kwan, T., *Shokubai* **15,** 1 (1958).
6. Ray, N. H., *J. Appl. Chem.* **4,** 21 (1954).
7. Greene, S. A., Moberg, M. L., and Wilson, E. M., *Anal. Chem.* **28,** 1369 (1956).
8. Greene, S. A., and Pust, H., *Anal. Chem.* **29,** 1055 (1957).
9. Morrow, H. N., and Buckley, K. B., *Petrol. Refiner* **36,** 157 (1957).
10. Taylor, G. W., and Dunlop, A. S., *in* "Gas Chromatography," I.S.A. Symposium, August, 1957 (V. J. Coates, H. J. Noebels, and I. S. Fagerson, eds.), p. 73. Academic Press, New York, 1958.
11. Fredericks, E. M., and Brooks, F. R., *Anal. Chem.* **28,** 297 (1956).
12. Bradford, B. W., Harvey, D., and Chalkley, D. E., *J. Inst. Petrol.* **41,** 80 (1955).
13. Primavesi, G. R., *Nature* **184,** 2010 (1959).
14. Barnard, J. A., and Hughes, H. W. D., *Nature* **183,** 250 (1959).
15. Dietz, W. A., and Dudenbostel, B. F., Advances in Gas Chromatography, *Am. Chem. Soc. Symposium, New York, Sept. 1957*, p. D 171.
16. van der Craats, F., *Anal. Chim. Acta* **14,** 136 (1956).

17. Wirth, M. M., *in* "Vapour Phase Chromatography," Proceedings of the First Symposium, London, June, 1956 (D. H. Desty, ed.), p. 154. Academic Press, New York, 1957.
18. I. P. Methods 169 (A, B, and C)/59 (tentative), Institute of Petroleum Standard Methods for Testing Petroleum and Its Products, 19th ed., 1960.
19. Hively, R. A., *J. Chem. Eng. Data* **5,** 237 (1960).
20. Keulemans, A. I. M., Kwantes, A., and Zaal, P., *Anal. Chim. Acta* **13,** 357 (1955).
21. McKenna, T. A., and Idleman, J. A , *Anal. Chem.* **31,** 2000 (1959).
22. McKenna, T. A., and Idleman, J. A., *Anal. Chem.* **31,** 1021 (1959).
23. Scott, C. G., *J. Inst. Petrol.* **45,** 118 (1959).
24. Favre, J. A., Hines, W. J., and Smith, D. E., *Proc. 37th Ann. Conv, Nat. Gasoline Assoc. Am.*, p. 27 (1958); see *J. Inst. Petrol.* **45,** 29A (1959).
25. Knight, H. S., *Anal. Chem.* **30,** 9 (1958).
26. Davies, R. E., and Schreiber, R. A., Advances in Gas Chromatography, *Am. Chem. Soc. Symposium, New York, Sept. 1957*, p. D 91.
27. Brenner, N., and Ciepelinski, E., *Ann. N.Y. Acad. Sci.* **72,** 705 (1959).

Section 11.3.

1. Desty, D. H., and Whyman, B. H. F., *Anal. Chem.* **29,** 320 (1957).
2. Brooks, V. T., and Collins, G. A., *Chem. & Ind. (London)* p. 921 (1956).
3. Scott, R. P. W., Benzol Producers Ltd., Watford, England, Research Paper 8-1957.
4. Kwantes, A., and Rijnders, G. W. A., *in* "Gas Chromatography 1958," Proceedings of the Second Symposium, Amsterdam May, 1958 (D. H. Desty, ed.), p. 125. Academic Press, New York, 1958.
5. James, A. T., and Martin, A. J. P., *J. Appl. Chem.* **6,** 105 (1956).
6. Eggertsen, F. T., and Groennings, S., *Anal. Chem.* **30,** 20 (1958).
7. Littlewood, A. B., unpublished results.
8. Porter, P. E., Deal, C. H., and Stross, F. H., *J. Am. Chem. Soc.* **78,** 2999 (1956).
9. Armitage, F., *J. Chromatog.* **2,** 655 (1959).
10. Adlard, E. R., *in* "Vapor Phase Chromatography," Proceedings of the First Symposium, London, June, 1956 (D. H. Desty, ed.), p. 98. Academic Press, New York, 1957.

10a. Knight, H. S., *Anal. Chem.* **30,** 9 (1958).

11. Sullivan, L. J., Lotz, J. R., and Willingham, C. B., *Anal. Chem.* **28,** 495 (1956).
12. Dietz, W. A., and Dudenbostel, B. F., Advances in Gas Chromatography, *Am. Chem. Soc. Symposium, New York, Sept. 1957*, p. D 171.
13. Hively, R. A., *J. Chem. Eng. Data* **5,** 237 (1960).
14. Desty, D. H., Goldup, A., and Whyman, B. H. F., *J. Inst. Petrol.* **45,** 287 (1959).
15. Zlatkis, A., *Anal. Chem.* **30,** 332 (1958).
16. Eggertsen, F. T., Knight, H. S., and Groennings, S., *Anal. Chem.* **28,** 303 (1956).
17. Zlatkis, A., and Lovelock, J. E., *Anal. Chem.* **31,** 620 (1959).
18. Eggertsen, F. T., and Knight, H. S., *Anal. Chem.* **30,** 15 (1958).
19. Tenney, H. M., *Anal. Chem.* **30,** 2 (1958).
20. Bradford, B. W., Harvey, D., and Chalkley, D. E., *J. Inst. Petrol.* **41,** 80 (1955).
21. Bednas, M. E. and Russell, D. S., *Can. J. Chem.* **36,** 1272 (1958).
22. I. P. Method 156/58, Institute of Petroleum Standard Methods for Testing Petroleum and Its Products, 19th ed., 1960.
23. Blundell, R. V., Griffiths, S. T., and Wilson, R. R., Third Symposium on Gas Chromatography, Edinburgh, June, 1960, Paper No. 25 (Preprint).
24. Martin, R. L., *Anal. Chem.* **32,** 336 (1960).

25. Rowan, R. Jr., Presented at the *137th Am. Chem. Soc. Meeting, April, 1960.*
26. Merritt, C., Jr., and Walsh, J. T., Presented at the Pittsburgh Conference on Analytical Instrumentation, March, 1960.
27. Mawson, J., *Ind. Eng. Chem.* **52,** 85A (1960).
28. Whitham, B. T., *Nature* **182,** 391 (1958).
29. Smith, B., and Ohlson, R., *Acta Chem. Scand.* **14,** 1317 (1960).
30. Nelson, K. H., Hines, W. J., Grimes, M.D., and Smith, D. E., *Anal. Chem.* **32,** 1110 (1960).
31. Murray, K. E., *Australian J. Chem.* **12,** 657 (1959).
32. Cason, J., Fessenden, J. S., and Agre, C. L., *Tetrahedron* **7,** 289 (1959).
33. Gohlke, R. S., *Anal. Chem.* **31,** 535 (1959).
34. Beynon, J. H., *Nature* **174,** 735 (1954).
35. Beynon, J. H., *Mikrochim. Acta* p. 437 (1956).
36. Beynon, J. H., Saunders, R. A., and Williams, A. E., *J. Sci. Inst.* **36,** 275 (1959).
37. Anderson, D. M. W., and Duncan, J. L., *Chem. & Ind.* (*London*) p. 1662 (1958).
38. Anderson, D. M. W., *Analyst* **84,** 50 (1959).

Section 11.4.

1. Scott, R. P. W., Benzol Producers Ltd., Watford, England, Research Paper 8-1957.
2. Brooks, V. T., and Collins, G. A., *Chem. & Ind.* (*London*) p. 921 (1956).
3. Jones, W. C., Advances in Gas Chromatography, *Am. Chem. Soc. Symposium, New York, Sept. 1957*, p. D 117.
4. Desty, D. H., Goldup, A., and Swanton, W. T., *Nature* **183,** 107 (1959).
5. Zlatkis, A., Ling, S., and Kaufman, H. R., *Anal. Chem.* **31,** 945 (1959).
6. Adlard, E. R., *in* "Vapour Phase Chromatography," Proceedings of the First Symposium, 1956 (D. H. Desty, ed.), p. 98. Academic Press, New York, 1957.
7. Adlard, E. R., Khan, M. A., and Whitham, B. T., Third Symposium on Gas Chromatography, Edinburgh, June, 1960, Paper No. 17 (Preprint).
8. Littlewood, A. B., unpublished results.
9. Langer, S. H., Zahn, C., and Pantazoplos, G. *Chem. & Ind.* (*London*) p. 1145 (1958).
10. Paterson, A. R., *in* "Gas Chromatography," I.S.A. Symposium, June, 1959 (H. J. Noebels, R. F. Wall, and N. Brenner, eds.), p. 323. Academic Press, New York, 1961.
11. Desty, D. H., Goldup, A., and Whyman, B. H. F., *J. Inst. Petrol.* **45,** 287 (1959).
12. Hughes, M. A., White, D., and Roberts, A. L., *Nature* **184,** 1796 (1959).
13. Franc, J., and Jokl, J., *Collection Czechoslov. Chem. Communs.* **24,** 144 (1959).
14. Hendriks, W. J., Soemantri, R. M., and Waterman, H. I., *J. Inst. Petrol.* **43,** 288 (1957).
15. Soemantri, R. M., and Waterman, H. I., *J. Inst. Petrol.* **43,** 94 (1957).
16. Soemantri, R. M., Proefschr. tech. Hogesch. (Delft) 1958; see *J. Appl. Chem.* **9** (9), Abstr. ii-259 (1959).
17. Castiglioni, A., *Z. anal. Chem.* **161,** 191 (1958).
18. Gordon, S., Dyken, A. R. van, and Doumani, T. F., *J. Phys. Chem.* **62,** 20 (1958).
19. Beaven, G. H., James, A. T., and Johnson, E. A., *Nature* **179,** 490 (1957).
20. Johnson, E. A., *J. Chem. Soc.* p. 4155 (1957).
21. Baxter, R. A., and Keen, R. T., *Anal. Chem.* **31,** 475 (1959).
22. Rosie, D. M., and Grob, R. L., *Anal. Chem.* **29,** 1263 (1957).

Section 11.5.

1. Scott, R. P. W., Benzol Producers Ltd., Watford, England, Research Paper 8-1957.
2. Adlard, E. R., *in* "Vapour Phase Chromatography," Proceedings of the First

Symposium, London, June, 1956 (D. H. Desty, ed.), p. 98. Academic Press, New York, 1957.
3. Hively, R. A., *J. Chem. Eng. Data* **5,** 237 (1960).
4. Anderson, J. R. A. and Napier, K. H., *Australian J. Chem.* **9,** 541 (1956).
5. Tenney, H. M., *Anal. Chem.* **30,** 2 (1958).
6. White, D., *Nature* **179,** 1075 (1957).
7. White, D. and Cowan, C. T., *Trans. Faraday Soc.* **54,** 557 (1958).
8. James, A. T., and Martin, A. J. P., *J. Appl. Chem.* **6,** 105 (1956).
9. Desty, D. H., and Whyman, B. H. F., *Anal. Chem.* **29,** 320 (1957).

Section 11.6.

1. James, A. T., and Martin, A. J. P., *Biochem. J.* **50,** 679 (1952).
2. Beerthuis, R. K., Dijkstra, G., Keppler, J. G., and Recourt, J. H., *Ann. N.Y. Acad. Sci.* **72,** 616 (1959).
3. James, A. T., and Martin, A. J. P., *Biochem. J.* **63,** 144 (1956).
4. Jones, C. E. Roland, Third Symposium on Gas Chromatography, Edinburgh, June, 1960, Paper No. 28 (Preprint).
5. Quin, L. D., and Hobbs, M. E., *Anal. Chem.* **30,** 1400 (1958).
6. Stoffel, W., Chu, F., and Ahrens, E. H., *Anal. Chem.* **31,** 307 (1959).
7. Luddy, F. E., Barford, R. A., and Riemenschneider, R. W., Am. Oil Chemists' Soc. Meeting, April, 1959.
8. Craig, B. M., Tulloch, A. P., and Murty, N. L., 33rd Fall Meeting, Am. Oil Chemists' Soc., Sept. 1959.
9. Huebner, V. R., 33rd Fall Meeting, Am. Oil Chemists' Soc., Sept. 1959.
10. Cropper, F. R., and Heywood, A., *Nature* **174,** 1063 (1954).
11. Cropper, F. R., and Heywood, A., *Nature* **172,** 1101 (1953).
12. Cropper, F. R., and Heywood, A., *in* "Vapour Phase Chromatography," Proceedings of the First Symposium, London, June, 1956 (D. H. Desty, ed.), p. 316. Academic Press, New York, 1957.
13. Khan, M. A., and Whitham, B. T., *J. Appl. Chem.* **8,** 549 (1958).
14. Adlard, E. R., and Whitham, B. T., *in* "Gas Chromatography 1958," Proceedings of the Second Symposium, Amsterdam, May, 1958 (D. H. Desty, ed.), p. 351. Academic Press, New York, 1958.
15. Beerthuis, R. K., and Keppler, J. G., *Nature* **179,** 731 (1957).
16. Hawke, J. C., Hansen, R. P., and Shorland, F. B., *J. Chromatog.* **2,** 547 (1959).
17. James, A. T., *J. Chromatog.* **2,** 552 (1959).
18. Insull, W., and Ahrens, E. H., *Biochem. J.* **72,** 27 (1959).
19. Orr, C. H., and Callen, J. E., *J. Am. Chem. Soc.* **80,** 249 (1958).
20. Hornstein, I., Elliott, L. E., and Crowe, P. F., *Nature* **184,** 1710 (1959).
21. Lipsky, S. R., Lovelock, J. E., and Landowne, R. A., *J. Am. Chem. Soc.* **81,** 1010 (1959).
22. Lipsky, S. R., and Landowne, R. A., *Ann. N.Y. Acad. Sci.* **72,** 666 (1959).
23. Lipsky, S. R., Landowne, R. A., and Lovelock, J. E., *Anal. Chem.* **31,** 852 (1959).
24. Orr, C. H., and Callen, J. E., *Ann. N.Y. Acad. Sci.* **72,** 649 (1959).
25. Lipsky, S. R., Landowne, R. A., and Godet, M. R., *Biochim. et Biophys. Acta* **31,** 336 (1959).
26. Craig, B. M., and Murty, N. L., *Can. J. Chem.* **36,** 1297 (1958).
27. Janak, J., Dobiasova, M., and Veres, K., *Collection Czechoslov. Chem. Communs.* **25,** 1566 (1960).
28. Daniels, N. W. R., and Richmond, J. W., *Nature* **187,** 55 (1960).

29. Miwa, T. K., Mikolajczak, K. L., Earle, F. R., and Wolff, I. A., Presented at the *137th Am. Chem. Soc. Meeting, April, 1960.*
30. Miwa, T. K., Mikolajczak, K. L., Earle, F. R., and Wolff, I. A., *Anal. Chem.* **32,** 1739 (1960).
31. Woodford, F. P., and van Gent, C. M., *J. Lipid Research* **1,** 188 (1960).
32. Landowne, R. A., and Lipsky, S. R., *Nature* **182,** 1731 (1958).
33. Bottcher, C. J. E., Clemens, C. F. G., and van Gent, C. M., *J. Chromatog.* **3,** 582 (1960).
34. Killheffer, J. V., and Jungermann, E., *J. Am. Oil Chemists' Soc.* **37,** 456 (1960).
35. Lipsky, S. R., and Landowne, R. A., *Ann. Rev. Biochem.* (1960).
36. James, A. T., *in* "Methods of Biochemical Analysis" (D. Glick, ed.). Interscience, New York, 1960.
37. Burchfield, H. P., and Storrs, E. E. (eds.), "Biochemical Applications of Gas Chromatography." Academic Press, New York, 1962.

Section 11.7.

1. Knight, H. S., *Anal. Chem.* **30,** 2030 (1958).
2. Littlewood, A. B., Phillips, C. S. G., and Price, D. T., *J. Chem. Soc.* p. 1480 (1955).
3. Adlard, E. R., *in* "Vapour Phase Chromatography," Proceedings of the First Symposium, London, June, 1956 (D. H. Desty, ed.), p. 98. Academic Press, New York, 1957.
4. Raupp, G., *Z. anal. Chem.* **164,** 135 (1958).
5. Kelker, H., *Angew. Chem.* **71,** 218 (1959).
6. Karagounis, G., and Lippold, G., *Naturwissenschaften* p. 145 (1959).
7. Kuffner, F , and Kallina, D., *Monatsh. Chem.* **90,** 463 (1959).
8. Warren, G. W., Haskin, J. F., Kourey, R. E., and Yarborough, V. A., *Anal. Chem.* **31,** 1624 (1959).
9. Kallina, D., and Kuffner, F., *Monatsh. Chem.* **91,** 289 (1960).
10. Ray, N. H., *J. Appl. Chem.* **4,** 21 (1954).
11. Broughton, B., and Wheatley, V. R., *Biochem. J.* **73,** 144 (1959).
12. Link, W. E., Hickman, H. M., and Morrissette, R. A., *J. Am. Oil Chemists' Soc.* **36,** 20 (1959).
13. Link, W. E., Hickman, H. M., and Morrissette, R. A., *J. Am. Oil Chemists' Soc.* **36,** 300 (1959).
14. Cropper, F. R., and Heywood, A., *in* "Vapour Phase Chromatography," Proceedings of the First Symposium, London, June, 1956 (D. H. Desty, ed.), p. 316. Academic Press, New York, 1957.
15. Ginsberg, L., *Anal. Chem.* **31,** 1822 (1959).
16. Nogare, S. D., and Safranski, L. W., *Anal. Chem.* **30,** 894 (1958).
17. Ring, R. D., *in* "Gas Chromatography," I.S.A. Symposium, August, 1957 (V. J. Coates, H. J. Noebels, and I. S. Fagerson, eds.), p. 195. Academic Press, New York, 1958.
18. Beerthuis, R. K., and Recourt, J. H., *Nature* **186,** 372 (1960).
19. Vandenheuvel, W. J. A., Sweeley, C. C., and Horning, E. C., *Biochem. Biophys. Research Communs.* **3,** 33 (1960).
20. Vandenheuvel, W. J. A., Sweeley, C. C., and Horning, E. C., *J. Am. Chem. Soc.* **82,** 3481 (1960).
21. Sweeley, C. C., and Horning, E. C., *Nature* **187,** 144 (1960).
22. Littlewood, A. B., Unpublished results.
23. Bartsch, R. C., Miller, F. D., and Trent, F. M., *Anal. Chem.* **32,** 1101 (1960).

24. Adlard, E. R., and Hill, D. W., *Nature* **186,** 1045 (1960).
25. Hill, D. W., Third Symposium on Gas Chromatography, Edinburgh, 1960, Paper No. 24 (Preprint).
26. McInnes, A. G., Ball, D. H., Cooper, F. P., and Bishop, C. T., *J. Chromatog.* **1,** 556 (1958).
27. Bishop, C. T., and Cooper, F. P., *Can. J. Chem.* **38,** 388 (1960).
28. Kircher, H. W., *Anal. Chem.* **32,** 1103 (1960).
29. Martin, F., and Vertalier, S., Presented at 15th Congress of Pure and Applied Chemistry, Lisbon, Sept. 1956.
30. Vertalier, S., and Martin, F., *Chim. anal.* **40,** 80 (1958).
31. Kratzl, K. and Gruber, K., *Monatsh. Chem.* **89,** 618 (1958).
32. Haslam, J., Hamilton, J. B., and Jeffs, A. R., *Analyst* **83,** 66 (1958).
33. Kovats, E., *Helv. Chim. Acta* **41,** 1915 (1958).
34. Matthews, J. S., Burow, F. H., and Snyder, R. E., *Anal. Chem.* **32,** 691 (1960).
35. Zlatkis, A., and Oro, J. F., *Anal. Chem.* **30,** 1156 (1958).
36. Schepartz, A. I., and McDowell, P. E., *Anal. Chem.* **32,** 723 (1960)
37. Kelker, H., *Z. anal. Chem.* **176,** 3 (1960).
38. Sandler, S., and Strom, R., *Anal. Chem.* **32,** 1890 (1960).
39. Cason, J., and Harris, E. R., *J. Org. Chem.* **24,** 676 (1959).
40. Gray, G. M., *J. Chromatog.* **4,** 52 (1960).
41. Ralls, J. W., *Anal. Chem.* **32,** 332 (1960).
42. Stephens, R. L., and Teszler, A. P., *Anal. Chem.* **32,** 1047 (1960).
43. Young, J. R., *Chem. & Ind.* (*London*), p. 594 (1958).
44. Irvine, L., and Mitchell, T. J., *J. Appl. Chem.* **8,** 3 (1958).
45. Irvine, L., and Mitchell, T. J., *J. Appl. Chem.* **8,** 425 (1958).
46. Janak, J., and Komers, R., *Z. anal. Chem.* **164,** 69 (1958).
47. Janak, J., and Komers, R., *in* "Gas Chromatography 1958," Proceedings of the Second Symposium, Amsterdam, May, 1958 (D. H. Desty, ed.), p. 343. Academic Press, New York, 1958.
48. Janak, J., and Komers, R., *Collection Czechoslov. Chem. Communs.* **24,** 1960 (1959).
49. Janak, J., Komers, R., and Sima, J., *Chem. Listy* **52,** 2296 (1958).
50. Bergmann, G., and Jentzsch, D., *Z. anal. Chem.* **164,** 10 (1958).
51. Karr, C., Brown, P. M., Estep, P. A., and Humphrey, G. L., *Anal. Chem.* **30,** 1413 (1958).
52. Brooks, V. T., *Chem. & Ind.* (*London*) p. 1317 (1959).
53. Kreyenbuhl, A., and Weiss, H., *Bull. soc. chim. France* p. 1880 (1959).
54. Carruthers, W., Johnstone, R. A. W., and Plimmer, J. R., *Chem. & Ind.* (*London*) p. 331 (1958).
55. Langer, S. H., Pantages, P., and Wender, I., *Chem. & Ind.* (*London*) p. 1664 (1958).
56. Komers, R., and Bazant, V., *Doklady Akad. Nauk S.S.S.R.*, **126,** 1268 (1959).
57. Brown, H. C., Marino, G., and Stock, L. M., *J. Am. Chem. Soc.* **81,** 3310 (1959).

Section 11.8.

1. James, A. T., Martin, A. J. P., and Smith, G. H., *Biochem. J.* **52,** 238 (1952).
2. James, A. T., and Martin, A. J. P., *Analyst* **77,** 915 (1952).
3. James, A. T. and Martin, A. J. P., *Brit. Med. Bull.* **10,** 170 (1954).
4. James, A. T., *Biochem. J.* **52,** 242 (1952).
5. Link, W. E., Morrissette, R. A., Cooper, A. D., and Smullin, C. F., *J. Am. Oil Chemists' Soc.* **37,** 364 (1960).
6. Nelson, J., and Milun, A., *Chem. & Ind.* (*London*) p. 663 (1960).

7. James, A. T., *Anal. Chem.* **28,** 1564 (1956).
8. Jones, J. H., Ritchie, C. D., and Heine, K. S., *J. Assoc. Offic. Agr. Chemists* **41,** 749 (1958).
9. Brooks, V. T., and Collins, G. A., *Chem. & Ind.* (*London*) p. 1021 (1956).
10. Decora, A. W., and Dineen, G. U., *Anal. Chem.* **32,** 164 (1960).
11. Murray, W. J., and Williams, A. F., *Chem. & Ind.* (*London*) p. 1020 (1956).
12. Janak, J., and Hrivnac, M., Presented at the Third Conference on Analytical Chemistry, Prague, September, 1959.
13. Janak, J., and Hrivnac, M., *Collection Czechoslov. Chem. Communs.* **25,** 1557 (1960).
14. Hunter, I. R., Dimick, K. P., and Corse, J. W., *Chem. & Ind.* (*London*) p. 294 (1956).
15. Zlatkis, A., and Oro, J. F., *Anal. Chem.* **30,** 1156 (1958).
16. Bier, M., and Teitelbaum, P., *Ann. N.Y. Acad. Sci.* **72,** 641 (1959).
17. Zlatkis, A., Oro, J. F., and Kimball, A. P., *Anal. Chem.* **32,** 162 (1960).
18. Baraud, J., *Bull. soc. chim. France* p. 785 (1960).
19. Warren, G. W., Haskin, J. F., Kourey, R. E., and Yarborough, V. A., *Anal. Chem.* **31,** 1624 (1959).
20. Bayer, E., *in* "Gas Chromatography 1958," Proceedings of the Second Symposium, Amsterdam, May, 1958 (D. H. Desty, ed.), p. 333. Academic Press, New York, 1958.
21. Bayer, E., Reuther, K. H., and Born, F., *Angew. Chem.* **69,** 640 (1957).
22. Youngs, C. G., *Anal. Chem.* **31,** 1019 (1959).
23. Saroff, H. A., and Karmen, A., *Anal. Biochem.* **1,** 344 (1960).
24. Johnson, D. E., Scott, S. J., and Meister, A., *Anal. Chem.* **33,** 669 (1961).
25. Melamed, M., and Renard, M., *J. Chromatog.* **4,** 339 (1960).
26. Quin, L. D., *Nature* **182,** 865 (1958).
27. Quin, L. D., *J. Org. Chem.* **24,** 911 (1959).
28. Lloyd, H. A., Fales, H. M., Highet, P. F., Vandenheuvel, W. J. A., and Wildman, W. C., *J. Am. Chem. Soc.* **82,** 3791 (1960).
29. Dietrich, P., and Mercier, D., *J. Chromatog.* **1,** 67 (1958).
30. Kjaer, A., and Jart, A., *Acta Chem. Scand.* **11,** 1423 (1957).
31. Bens, E. M., and McBride, W. R., *Anal. Chem.* **31,** 1379 (1959).
32. Cason, J., and Harris, E. R., *J. Org. Chem.* **24,** 676 (1959).
33. Barber, D. W., Phillips, C. S. G., Tusa, G. F., and Verdin, A., *J. Chem. Soc.* p. 18 (1959).

Section 11.9.

1. Pollard, F. H., and Hardy, C. J., *Anal. Chim. Acta* **16,** 135 (1957).
2. Pollard, F. H., and Hardy, C. J., *in* "Vapour Phase Chromatography," Proceedings of the First Symposium, London, June, 1956 (D. H. Desty, ed.), p. 115. Academic Press, New York, 1958.
3. Harrison, G. F., *in* "Vapour Phase Chromatography," Proceedings of the First Symposium, London, June, 1956 (D. H. Desty, ed.), p. 332. Academic Press, New York, 1957.
4. Kelker, H., *Angew. Chem.* **71,** 218 (1959).
5. Hardy, C. J., *J. Chromatog.* **2,** 490 (1959).
6. Purnell, J. H., and Spencer, M. S., *Nature* **175,** 988 (1955).
7. Harrison, G. F., Knight, P., Kelly, R. P., and Heath, M. T., "Gas Chromatography 1958," Proceedings of the Second Symposium, Amsterdam, May, 1958 (D. H. Desty, ed.), p. 216. Academic Press, New York, 1958.
8. Gloesener, E., Lapiere, C. L., and Versie, J., *J. pharm. Belg.* [N.S.] **13,** 389 (1958).

9. Domange, L., and Longuevalle, S., *Ann. pharm. franç.* **15,** 448 (1957).
10. Adlard, E. R., and Hill, D. W., *Nature* **186,** 1045 (1960).
11. James, A. T., and Martin, A. J. P., *Brit. Med. Bull.* **10,** 170 (1954).
12. Kovats, E., *Helv. Chim. Acta* **41,** 1915 (1958).
13. McFadden, W. H., *Anal. Chem.* **30,** 479 (1958).
14. Harris, W. E., and McFadden, W. H., *Anal. Chem.* **31,** 114 (1959).
15. Nystrom, R. F., and Berger, C. R. A., *Chem. & Ind.* (*London*) p. 559 (1958).
16. Karagounis, G., and Lippold, G., *Naturwissenschaften* p. 145 (1959).
17. Hatch, L. F., and Payne, J. S., *Ann. N.Y. Acad. Sci.* **72,** 698 (1959).
18. Moussebois, C., and Duyckaerts, G., *J. Chromatog.* **1,** 200 (1958).
19. Littlewood, A. B., Unpublished results.
20. Troupe, R. A., and Golner, J. J., *Anal. Chem.* **30,** 129 (1958).
21. Freeman, S. K., *Anal. Chem.* **32,** 1304 (1960).
22. Root, M. J., *in* "Gas Chromatography," I.S.A. Symposium, August, 1957 (V. J. Coates, H. J. Noebels, and I. S. Fagerson, eds.), p. 99. Academic Press, New York, 1958.
23. Green, S. W., *in* "Vapour Phase Chromatography," Proceedings of the First Symposium, London, June, 1956 (D. H. Desty, ed.), p. 388. Academic Press, New York, 1957.
24. Reed, T. M., *Anal. Chem.* **30,** 221 (1958).
25. Serpinet, J., *Chim. Anal.* **41,** 146 (1959).
26. Godsell, J. A., Stacey, M., and Tatlow, J. C., *Nature* **178,** 199 (1956).
27. Stephens, R., and Tatlow, J. C., *Chem. & Ind.* (*London*) p. 821 (1957).
28. Smith, R. P., and Tatlow, J. C., *J. Chem. Soc.* p. 2505 (1957).
29. Evans, D. E. M., and Tatlow, J. C., *J. Chem. Soc.* p. 1184 (1955).
30. Evans, D. E. M., and Tatlow, J. C., *in* "Vapour Phase Chromatography," Proceedings of the First Symposium, London, June, 1956 (D. H. Desty, ed.), p. 256. Academic Press, New York, 1957.

Section 11.10.

1. Spencer, C. F., Baumann, F., and Johnson, J. F., *Anal. Chem.* **30,** 1473 (1958).
2. Amberg, C. H., *Can. J. Chem.* **36,** 590 (1958).
3. Ryce, S. A., and Bryce, W. A., *Anal. Chem.* **29,** 925 (1957).
4. Sunner, S., Karrman, K. J., and Sunden, V., *Mikrochim. Acta* p. 1144 (1956).
5. Karchmer, J. H., *Anal. Chem.* **31,** 1377 (1959).
6. Sullivan, J. H., Walsh, J. T., and Merritt, C., *Anal. Chem.* **31,** 1826 (1959).
7. Carson, J. R., Weston, W. J., and Ralls, J. W., *Nature* **186,** 801 (1960).
8. Desty, D. H., and Whyman, B. H. F., *Anal. Chem.* **29,** 320 (1959).
9. Petranek, J., *J. Chromatog.* **5,** 254 (1961).
10. Carson, J. F., and Wong, F. F., *J. Org. Chem.* **24,** 175 (1959).
11. Hrivnac, M., and Janak, J., *Chem. & Ind.* (*London*) p. 930 (1960).
12. Thompson, C. J., Coleman, H. J., Ward, C. C. and Rall, H. T., *Anal. Chem.* **32,** 424 (1960).

Section 11.11.

1. Davison, W. H. T., Slaney, S., and Wragg, A. L., *Chem. & Ind.* (*London*) p. 1356 (1954).
2. Strassburger, J., Brauer, G. M., Tryon, M., and Forziati, A. F., *Anal. Chem.* **32,** 454 (1960).

3. Radell, E. A., and Strultz, H. C., *Anal. Chem.* **31,** 1890 (1959).
4. Roland-Jones, C. E., Informal Symposium, Gas Chromatography Discussion Group Birmingham, April, 1961.
5. Miller, D. L., Samsel, E. P., and Cobler, J. G., *Anal. Chem.* **33,** 677 (1961).
6. Barlow, A., Lehrle, R. A., and Robb, J. C., *Polymer* **2,** 27 (1961).
7. Lehrle, R. S., and Robb, J. C., *Nature* **183,** 1671 (1959).
8. Lehmann, F. A., and Brauer, C. M., *Anal. Chem.* **33,** 673 (1961).
9. Jones, C. E. R., and Moyles, A. E., *Nature* **189,** 222 (1961).
10. Blenkin, J., Informal Symposium, Gas Chromatography Discussion Group, London, April, 1960.
11. Janak, J., Informal Symposium, Gas Chromatography Discussion Group, Bristol, September, 1959.
12. Janak, J., Third Symposium on Gas Chromatography, Edinburgh, June, 1960. Paper No. 27 (Preprint).
13. Janak, J., *Nature* **185,** 684 (1960).

Section 11.12.

1. Keller, R. A., and Freiser, H., Third Symposium on Gas Chromatography, Edinburgh, June, 1960, Paper No. 20 (Preprint).
2. Wachi, F. M., *Dissertation Abstr.* **20,** 53 (1959).
3. Juvet, R. S., and Wachi, F. M., *Anal. Chem.* **32,** 290 (1960).
4. Keller, R. A., *J. Chromatog.* **5,** 225 (1961).
5. Freiser, H., *Anal. Chem.* **31,** 1440 (1959).
6. Duswalt, A. A., *Dissertation Abstr.* **20,** 52 (1959).
7. Bierman, W. J., and Gesser, H., *Anal. Chem.* **32,** 1525 (1960).
8. Abel, E. W., Nickless, G., and Pollard, F. H., *Proc. Chem. Soc.* (*London*) p. 288 (1960).
9. DeBoer, F. E., *Nature* **185,** 915 (1960).
10. Kaufman, J. J., Todd, J. E., and Koski, W. S., *Anal. Chem.* **29,** 1032 (1957).
11. Borer, K., Littlewood, A. B., and Phillips, C. S. G., *J. Inorg. & Nuclear Chem.* **15,** 316 (1960).
12. Boone, J. L., and Burg, A. B., *J. Am. Chem. Soc.* **80,** 1519 (1958); **81,** 1766 (1959).
13. Schomburg, G., Koster, R., and Henneberg, D., *Z. anal. chem.* **170,** 285 (1959).
14. Koster, R., and Bruno, G., *Ann.* **629,** 89 (1960).
15. Seely, G. R., Oliver, J. P., and Ritter, D. M., *Anal. Chem.* **31,** 2000 (1959).
16. Blay, N. J., Dunstan, I., and Williams, R. L., *J. Chem. Soc.* p. 430 (1960).
17. Blay, N. J., Williams, J., and Williams, R. L., *J. Chem. Soc.* p. 424 (1960).
18. Borer, K., and Phillips, C. S. G., *Proc. Chem. Soc.* (*London*) p. 189 (1959).
19. Russell, G. A., *J. Am. Chem. Soc.* **81,** 4815 (1959).
20. Fritz, G. and Ksinsik, D., *Z. anorg. u. allgem. Chem.* **304,** 241 (1960).
21. Friedrich, K., *Chem. & Ind.* (*London*) p. 47 (1957).
22. Franc, J., Wirst, M., and Moudry, V., *Collection Czechoslov. Chem. Communs.* **26,** 1313 (1961).
23. Stanford, F. G., *J. Chromatog.* **4,** 419 (1960).
24. Shipotofsky, S. F., and Moser, H. C., *Anal. Chem.* **33,** 521 (1961).
25. Gimblett, F. G. R., *Chem. & Ind.* (*London*) p. 365 (1958).
26. Ellis, J. F., and Iveson, G., *in* "Gas Chromatography 1958," Proceedings of the Second Symposium, Amsterdam, May, 1958 (D. H. Desty, ed.), Academic Press, New York, 1958, p. 300.

27. Ellis, J. F., Forrest, C. W., and Allen, P. L., *Anal. Chim. Acta* **22,** 27 (1960).
28. Iveson, G. and Hamlin, A. G., Third Symposium on Gas Chromatography, Edinburgh, June, 1960, Paper No. 23 (Preprint).
29. Phillips, T. R., and Owens, D. R., Third Symposium on Gas Chromatography, Edinburgh, June, 1960, Paper No. 21 (Preprint).
30. Neely, E. E., *Anal. Chem.* **32,** 1382 (1960).
31. Janak, J., Nedorost, M., and Bubenikova, V., *Chem. Listy* **51,** 890 (1957).

LIST OF SYMBOLS

The number at the right-hand margin indicates the section in which the symbol is first mentioned or defined. Symbols conform where possible to standard usage, and symbols used specifically in gas chromatography conform to the recommendations of the Committee of the Gas Chromatography Discussion Group of the Institute of Petroleum, London, except for the symbols for plate-number and partition coefficient.

Symbol	Meaning	Section
A	constant of integration in Young's or Antoine's equation	3.4
	constant in equation for $\ln \gamma$ by Pierotti *et al.*	3.5
	surface area of solvent phase	5.4
	constant in simplified form of van Deemter's equation (u as variable)	5.11
	area of a peak	7.1
A^*	constant in simplified form of van Deemter's equation ($\dot{V}$ as variable)	5.11
A'	area of triangle formed by base-line and the tangents at the points of inflection of a peak	7.2
B	constant in Antoine's equation	3.4
	constant in equation for $\ln \gamma$ by Pierotti *et al.*	3.5
	constant in simplified form of van Deemter's equation (u as variable)	5.11
B^*	constant in simplified form of van Deemter's equation ($\dot{V}$ as variable)	5.11
C	constant in Antoine's equation	3.4
C, C'	constants in equation for $\ln \gamma$ by Pierotti *et al.*	3.5
C	constant in simplified form of van Deemter's equation (u as variable)	5.11
C^*	constant in simplified form of van Deemter's equation ($\dot{V}$ as variable)	5.11
C_1	reciprocal chart speed	7.1
C_2	reciprocal recorder sensitivity	7.1
C_p	molar specific heat of carrier gas at constant pressure	9.2
D	constant in equation for $\ln \gamma$ by Pierotti *et al.*	3.5
	dissipation constant of a thermistor	9.10
D_g	diffusion coefficient of a solute in the gas phase	5.2
D_l	diffusion coefficient of a solute in the solvent phase	5.4
E	EMF across the Wheatstone's Bridge of a catharometer	9.2

Symbol	Meaning	Section
E_g	EMF across the galvanometer of a catharometer	9.2
E_n	EMF across the arm of a Wheatstone's Bridge, R_n	9.2
F,F'	constants in equation for ln γ by Pierotti *et al.*	3.5
G	Gibbs free energy	3.4
ΔG_{xs}	excess free energy of mixing of solute and solvent	3.5
G	geometrical catharometer constant	9.2
H	height equivalent to a theoretical plate	4.2
ΔH_s	molar heat of evaporation of solute from solution	3.3
ΔH_v	molar heat of evaporation of pure liquid solute	3.3
I	electrical current	8.4, 9.2
I_n	electrical current in arm of a Wheatstone's Bridge, R_n	9.2
J	Joule's constant	9.2
K,K'	used as constants in a particular discussion, and applying to that discussion only	
L	peak retention measured as a distance on the chart paper	4.5
M	molecular weight	
	distance apart at the base-line of tangents drawn at the points of inflection of a peak	4.5
M_1	molecular weight of solvent	3.3
M_2	molecular weight of solute	3.3
N_1	inverse molar volume of solvent	3.3
P	hydrostatic pressure	2.5
P_o	pressure at column outlet	2.5
P_i	pressure at column inlet	2.5
$P^\dagger$	standard pressure	3.4
Q	molecular ionisation cross section	8.4
R	gas constant	3.3
	column resolution	4.7
	helix radius of a helically wound column	5.3
	resistance of the hot element of a catharometer	9.2
R_F	retardation factor	2.4
R_0	resistance of the hot element of a catharometer at T_0	9.2
R_n	resistance of arm of a Wheatstone's bridge, R_n	9.2
S	sharpness of a saturation or elution front	5.6
S,S'	detector sensitivity	7.1
T	temperature (°K)	2.6
T_f	temperature at which flowmeter is calibrated	2.6
T_c	temperature of column	2.6
T_B	boiling point of a pure liquid solute	3.4

T_0	starting temperature in programmed temperature operation	6.5
T_R	emergence temperature of a peak in programmed temperature operation	6.5
T_1	temperature of catharometer walls	9.2
T_2	temperature of catharometer hot element	9.2
T'	average temperature difference between gas entering and leaving a catharometer	9.2
U_g	adsorption volume; formal equivalent of V_g for adsorbents	3.11
V	volume of gas passed through the column	1.2
V_R^0	corrected retention volume	2.3
V_M	gas hold-up of the column	2.3
V_R	measured retention volume	2.5
V_R'	adjusted retention volume	2.5
V_N	net retention volume	2.5
V_a, V_{ab}, etc.	variously corrected retention volumes	2.7
V_g	specific retention volume	2.7
V_g^c	(quantity not named)	2.7
V_i	volume of sample injector cavity	2.9
V_I	volume occupied by the input distribution	5.7
V_r^0	V_R^0 corrected for sample injector volume	2.9
$\dot{V}$	volume flow rate of carrier gas	2.4
$\dot{V}'$	molar flow rate of carrier gas	9.2
$\dot{V}_o$	volume flow rate of carrier gas at column outlet	2.5
$\dot{V}_0$	volume flow rate of carrier gas at 0°C	2.6
$\dot{V}_T$	volume flow rate of carrier gas at T°C	2.6
V_1	molar volume of solvent in liquid state	3.5
V_2	molar volume of solute in liquid state	3.5
W	weight of stationary phase in column	2.3
	power dissipated by the hot element of a catharometer	9.10
X	$\Delta H/RT$ (subscripts on X correspond to subscripts on T)	6.5
a	constant in the Langmuir isotherm	1.4
	volume of gas phase per unit length of column, i.e.,	2.2
	cross-sectional area of column occupied by gas phase	4.2
	drift coefficient in catharometers	9.4
b	constant in the Langmuir isotherm	1.4
	cross-sectional area of column occupied by the solvent phase	4.2

$'$	drift coefficient for catharometers	9.4
c	concentration of vapour in the gas phase	1.1
d_p	average particle diameter of column packing	5.3
d_f	equivalent thickness of liquid film in a packed column	5.4
e_0	rate of production of electrons in pure argon in an argon detector	8.5
e_x	rate of production of electrons in presence of a mole fraction x of organic species	8.5
g	pressure correction factor for A and B terms of van Deemter's equation	5.19
h	peak height	4.5
j	pressure correction factor	2.5
k	retardation ratio, $= m\beta/a$	2.4
l	length of column	2.2
	length of catharometer filament	9.2
m	mass of stationary phase per unit length of column	2.2
	molecular weight of solute	10.2
n	number of incremental volumes V in plate theory	4.2
	carbon number	3.4
n_1	number of moles of solvent in a solution	3.3
	carbon number of solvent	3.5
n_2	number of moles of solute in a solution	3.3
	carbon number of solute	3.5
p	quantity used in discussion of plate theory	4.2
p_2	vapour pressure of solute above its solution	3.3
$p_2{}^0$	vapour pressure of solute above pure liquid solute	3.3
q	quantity used in discussion of plate theory	4.2
	concentration of solute in the stationary phase	1.1
q_m	quantity of adsorbate required to make a monomolecular layer on an adsorbent	3.11
r	relative retention	3.2
	serial number of a theoretical plate	4.2
	column radius	5.3
	heating rate in programmed temperature operation	6.5
r_{nm}	relative retention of components n and m	3.2
r_1	radius of catharometer cavity	9.2
r_2	radius of catharometer hot element	9.2
t	time	2.4
	temperature (°C)	3.4
t_R	retention time	2.4
t_M	gas hold-up time	2.4

t_B	boiling point of solute (°C)	3.4
u	linear flow rate of carrier gas	2.4
v_a	speed of excited argon atoms in an argon detector	8.5
v_m	speed of excited argon atoms relative to organic molecules in an argon detector	8.5
w	mass of solute	1.2
	coordinate of length along the column moving with the peak maximum	5.2
w_1	weight of solvent in a solution	3.3
w_2	weight of solute in a solution	3.3
x	distance from inlet end of the column	2.2
	length coordinate on chart paper	7.1
x_2	mole fraction of solute	3.3
y	recorder deflection	7.1
z	(in general) argument of a function	
	smaller dimension of the cross section of a flat rectangular column	5.4
$z(t)$	chromatogram as plotted by a recorder	5.8
α	dimensionless partition coefficient	3.2
	temperature coefficient of resistance of hot element of a catharometer	9.2
α_0	rate of production of metastable argon atoms in an argon detector	8.5
β	partition coefficient with dimensions ml^{-3}	1.1
γ	activity coefficient	3.3
	tortuosity factor	5.2
ζ	partition coefficient in dimensions ml^{-3}	3.2
η	gas viscosity	2.5
	coefficient of thermal expansion of solvent	3.6
$\eta_{m_2:m_3}$	impurity fraction of solute 2 in solute 3 and vice versa for components divided by a single cut	4.6
θ	fraction of adsorbent surface covered by adsorbate	3.11
	$T_2 - T_1$ for catharometers	9.10
λ	constant in expression for geometrical peak broadening	5.3
	thermal conductivity (in general)	9.2
λ_1	thermal conductivity of carrier gas	9.2
λ_2	thermal conductivity of vapour	9.2
λ_{12}	thermal conductivity of mixed vapour and carrier gas	9.2
ρ	density of stationary phase	3.2
σ	standard deviation of a peak	4.2

	collision diameter of a molecule	9.3
$\sigma_{(V)}$	standard deviation of a peak measured as a volume of carrier gas	4.2
$\sigma_{(r)}$	standard deviation of a peak measured as a number of plates	4.2
$\sigma_{(x)}$	standard deviation of a peak measured as a length along the column	4.3
$\sigma_{(L)}$	standard deviation of a peak measured as a distance on chart paper	4.5
$\sigma_{(t)}$	standard deviation of a peak measured in time units	5.3
σ_g	standard deviation as a result of lateral diffusion of solute in the gas phase	5.4
σ_l	standard deviation as a result of lateral diffusion in the liquid phase	5.4
σ_C	standard deviation as a result of the column	5.7
σ_I	standard deviation as a result of the sample injector	5.7
σ_T	$\sqrt{\sigma_C^2 + \sigma_I^2}$	5.7
σ_a	collision cross section of excited argon atoms	8.5
σ_M	collision cross section of excited argon atoms in collision with organic molecules	8.5
φ	arbitrary function	2.3
	multiplication factor for the rate of electron production in irradiated argon in an electric field	8.5
	function of temperature	9.2
$\omega_{1/2}$	peak width half-way up the peak	4.5
$\mathcal{H}$	phenomenological plate-height	5.19
$\mathfrak{N}$	number of theoretical plates in a column	4.2
$\mathfrak{N}'$	number of theoretical plates as measured from a chromatogram	5.7
$\mathcal{W}', \mathcal{W}''$	quantities used in Section 3.3	

Subscripts

1	pertaining to solvent	
2	pertaining to solute	
23	pertaining to two solutes	

Superscripts

†	pertaining to standard state	
–	mean value	

Author Index

Numbers in parentheses are reference numbers and are included to assist in locating the reference where the authors' names are not mentioned in the text. Numbers in italics refer to the page on which the reference is listed.*

* *Note:* In Chapter 11 references are listed according to sections. Please see footnotes on pages 372 and 472.

Subject Index

Index of Chemicals